TRANSPORT PHENOMENA IN SOLIDIFICATION

presented at
1994 International Mechanical Engineering Congress and Exposition
Chicago, Illinois
November 6–11, 1994

sponsored by
The Heat Transfer Division,
The Applied Mechanics Division, and
The Materials Division, ASME

edited by
C. Beckermann
University of Iowa

H. P. Wang
General Electric

L. A. Bertram
Sandia National Laboratories

M. S. Sohal
Idaho National Engineering Laboratory

S. I. Guceri
University of Illinois at Chicago

THE AMERICAN SOCIETY OF MECHANICAL ENGINEERS
UNITED ENGINEERING CENTER / 345 EAST 47TH STREET / NEW YORK, NEW YORK 10017

Statement from By-Laws: The Society shall not be responsible for statements or opinions advanced in papers. . . or printed in its publications (7.1.3)

Authorization to photocopy material for internal or personal use under circumstance not failling within the fair use provisions of the Copyright Act is granted by ASME to libraries and other users registered with the Copyright Clearance Center (CCC) Transactional Reporting Service provided that the base fee of $0.30 per page is paid directly to the CCC, 27 Congress Street, Salem MA 01970. Requests for special permission or bulk reproduction should be addressed to the ASME Technical Publishing Department.

ISBN No. 0-7918-1392-4

Library of Congress Catalog Number 94-78966

Copyright © 1994 by
THE AMERICAN SOCIETY OF MECHANICAL ENGINEERS
All Rights Reserved
Printed in U.S.A.

FOREWORD

Heat, mass, and momentum transport during solidification processes is a broad field that has experienced renewed interest in recent years. Applications range from metal casting, welding, crystal growth, and casting of composites to ice formation in heat exchangers. In addition to the transport phenomena at the system scale, the interactions with microscale effects are receiving increased attention due to their importance in determining the properties of the solidified material. The field is of a multidisciplinary nature, and this symposium is designed to bring together researchers from a variety of disciplines and provide an overview of recent research efforts. Experimental, numerical, and analytical studies are reported.

The papers contained in this volume were presented in six sessions on *Transport Phenomena in Solidification* at the 1994 International Mechanical Engineering Congress and Exposition, November 6–11, 1994, in Chicago, Illinois. The symposium was jointly sponsored by the K-15 Committee on Heat and Mass Transfer in Manufacturing and Materials Processing and the K-6 Committee on Heat Transfer in Energy Systems, both of the Heat Transfer Division; the Fluid Mechanics Committee of the Applied Mechanics Division; and the Materials Processing Committee of the Materials Division of ASME.

We wish to extend our thanks and appreciation to the authors for their contributions and to the reviewers for their effort in evaluating the papers.

C. Beckermann
H. P. Wang
L. A. Bertram
M. S. Sohal
S. I. Güçeri

LIST OF REVIEWERS

C. Batur
C. Beckermann
T. L. Bergman
L. A. Bertram
A. Chait
J. A. Dantzig
H. C. de Groh III
R. J. Feller
S. Fukusako
S. I. Güçeri
A. Hellawell
F. P. Incropera
G. A. Irons
M. P. Kanouff
L. Katgerman
M. Kazmierczak
M. H. McCay
B. T. Murray
S. Nair
D. L. O'Neal
D. R. Poirier
A. V. Reddy
M. C. Schneider
M. Sen
W. Shyy
R. N. Smith
M. S. Sohal
D. M. Stefanescu
H. L. Tsai
R. Viskanta
V. R. Voller
C. Y. Wang
H. P. Wang
K. H. Yae

CONTENTS

HTD-Vol. 284/AMD-Vol. 182, Transport Phenomena in Solidification
ASME 1994

FORMATION AND SUPPRESSION OF CHANNELS DURING UNIDIRECTIONAL SOLIDIFICATION OF AQUEOUS AMMONIUM CHLORIDE

James P. McNulty, Suresh V. Garimella and **Lei Z. Schlitz**
Department of Mechanical Engineering
University of Wisconsin-Milwaukee
Milwaukee, Wisconsin

ABSTRACT

Characteristics of the mushy zone were experimentally investigated in the upward solidification of a binary mixture. The formation of channels and techniques for their suppression were explored. The experiments were carried out in a rectangular test section using aqueous ammonium chloride as the phase change material at hypo- and hypereutectic concentrations ranging from 15 to 33 weight percent of salt. The cold plate temperature was varied in the range of −60 to −14°C. Transient temperature profiles as well as the positions of the liquidus and solidus interfaces were obtained. The mushy-zone characteristics, the nature and distribution of channels, and the associated fluid flows were studied as a function of initial solution concentration and cold plate temperature. The application of low-amplitude vibration to the test cell was found to reduce the mushy zone thickness and the number of channels for all concentrations; channeling was almost completely suppressed at the lower concentrations. Channel suppression was influenced by vibration amplitude rather than frequency, with the larger-amplitude vibration being the more effective. The vibration results suggest that the formation and sustenance of channels is influenced more by developments within the mushy zone than by bulk liquid behavior.

INTRODUCTION

When an alloy melt is solidified by cooling from one wall of the mold, a homogeneous casting is produced with columnar grains aligned in the primary growth direction and with few transverse grain boundaries formed. The material produced by this process of *unidirectional solidification* has improved thermal fatigue strength and increased creep rupture strain, and is used in the manufacture of products such as high-performance gas turbine blades. However, these castings may be characterized by large-scale inhomogeneities in the form of longitudinal solute-rich imperfections (freckles) caused by compositional convection in the melt and in the mushy zone during solidification. Although much attention has been devoted to the study of this defect, the precise mechanisms of when and how the parent channels form in the mushy zone are still not clear.

Unidirectional solidification has been investigated experimentally in aqueous salt solutions and organic systems, in addition to metallic systems. The aqueous salt system is preferred for experimentation in view of its translucency, similarity to liquid metal solidification in terms of dendritic growth (Jackson et al., 1966) due to its low entropy of fusion, availability of thermophysical property data, and ease of experimentation due to its low melting temperature and small latent heat. In some of the first such experiments conducted by Copley et al. (1970), a 30 wt.% NH_4Cl-H_2O solution was solidified upwards in a cylindrical mold. They found that channels were caused by upward-flowing liquid jets that eroded the mushy zone and led to localized segregation. The erosion by the jets was shown to decrease as the imposed temperature gradient and growth velocity were increased. It was further shown that the tendency to channel is greatest in alloys with a large density difference between the primary phase and the melt, high thermal diffusivity, and low solute diffusivity and viscosity. Other visualization studies of solidification in aqueous solutions (Asai and Muchi, 1978; McDonald and Hunt, 1969) attributed macrosegregation and the formation of channel-type segregates to gravity-induced interdendritic flows. Chen and Chen (1991) discussed the differences between finger and plume-type convection in upward solidification in a 26% NH_4Cl solution for a range of cold-plate temperatures; the tendency for plume formation decreased as the cold plate temperature was increased. Based on estimates of the porosity and permeability of the mushy zone, Rayleigh numbers for the onset of plume convection were predicted. Magirl and Incropera (1993) also visualized salt-fingers and plumes during the solidification of a 27% NH_4Cl

solution. Other experimental investigations have been conducted in aqueous salt systems by Bennon and Incropera (1989), Chen and Turner (1980), and Christenson and Incropera (1989); additional studies are reviewed in Hellawell et al. (1993).

Solidification experiments have also been conducted in metallic alloys such as the Al-Cu and Pb-Sn systems. Streat and Weinberg (1972) attributed the formation of channels (pipes) in Pb-Sn alloys to a density inversion in the mushy zone. Sarazin and Hellawell (1988) investigated macrosegregation and the channeling phenomenon in Pb-Sn, Pb-Sb, and Pb-Sn-Sb alloy ingots. Channel distribution was found to be a function of temperature gradient, growth rate, dendrite spacing, and interdendritic permeability. Upper and lower limits to the permeability of the dendritic array were related to the composition range over which channeling is supported. Tewari and Shah (1992) directionally solidified Pb-Sn alloys in controlled experiments which examined the influence of the volume fraction of interdendritic liquid, the primary dendrite spacing and the mushy zone length on longitudinal macrosegregation and the formation of channel segregates.

In spite of the popularity of aqueous systems for experimental visualization, some doubt exists as to the strength of their analogy to metallic alloys (Standish, 1970). The robustness of the analogy has also been examined by Hellawell et al. (1993). In fact, even among the aqueous systems, different types of convection are realized. According to Huppert (1990), distinct plumes and channels have been observed only in the ammonium chloride-water system. Some reasons offered for the distinct behavior of this system were: the low solid fraction in the mushy zone; the high energy of formation; the steep liquidus curve; and the less-faceted crystals than other salts. An important difference between metallic and aqueous systems is that the structure of the mushy zone is weaker in the latter, as characterized, for instance, by the solid fraction. The results of the present study should be interpreted with this difference noted.

Computational investigations of unidirectional solidification have been refined in recent years. Early models such as that of Mehrabian et al. (1970), where the mushy region was treated as a porous medium and the flow due to buoyancy and thermal contraction was explicitly determined, were limited in that solidification rates and temperature gradients were still to be prescribed. Fujii et al. (1979) presented a model in which coupled momentum and energy conservation equations were solved. The mushy region was uncoupled from the solid and melt, and the transient progression of planar solidus and liquidus interfaces was arbitrarily prescribed. Szekely and Jassal (1978) considered momentum and energy transport in the solid, mushy and liquid regions of a binary system, but did not account for species transfer and hence were unable to predict macrosegregation effects. Felicelli et al. (1991) performed a finite-element analysis of the vertical solidification of Pb-Sn alloy, in which the mushy zone was allowed to have variable porosity depending on local thermodynamic constraints. It was found possible to induce channels by establishing a column of upward flow in the bulk liquid (as in the experiments of Sample and Hellawell, 1984), or by enhancing vertical convection. Mechanisms for the creation, growth and termination of channels were discussed in this and other studies (Magirl and Incropera, 1993; Neilson and Incropera, 1991, 1993b). Channels were shown to develop at the liquidus front and grow downward into the mush by remelting due to compositionally induced local freezing point depression. The final as-cast product revealing segregation patterns was modeled recently in a simulation by Combeau and Lesoult (1993), revealing the influence of alloy composition, cooling intensity and initial superheat. Comprehensive reviews of advanced mathematical models are available in Rappaz and Voller (1990), and Viskanta (1990).

The picture that emerges about the formation of channels is clear in some respects. During unidirectional upward solidification, three stages have been observed in the literature (for instance, Neilson and Incropera, 1993c), using experiments with aqueous salt solutions. After nucleation of solid at the cold plate, as convection patterns are established, finger-type convection is set up in a so-called *boundary-layer mode* (Worster, 1992). The fingers are rich in solute (water in aqueous salt systems), and extend a limited distance ahead of the mushy zone into the melt. In time, a transformation occurs in which some of the fingers get stronger and form plumes which rise to a much greater distance into the melt. These plumes have higher flow rates, and are fed by local segregation in the mushy-zone interior; hence this stage of the solidification process has been referred to as the *mushy-layer mode*. Each plume gives rise to a channel in the mushy zone that has nearly zero solid-fraction. The ascending plumes induce salt-rich fluid to descend towards the mushy zone, crystallizing into volcano-like hills around the channel exits. The third and final phase sees some of the channels close as the potential that drives the plume flow wanes.

There is less certainty, however, about the origin of the plumes and channels. Two alternative models have been proposed. In the one (Hellawell et al., 1993; Magirl and Incropera, 1993; Neilson and Incropera, 1993c), a plume is thought to result from an unstable perturbation in the bulk liquid at or close to the level of the growth front. Observations in support of this model are presented in detail in these references. The other model (Chen and Chen, 1991; Huppert, 1990; Tait and Jaupart, 1992; Worster, 1992) attributes the origin of plumes to compositional buoyant convection within the mushy zone. In fact, Worster (1992) concluded that fingers and plumes were two independent modes of convection which may interact but are independently formed. An understanding of the origins of the plumes could guide a rational approach to the suppression of channels. Irrespective of origin, however, it is clear that plume flow must be fed and sustained by the solute rejected in the mushy zone. The vibration experiments in the present study tend to support the latter model, as will be discussed.

Several studies in the literature have attempted to develop practical means to prevent channeling in castings. An accepted approach to channel suppression is to increase the cooling rate in order to suppress convection which in turn suppresses macrosegregation, as shown in experiments by Copley et al. (1970) and in recent computations by Poirier and Heinrich (1993). Sample and Hellawell (1982, 1984) effectively prevented the formation and propagation of channels in salt solutions and Pb-Sn alloys by precessing (< 10 rpm) the molds about an inclined axis. It was shown through novel experiments that channels originate at the top of the mushy zone due to convective perturbations, even though they are then sustained by buoyant interdendritic fluid. The success of mold precession in channel suppression was attributed to translation of bulk liquid across the dendritic growth front, which sheared off the convective perturbations from the solute boundary layer before they had a chance to destabilize and grow. Neilson and Incropera (1993a, c) confirmed that intermittent rotation of a cylindrical mold may be used to reduce channel formation. Solidification under alternately increasing and decreasing gravity conditions was studied by McCay and McCay (1988) who found that the plumes arising from the mushy zone were completely suppressed during low-gravity conditions.

In this paper, results of an experimental investigation into the upward unidirectional solidification of a binary mixture are presented. The mushy-zone characteristics, the nature and distribution of channels, and the associated fluid flows were studied as a function of initial solution concentration and cold plate temperature using aqueous ammonium chloride as the phase change material. Results from this study will serve as a baseline for a subsequent investigation that will study the solidification of (metal-matrix) composite systems, and will also be used to provide experimental verification for mathematical models. Transient temperature profiles in the growth direction were obtained and the liquidus and solidus interfaces were tracked visually. Low-amplitude vibration was investigated as a means for suppressing channel formation. It was hoped that channeling would be suppressed either by dissipating bulk liquid perturbations and thus preventing plume formation, or by causing dendrite fragmentation in the mushy zone. The latter process could result in a diffused set of flow ejection paths instead of the preferential channels for plume flow observed in static solidification. It is likely that this work would best be accomplished in conjunction with stability analyses such as those of Heinrich et al. (1989) and Worster (1992), which might enable the evaluation of any suppression technique based on its effect on the stability of incipient plumes.

EXPERIMENTAL METHODS

The solidification process was carried out in a rectangular test cell consisting of a stainless steel heat exchanger cold plate as the bottom wall and a plexiglass center section and top wall to allow visual access from the sides as well as the top. The cavity used was 40.5 mm high in the growth direction, with side dimensions of 200 and 144 mm. The plexiglass side and top walls were 25.4 mm thick to reduce heat losses. Thermal control of the cold plate was accomplished by passing ethanol through a multiple-pass serpentine passage machined into the stainless steel plate. A low-temperature bath circulator maintained the required cold plate temperatures ($-60°C < T_c < -14°C$).

Aqueous solutions of ammonium chloride at several different concentrations were chosen to model metallic alloy solidification. This system has a eutectic temperature of −15.4°C and concentration of 19.7%. Since ammonium chloride is hygroscopic, the concentration of each sample was accurately analyzed by titrating for the chloride ion against aqueous silver nitrate to within ±0.5 wt.% of the desired nominal value.

Temperature profiles along the midplane of the test cell were obtained by means of two vertical rakes containing ten T-type, 30-gage thermocouples each. The thermocouple beads were irregularly spaced, with more junctions installed near the cold wall. One set of rake thermocouple locations corresponded to x = 37.7, 33.0, 27.8, 22.6, 17.9, 13.1, 9.5, 6.4, 3.2, and 0.8 mm, measured upwards from the bottom wall (cold plate). The position of each junction in a thermocouple rake was periodically measured and adjusted when necessary, yielding an uncertainty in thermocouple location of ±0.5 mm. Each polycarbonate rake was 6.35 mm in diameter and was filled with silicone after the thermocouples were properly positioned. Three additional thermocouples were used to monitor temperatures of the top wall, the cold plate, and the ambient. The thermocouple beads were protected from corrosion by a thinned polyurethane coating. All thermocouples were connected to two Fluke Hydra data loggers and scanned at five-second intervals. The positions of the liquidus and solidus were visually observed and recorded to within ±0.5 mm at intervals of 250 s using two transparent scales mounted on the inside of adjacent side walls in the test cell. A videographic record of the transient interface progression was also obtained.

The channeling that occurred in many of the experiments was distinctly observed from both the sides and the top of the test cell. The number and distribution of channels was recorded at 250-second time intervals by marking them on clear transparency film mounted on top of one half of the apparatus. For the experiments in which vibration was applied, one of two pneumatic vibrators was securely bolted to one corner of the cold plate, and driven by compressed air at a pressure of about 50 psi. The characteristics of the vibration applied to the test cell were monitored for frequency and amplitude with an accelerometric transducer mounted on the test cell and read using an oscilloscope. Both vibrators had roughly the same frequency, but the force and amplitude of vibration were larger for the larger vibrator. At a compressed air supply pressure of 50 psi, the smaller vibrator provided an amplitude of 0.1 mm and a frequency of 150 Hz, while the larger vibrator yielded a 0.6-mm amplitude and a frequency of 130 Hz.

The apparatus was brought to a uniform temperature before the start of an experiment. The chiller (with the circulation valve closed) first cooled the reservoir of ethanol to the desired cold plate temperature. The solidification process commenced when the circulation valve on the chiller was opened. In experiments with solution concentrations of 30 and 33 wt.% where the liquidus temperature could be greater than the ambient, the melt was heated to roughly 45°C to prevent inadvertent nucleation of solid until the solution was chilled by the cold plate.

Experiments were conducted for hypoeutectic, eutectic and hypereutectic solution concentrations of 15, 19.7, 24, 26, 27, 28, 30 and 33 wt.%, and for cold plate temperatures of −14, −20, −30, −40, −50 and −60°C, without applied vibration. Vibration was applied to the test cell with solution concentrations of 26% and more.

RESULTS AND DISCUSSION

Cooling curves, temperature gradients, interface positions, and channeling distribution and frequency are first presented for a representative case with a solution concentration of 30 wt.% and a cold plate temperature of −50°C. The effect of varying the solution concentration and cold plate temperature on the solidification process are then explored. Finally results are presented from experiments where vibration was applied to the test cell as a means of suppressing channels.

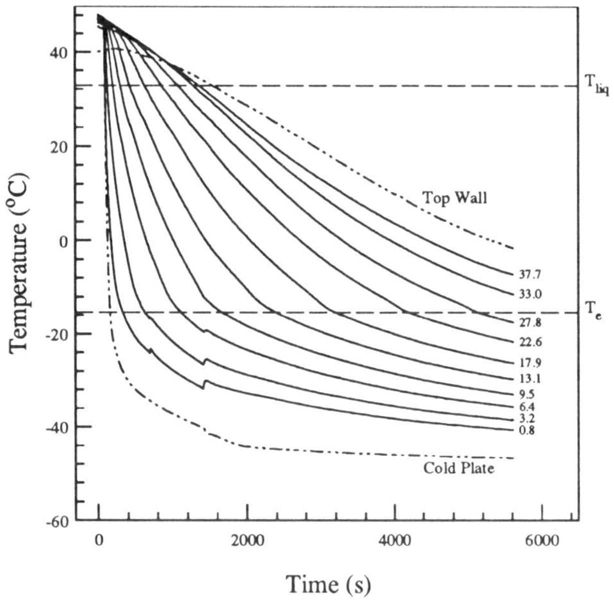

Fig. 1. Cooling curves for the 30% solution with a cold plate temperature of –50°C. Rake thermocouple readings are shown as solid lines with distances from the cold plate in mm indicated alongside.

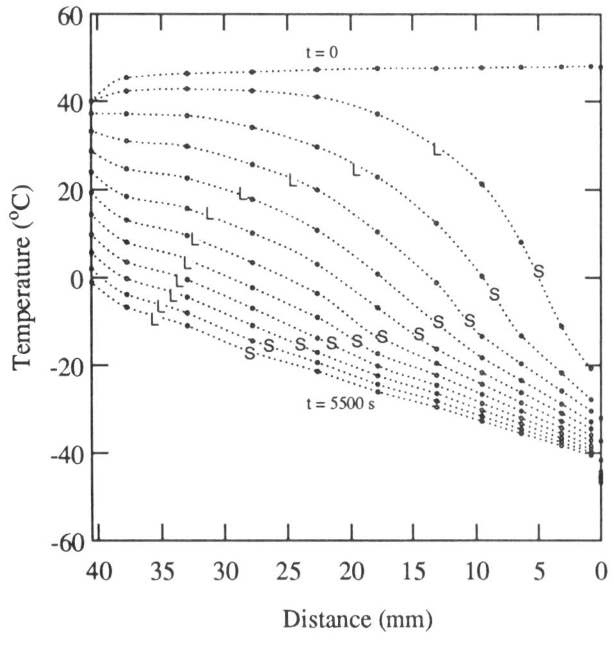

Fig. 2. Transient temperature readings at time intervals of 500 s as a function of distance from the cold plate for the 30% solution (T_c = –50°C). Observed liquidus (L) and solidus (S) locations are marked on the curves.

Static Solidification

At the start of a solidification experiment, macroscopic hexagonal crystals (for hypereutectic solutions) were nucleated all over the stainless steel surface of the cold plate and grew rapidly. The initial solidification in the 24% solution was different from that at higher concentrations in that it began eutectically. Solid NH_4Cl and ice formed simultaneously as fine crystals of the two phases in an alternating-plate morphology. Unlike the square and hexagonal shapes of the crystals of pure NH_4Cl formed at the higher concentrations, the eutectic grains for the 24% solution had rounded perimeters. As growth of the solid continued upward, solidus and liquidus interfaces became distinguishable within minutes. The rate of solidification, the character and thickness of the mushy zone, and the presence or absence of channels were dependent on cold plate temperature and solution concentration.

Cooling curves are presented in Figure 1 for a 30% solution with a cold plate temperature of –50°C. The equilibrium phase diagram indicates that only solid is present (solidification is complete) below the eutectic temperature of –15.4°C, indicated on the plots by a dashed line. The cooling curves display a change in slope at the eutectic (solidus) temperature as expected, due to the different thermal properties of the mushy zone and solid phases. The growth rate is initially very high, but decreases steadily as the extent of the solid phase increases.

An interesting feature in the cooling curves of Figure 1 is the "bumps" that occur in the temperatures read closest to the cold wall at approximately 1400 s, a time when the liquidus and solidus are 24 mm and 11 mm respectively from the cold plate. The bumps typically occur when the cold plate reaches a temperature of about –38 to –40°C; the increase in solid temperature is accompanied by a simultaneous *decrease* in cold plate temperature. Since these bumps occur in the interior of the solid close to the cold plate, they cannot be due to recalescence effects. The bumps correspond instead to a mold breakaway from the solid. At the exact moment when the cold plate temperature drops and the temperature in the solid closest to the cold plate rises, a distinct sharp cracking sound was heard: the cold plate drops in temperature when it loses contact with the warmer solidifying material, and the solid rises in temperature upon losing contact with the heat sink. Less intensely audible cracks were associated with smaller bumps in the temperature curves (one such bump is seen in the figure at 800 s).

The temperature profile in the growth direction at successive times in an experiment is illustrated in Figure 2. The letters L and S correspond to the visually determined liquidus and solidus positions which agree fairly well with T_{liq} and T_e from the phase diagram for the given concentration, except towards the top wall where the concentration of the melt has changed significantly and is highly water-rich. There is also increased uncertainty in pinpointing the solidus position near the cold plate very early in the solidification process, which might explain the S locations being well above T_e. The slope of the curves is constant in the solid region, and changes discretely upon entering the mushy zone. The temperature gradient in the mushy zone is, however, not linear in contrast to the observations of Chen and Chen (1991). The decrease in solid fraction in the mushy zone with distance away from the solid phase would result in changing thermophysical properties; the more porous regions of the mushy

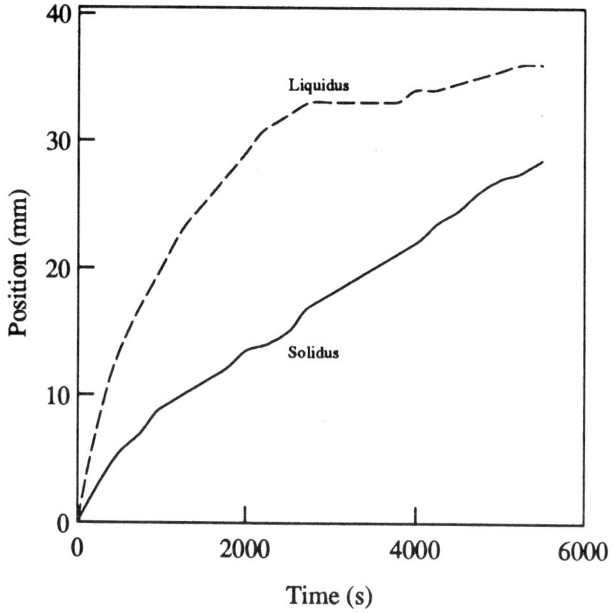

Fig. 3. Progression of observed interface positions (measured upwards from the cold plate) with time for the 30% solution (T_c = −50°C).

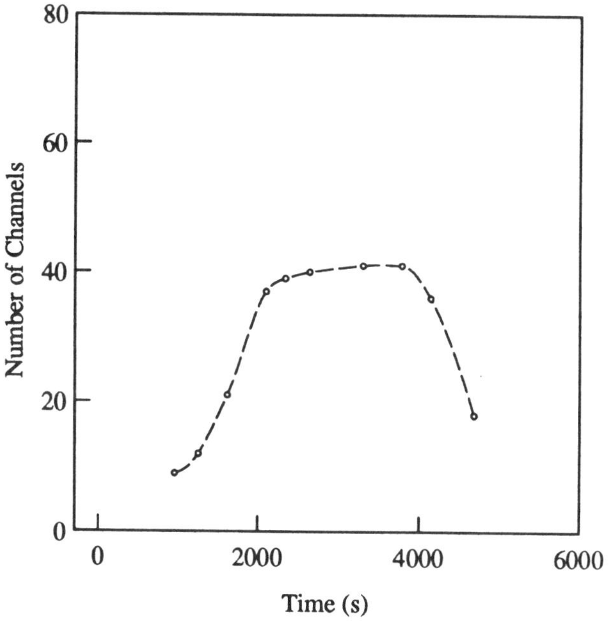

Fig. 4. Occurrence of channels as a function of time with the 30% solution (T_c = −50°C) over half of the test cell.

zone would also support greater convection, leading to a non-linear temperature gradient.

Interface positions at time intervals of 500 s for this case areshown in Figure 3. The mushy zone thickness increases with time to a maximum of 16 mm as the liquidus and solidus interfaces progress in the growth direction. While the solidus continues to grow with time at a steady rate, the subsequent levelling off of the liquidus is due to the presence of the top wall, because of which steady state conditions are not reached. The melt at the top is enriched in solute (water) and has a progressively lower liquidus temperature and thus stays molten; the heat gain from the top wall also contributes to keeping the melt from solidifying.

Channeling was observed in the experiments conducted with solution concentrations of roughly 26% and greater. The number of channels as a function of time for the 30% solution is shown in Figure 4. As the plot indicates, the first channels did not appear until about 1000 s into the experiment, suggesting that a well-established mushy zone is necessary before channels can develop. The onset of channeling coincided with the finger-convection regime being replaced by well-established plumes, consistent with observations in the literature. The transformation in convection regime from fingers to plumes was marked by a dramatic and fairly sudden change in the appearance of the melt just ahead of the growth front: the finger regime was characterized by a dense forest of dendritic fragments entrained in the boundary layer just ahead of the mushy zone. With the onset of plumes, the melt became much clearer and the ejection of particulates was greatly reduced and limited to a few localized columns. As noted in Copley et al. (1970) and Sample and Hellawell (1984), the start of channeling occurs when the growth rate has reached a near-constant value. After the onset of channeling, the number of channels increased steadily until about 2200 s into the experiment, when 40 were present over one half of the test cell. These channels persisted, ejecting the water-rich interdendritic liquid and forming craters at their mouths, for an additional 2000 s. Roughly 4500 s into the experiment, the liquidus was about 5 mm from the top of the cavity and solidification slowed considerably. This was followed by channel closure as the potential sustaining the flow in the plumes was progressively reduced. The channels existed in the solid as severe segregates as illustrated in Figure 5 because the liquid that

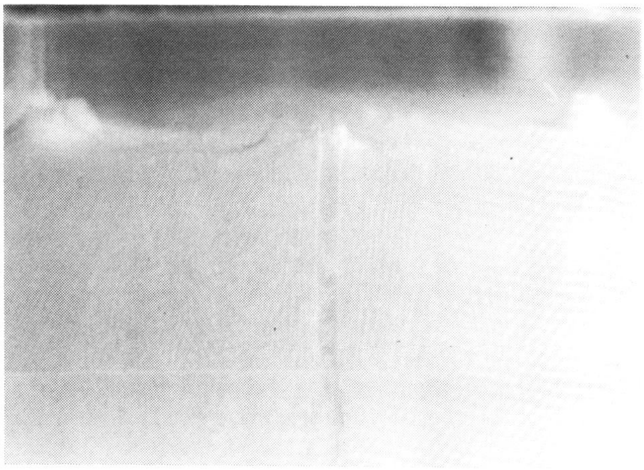

Fig. 5. Channel formed at the side wall of the test section for a 30% solution (T_c = −50°C). The signature of the channel extends into the solid.

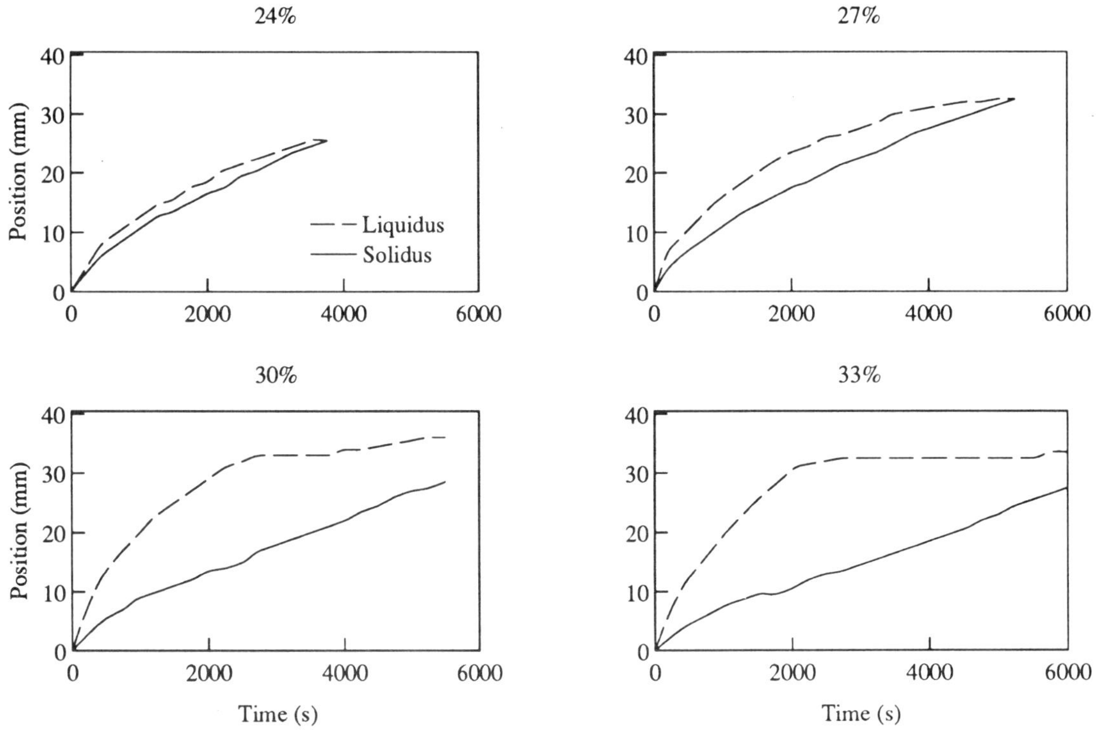

Fig. 6. Effect of solution concentration on interface progression and mushy zone thickness during solidification for a constant cold plate temperature of –50°C.

eventually solidified in them is of a concentration very different from that of the surrounding solid. Figure 5 also illustrates the craters formed at the mouths of the channels when dendrite fragments carried out of the mushy zone with plumes of water-rich liquid were deposited on top. The rising cold plumes also displace salt-rich fluid which descends and contributes to crystal formation at the channel mouth (Chen and Chen, 1991).

Effect of Initial Concentration

Solution concentration strongly influenced the solidification process, corresponding to the difference in freezing range at each concentration, which in turn determines the extent and character of the mushy zone. Interface positions for four hypereutectic solutions are presented as a function of time in Figure 6 with T_c = –50°C. As solution concentration increased, the growth velocity of the solidus decreased almost linearly from roughly 0.33 mm/min at 24% to 0.24 mm/min at 33%. The liquidus, however, advanced more quickly in the more concentrated solutions resulting in a thicker mushy zone.

The nature and extent of the channeling observed was also strongly affected by solution concentration. Unlike the sharp, distinct channels that were observed in the 30 and 33% solutions, those at 27% were less defined, greater in number, and possessed large and diffuse craters at the mouths. There was no discernible channeling at 24%. The number of channels is presented as a function of time for three solution concentrations in Figure 7. The 27% solution showed a peaked distribution of channels with time, with a maximum of about 80 over one half of the test cell, twice that with the 30% solution. The 33% solution displayed the fewest with about 30 in the same area. The higher concentrations also exhibited a more gradual rise, with a plateau distribution.

Channeling occurs over a specific range of hypereutectic concentrations. As the solution concentration increases to around 25%, the mushy zone gets well-established and the driving force for interdendritic thermosolutal convection increases, resulting in plumes and channels. The channels get more defined with an increase in concentration up to 30%, with the structure of the mushy zone getting stronger and denser. However, at an even higher concentration of 33%, the volume fraction of solid in the mushy zone appears to be high enough (roughly 15% compared to less than 5% for the 24% solution) that the structure of the porous array resists channel formation. Upper and lower concentration limits for the occurrence of channeling have also been observed by Sample and Hellawell (1984), Sarazin and Hellawell (1988), and Tewari and Shah (1992).

Effect of Cold Wall Temperature

The cold wall temperature affects only the rate of interface progression and not the mushy zone thickness, for a fixed concentration. The solidus position versus time curves in Figure 8 (24% solution) show that while the temperature gradients (dx/dt) increase as the cold plate temperature decreases, the mushy zone thickness remains roughly constant. This would be expected since the mushy zone thickness is directly related to thefreezing range, which is a constant for a given solution concentration.

The effect of cold plate temperature on channeling is illustrated in Figure 9 for a 28% solution solidified at three

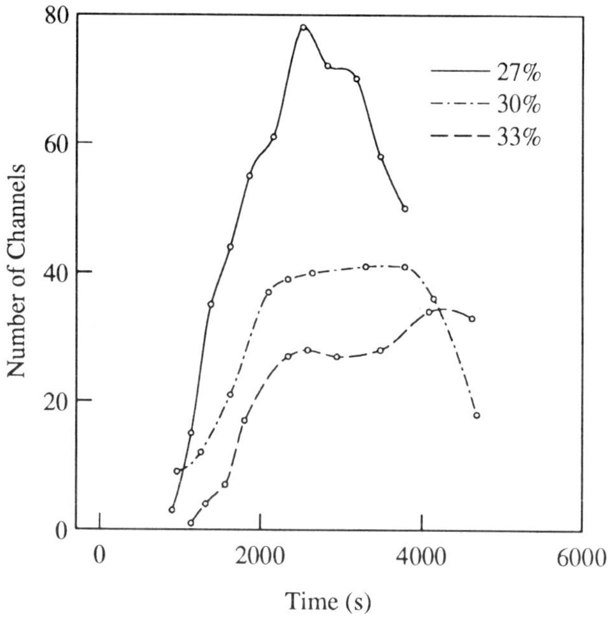

Fig. 7. Effect of solution concentration on number of channels with a constant cold plate temperature of −50°C.

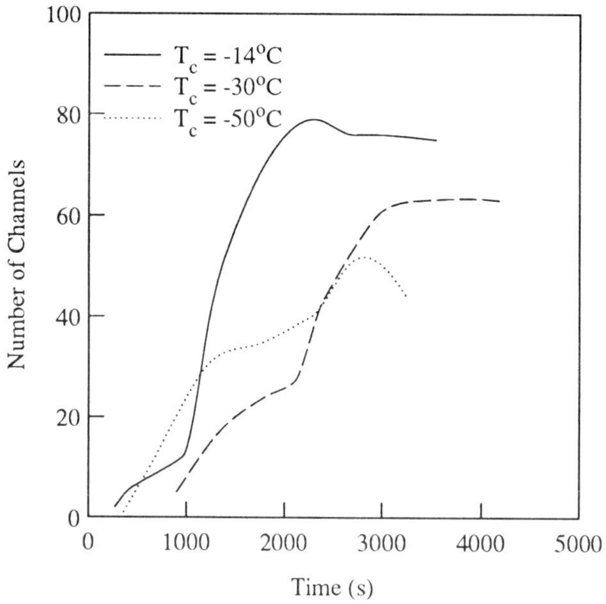

Fig. 9. Effect of cold plate temperature on the number of channels for a 28% solution.

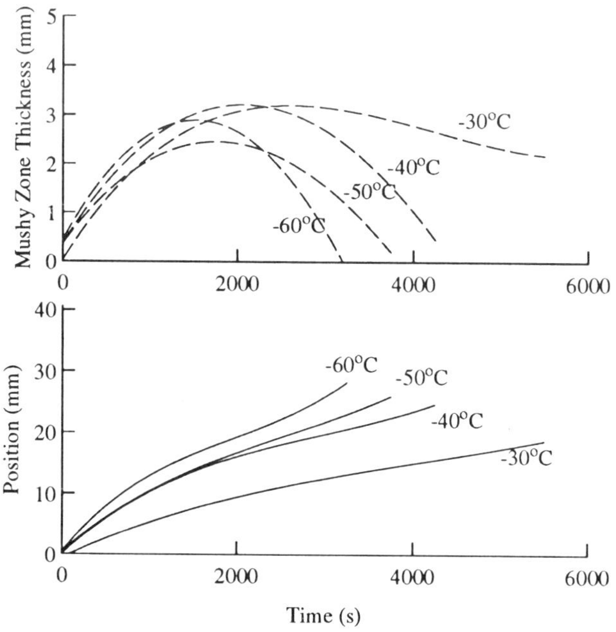

Fig. 8. Effect of cold plate temperature on solidus progression and mushy zone thickness for the 24% solution.

different cold plate temperatures. Differences in the slopes of the curves are in response to the different rates of heat extraction and growth of the mushy zone. The experiments were discontinued when the growth of the mushy zone tapered off. The peak number of channels for the three cases was 80, 64 and 58, decreasing with a decrease in T_c. This observed decrease in channeling with an increase in the solidification rate is an accepted method of reducing macrosegregation.

Suppression of Channeling: Vibration

The solution concentrations that exhibited distinctive channeling (26% NH_4Cl and above) were retested with vibration applied to the test cell at cold plate temperatures of −14 and −50°C. The key differences between static solidification and that with vibration were three-fold. With vibration, although plumes were associated with any channels that were present (as expected), finger convection persisted throughout the solidification process whether or not channels were formed. This was in contrast with static solidification where finger convection was usually present early in the process, and was subsequently replaced by plumes. Secondly, the structure of the mushy zone and its packing density (solid fraction) were modified upon the application of vibration. Thirdly, channeling was suppressed at the lower concentrations by vibration, and the amplitude of vibration rather than the frequency was found to be the determining factor. These observations are discussed further in the following.

At the start of solidification with vibration applied to the test cell, the first crystals grew in fuzzy, rounded shapes at all concentrations, unlike the polygonal shapes observed in static solidification. For concentrations of 28% and greater, solute-rich flows, half-way in character between fingers and plumes, were set up almost immediately after the start of solidification. In fact, even the first clusters of solid to form had holes at their centers with plume-like ejections, especially at the lower cold plate temperatures. Solidification progressed more rapidly than in the static case.

The mushy zone thickness was decreased due to the applied vibration in all cases. This is illustrated for a cold wall temperature of −14°C in Figure 10 for three different

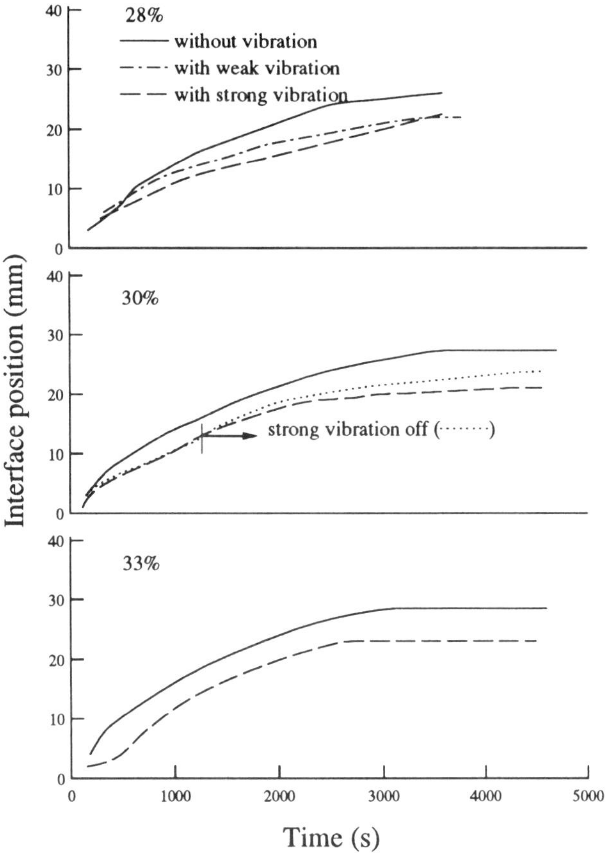

Fig. 10. Effect of vibration on growth front progression at solution concentrations of 28, 30 and 33% with a cold plate temperature of −14°C.

concentrations (only liquidus lines exist for this T_c). "Weak" and "strong" vibrations in the figure indicate vibration amplitudes of about 0.1 and 0.6 mm respectively; the frequency in both cases is nearly the same and equal to about 150 Hz. It is clear from the top part of this figure that the stronger vibration resulted in a thinner mushy zone. Also, as the 30% solution shows, the rate of mushy zone growth increased noticeably as soon as vibration was turned off. While weak vibration had some effect on channeling for the 28% solution, the higher concentrations were influenced only by the strong (larger-amplitude) vibration.

The number of channels over half the test cell in a variety of solidification experiments, with and without applied (strong) vibration, are listed in Table 1. The numbers reported include channels formed at the walls of the test cell. These channels were generally not suppressed by vibration. Thus the percentage drop in channels in the table would be more dramatic if only channels away from the walls were considered. Several important observations can be made based on this table. Clearly, the applied vibration almost completely suppressed channel formation at the lowest concentration. Experiments with 25.5 and 27% solutions yielded almost identical results as the 26.5% case. Even the 21 channels recorded did not display the characteristic well-defined craters or the attendant holes and plumes. Rather, they were manifested as fluffy bumps on the surface. The photograph

Table 1. Suppression of channels under applied vibration.

wt.% NH_4Cl	T_c(°C)	Number of channels		
		without vibration	with strong vibration	% decrease
26.5%	-50	140	21	85.0
28%	-14	79	19	75.9
	-50	49	20	59.2
30%	-14	48	27	44.0
	-50	38	26	31.6
33%	-14	30	22	26.7

in Figure 11, taken 2000 s into an experiment with the 27% solution (T_c = −50°C), shows a part of the mushy zone that is free of channels under applied vibration. Without vibration there were nearly 60 channels present in this case. At the higher concentrations of 28% and above, the channels noted during vibration were quite distinct and were associated with holes in the mushy zone. As the concentration was increased, the ability of the vibration to suppress channeling was reduced. Although a decrease in the number of channels was noticed at every concentration, the efficacy of suppression due to vibration dropped as the concentration was increased from 26% to 33%.

Figure 12 further illustrates the suppression of channels upon the application of vibration for three different concentrations and cold plate temperatures. The effect was clearly strongest at the lowest salt concentration. An important demonstration with the 28% solution in the figure is the effect of the nature of vibration on channel suppression. The larger vibrator was more successful than the smaller one. For instance, with the 28% solution, 79 channels were observed for static solidification, 31 with the smaller vibrator, and 19 with the larger (see Table 1). Similarly, in the case of the 30% solution, the smaller vibrator had hardly any suppression effect at all, while the larger one caused a 44% decrease in the number of channels. Since both vibrators had nearly the same frequency, it was the amplitude which was the significant descriptor of vibration: a larger-amplitude vibration is probably more able to cause dendrite fragmentation and plume suppression, which appears to be the mechanism by which channeling is suppressed as discussed below. The effect of vibration on reducing channeling even at the higher concentrations is illustrated in the bottom graph of Figure 12, where the number of channels increased rapidly as soon as vibration was turned off.

It is unclear whether stronger vibrations could suppress channeling at the higher concentrations while still achieving ordered, unidirectional growth. The objective of the vibration experiments here was to suppress channeling without materially affecting the overall solidification process or the final product. When much larger amplitudes than those reported above were imposed, the growth process was completely disturbed: crystals

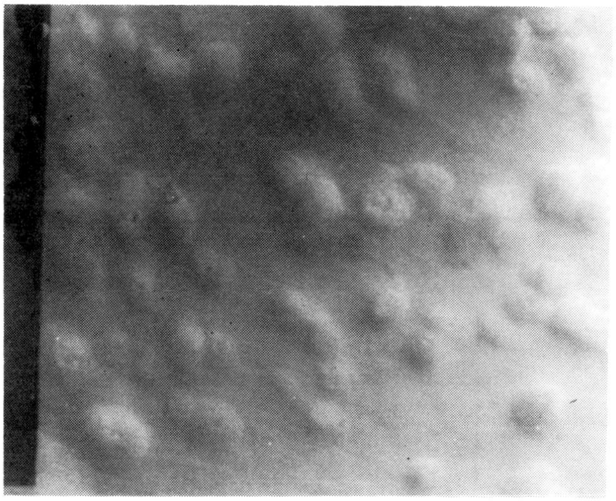

(a) without vibration

(b) with applied vibration (channeling suppressed).

Fig. 11. Top view of channels in the 27% solution at a cold plate temperature of −50°C.

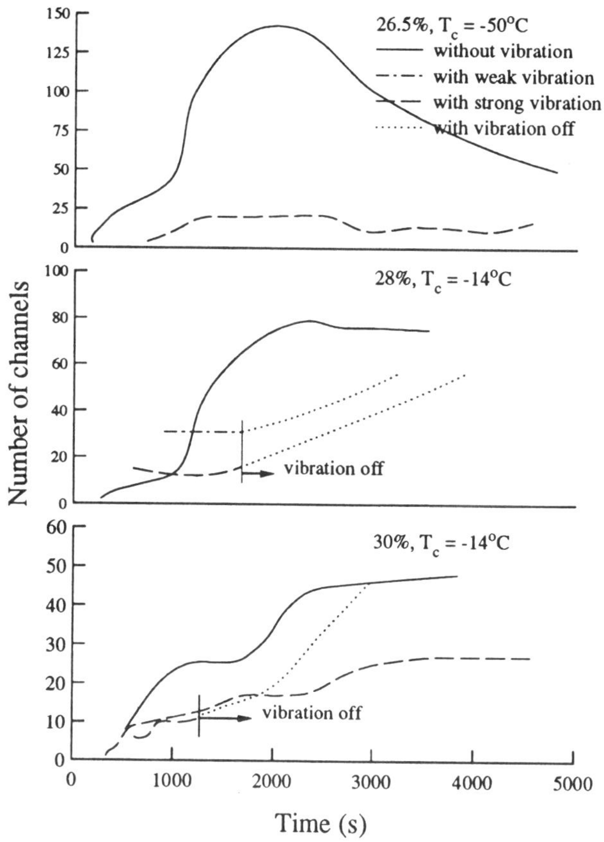

Fig. 12. Effect of vibration on the number of channels at different solution concentrations and cold plate temperatures.

that formed at the cold plate were immediately shaken off, giving rise to an equiaxed-type growth. This would presumably no longer lead to unidirectional solidification.

Based on the observations from these experiments, it appears that vibration breaks up the secondary and tertiary dendrite arms. This dendrite fragmentation decreases the resistance to fluid ejection globally in the mushy zone, in contrast to static solidification where fluid is preferentially ejected through localized columns of low solid fraction. This is consistent with the presence of diffused, weak plumes and fingers co-existing throughout most of the solidification process. When the cold wall temperature was below eutectic, and a solid layer was present, the structure of the solid layer was found to be different with vibration, with vertical striations seen in the solid structure. This confirmed that the mushy zone structure was indeed altered by the applied vibration. However, it is not clear whether this structural difference observed near the side wall of the test section is also present in the interior.

While vibration appears to suppress channeling to a certain degree for all concentrations, it is more effective at the smaller concentrations. This is attributable to the difference in mushy zone structure between the smaller and larger concentrations: in the former, the skeleton of the mushy zone is weak and less dense (low solid fraction) and lends itself to fragmentation; at the larger concentrations, the larger solid fraction and greater integrity of the mushy zone resists fragmentation and thus sustains channels in spite of applied vibration. These results would seem to support the mechanism proposed in the literature (for instance, Worster, 1992) for channel development from within the mushy zone, rather than due to bulk liquid perturbations (Hellawell et al., 1993). The decreased permeability of the mushy zone due to the tighter packing induced by vibration would make it less likely that the solutal Rayleigh numbers (defined in Chen and Chen, 1991; Worster, 1992) would exceed the critical value required for channel formation. If the origins of channels lay in bulk liquid perturbations, and applied vibration suppressed channels by shearing off these perturbations, the dependence of the success of vibration on the solution concentration could not be reasonably explained.

CONCLUSIONS

The mushy zone characteristics and the nature and distribution of channel segregates in unidirectional upward alloy solidification have been investigated, with particular reference to the effects of initial concentration and cold plate temperature. With an increase in concentration, the growth velocity of the solidus decreased while that of the liquidus increased, resulting in a thicker mushy zone, corresponding to the larger freezing range. The nature and extent of the channeling was also strongly affected by concentration. Sharp, pronounced channels were observed in the 30 and 33 wt.% solutions, while those in the 27 wt.% solution were less defined, double in number, and topped by large, diffuse craters. Competing effects that result in the existence of upper and lower limits for the concentration range over which channeling occurs are discussed. Channels start "nucleating" when the growth rate has reduced to a nearly constant level, at which time finger convection is replaced by plume convection. While the cold plate temperature affected the rate of interface progression, the mushy zone thickness was unaffected. Also, at a given concentration, the number of channels decreased as the cold plate temperature was lowered.

Vibration applied to the test cell during the solidification process was found to suppress channel formation at all concentrations, but particularly effectively at about 26 to 27%. Solidification with vibration differed from the static case in that finger convection persisted throughout the solidification process in the former. Vibration reduced the mushy zone thickness by dendrite fragmentation and settling at all concentrations. The amplitude of the applied vibration, rather than the frequency was found to be the important factor; larger-amplitude vibration (of about 0.6 mm) affected channeling at all concentrations, whereas the smaller amplitude suppressed channeling only at concentrations of 28% or less. The mushy zone thickness and the number of channels grew as soon as vibration was turned off during solidification. The channel suppression results of this study support the mechanism proposed in the literature for channel development from within the mushy zone, rather than due to bulk liquid perturbations.

ACKNOWLEDGEMENT

Support for this work from the National Science Foundation (Grant No. CTS-9210612) is gratefully acknowledged.

REFERENCES

Asai, S. and Muchi, I, 1978, "Theoretical Analysis and Model Experiments on the Formation Mechanism of Channel-type Segregation," *Trans. ISIJ*, Vol. 18, pp. 90-98.

Bennon, W. D. and Incropera, F. P., 1989, "An Experimental Investigation of Binary Solidification in a Vertical Channel With Thermal and Solutal Mixed Convection," *J. Heat Transfer*, Vol. 111, pp. 706-712.

Chen, C. F. and Chen, F., 1991, "Experimental Study of Directional Solidification of Aqueous Ammonium Chloride Solution," *J. Fluid Mechanics*, Vol. 227, pp. 567-586.

Chen, C. F. and Turner, J. S., 1980, "Crystallization in a Double-Diffusive System," *J. Geophysical Res.*, Vol. 85, pp. 2573-2593.

Christenson, M. S. and Incropera, F. P., 1989, "Solidification of an Aqueous Ammonium Chloride Solution in a Rectangular Cavity - I. Experimental Study," *Int. J. Heat Mass Transfer*, Vol. 32, pp. 47-68.

Combeau, H. and Lesoult, G., 1993, "Simulation of Freckles Formation and Related Segregation during Directional Solidification of Metallic Alloys," *Modeling of Casting, Welding and Advanced Solidification Processes VI*, TMS, pp. 201-208.

Copley, S. M., Giamei, A. F, Johnson, S. M., and Hornbecker, M. F., 1970, "The Origin of Freckles in Unidirectionally Solidified Castings," *Metall. Trans.*, Vol. 1, pp. 2193-2204.

Felicelli, S. D., Heinrich, J. C., and Poirier, D. R., 1991, "Simulation of Freckles during Vertical Solidification of Binary Alloys," *Metall. Trans.*, Vol. 22B, pp. 847-859.

Fujii, T., Poirier, D. R., and Flemings, M. C., 1968, "Macrosegregation in a Multicomponent Low Alloy Steel," *Metall. Trans.*, Vol. 10B, pp. 331-339.

Heinrich, J. C., Felicelli, S., Nandapurkar, P., and Poirier, D. R., 1989, "Thermosolutal Convection during Dendritic Solidification of Alloys: Part II. Nonlinear Convection," *Metall. Trans.*, Vol. 20B, pp. 883-891.

Hellawell, A., Sarazin, J. A., and Steube, R. S., 1993, "Channel Convection in Partly Solidified Systems," *Phil. Trans. R. Soc. Lond.*, Vol. 345A, pp. 507-544.

Huppert, H. E., 1990, "The Fluid Mechanics of Solidification," *J. Fluid Mechanics*, Vol. 212, pp. 209-240.

Jackson, K. A., Hunt J. D., Uhlmann, D. R., and Seward III, T. P., 1966, "On the Origin of the Equiaxed Zone in Castings," *Trans. AIME*, Vol. 236, pp. 149-158.

Magirl, C. S. and Incropera, F. P., 1993, "Flow and Morphological Conditions Associated with Unidirectional Solidification of Aqueous Ammonium Chloride," *J. Heat Transfer*, Vol. 115, pp. 1036-1043.

McCay, M. H. and McCay T. D., "Experimental Measurements of Solutal Layers in Unidirectional Solidification," *J. Thermophysics*, Vol. 2, pp. 197-202.

McDonald, R. J. and Hunt, J. D., 1969, "Fluid Motion Through the Partially Solid Regions of a Casting and Its Importance in Understanding A Type Segregation," *Trans. AIME*, Vol. 245, pp. 1993-1997.

Mehrabian, R., Keane, M., and Flemings, M. C., 1970, "Interdendritic Fluid Flow and Macrosegregation; Influence of Gravity," *Metall. Trans.*, Vol. 1, pp. 1209-1220.

Neilson, D. G. and Incropera, F. P., 1991, "Unidirectional Solidification of a Binary Alloy and the Effects of Induced Fluid Motion," *Int. J. Heat Mass Transfer*, Vol. 34, pp. 1717-1732.

Neilson, D. G. and Incropera, F. P., 1993a, "Effect of Rotation on Fluid Motion and Channel Formation during Unidirectional Solidification of a Binary Alloy," *Int. J. Heat Mass Transfer*, Vol. 36, pp. 489-505.

Neilson, D. G. and Incropera, F. P., 1993b, "Three-Dimensional Considerations of Unidirectional Solidification in a Binary Liquid," *Num. Heat Transfer*, Part A, Vol. 23, pp. 1-20.

Neilson, D. G. and Incropera, F. P., 1993c, "Experimental Study of Unidirectional Solidification of Aqueous Ammonium Chloride in a Cylindrical Mold with and without Rotation," *Experimental Heat Transfer*, Vol. 6, pp. 131-155.

Poirier, D. R. and Heinrich, J. C., 1993, "Simulations of Thermosolutal Convection in Directional Solidification," *Modeling of Casting, Welding and Advanced Solidification Processes VI*, ed. Piwonka et al., TMS, pp. 227-234.

Rappaz, M. and Voller, V., 1990, "Modeling of Micro-macrosegregation in Solidification Processes," *Metall. Trans.*, Vol. 21A, pp. 749-753.

Sample, A. K. and Hellawell, A., 1982, "The Effect of Mold Precession on Channel and Macro-Segregation in Ammonium Chloride-Water Analog Castings," *Metall. Trans.*, Vol. 13B, pp. 495-501.

Sample, A. K. and Hellawell, A., 1984, "The Mechanisms of Formation and Prevention of Channel Segregation during Alloy Solidification," *Metall. Trans.*, Vol. 15A, pp. 2163-2173.

Sarazin, J. R. and Hellawell, A., 1988, "Channel Formation in Pb-Sn, Pb-Sb, and Pb-Sn-Sb Alloy Ingots and Comparison with the System NH_4Cl-H_2O," *Metall. Trans.*, Vol. 19A, pp. 1861-1871.

Standish, N., 1970, Discussion of "Fluid Motion through Partially Solidified Regions of a Casting and its Importance in Understanding A Type Segregation," *Metall. Trans.*, Vol. 1, pp. 2026-2029.

Streat, N. and Weinberg, F., 1972, "Pipe Formation in Pb-Sn Alloys," *Metall. Trans.*, Vol. 3, pp. 3181-3184.

Szekely, J. and Jassal, A. S., 1978, "An Experimental and Analytical Study of the Solidification of a Binary Dendritic System," *Metall. Trans.*, Vol. 9B, pp. 389-398.

Tait, S. and Jaupart, C., 1992, "Compositional Convection in a Reactive Crystalline Mush and Melt Differentiation," *J. Geophysical Research*, Vol. 97, B5, pp. 6735-6756.

Tewari, S. N., and Shah, R., 1992, "Thermosolutal Convection During Unidirectional Dendritic Growth and its Effect on Macrosegregation," *Micro/Macro Scale Phenomena in Solidification* ASME HTD-Vol. 218, pp. 9-16.

Viskanta, R., 1990, "Mathematical Modeling of Transport Processes during Solidification of Binary Systems," *JSME Int. Journal*, Series II, Vol. 33, pp. 409-423.

Worster, M. G., 1992, "Instabilities of the Liquid and Mushy Regions during Solidification of Alloys," *J. Fluid Mechanics*, Vol. 237, pp. 649-669.

HTD-Vol. 284/AMD-Vol. 182, Transport Phenomena in Solidification
ASME 1994

ANALYSIS OF THE EFFECT OF SHRINKAGE ON MACROSEGREGATION IN ALLOY SOLIDIFICATION

Matthew John M. Krane and Frank P. Incropera
Heat Transfer Laboratory
School of Mechanical Engineering
Purdue University
West Lafayette, Indiana

ABSTRACT

Numerical calculations based on a continuum model are used to examine the effects of solidification shrinkage on the redistribution of solute in a Pb-19.2%Sn mixture which is convectively cooled at a side wall. For each of three different cooling rates, separate calculations are performed for shrinkage and buoyancy-induced flows, as well as for the combined influence of shrinkage and buoyancy effects. The calculations reveal that flow and macrosegregation patterns are more strongly influenced by buoyancy effects over a wide range of solidification rates. Although extremely large solidification rates yield small regions near the chilled wall in which shrinkage induced flows control the redistribution of solute, the overall effect on macrosegregation is small relative to that associated with buoyancy. Scaling analysis of the governing equations produces reference shrinkage and buoyancy velocities which can be used to extend the current numerical results to other binary systems.

NOMENCLATURE

A_m	frontal area of mushy zone (m^2)
c	specific heat [J/kg K]
D_l	mass diffusion coefficient [m^2/s]
f	mass fraction
f^α	mass fraction of species α
g	volume fraction or gravitational acceleration [m/s^2]
h	enthalpy [J]
h_f	heat of fusion [J/kg]
H	height of domain [m]
k	thermal conductivity [W/m K]
K	permeability [m^2]
L_1	length of bottom wall [m]
L_2	length of top wall [m]
m	mass [kg]
P	pressure [N/m^2]
q_{lat}	latent heat extraction rate [W]
t	time [s]
T	temperature [K]
u	x-velocity [m/s]
U	reference velocity [m/s], overall heat transfer coefficient (W/m^2K)
v	y-velocity [m/s]
V	velocity vector [m/s]
V	volume [m^3]
x,y	Cartesian coordinates [m]

Greek Symbols

α	thermal diffusivity [m^2/s]
β	contraction ratio
β_S	solutal expansion coefficient
β_T	thermal expansion coefficient [1/K]

δ mushy zone thickness [m]
κ_o permeability constant [m^2]
μ_l dynamic viscosity [kg/s m]
ν kinematic viscosity [m^2/s]
ρ density [kg/m^3]

Subscripts

b buoyancy driven
c chill
d diffusion driven
e eutectic
l liquid
o initial
s solid, shrinkage driven
S solutal
T thermal

Superscripts

α constituent of binary mixture

INTRODUCTION

Recently, numerous studies have addressed means by which the solidification of binary metal alloys may be modelled, with particular attention given to continuum formulations based on classic mixing theory or volume averaging methods (Bennon and Incropera, 1987; Voller and Prakash, 1987; Beckermann and Viskanta, 1988; Ganesan and Poirier, 1990; Amberg, 1991; Ni and Beckermann, 1991; Prescott *et al.*, 1991). In these models, it is possible to track the freezing fronts without specifying interface conditions or explicitly computing the size of the different regions (solid, liquid and mush). Important features of such models include prediction of the nonuniform redistribution of solute (macrosegregation) during freezing, as well as determination of growth rates for the solid and two-phase (mushy) regions and convection in the mush and bulk liquid. Recent successes include the prediction of channel development in the mushy zone for unidirectional solidification of an off-eutectic solution cooled from below and its relationship to the formation of freckle segregates in the final casting (Felicelli *et al.*, 1991; Neilson and Incropera, 1991). The freckles are regions of high concentration gradients in the frozen ingot and therefore of severe nonuniformity in mechanical properties.

Although the foregoing studies assume that the density of the alloy does not change during solidification, it is well known that most alloys shrink as they are cast. The attendant volume change can cause the casting to pull away from the mold wall and can induce defects such as hot tears and porosity. The objective of this study is to determine conditions under which shrinkage induced flow significantly alters macrosegregation in a casting through its influence on concentration fields during freezing.

Many early attempts to model macrosegregation in binary alloys examined shrinkage effects as the only source of interdendritic liquid motion (Flemings and Nereo, 1967, 1968; Flemings *et al.*, 1968). In these studies, all of which used globally stable Al-Cu mixtures chilled from below, experiments and analysis were in good agreement, showing the sometimes significant effect of solidification contraction on macrosegregation. Mehrabian *et al.* (1970a) extended the model to study side cooled Al-Cu ingots in which buoyancy effects had a major role. They predicted that, at higher solidification rates, shrinkage induced flows would have a significant effect on the velocity field, but that such effects would be negligible at lower rates. Lead-tin solutions were solidified from below at moderate freezing rates by Streat and Weinberg (1974), whose results indicated that, for the solutally unstable cases (20% Sn), shrinkage does not play a significant role in macrosegregation.

The effect of shrinkage on the temperature field was considered by Chang and Tsai (1990), who numerically solved the governing equations for one-dimensional freezing of a pure substance. An approximate solution to this problem is described by Viskanta (1983). Although Chang and Tsai concluded that "the temperature history...is significantly affected by shrinkage," inspection of their temperature and phase front histories indicates that differences are within a few per cent, which is well within normal model uncertainties.

Using a continuum model to simulate solidification induced at the side wall of a mold, Xu and Li (1991) were the first to examine the shrinkage phenomenon in a binary alloy (Cu-Al). They showed that a large pressure gradient is needed deep in the mushy zone to supply liquid to feed associated volume changes. Because the pressure gradient is orders of magnitude larger than that which could be generated by buoyancy forces, shrinkage induced flows might be expected to dominate buoyant flows in regions close to the solidus. Xu and Li also showed macrosegregation patterns for the fully solidified ingot, but did not compare them with predictions based on neglecting shrinkage effects.

Adapting the continuum model of Bennon and Incropera (1987), Chiang and Tsai (1992a,b) considered the effects of shrinkage on the solidification of a 1% Cr steel alloy. In their first paper (1992a), they computed velocity and temperature fields, but neglected solutal redistribution. Shrinkage was accommodated by moving the free surface in a riser to account for the volume change at each time step. They compared predicted temperature histories for conduction dominated freezing with predictions which included the effects of convection due to volume change. While they concluded that the influence of shrinkage induced flow "on the casting cooling curve could be significant," inspection of the temperature histories reveals negligible differences between the two cases. It is noteworthy that differences were negligible, despite the use of a solidification contraction ratio, $\beta = (\rho_s/\rho_l - 1) = 0.2$, which substantially exceeds values normally associated with metallic systems ($0.02 \leq \beta \leq 0.10$) (Brandes and Brook, 1992).

In their second paper, Chiang and Tsai (1992b) added the effect of natural convection due to temperature differences and performed three simulations: (i) with shrinkage induced flow, (ii) with buoyancy induced flow, and (iii) with both shrinkage and buoyancy induced flows. The authors concluded that: (1) "although the isotherms and temperature fields (*sic*) in the casting caused by shrinkage and/or natural convection are usually the same, their flow patterns are different;" (2) volume change effects dominate flow patterns in the melt during the early and late stages of solidification, while thermally driven convection dominates in the interim; and (3) flows in the mushy zone are driven primarily by volume change rather than natural convection. However, they did not determine under what conditions the isotherms would be changed by any of the flows. Also, because they used a thermal expansion coefficient ($\beta_T = 7.85579 \times 10^{-9}$ K^{-1}) which is approximately five orders of magnitude smaller than the appropriate value of 1.26×10^{-4} K^{-1} (Brandes and Brook, 1992), their conclusions should be viewed with caution.

In a similar study, Diao and Tsai (1993) looked at a 4.1% wt Cu-Al system convectively cooled from below. They used the same version of the Bennon and Incropera model (1987) adopted by Chiang and Tsai (1992a), but this time they considered the effects of solute transport and therefore macrosegregation in the ingot. However, the geometry and choice of materials dictated thermally and solutally stable conditions. With no buoyancy driven convection, it was the relative effects of diffusion and shrinkage induced flow which were studied. The results showed that, while there was a tendency for the rejected copper to diffuse upwards and therefore to provide a more uniform distribution, the downward flow caused by volume change tended to overwhelm the effects of diffusion, causing more copper to be transported from the bulk liquid towards the solidus. Hence, solid close to the bottom of the ingot was predicted to be copper rich, instead of slightly copper poor, as for diffusion-dominated conditions.

In the foregoing studies, no attempt was made to generalize the results. In fact, few attempts have been made to apply any sort of scale analysis to alloy solidification. Amberg (1992,1993) identified several dimensionless parameters for alloy freezing from a vertical boundary, deriving them from physically meaningful reference scales. These parameters were used to delineate different solidification regimes and to estimate the solidification time, global macrosegregation parameters, the degree of undercooling, and the onset of buoyancy induced flows.

In this study, a numerical study is performed to identify the relative influence of shrinkage and buoyancy induced flows on macrosegregation. Also, the momentum equations are scaled inside the mushy zone to derive shrinkage and buoyancy reference velocities and to delineate the physical variables which govern shrinkage and buoyancy driven flows. The material used for these simulations is a Pb-19.2% wt Sn system, which has the advantages of a relatively simple phase diagram and well known properties (Table 1), as well as a large temperature range in the two-phase region and a large density difference between components. Both of these characteristics enhance macrosegregation. The alloy is chilled from a vertical side wall with an opening provided at the opposite side for a riser in the top surface (Figure 1). The size of the domain

TABLE 1: MATERIAL PROPERTIES AND CASTING CONDITIONS

c_l	= 177.9 J/kg K	T_e = 456 K	
c_s	= 154.7 J/kg K	T_o = 560 K	
D_l	= 1.05 X 10^{-9} m²/s	T_c = 293 K	
f^{Sn}_e	= 0.619	β = 0.08	
f^{Sn}_o	= 0.192	β_S = 0.354	
h_f	= 30,162 J/kg	β_T = 1.09 X 10^{-4} K^{-1}	
H	= 0.05 m	K_o = 2.8 X 10^{-11} m²	
k_l	= 22.9 W/m K	μ_l = 0.0023 kg/s m	
k_s	= 39.7 W/m K	ρ_l = 10,000 kg/m³	
L_1	= 0.2 m	ρ_s = 10,800 kg/m³	
L_2	= 0.15 m		

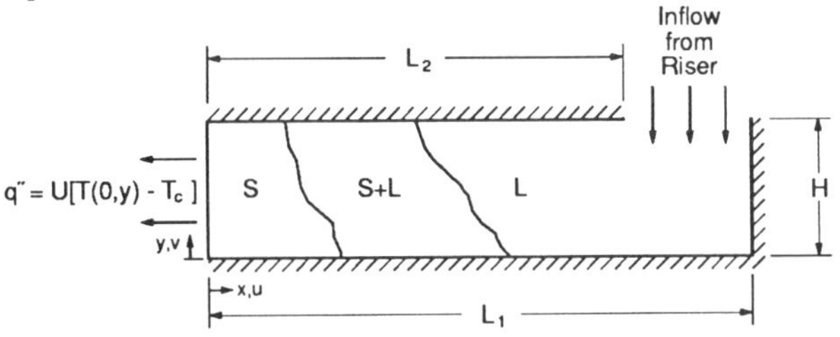

Figure 1: System Geometry

is L_1 = 200 mm, L_2 = 150 mm and H = 50 mm.

MATHEMATICAL FORMULATION AND NUMERICAL METHODS

Simulation of the solidification of a binary metal alloy is considered in a two-dimensional domain. Adopting the continuum model of previous studies (Bennon and Incropera, 1987; Prescott *et al.*, 1991), the equations of mass, momentum, energy and species conservation are written in terms of the *mixture* density, velocity, enthalpy and species concentration.

$$\frac{\partial \rho}{\partial t} + \frac{\partial}{\partial x}(\rho u) + \frac{\partial}{\partial y}(\rho v) = 0 \tag{1}$$

$$\frac{\partial}{\partial t}(\rho u) + \nabla\cdot(\rho V u) = \nabla\cdot\nabla\left(\mu_l \frac{\rho}{\rho_l} u\right) - \frac{\mu_l}{K_x}\frac{\rho}{\rho_l}(u-u_s) - \frac{\partial P}{\partial x} \tag{2}$$

$$\frac{\partial}{\partial t}(\rho v) + \nabla\cdot(\rho V v) = \nabla\cdot\nabla\left(\mu_l \frac{\rho}{\rho_l} v\right) - \frac{\mu_l}{K_y}\frac{\rho}{\rho_l}(v-v_s)$$
$$+ \rho_l g(\beta_T(T-T_o) + \beta_S(f_l^\alpha - f_{l,o}^\alpha)) - \frac{\partial P}{\partial y} \tag{3}$$

$$\frac{\partial}{\partial t}(\rho h) + \nabla\cdot(\rho V h) = \nabla\cdot\left(\frac{k}{c_s}\nabla h\right) +$$
$$\nabla\cdot\left(\frac{k}{c_s}\nabla(h_s - h)\right) - \nabla\cdot(\rho(V-V_s)(h_l - h)) \tag{4}$$

$$\frac{\partial}{\partial t}(\rho f^\alpha) + \nabla\cdot(\rho V f^\alpha) = \nabla\cdot(\rho D_l \nabla f^\alpha) +$$
$$\nabla\cdot(\rho D_l \nabla(f_l^\alpha - f^\alpha)) - \nabla\cdot(\rho(V-V_s)(f_l^\alpha - f^\alpha)) \tag{5}$$

Although several terms in these equations are written as source terms, not all should be construed as such. This approach is motivated by the fact that many numerical techniques employ the following standard form for advection-diffusion equations:

$$\frac{\partial}{\partial t}(\rho\phi) + \nabla\cdot(\rho V\phi) = \nabla\cdot\Gamma\nabla\phi + S. \tag{6}$$

In order to fit this form, where ϕ is a mixture quantity such as enthalpy, composition, or velocity, certain quantities must be artificially designated as source terms. For instance, although the last two terms in equations (4) and (5) are actually components of the advection and diffusion terms, they have been extracted to facilitate writing the conservation equations in the standard advection-diffusion form of equation (6). Hence, as previously noted (Bennon and Incropera, 1987), one must be careful when providing physical explanations for these "source-like" terms.

One such misunderstanding has arisen regarding the viscous diffusion terms in equations (2) and (3). For the x-momentum equation, this term can be divided into two parts,

$$\nabla\cdot\nabla\left(\mu_l \frac{\rho}{\rho_l} u\right) = \nabla\cdot(\mu_l \frac{\rho}{\rho_l}\nabla u) + \nabla\cdot\left(\mu_l u \nabla\left(\frac{\rho}{\rho_l}\right)\right), \tag{7}$$

or, assuming uniform densities for each phase,

$$\nabla\cdot\nabla(\mu_l \frac{\rho}{\rho_l} u) = \nabla\cdot(\mu_l \frac{\rho}{\rho_l}\nabla u) + \nabla\cdot(\mu_l u\left(\frac{\rho_s}{\rho_l} - 1\right)\nabla g_s). \tag{8}$$

As noted by Prescott *et al.* (1991), when there is no density difference between the phases, viscous stresses arising from local density variations are negligible and the last term in equations (7) and (8) is neglected. Although this term was included in the formulations of Tsai and coworkers, who examine the effects of volume change, it was misinterpreted. Chiang and Tsai (1992b) state that "shrinkage-induced flow is accounted for" by this term and Diao and Tsai (1993) note that this term "represent(s) the effect of shrinkage." However, in their derivation, Prescott *et al.* (1991) have shown that the term represents a momentum sink resulting from viscous effects related to the different phase densities and is not a shrinkage source term.

Because the foregoing viscous term is not responsible for shrinkage-induced flow, the flow must be driven by some other mechanism. Tsai and coworkers use a front tracking method, which relies on global mass continuity to determine the velocity perpendicular to a free surface in a riser (Chiang and Tsai, 1992a,b; Diao and Tsai, 1993). The average velocity of the free surface is then used to displace that surface, thus changing the domain size. In this study, the riser opening is modelled as a boundary of uniform velocity. This velocity is calculated at each time step and is determined by the mass inflow required to compensate for the volume change due to solidification during that time step. In both methods, shrinkage induced flow arises from a need to satisfy equation (1) throughout the domain. However, the present method eliminates the need for changing the domain size. The effect of this velocity boundary condition is to trap tin rich liquid in the ingot, rather than to let it escape to the riser, and, therefore, to produce more macrosegregation at that end of the ingot than would occur otherwise. The degree of overprediction depends on the size of the riser. If the riser is small, the tin rich liquid would eventually be transported back into the mold by shrinkage, and the effect of the boundary condition on macrosegregation would be small. Such effects are ignored in this study and the results will show that this region is not one in which shrinkage induced flows are important.

Additional boundary conditions are prescribed by assuming inflow from the riser to have the initial composition of the melt and the riser itself to have the same local temperature as the melt at the boundary. Effectively, this is an insulated boundary condition ($\partial T/\partial y = 0$) at the opening of the riser. While these assumptions might cause some inaccuracies in the temperature and composition fields near the riser towards the end of solidification, they eliminate the need to calculate details of the riser and preserve the rectangular domain required by the numerical method.

The permeability components, K_x and K_y in equations (2) and (3), depend on the model linking the macroscopic equations to microscopic effects. Although many models have been proposed, we use the relatively simple Blake-Kozeny expression (Bennon and Incropera, 1988):

$$K = \kappa_o \frac{g_l^3}{(1 - g_l)^2}. \tag{9}$$

Because the anisotropy of the mushy region permeability is not well understood, it is assumed that $K_x = K_y = K$, with the permeability constant, κ_o, based on the dendritic arm spacing (DAS). A reasonable average value for the arm spacing in Pb-20% wt Sn (DAS = 71 μm) is provided by Nasser-Rafi *et al.* (1985) and was used to compute the value of κ_o cited in Table 1.

The numerical scheme used to solve the conservation equations (the SIMPLER algorithm) is a control-volume-based finite difference method, with a fully implicit time marching technique (Patankar, 1980). The program uses a TDMA line-by-line solver with a block correction method, solving first for the pressure and velocity fields and then for the mixture enthalpy and composition. Using these mixture quantities, the linearized equilibrium phase diagram for Pb-Sn is then used with the lever law to determine the local temperature, the fraction solid, and the composition of the solid and liquid phases. Use of the lever law, rather than the Sheil model, results in less eutectic solid in the final casting. (The model can account for both primary and eutectic solidification.) However, experimental work by Wang *et al.* (1988) indicates that the actual production of eutectic solid may be much lower than that predicted by the Sheil model, except near the regions which are last to solidify. The expressions based on the phase diagram are well documented (Bennon and Incropera, 1987; 1988) and are not repeated here. The grid (85 x 41) provides a compromise between computational accuracy and speed and is comparable to that used in a previous simulation of a lead-tin system (Prescott and Incropera, 1994a). The system was initially at a uniform temperature (T_o = 560 K) before being cooled convectively at the left wall.

$$q'' = U\,[T(0,y) - T_c] \tag{10}$$

Three different values of the overall heat transfer coefficient were used ($U = 10^2, 10^3, 10^4$ W/m^{2}K), ranging from very slow solidification to rapid solidification associated with a boundary condition which is *nearly* isothermal. The largest time steps which yielded quickly converged results varied with cooling rate, ranging from

0.5s to 0.05 s for slow and rapid cooling, respectively. Solutions were considered converged if they had residuals of mass, energy and species less than 10^{-4} for at least 5 consecutive iterations. The calculations were performed on an HP-715 workstation and used approximately 250 CPU seconds per time step.

SCALE ANALYSIS

To enhance interpretation of the numerical results of this study, a scaling analysis is performed for equations pertinent to the mushy zone within which flow strongly influences redistribution of the components during freezing.

The method used to determine a reference velocity in the mushy zone for buoyancy induced flow follows the approach adopted by Bejan (1984). Equations (2) and (3) are derived assuming that deep inside a mushy zone, characterized by a rigid solid, D'Arcy forces dominate the resistance to flow and transient, advective and diffusive effects can be neglected (Prescott, *et al.*, 1991). Therefore, equations (1-3) can be approximated as

$$\frac{\partial(\rho u)}{\partial x} + \frac{\partial(\rho v)}{\partial y} \sim 0 \qquad \textbf{(11)}$$

$$-\frac{\mu_l}{K}\frac{\rho}{\rho_l}u \sim \frac{\partial P}{\partial x} \qquad \textbf{(12)}$$

$$-\frac{\mu_l}{K}\frac{\rho}{\rho_l}v \sim \frac{\partial P}{\partial y} + \rho_l g\left[\beta_T(T-T_o) + \beta_S(f_l^\alpha - f_{l,o}^\alpha)\right]. \qquad \textbf{(13)}$$

Differentiating equations (12) and (13) with respect to y and x, respectively, and subtracting one from the other to eliminate the pressure gradients, it follows that

$$\frac{\mu_l}{K}\frac{1}{\rho_l}\left(\frac{\partial \rho u}{\partial y} - \frac{\partial \rho v}{\partial x}\right) \sim \rho_l g\left(\beta_S\frac{\partial f_l^\alpha}{\partial x} + \beta_T\frac{\partial T}{\partial x}\right). \qquad \textbf{(14)}$$

However, because $(\beta_S\, \Delta f^\alpha_l / \beta_T\, \Delta T) >> 1$ for Pb-Sn, as well as for many other liquid metal alloys, only the solutal buoyancy force will be retained in subsequent considerations, although similar results are readily obtained for the thermal buoyancy force. With freezing from the side, the mushy zone thickness, δ, and the height of the domain, H, are used as length scales ($x \sim \delta$, $y \sim H$) and the three remaining terms of equation (14) may be scaled as u / H, v / δ, and $(\rho_l\, g\, \beta_S\, \Delta f^\alpha_l\, K) / (\mu_l \delta)$. The liquid composition difference is the difference between the initial value and the composition of the liquid as the mixture approaches the solidus line, $\Delta f^\alpha_l = (f^\alpha_o - f^\alpha_{l,s})$.

From continuity, it follows that $u/\delta \sim v/H$, or $(u/H)/(v/\delta) \sim (\delta/H)^2$. If the ingot has an aspect ratio of order unity, δ/H may range from much less than unity to order unity during the course of solidification. Thus, u/H is initially much less than v/δ and becomes, at most, of order v/δ as solidification proceeds. From equation (14), we obtain

$$v/\delta \sim \frac{\rho_l g \beta_S \Delta f_l^\alpha K}{\mu_l \delta}, \qquad \textbf{(15)}$$

which provides an order-of-magnitude estimate of the buoyancy driven flow velocity in the mushy zone. That is, with $U_b \sim v$,

$$U_b \sim \frac{\rho_l g \beta_S \Delta f_l^\alpha K}{\mu_l}. \qquad \textbf{(16)}$$

Because the permeability, K, varies widely over time and space, equation (16) should be interpreted as a *local* estimate of the strength of the buoyancy induced flow.

To obtain an order-of-magnitude estimate of the shrinkage induced velocity, U_s, the two-phase region is treated as a control volume for which mass inflow is balanced by mass storage. That is,

$$\rho_l A_m U_s = \frac{dm}{dt} = (\rho_s - \rho_l)\frac{dV_s}{dt}, \qquad \textbf{(17)}$$

where A_m is the frontal area of the mushy zone. This area may be approximated as the product of the mold height and a unit depth ($A_m \approx H \cdot 1$). It follows that

$$U_s \sim \left(\frac{\rho_s - \rho_l}{\rho_l}\right)\frac{1}{H}\left(\frac{1}{\rho_s}\frac{dm}{dt}\right). \qquad \textbf{(18)}$$

If the solidification rate is expressed as

$$\frac{dm}{dt} = q_{lat} / h_f, \qquad \textbf{(19)}$$

where q_{lat} is the rate at which latent heat is removed from the mushy zone, the shrinkage induced velocity may be approximated as

$$U_s \sim \frac{\beta\, q_{lat}}{H\, \rho_s\, h_f}. \qquad \textbf{(20)}$$

The heat released due to freezing, q_{lat}, is of the same order as that removed through the mold wall, particularly during the early stages of solidification.

NUMERICAL RESULTS AND DISCUSSION

To assess the influence of solidification shrinkage, nine numerical simulations are performed. The objective was to determine if and when shrinkage induced flows are vigorous enough to significantly affect the redistribution of solute. For each value of U, three numerical simulations were performed, corresponding to: (i) buoyancy induced flow ($\rho_s = \rho_l$), (ii) combined buoyancy and shrinkage induced flow, and (iii) shrinkage induced flow ($\beta_S \approx \beta_T \approx 0$). In each case, the simulations were taken to the point of complete solidification. Numerical results are restricted to the consideration of component redistribution and macrosegregation effects. They are presented as plots of tin concentration over the entire domain at various times and, to facilitate comparisons for the three flow conditions, as plots of the tin concentration along the midheight of the ingot.

The thermal boundary condition for the slowest freezing rate case (U = 100 W/m^2 K) is close to that considered in previous laboratory experiments and numerical studies (Diao and Tsai, 1993; Prescott and Incropera, 1994a,b). The coefficient can be achieved by transferring heat by radiation over a small air gap between the mold and a cold plate maintained near room temperature. With this boundary condition, the ingot was completely solid in just less than 6000 s.

The redistribution of solute for this first case is shown in Figure 2, which provides the midheight composition at 1000, 2000 and 6000 s for the three flow conditions, and Figures 3-5, which indicate the extent of macrosegregation for the entire domain at the selected times. From the excellent agreement between predictions for the buoyancy and buoyancy/shrinkage driven flows, it is evident that, throughout the solidification process, shrinkage has only a small, if not negligible, effect on macrosegregation.

The distribution of solute at t = 1000 s is shown in Figures 2a and 3. When the flow is driven only by solidification contraction, there is a small increase in tin concentration near the chilled wall and a correspondingly slight reduction further in the mushy zone. This condition results from the one-dimensional velocity field, which is perpendicular to the gravity vector and draws tin-rich interdendritic fluid towards the cold wall (Diao and Tsai, 1993). Macrosegregation patterns for the two cases with buoyancy driven flows are very different from that associated solely with shrinkage, but are very similar to each other. When present, buoyancy effects are strong enough to move the rejected tin upward and out of the mush, into the bulk liquid along the top wall. In the combined case, shrinkage does have a small effect on macrosegregation in the upper left corner of the domain. There is some evidence of channels forming in that region, induced by solutal remelting of the dendritic structure. Because some tin-rich liquid is drawn towards the chilled wall, remelting, and consequent channelling, are predicted closer to the wall for the combined case than for buoyancy alone. Near the top of the mushy zone, the flows are

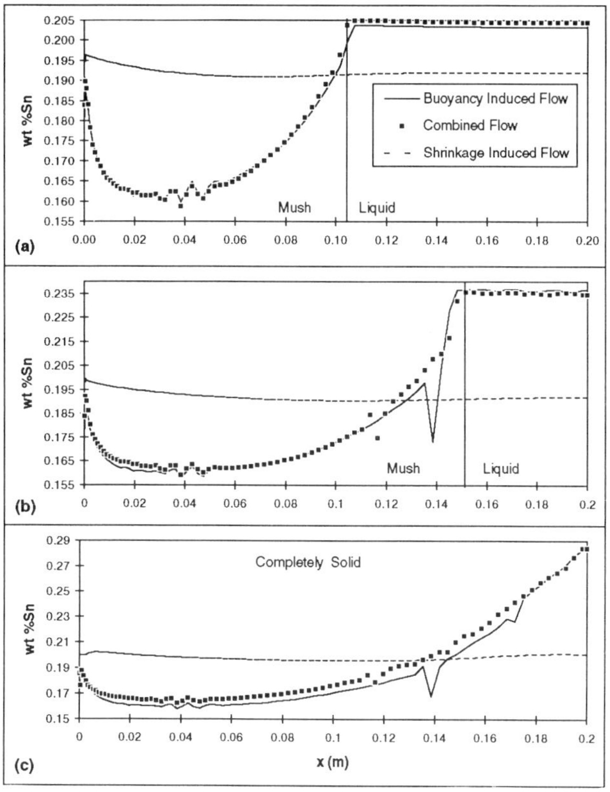

Figure 2: Midheight composition profiles, U = 100 W/m^2 K at (a) 1000 s, (b) 2000 s, (c) 6000 s.

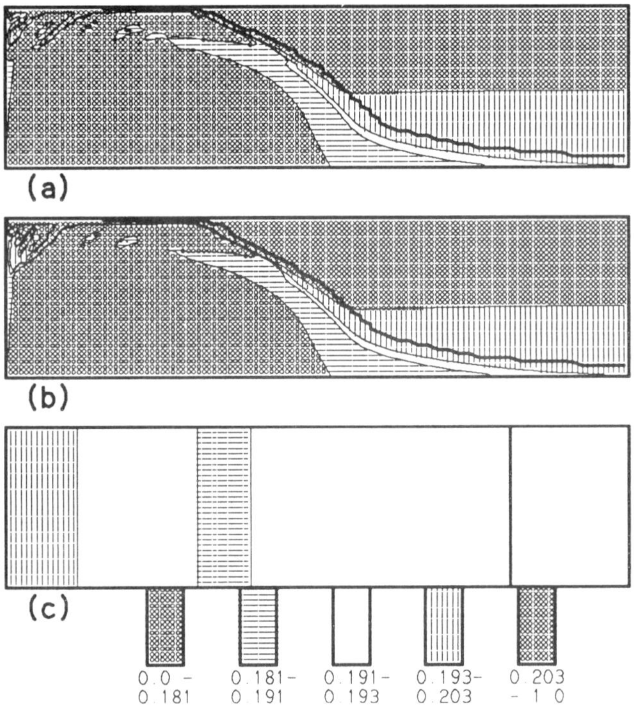

Figure 3: Macrosegregation plots at 1000 s, for U = 100 W/m^2 K: (a) buoyancy induced flow,(b) combined buoyancy and shrinkage induced flow, (c) shrinkage induced flow.

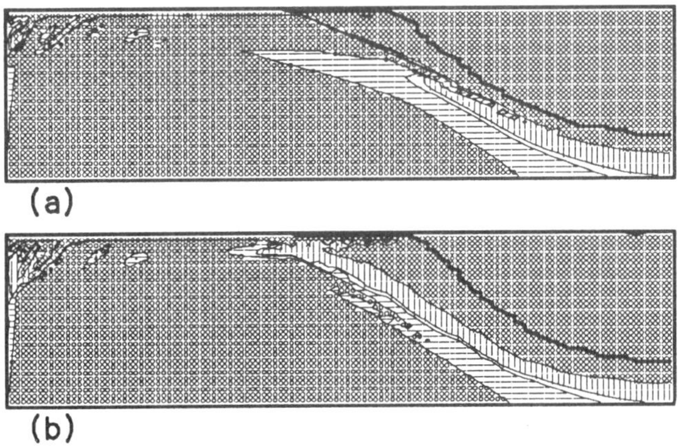

Figure 4: Macrosegregation plots at 2000 s, for U = 100 W/m^2 K: (a) buoyancy induced flow,(b) combined buoyancy and shrinkage induced flow.(See Figure 3 for legend.)

slowed and turned by the top wall, allowing shrinkage to have a small effect, while at the midheight, the buoyancy driven flow overwhelms the shrinkage driven flow, as seen in Figure 2a. As the mushy zone slowly develops and buoyancy driven flow expels tin-rich liquid into the melt,

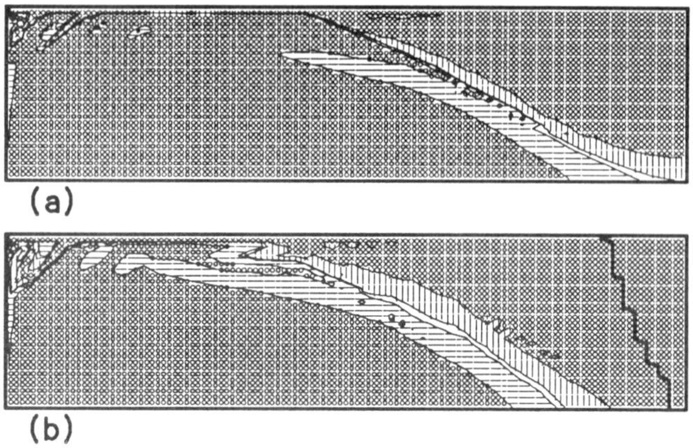

Figure 5: Macrosegregation plots at 6000 s, for U = 100 W/m^2 K: (a) buoyancy induced flow, (b) combined buoyancy and shrinkage induced flow. (See Figure 3 for legend.)

a large zone of negative segregation is produced inside the mush. In that zone, the midheight profiles show some irregularities, which are small channels forming due to local solutal remelting.

With increasing time, the two phase region continues to widen. At t = 2000 s (Figures 2b and 4), the liquidus front is at $x \approx$ 150 mm at the midheight, while, at the chilled wall, the solid fraction is still less than unity, $g_s(x=0) \approx 0.9$. The mush is now large enough to include the tin-rich section created by the earlier expulsion of liquid from the mushy zone. Close inspection of the macrosegregation patterns in Figures 4a and 4b shows again that several tin-rich areas are slightly closer to the cold wall for the combined flow, but there is still little qualitative difference between the two. As seen in Figure 2b, the influence of shrinkage remains the same, involving a small rise in Sn near the chilled wall and a slight decrease inside the mush near the liquidus front. Because conditions are nearly one-dimensional, the full macrosegregation patterns caused by shrinkage driven flows will only be shown when necessary.

In the completely solidified ingot at t = 6000 s (Figures 2c and 5), the final macrosegregation plots show some influence of shrinkage in the combined case, where tin-rich regions are slightly shifted towards the cold wall compared to the buoyancy case. In the final stages of solidification, the shrinkage becomes relatively more important, as the permeability and the composition gradients decrease. The shrinkage midheight profile (Figure 2c) is qualitatively the same as the profiles at the previous times and indicates relatively mild macrosegregation compared to the large spatial variations in composition caused by buoyancy induced flows.

The low heat transfer coefficient of the foregoing case results in a relatively low latent heat release rate and, therefore, a weak shrinkage effect. The second case corresponds to an order of magnitude increase in the heat transfer coefficient (U = 1000 W/m^2 K) and hence to much higher values of q_{lat}, especially during the early stages of solidification when the difference between the wall (T_w) and sink (T_∞) temperatures is large. The wall temperature decays more rapidly than in the first case, but not fast enough to be approximated as an isothermal boundary.

Figure 6 shows midheight composition profiles at times ranging from 25 to 1750 s (complete solidification). In Figure 6a (t = 25 s), profiles for the shrinkage and combined flows match almost exactly, with discernable differences existing only in proximity to the liquidus front. As indicated by equation (16), the buoyancy velocity increases with the permeability and if deviations from a shrinkage dominated flow are to occur, they would do so first at the liquidus ($K \Rightarrow \infty$). At 50 s (Figure 6b), a completely solid region is beginning to form at the chilled wall, and near this interface, solutal redistribution is still dominated by the shrinkage induced flow. However, as the

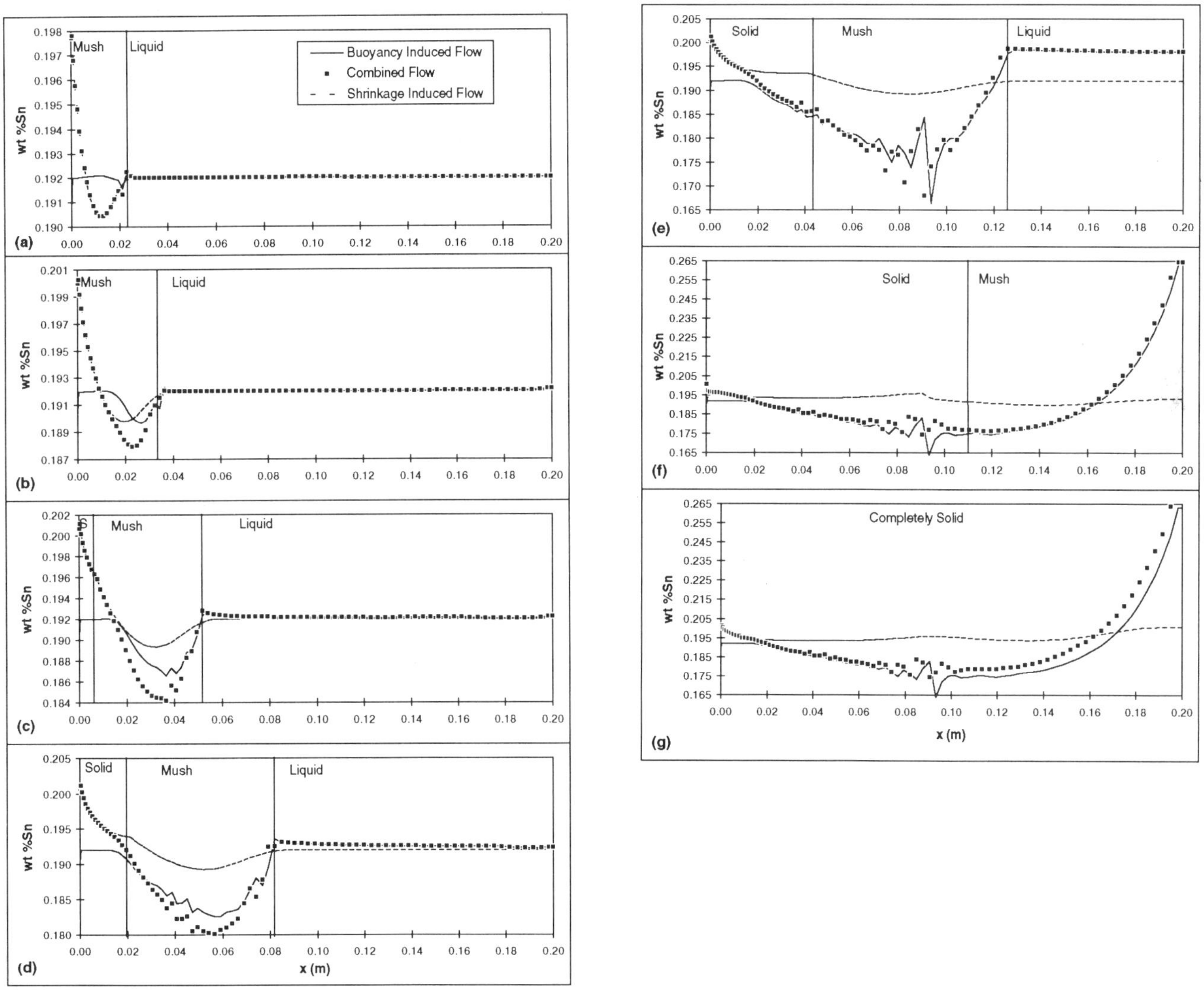

Figure 6: Midheight composition profiles, U = 1000 W/m^2 K at (a) 25 s, (b) 50 s, (c) 100 s, (d) 200s, (e) 400 s, (f) 1000 s, (g) 1750 s.

liquidus front is approached, the tin concentration begins to follow the predictions based on a buoyancy induced flow. Note that the concentration at the far end of the mold (x = 200 mm) increases slightly, as tin-rich liquid escapes the mushy zone and begins to displace the bulk liquid.

Macrosegregation over the entire domain at 50 s is shown in Figure 7 for all three flow conditions. While the Sn concentration in the near wall region remains close to the initial composition for the buoyancy induced flow (Figure 7a), the shrinkage flow (Figure 7c) yields elevated tin concentrations in this region. This result suggests that, while the shrinkage induced flow transports tin-rich liquid towards the chilled surface, buoyancy forces are insufficient to transport interdendritic liquid very far before it is overtaken by the freezing front. As solidification progresses, buoyancy induced flow does begin to advect a significant amount of tin-rich liquid up and out of the mush, creating the cone-like segregates of Figures 7a and 7b. A comparison of the two cones shows that shrinkage affects the cone shape, making it look more like the tin-depleted band in Figure 7c. At the midheight (Figure 6b), the combined flow yields a much lower Sn concentration in the middle of the mush, where buoyancy *and* shrinkage are both important, with buoyancy causing the tin to ascend, while shrinkage pulls it towards the chilled wall. The first effect causes tin-depleted liquid to ascend from lower regions of the mush to the central region, while the second effect causes fluid at the initial composition to be drawn in from the melt.

Figures 6c, 6d and 6e show a progression of midheight concentration profiles during a transitional time in which shrinkage loses its ability to significantly affect the fluid flow. As the wall temperature decreases, thereby decreasing q_{lat}, the shrinkage induced velocity (U_s) decreases proportionally. At t = 100 s, the profiles are similar to those at 50 s, but with significantly more macrosegregation for the combined predictions. This increase in macrosegregation is entirely due to the increased influence of buoyancy driven solute redistribution. For t = 200 s, shrinkage effects cease to dominate at any location in the mushy zone and, for t = 400 s, shrinkage induced flow ceases to have any discernable effect within the mushy zone. Macrosegregation plots for the entire domain at 200

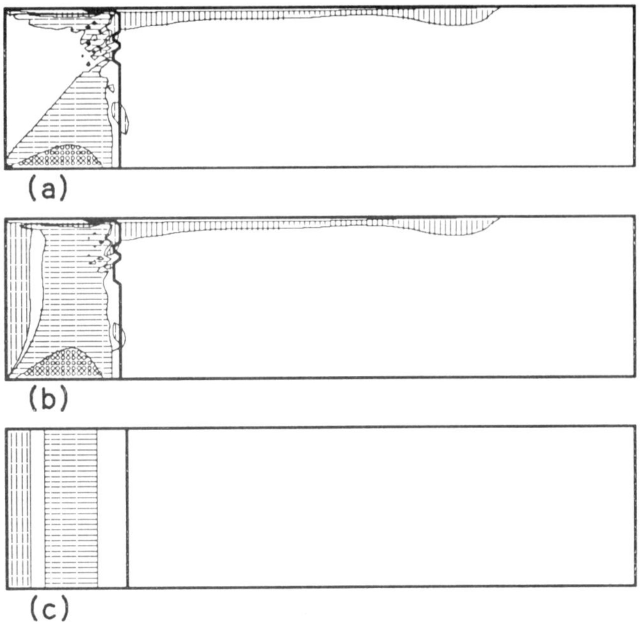

Figure 7: Macrosegregation plots at 50 s, U = 1000 W/m^2 K: (a) buoyancy induced flow, (b) combined buoyancy and shrinkage induced flow, (c) shrinkage induced flow. (See Figure 3 for legend.)

s (Figure 8) reveal a vestigial influence of shrinkage, with Figure 8b exhibiting a larger cone than Figure 8a.

At t = 1000 seconds (Figure 6f), the solid region covers more than half the domain. In the mushy zone, which encompasses the rest of the mold, solute redistribution is completely controlled by buoyancy driven flows, and there is little change in the Sn profile to the time of complete solidification at t = 1750 s (Figures 6g and 9). These plots show three prominent regions of macrosegregation. The tin-rich zone near the chilled wall results from the relatively strong shrinkage induced flow early in the process. In the middle of the domain, a large, broad tin-depleted cone rises from the bottom of the ingot. In this region, negative segregation is compounded by the presence of several freckles. Most of the tin rejected during primary solidification is found in a third region near the riser, which is the last to solidify and therefore is characterized by a large Sn concentration.

Re-examining concentration distributions for the earlier stages of solidification, one is prompted to conclude that shrinkage strongly influences the model predictions. Certainly, at those times, shrinkage driven flows play a major role in transporting solute through the mushy zone.

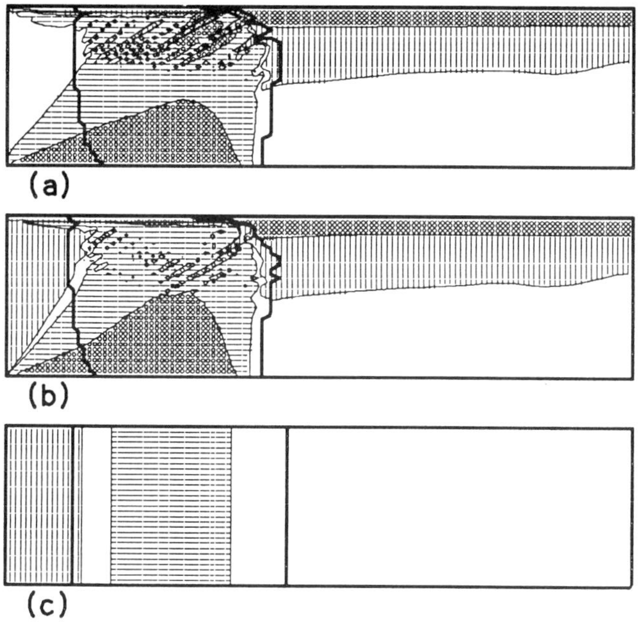

Figure 8: Macrosegregation plots at 200 s, $U = 1000$ W/m^2 K: (a) buoyancy induced flow, (b) combined buoyancy and shrinkage induced flow, (c) shrinkage induced flow. (See Figure 3 for legend.)

However, while positive segregation near the cold wall caused by contraction of the alloy (+ 0.9%) is about half that associated with the negative cone segregate in the primary center of the ingot (- 1.5%), the banded segregation at the right wall is dominant (+7.0%). Given that the region in which shrinkage dominates the distribution of solute is relatively small (less than 10% of the total ingot) and that the level of macrosegregation in this region is approximately 10% of that in the far end of the domain, one can conclude that, in this case, shrinkage has a second order effect on macrosegregation.

With $U = 10{,}000$ W/m^2 K, the rate of heat extraction is large and the chilled wall temperature decreases from its initial value of 560 K to 315 K (≈95% of the difference between the initial and coolant temperatures) in approximately 60 s. Such a large heat transfer coefficient approximates the use of nucleate boiling to cool the ingot and yields a thermal boundary condition comparable to that associated with maintaining an isothermal mold wall. This condition is extremely favorable to enhancing the effect of shrinkage induced flow on solutal redistribution.

Figure 10a shows the midheight composition profiles at t = 10 seconds. In a 5 mm thick region adjoining the

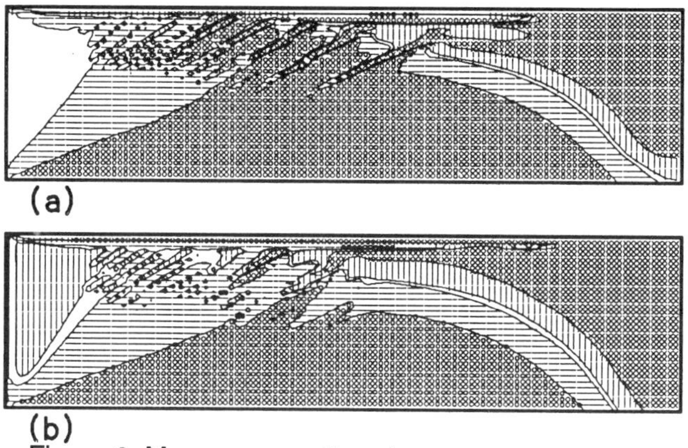

Figure 9: Macrosegregation plots at 1750 s, $U = 1000$ W/m^2 K: (a) buoyancy induced flow, (b) combined buoyancy and shrinkage induced flow. (See Figure 3 for legend.)

chilled wall, there is significant positive segregation (+1.8%) due to the large rate of latent heat release occurring within the first few seconds. The correspondingly large shrinkage induced velocity advects most of the rejected tin towards the chilled surface, and there is excellent agreement between the solute profiles in the mush for predictions based on the combined and shrinkage flow conditions. As shown in Figure 11, the macrosegregation pattern for the combined flow is controlled almost entirely by shrinkage effects. If the flow is assumed to be driven solely by buoyancy, the progression of the solidification fronts is so rapid as to fix the initial composition everywhere but very close to the top and bottom of the ingot.

At t = 50 s, Figure 12 reveals that, while becoming more significant, buoyancy effects influence macrosegregation only near the top and bottom of the domain. Figure 10b suggests that buoyancy is becoming influential near the liquidus interface, but nowhere is it the dominant effect. Figures 10c, 10d and 10e demonstrate the same type of progression from shrinkage to buoyancy controlled conditions in the mush which occurred for $U = 1000$ W/m^{2}K. The time period over which this transition occurs is only slightly shorter for $U = 10{,}000$ W/m^{2}K than $U = 1000$ W/m^{2}K.

Complete solidification occurs at approximately 1400 s (Figure 13), and the region in which macrosegregation is controlled by shrinkage effects encompasses approximately 15% to 20% of the total domain. Although the extent of

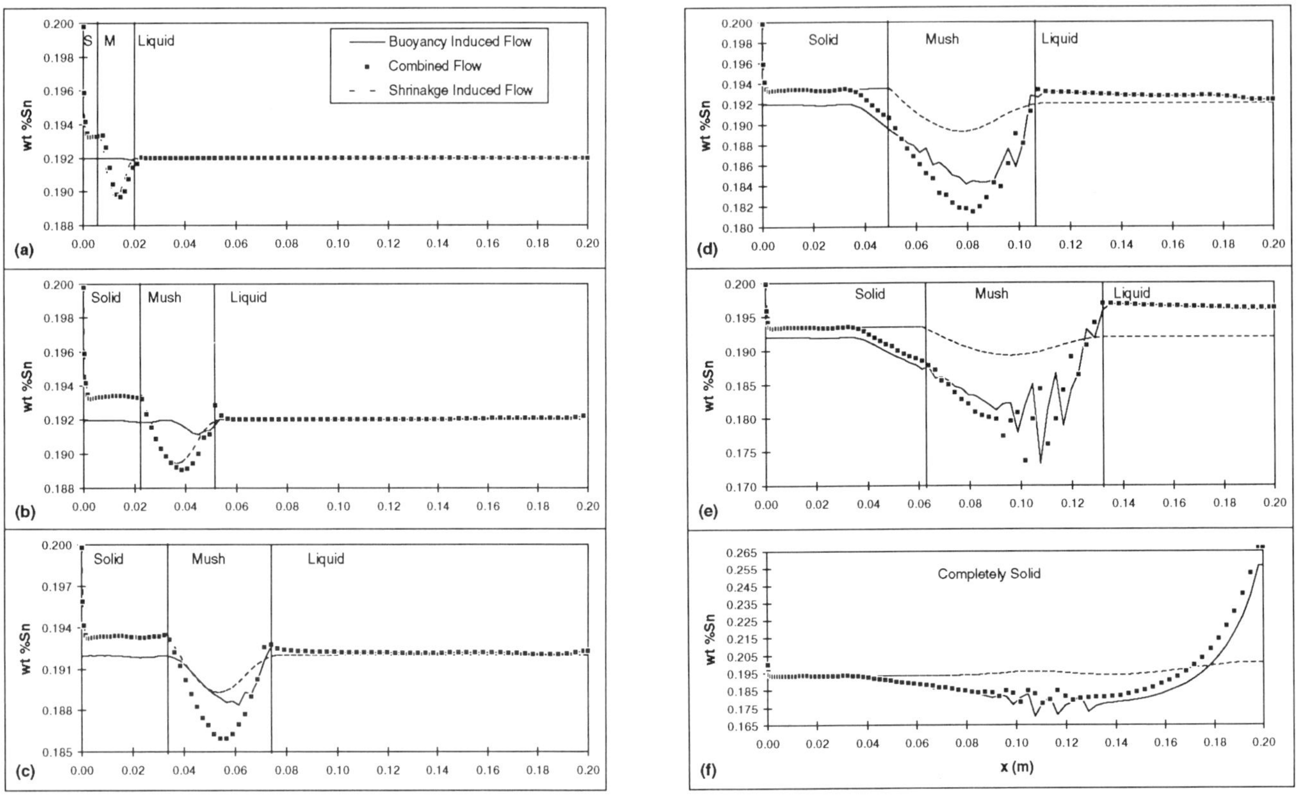

Figure 10: Midheight composition profiles, U = 10,000 W/m^2 K at (a) 10 s, (b) 50 s, (c) 100 s, (d) 200s, (e) 300 s, (f) 1400 s.

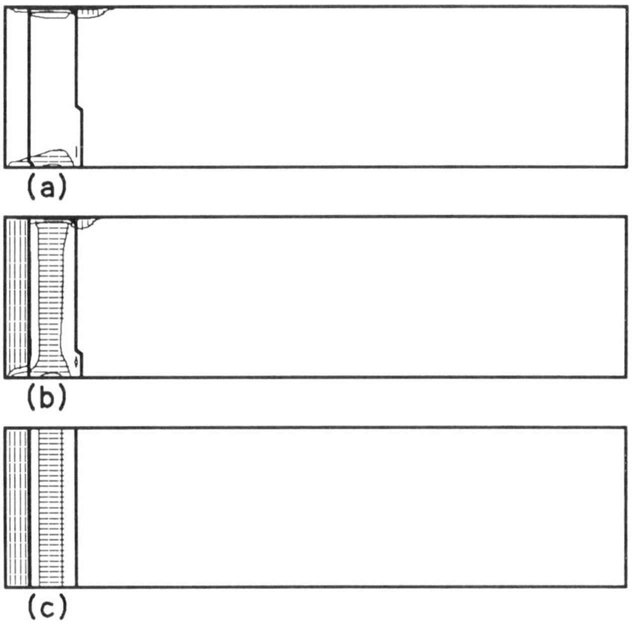

Figure 11: Macrosegregation plots at 10 s, for U = 10,000 W/m^2 K: (a) buoyancy induced flow, (b) combined buoyancy and shrinkage induced flow, (c) shrinkage induced flow. (See Figure 3 for legend.)

this region exceeds that associated with U = 1000 W/m^{2}K, concentrations in this part of the ingot are within ≈ 0.2% of the composition in the buoyancy case. Due to the high solidification rate, especially early in the process, there is less buoyancy driven macrosegregation than for the previous cases. However, the negatively segregated cone in the middle of the domain (-1.5% along the midheight) and the tin-rich band at the far end (+7.0%) are still much larger than the shrinkage induced redistribution at the chilled wall. Even at this high level of heat extraction, and, therefore large U_s, the shrinkage driven transport of solute is only significant near the chilled wall and makes a small contribution to overall macrosegregation in the final ingot.

SIMILARITY CONSIDERATIONS

The foregoing numerical simulations have shown that shrinkage induced flows have a small effect on the final macrosegregation patterns for a particular Pb-Sn system. Thermal boundary conditions ranged from a comparatively small heat extraction rate, for which shrinkage had no

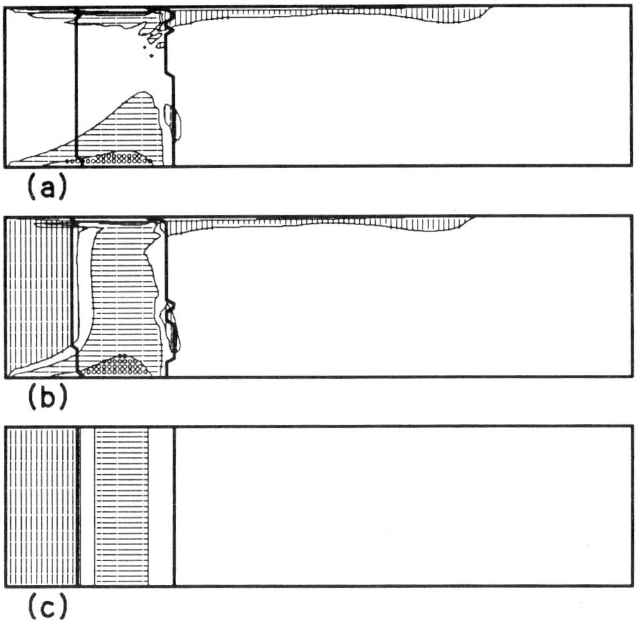

Figure 12: Macrosegregation plots at 50 s, for U = 10,000 W/m^2 K: (a) buoyancy induced flow, (b) combined buoyancy and shrinkage induced flow, (c) shrinkage induced flow. (See Figure 3 for legend.)

discernable effect, to a large rate, for which shrinkage effects were restricted to early flow and solute redistribution patterns in the mushy zone. The question of applicability of these results to other binary systems is addressed by considering the reference velocities developed in the scaling analysis. The reference velocities provide a measure of the strength of the buoyancy and shrinkage induced flows in a side cooled alloy and can be contrasted for different alloys. As examples, Al-5.65%Cu and Cu-13.5%Sn will be compared to the Pb-19.2%Sn system.

From equation (16), the ratio of buoyancy velocities for Pb-Sn and Al-Cu may be expressed as

$$U_b|_{Al-Cu} \;/\; U_b|_{Pb-Sn} = \left[\frac{\rho_l \beta_S \Delta f_l^{\alpha}}{\mu_l}\right]_{Al-Cu} \left[\frac{\mu_l}{\rho_l \beta_S \Delta f_l^{\alpha}}\right]_{Pb-Sn} \qquad \textbf{(21)}$$

which assumes an equivalent dependence of the permeability of the two systems on the solid volume fraction. Although the solutal and thermal buoyancy forces for the Al-Cu mixture are both downward, Mehrabian *et al.* (1970b) and Mori and Ogi (1990) have shown that macrosegregation patterns in a side cooled Al-Cu ingot are

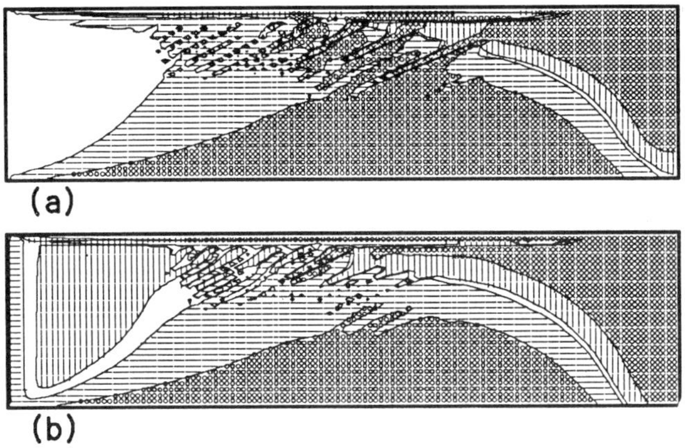

Figure 13: Macrosegregation plots at 1400 s, for U = 10,000 W/m^2 K: (a) buoyancy induced flow, (b) combined buoyancy and shrinkage induced flow. (See Figure 3 for legend.)

similar to the numerical results of this study (Figures 5, 9 and 13). The major difference is that, due to the downward buoyancy force, the channels are oriented down and to the right (as opposed to the current Pb-Sn results, in which channels extend up and to the right). The scaling parameters of this study remain valid because the buoyancy force is still perpendicular to the direction of shrinkage induced flow. Using properties from Table 1, Diao and Tsai (1993) and Brandes and Brook (1992), equation (21) yields

$$|U_b|_{Al-Cu} \;/\; |U_b|_{Pb-Sn} \approx 1.91\,. \qquad \textbf{(22)}$$

For the Cu-Sn system, ($\beta_S\, \Delta f^{\alpha}_{l} \,/\, \beta_T\, \Delta T$) is close to unity. Therefore, the buoyancy velocity must account for both thermal and solutal effects and is written as

$$U_b \sim \frac{\rho_l g\, (\beta_S\, \Delta f_l^{\alpha} + \beta_T\, \Delta T) K}{\mu_l}\,. \qquad \textbf{(23)}$$

Using equation (23) for the Cu-Sn system and equation (16) for Pb-Sn, the ratio of buoyancy velocities is

$$U_b|_{Cu-Sn} \;/\; U_b|_{Pb-Sn} \approx 0.0066\,. \qquad \textbf{(24)}$$

From equation (20), the ratio of shrinkage velocities may be expressed as

$$U_s|_{Al-Cu} \;/\; U_s|_{Pb-Sn} \;=$$

$$\left[\left(\frac{q_{lat}}{H}\right)\frac{\beta}{\rho_s h_f}\right]_{Al-Cu} \left[\left(\frac{H}{q_{lat}}\right)\frac{\rho_s h_f}{\beta}\right]_{Pb-Sn} . \quad (25)$$

The latent heat release rate per unit surface area may be reasonably approximated as $(q_{lat} \;/\; H) \;\sim\; U\;(T_s\; -\; T_c)$. Assuming equivalent heat transfer coefficients for both systems, it follows that

$$U_s|_{Al-Cu} \;/\; U_s|_{Pb-Sn} \;=$$

$$\left[\frac{(T_s - T_c)\;\beta}{\rho_s h_f}\right]_{Al-Cu} \left[\frac{\rho_s h_f}{(T_s - T_c)\;\beta}\right]_{Pb-Sn} \approx 0.83 . \quad (26)$$

and

$$U_s|_{Cu-Sn} \;/\; U_s|_{Pb-Sn} \;\approx\; 1.11 . \quad (27)$$

While equations (22) and (26) indicate that the characteristic shrinkage and buoyancy velocities for the Al-Cu system are approximately 20% smaller and 100% larger, respectively, than those of the Pb-Sn system, the ratios are of order unity, suggesting similar macrosegregation trends for the two cases. Hence, relative to the influence of buoyancy, one would not expect the Al-Cu system to experience significant macrosegregation due to shrinkage effects. However, for Cu-Sn, the two orders-of-magnitude reduction in the buoyancy velocity and the slight increase in the shrinkage velocity suggest that shrinkage effects would strongly influence macrosegregation in this system.

CONCLUSIONS

The effect of solidification shrinkage on macrosegregation in a binary alloy chilled from one side has been examined using a continuum model. A scaling analysis of the momentum equations produces reference velocities for shrinkage and buoyancy induced flows, which may be used to assess their relative strength for different alloys. For a Pb-19.2%Sn system, predicted macrosegregation patterns were compared at three different cooling rates for shrinkage induced flow, buoyancy induced flow, and a combined flow condition. The comparisons show that, except for large cooling rates, macrosegregation patterns are dominated by buoyancy effects. Shrinkage effects become more important with increasing cooling rate, but even for the largest rate considered in this study, the influence on macrosegregation is restricted to a small region near the chilled surface. Comparisons of the reference velocities suggest that similar behavior characterizes an Al-5.65%Cu system, but that shrinkage effects are more important for a Cu-13.5%Sn alloy.

ACKNOWLEDGEMENTS

The authors would like to thank the Department of Energy for support through Award Number DE-FG02-87ER13759. The first author would also like to thank Dr. Jun Ni and Professor Satish Ramadhyani for many useful discussions during the course of this work.

REFERENCES

G. Amberg, 1991, Computation of macrosegregation in an iron-carbon cast, *Int.J.Heat Mass Transfer,* v. 34, pp. 217-227.

G. Amberg, 1992, Scale analysis and numerical simulation of the solidification of an alloy cooled at a vertical boundary, in *Interactive Dynamics of Convection and Solidification*, S. H. Davis, H. E. Huppert, U. Müller and M. G. Worster, eds., Kluwer.

G. Amberg, 1993, Derivation of parameter ranges in binary solidification, TR 1993:9, Department of Mechanics, The Royal Institute of Technology, Stockholm, Sweden.

C. Beckermann and R. Viskanta, 1988, Double-diffusive convection during dendritic solidification of a binary mixture, *PCH PhysicoChemical Hydrodynamics*, v. 10, pp. 195-213.

A. Bejan, 1984, *Convective Heat Transfer*, Wiley-Interscience, New York.

W. D. Bennon and F. P. Incropera, 1987, A continuum model for momentum, heat and species transport in binary solid-liquid phase change systems-I. Model formulation, *Int.J.Heat Mass Transfer*, v. 30, pp. 2161-2170.

W. D. Bennon and F. P. Incropera, 1988, Numerical analysis of binary solid-liquid phase change using a continuum model, *Numer. Heat Transfer*, v. 13, pp. 277-296.

E. A. Brandes and G. B. Brook, eds., 1992, *Smithell's Metals Reference Handbook*, 7th edition, Butterworth-Heinemann, Ltd., Oxford.

F. C. Chang and H. L. Tsai, 1990, Shrinkage-induced flow and domain change during solidification of pure substances, in *Transport Phenomena in Material Processing*, ASME HTD v. 132, M. Charmichi, M. K. Chyu, Y. Joshi and S. M. Walsh, eds., pp. 73-80.

K. C. Chiang and H. L. Tsai, 1992a, Shrinkage-induced fluid flow and domain change in two-dimensional alloy solidification, *Int.J.Heat Mass Transfer*, v. 35, pp. 1763-1770.

K. C. Chiang and H. L. Tsai, 1992b, Interaction between shrinkage-induced fluid flow and natural convection during alloy solidification, *Int.J.Heat Mass Transfer*, v. 35, pp. 1771-1778.

Q. Z. Diao and H. L. Tsai, 1993, Modeling of solute redistribution in the mushy zone during solidification of aluminum-copper alloys, *Met. Trans. A*, v. 24A, pp. 963-973.

S. D. Felicelli, J. C. Heinrich and D. R. Poirier, 1991, Simulation of freckles during vertical solidification of binary alloys, *Met. Trans. B*, v. 22B, pp. 847-859.

Flemings, M. C., and G. E. Nereo, 1967, Macrosegregation, Part I, *Trans. TMS-AIME*, v. 239, pp. 1449-1461.

Flemings, M. C., R. Mehrabian and G. E. Nereo, 1968, Macrosegregation, Part II, *Trans. TMS-AIME*, v. 242, pp. 41-49.

Flemings, M. C., and G. E. Nereo, 1968, Macrosegregation, Part III, *Trans. TMS-AIME*, v. 242, pp. 50-55.

S. Ganesan and D. R. Poirier, 1990, Conservation of mass and momentum for the flow of interdendritic liquid during solidification, *Met. Trans. B*, v. 21B, pp. 173-181.

Mehrabian, R., M. Keane and M. C. Flemings, 1970a, Interdendritic fluid flow and macrosegregation: Influence of gravity, *Met. Trans.* v.1, pp.1209-1220.

Mehrabian, R., M. Keane and M. C. Flemings, 1970a, Experiments on macrosegregation and freckle formation, *Met. Trans.* v.1, pp.3238-3241.

Mori, N., and K. Ogi, 1991, Study on formation of channel-type segregation, *Met. Trans. A*, v. 22A, pp. 1663-1672.

R. Nasser-Rafi, R. Deshmukh and D. R. Poirier, 1985, Flow of interdendritic liquid and permeability in Pb-20 wt pct Sn alloys, *Met. Trans. A*, v. 16A, pp. 2263-2271.

D. G. Neilson and F. P. Incropera, 1991, Unidirectional solidification of a binary alloy and the effects of induced fluid motion , *Int.J.Heat Mass Transfer*, v. 34, pp. 1717-1732.

J. Ni and C. Beckermann, 1991, A volume-averaged two-phase model for transport phenomena during solidification, *Met. Trans. B*, v. 22B, pp. 349-361.

S. Patankar, 1980, *Numerical Heat Transfer and Fluid Flow*, Hemisphere, New York.

P. J. Prescott, F. P. Incropera and W. D. Bennon, 1991, Modeling of dendritic solidification systems: reassessment of the continuum momentum equation, *Int.J.Heat Mass Transfer*, v. 34, pp. 2351-2359.

P. J. Prescott and F. P. Incropera, 1994, Convective transport phenomena and macrosegregation during solidification of a binary metal alloy - I. Numerical predictions, *ASME JHT*, in press.

P. J. Prescott, F. P. Incropera and D. R. Gaskell, 1994, Convective transport phenomena and macrosegregation during solidification of a binary metal alloy - II. Experiments and comparisons with numerical predictions, *ASME JHT*, in press.

Streat and Weinberg, 1974, Macrosegregation during solidification resulting from density differences in the liquid, *Met. Trans.* v. 5, pp. 2539-2548.

R. Viskanta, 1983, Phase-change heat transfer, in *Solar Heat Storage: Latent Heat Materials*, Volume I, G.A.Lane, ed., CRC Press, pp. 153-222.

V. R. Voller and C. Prakash, 1987, A fixed grid numerical modelling methodology for convection-diffusion mushy region phase-change problems, *Int.J.Heat Mass Transfer*, v. 30, pp. 1709-1719.

Wang, L., V. Laxmanan and J. F. Wallace, 1988, Gravitational macrosegregation in unidirectionally solidified lead-tin alloy, *Met. Trans. A*, v. 19A, pp. 2687-2694.

D. Xu and Q. Li, 1991, Gravity- and solidification-shrinkage-induced liquid flow in a horizontally solidified alloy ingot, *Numerical Heat Transfer (A)*, v. 20, pp. 203-211.

HTD-Vol. 284/AMD-Vol. 182, Transport Phenomena in Solidification
ASME 1994

A DUAL SCALE MODEL OF SEGREGATION PHENOMENA

Suresh Sundarraj and Vaughan R. Voller
Department of Civil and Mineral Engineering
University of Minnesota
Minneapolis, Minnesota

ABSTRACT

Segregation processes in solidifying metal alloys occur at two distinct length scales; microsegregation (controlled by mass diffusion in the dendritic arm spaces) and macrosegregation (controlled by convection over the scale of the casting). In modeling macrosegregation, microsegregation effects are accounted for on assuming limiting mass diffusion behavior. In modeling microsegregation, the macro scale effects are accounted for on prescribing the cooling rate and concentration history. The aim in this paper is to develop a dual length scale model of segregation which attempts to couple the micro- and macro- segregation processes more closely. In the first place, the development of separate macro- and micro-segregation models are described. On defining a dual scale numerical grid, consisting of a single macro scale mesh and a set of distinct micro scale meshes (each associated with a macro scale node point), the macro and micro models are coupled and a dual scale segregation model is developed. Initial results indicate that the choice of microsegregation model does affect the macrosegregation results, in particular the level of macrosegregation achieved is proportional to the amount of eutectic formed at the micro scale.

NOMENCLATURE

List of Symbols

C	concentration
$[C]$	average concentration
C_{eut}	eutectic concentration
C_l	liquid concentration
C_o	nominal concentration
c_p	specific heat
D	mass diffusivity
F	mass flow rate
g	volume fraction
h_{amb}	heat transfer coefficient
k_o	partition coefficient
K	thermal conductivity
L	latent heat of fusion
M_s	Solute mass in the arm spacing
q_C	solute mass flux term
q_H	heat flux term
$s(t)$	front position
S	source term
t	time
T	temperature
T_{amb}	ambient temperature
T_{eut}	eutectic temperature
T_f	fusion temperature
T_i	initial temperature
T_{liq}	liquidus temperature
u	system velocity
V	chemical activity
x	coordinate position
X_b	length of the solution domain
$X(t)$	length of the expanding microscopic domain

Greek Symbols

γ	interfacial surface energy
Δg_s	change in solid volume fraction
ΔH_f	latent heat (J/m^3)
Δt	time step
Δx	space step in macro domain
$\Delta \xi$	space step in micro domain

ξ coordinate in micro domain
ρ mass density of the alloy
$[\rho]$ mixture density of the alloy
$[\rho C]$ mixture solute density
$[\rho H]$ mixture enthalpy
ρ_s^{eut} solid eutectic density
χ phase function
$<\psi>$ intrinsic volume averaged quantity

Subscripts
eut eutectic
equ equilibrium
f fusion
k phase (solid or liquid)
l liquid
P,W,E node point position
s solid

Superscripts
L local value
old old value
s solid
* value at the solid/liquid interface

INTRODUCTION

Solidification phenomena occur over a wide range of length and time scales. An example is segregation which occurs during an alloy solidification process. Segregation results from solute partitioning at the solid/liquid interface, in the mushy region, and its subsequent redistribution by mass diffusion at the microscopic scale (microsegregation) and by fluid flow at the macroscopic scale (macrosegregation). The micro- and macro- segregation processes are coupled. A number of numerical micro- (Roosz et al. (1986), Battle and Pehlke (1990), Voller and Sundarraj (1993)) and macro- (Bennon and Incropera (1987), Beckermann and Viskanta (1988), Voller et al. (1989), Rappaz and Voller (1990) Amberg (1991), Diao and Tsai (1993), Voller and Sundarraj (1993)) segregation models have been reported in the literature. Typically, in microsegregation modeling, the model domain is taken as the one-dimensional region defined by a dendrite arm spacing. In nearly all microsegregation models a very limited treatment of the macro scale effects are considered; usually a constant domain cooling rate is prescribed and macrosegregation effects are neglected (i.e., the average concentration in the micro domain is fixed at the nominal value, C_o). In macrosegregation modeling, microsegregation is accounted for on making limiting assumptions for the local scale mass diffusion; usually a lever assumption (infinite mass diffusion in the solid) (Bennon and Incropera (1987), Beckermann and Viskanta (1988), Amberg (1991), Diao and Tsai (1993)) or a Scheil assumption (zero mass diffusion in the solid) (Voller et al. (1989), Rappaz and Voller (1990) Voller and Sundarraj (1993))

The work presented in this paper is aimed at developing a dual scale model which more completely couples the micro- and macro- segregation processes. A model is developed which describes coupled micro- and macro- segregation occurring in a uni-directionally solidified Aluminum-Copper system (see Figure 1). The paper is divided into three sections. In the first section, a macro model describing inverse segregation is presented. In this model microsegregation effects are accounted for on using a Scheil assumption. In the second section a comprehensive and efficient microsegregation model is introduced. A key feature in this model is its ability to account for mass flow into or out of the microsegregation domain. This provides an immediate link to the macro scale. In the third section a dual scale model which incorporates both the micro- and the inverse segregation models is developed. Note that both the macro- and micro- segregation models have been previously presented in the literature (Voller and Sundarraj, 1993 and Voller and Sundarraj 1994). The central contribution of this paper is the coupling of these models into a single segregation model.

AN INVERSE SEGREGATION MODEL

Inverse segregation is a macrosegregation resulting from redistribution of rejected solute in the mushy region by shrinkage driven fluid flows. In this paper a model of inverse segregation in an Aluminum-Copper system which is solidifying uni-directionally from below, will be presented, see Figure 1. The assumptions and governing equations used in this model are summarized below.

Assumptions

1. The domain is one-dimensional defined by $0<x<X_b$ where X_b is the macro-porosity free domain length on complete solidification.
2. Mass transport of solute in the solid phase by diffusion is neglected.
3. No surface exudation occurs.
4. The solid phase is stationary.
5. The specific heats, c_{p_s} and c_{p_l}, and thermal conductivities, K_s and K_l, are constant within each phase.
6. The latent heat of fusion L is constant.
7. Equilibrium conditions exist at the solid/liquid interface, i.e.,

$$C_s^* = k_o C_l^* \quad (1)$$

and

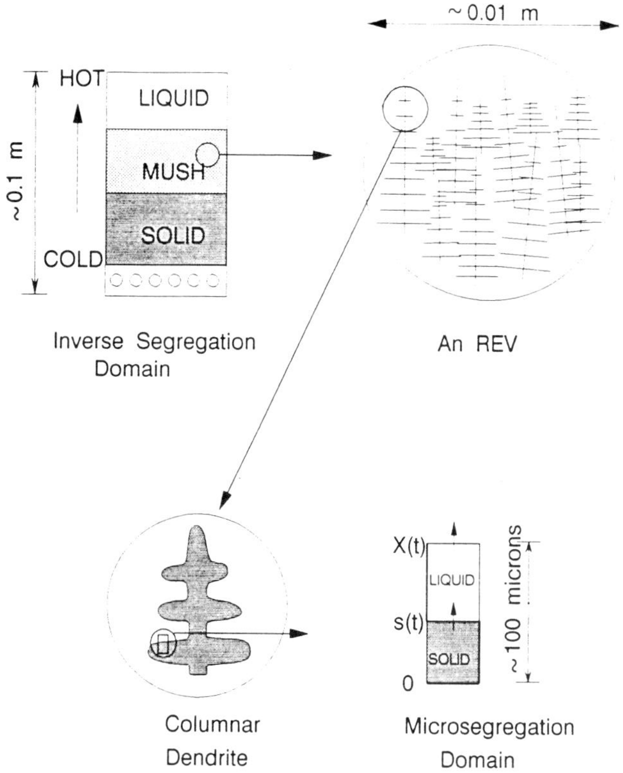

Figure 1. Schematic of macro- and micro- segregation domains

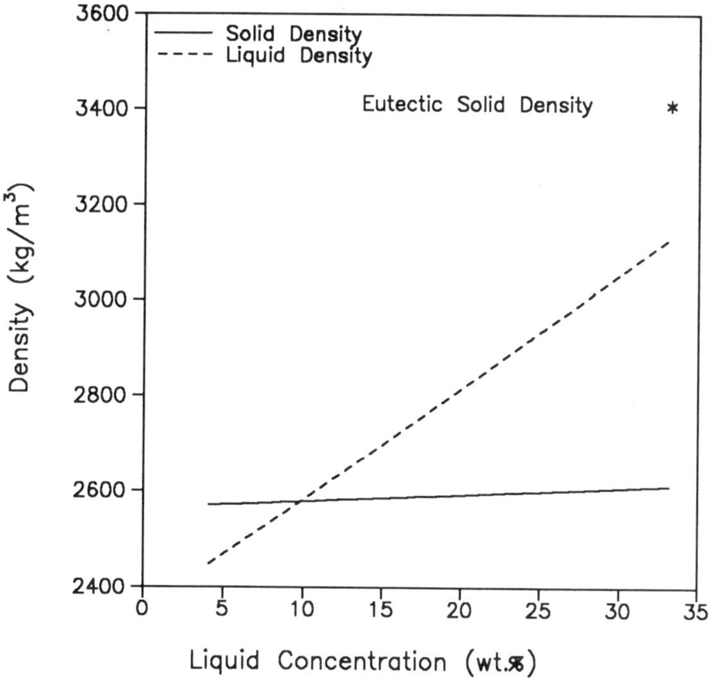

Figure 2. Density variation with concentration (Ganesan and Poirier (1987))

$$C_l = \left(\frac{T_f - T}{m_l}\right) \qquad (2)$$

where T is the temperature, C is the concentration, $m_l=(T_f-T_{eut})/C_{eut}$ is a representative liquidus slope in the phase diagram, superscript * denotes the value at the solid/liquid interface and subscripts s and l stand for solid and liquid phases respectively.

8. The temperature T, the liquid concentration C_l, the density ρ_l and the liquid velocity u_l are assumed to be uniform over a microscopic representative elementary volume (REV).
9. The REV can be chosen such that it includes several arm spaces and has a reasonably uniform microstructure, e.g. see Figure 1a in Ni and Beckermann (1991).

Governing Equations (Macroscopic)

With the above assumptions, the single domain equations describing the inverse segregation process in the domain $0<x<X_b$ can be derived from the two phase volume averaging approach presented by Ni and Beckermann (1991). These macroscopic governing equations are:

Energy

$$\frac{\partial[\rho H]}{\partial t} + \frac{\partial}{\partial x}(\rho_l u c_{p_l} T) + \frac{\partial}{\partial x}(\rho_l u L = \frac{\partial}{\partial x}\left([K]\frac{\partial T}{\partial x}\right) \qquad (3)$$

Species

$$\frac{\partial[\rho C]}{\partial t} + \frac{\partial}{\partial x}(\rho_l u C_l) = 0 \qquad (4)$$

Mass

$$\frac{\partial[\rho]}{\partial t} + \frac{\partial}{\partial x}(\rho_l u) = 0 \qquad (5)$$

In the above equations, the mixture density

$$[\rho] = g_s \langle\rho_s\rangle^s + g_l \rho_l \qquad (6)$$

the mixture enthalpy

$$[\rho H] = g_s \langle\rho_s\rangle^s c_{p_s} T + g_l \rho_l c_{p_l} T + g_l \rho_l L \qquad (7)$$

the mixture solute density

$$[\rho C] = g_s \langle\rho_s C_s\rangle^s + g_l \rho_l C_l \qquad (8)$$

the mixture thermal conductivity

$$[K] = g_s K_s + g_l K_l \qquad (9)$$

and the "system velocity"

$$u = g_l u_l \qquad (10)$$

The terms in the brackets < > are intrinsic volume averages over the REV.

Boundary Conditions

Appropriate boundary conditions for the above macroscopic equations are:

At x=0,

$$F = 0\ ;\ [K]\frac{\partial T}{\partial x} = h_{amb}(T_{amb} - T|_{x=0})\ ;\ \frac{\partial C_l}{\partial x} = 0 \qquad (11)$$

where h_{amb} is the heat transfer coefficient, T_{amb} is the ambient temperature of the chill and $F=\rho_l u$ is the mass flow rate of liquid per unit area.

At $x=X_b$,

$$F = F_b = \rho_l u_b\ ;\ \frac{\partial T}{\partial x} = 0\ ;\ \frac{\partial C_l}{\partial x} = 0 \qquad (12)$$

where F_b is the mass flow rate of the liquid metal per unit area that enters the system to compensate for the shrinkage in $0<x<X_b$. Note that this mass flux will result in a convective heat flux and solutal mass flux at $x=X_b$ of the form

$$q_h = F_b\,(c_{p_l} T|_{x=X_b} + L) \qquad (13)$$

and

$$q_c = F_b\, C_l|_{x=X_b} \qquad (14)$$

The boundary $X_b=\rho_l/\rho_s X_m$ (where X_m is the total height of the mold, ρ_l=2438 kg/m^3 and ρ_s=2580 kg/m^3 are representative density values) is the final macro-porosity free casting length on complete solidification.

Simplification of the Terms [ρ], [ρH] and [ρC]

Application of the model as it stands will require evaluation of the volume averaged terms appearing in the definitions of

Table 1. Thermal Properties of Al-Cu alloy system

Property	Value	Unit
c_{p_s}	900	J/kg-K
c_{p_l}	1100	J/kg-K
C_{eut}	33.2	wt.%
C_o	4.1	wt.%
h_{amb}	$1684.21-4.3443\ t + 0.00449561\ t^2$	W/m^2-K
k_o	0.172	---
K_l	100	W/m-K
K_s	200	W/m-K
L	3.95×10^5	J/kg
T_{amb}	293	K
T_{eut}	821.2	K
T_i	1020	K
T_f	933.2	K
X_b	0.1323	m
ρ_l	$2358.5 + 21.685\ C_l + 7.2914 \times 10^{-2}\ C_l^2 - 7.2351 \times 10^{-4}\ C_l^3$	kg/m^3
ρ_s	$2564.7 + 1.4023\ C_l$	kg/m^3

the mixture values $[\rho]$, $[\rho H]$ and $[\rho C]$, see Eq.(6), (7) and (8). More precise definitions of these terms can be obtained as follows. Consider the solid fraction, Δg_s say, formed in the REV over a given small time step. When this solid fraction forms, assumptions 7 and 8 above imply that its initial concentration is constant. As the solidification process continues, due to local mass diffusion, the concentration in this solid fraction will change. Since the microstructure is uniform over the REV, we content, however, that it is reasonable to assume that the concentration in this solid fraction, although different from the initial concentration, will still be uniform. Using this argument, simplified definitions for the mixture quantities are

$$[\rho] = \int_0^{g_s} \rho_s \, d\alpha + g_l \, \rho_l \tag{15}$$

$$[\rho\, H] = c_{p_s} T \int_0^{g_s} \rho_s \, d\alpha + g_l \, \rho_l \, c_{p_l} T + g_l \, \rho_l \, L \tag{16}$$

and

$$[\rho C] = \int_0^{g_s} \rho_s \, C_s \, d\alpha + g_l \, \rho_l \, C_l \tag{17}$$

Evaluation of the integrals in Eq.(15)-(17) will require an accounting of the microsegregation in the REV. Under the limiting assumption of no solid mass diffusion (the Scheil assumption) the concentration of the solid formed in a given time step will always remain fixed at its initial value and the integrals can be readily evaluated. Cases where there is mass diffusion in the solid (back diffusion), however, will

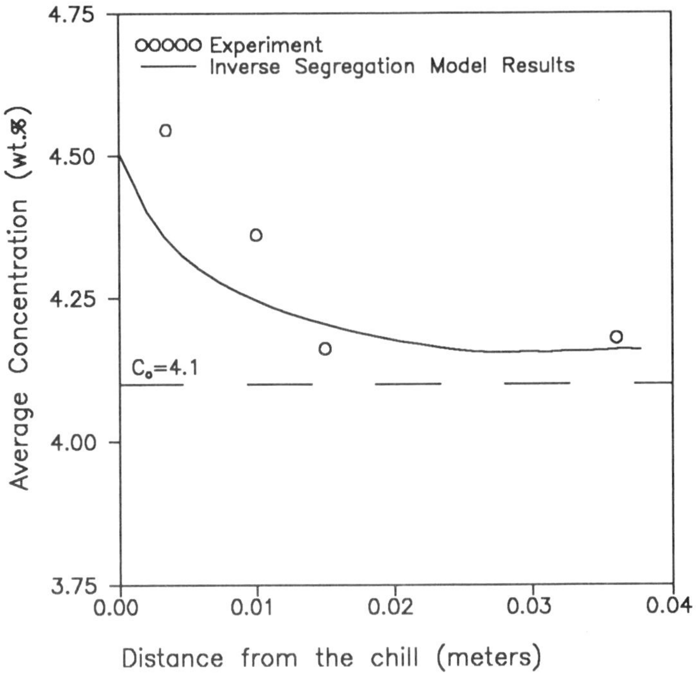

Figure 3. Near chill face segregation

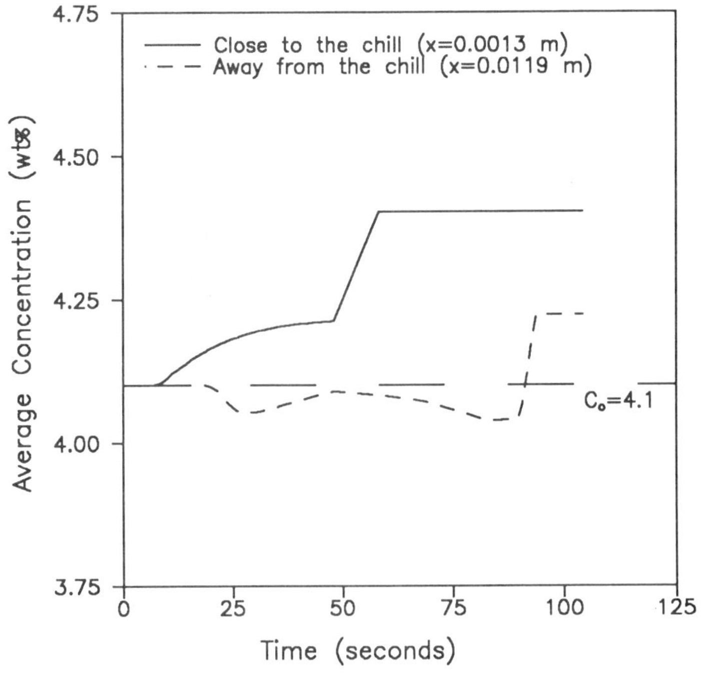

Figure 4. Concentration histories

require a more detailed accounting for microsegregation. Such an analysis will be attempted later in this paper on solving for microsegregation in a representative one-dimensional domain located on the solid/liquid interface of the REV.

Solution Procedure

After suitable space discretization the governing equations are solved via explicit time integration. When a Scheil assumption is used, the numerical scheme, over one time step, is as follows:

1. From the temperature T, the liquid concentration C_l and the liquid fraction g_l fields at the previous time step, the current $[\rho H]$ and $[\rho C]$ fields are obtained.
2. The current T, C_l and g_l fields are then obtained by solving, at each node, the non-linear equations formed by the definitions of $[\rho H]$ and $[\rho C]$, see Eqs.(16) and (17), and using the equilibrium conditions, Eqs.(1) and (2).
3. The equation solver in step 2 includes special procedures to deal with the eutectic formation, see Voller and Sundarraj (1994).
4. The g_l field, obtained from step 2, is used to evaluate the mixture density $[\rho]$ field.
5. Finally the current flow field, F, is determined explicitly from the mass continuity equation.

The objective in the model is to evaluate the nodal distribution of the mixture average concentration ($[C](x,t)=[\rho C]/[\rho]$). The proposed numerical solution approach has been validated on comparison with limiting analytical and semi-analytical solutions (Voller and Sundarraj (1994). Grid independent solutions are obtained with 100 node points and a time step equal to 0.9 times the explicit criteria limit.

The predictive ability of the model is validated on comparing predictions of the mixture concentration [C] distribution in the chill face region, i.e. the first 20 node points in the domain, with inverse segregation measurements in the literature. In this case the appropriate measurements are taken from the uni-directional solidification experiments on an Aluminum-4.1 wt.% Copper alloy reported by Kato and Cahoon (1985). The relevant boundary conditions and properties for this experiment are given in Table 1. A key part of this data is the variable density model taken from Ganesan and Poirier (1987) (see Figure 2). Although the comparison between the model predictions and the experimental measurements throughout the casting is reasonable, in the inverse segregation region, near the chill face, the model underpredicts the experiment, see Figure 3. Two possible reasons for this are: (i) the exudation phenomena, not included in the model, that results in higher levels of segregation at the chill face, and (ii) an incorrect choice of the density model.

Insight into the inverse segregation behavior can be obtained on studying the concentration history in a computational cell adjacent to the chill, see Figure 4. Initially the concentration in the cell is at the nominal value C_o. As solidification commences, the influx of mass entering the cell to compensate for shrinkage results in an increase in the average concentration. As the process continues the rate of increase in the average concentration diminishes. This is due to the fact that the rate of solidification decreases and thereby the rate of shrinkage decreases. When the eutectic is reached, however, there is a dramatic increase in the cell concentration. This increase is driven by (i) an increase in the solidification rate (rate of change of liquid fraction) at the eutectic, and (ii) the large differences in the solid and liquid densities at the eutectic (see Figure 2). Although the concentration history in a computational cell away from the chill is different, see the dashed line in Figure 4, the rapid concentration increase when the eutectic is reached is always observed. This observation suggests that the amount of eutectic could influence the amount of inverse segregation. Complete evidence for this view point will be presented later when the dual scale segregation model is discussed.

A MICROSEGREGATION MODEL

In this section a previously developed model of microsegregation (Voller and Sundarraj, 1993) in a dendritic binary alloy is presented. The key assumptions are:

1. The microsegregation domain is one-dimensional and nominally associated with a secondary dendrite arm spacing.
2. Due to the coarsening process, the size of the microsegregation domain X(t) increases with time (the model proposed by Roosz et. al. (1986) will be used in this work).
3. The moving solid/liquid interface, s(t), is planar and sharp.
4. Heat transfer is very rapid, and at each point in the domain a uniform temperature T(t) can be assumed.
5. Mass transfer in the domain is controlled by diffusion alone.
6. Thermal and solutal equilibrium holds at the solid/liquid interface s(t).

Governing Equation (Microscopic)

The microsegregation problem requires the separate solutions of a solid and liquid mass diffusion equations in an expanding domain, $0<x<X(t)$. On defining a variable V, the "chemical activity"

$$V = \begin{Bmatrix} C_s & x \le s(t) \\ k_o(T)\, C_l & x > s(t) \end{Bmatrix} \tag{18}$$

and using the Landau transformation

$$\xi = \frac{x}{X(t)} \tag{19}$$

the problem can be reduced to a single equation in a fixed domain $0 \le \xi \le 1$, viz.,

$$\frac{\partial(\rho C)}{\partial t}\Big|_{\xi} = \frac{1}{X^2}\frac{\partial}{\partial \xi}\left[\rho D \frac{\partial V}{\partial \xi}\right] + \frac{1}{X}\frac{dX}{dt}\left[\frac{\partial(\xi \rho C)}{\partial \xi} - \rho C\right] \tag{20}$$

where

$$\rho D = \left[\rho_s (1-g_l^L) D_s + \rho_l g_l^L \left(\frac{D_l}{k_o}\right)\right] \tag{21}$$

$$\rho C = \left[\rho_s (1-g_l^L) + \rho_l g_l^L \left(\frac{1}{k_o}\right)\right] V \tag{22}$$

$$\rho = \rho_s (1-g_l^L) + \rho_l g_l^L \tag{23}$$

and, g_l^L, is the local liquid fraction at a point in the micro domain.

Boundary Conditions

The boundary conditions for Eq.(20) are zero concentration gradients $\partial V/\partial \xi = 0$ at $\xi=0$ and $\xi=1$, and an imposed solute mass flux

$$q_C = \frac{d}{dt}\left([\rho C] X\right) \tag{24}$$

at $\xi=1$.

Closing the Microsegregation Model

To completely define the microsegregation system we need to prescribe the RHS of Eq.(24), in particular, the mixture solutal density $[\rho C](t)$. In addition, the cooling of the microscopic domain, which can be specified by a mixture enthalpy $[\rho H](t)$, or a cooling rate T(t), also needs to be prescribed. In this section of the paper suitable prescriptions of these quantities will be externally provided. Note, however, that the terms $[\rho H](t)$ and $[\rho C](t)$, defined in Eq.(16) and (17), are macroscopic quantities and could come from the solution of macroscopic equations; an approach that will be investigated later in this paper.

Numerical Solution

The numerical solution of the microsegregation model is based on a fully implicit time integration on a node centered control volume space grid. The solution based on a fixed space and time step and has been previously outlined by Sundarraj and Voller (1992) and Sundarraj and Voller (1994). Briefly, the iterative solution of the discrete microsegregation equations in one time step is as follows:

1. At the start of the time step the current externally prescribed values of T and $[\rho C]$ are known; the current equilibrium concentration value V_{equ} at the solid/liquid interface is obtained from the phase diagram and the total liquid fraction in the domain $0<x<X(t)$ is set to its previous value.
2. The current guessed value for the liquid fraction can be used to indicate the computational cell in which the solid/liquid interface is located, referred to as the phase change cell.
3. Using the values in steps 1 and 2 the discrete microsegregation equations are solved using a TDMA solver to obtain the concentration field, specified by the nodal values of V. In this solution the concentration in the phase change cell is forced to take the equilibrium value V_{equ}.
4. The predicted concentration values are then used to determine the value of $[\rho C]$; effectively these values are used in a numerical integration of the definition given in Eq.(17).
5. Due to the guessed value of the liquid fraction, the calculated value of $[\rho C]$ may not agree with the prescribed value. This difference is used to drive a correction in the domain liquid fraction.
6. Steps 2 to 5 are repeated until convergence, i.e., until the prescribed and the calculated values of $[\rho C]$ agree within a specified tolerance.

Model Predictions

The initial concentration in the domain is set at the nominal concentration of the alloy in question, C_o. Calculations, in time, continue until the domain liquid concentration reaches the eutectic. At this point the volume of eutectic and the final length of the arm spacing are recorded and the calculations are terminated. Eutectic fraction predictions and final secondary arm spaces, at different cooling rates, for an Aluminum-4.9% Copper alloy (see data in Table 2) are compared with the experiments measurements reported by Sarreal and Abbaschian (1985) in Figures 5 and 6. In these predictions, in order to match the experimental conditions, constant cooling rates T(t) are used and the mixture solutal density is prescribed such that $[\rho C]=[\rho]C_o$ (i.e., no macrosegregation occurs).

The Nature of the Microsegregation Model

Usually in 'stand alone' microsegregation models, the domain $0<x<X(t)$ is nominally associated with a secondary

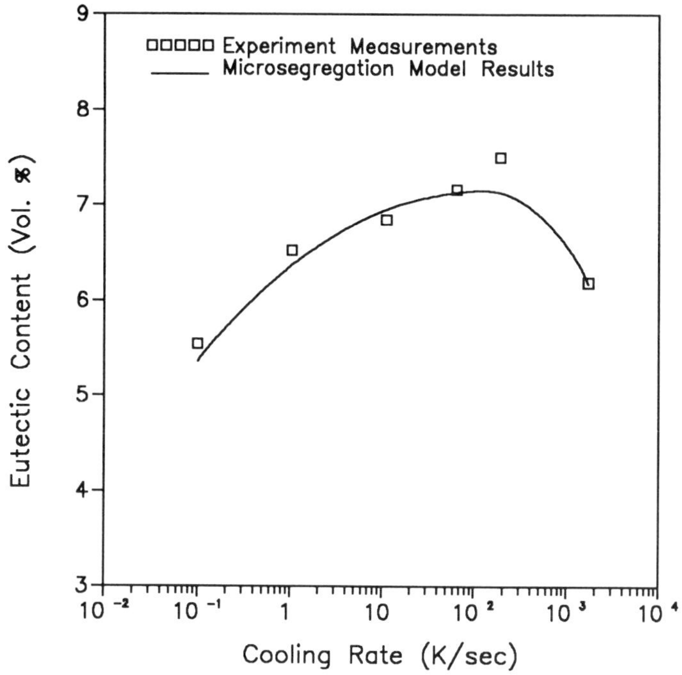

Figure 5. Fraction eutectic predictions

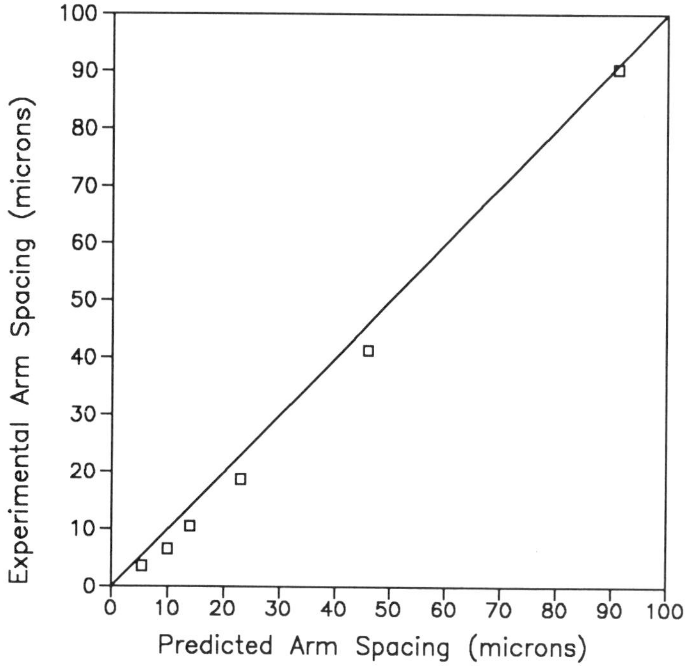

Figure 6. Comparison of predicted arm spacings with experimental measurements

Table 2. Properties for the Aluminum-Copper system

Property	Value	Unit
C_{eut}	33.2	wt.%
C_o	4.9	wt.%
$C_l(T)$	$3371.84 - 11.4464\ T + 0.01333\ T^2 - 5.2955 \times 10^{-6}\ T^3$	wt.%
$C_s(T)$	$47.1311 - 0.0505141\ T$	wt.%
D_l	$1.05 \times 10^{-7}\ \exp(-2856/T)$	m^2/sec
D_s	$0.29 \times 10^{-4}\ \exp(-15610/T)$	m^2/sec
$k_o(T)$	$C_s(T)/C_l(T)$	---
T_{eut}	821.2	K
T_f	933.2	K
T_{liq}	921.73	K
ρ_l	$2358.5 + 21.685\ C_l + 7.2914\text{x}10^{-2}\ C_l^2 - 7.2351\text{x}10^{-4}\ C_l^3$	kg/m^3
ρ_s	$2564.7 + 1.4023\ C_l$	kg/m^3
ρ_s^{eut}	3409	kg/m^3
ΔH_f	1.07×10^9	J/m^3
γ	0.093	J/m^2

dendrite arm space in the mushy region. Note, however, the experimental measurements of fraction eutectic and arm spaces are by their nature averaged values over an REV in the mushy region. Since the comparison between experimental measurements and microsegregation model predictions are close (Figures 5 and 6), in a more general context we feel that it is very reasonable to assume that a one-dimensional microsegregation domain $0<x<X(t)$, with the characteristic size of the secondary arm spacing, can be used to represent the averaged microsegregation behavior in a given REV.

A DUAL SCALE MODEL

Basic Concepts

The microsegregation and inverse segregation models, presented above, by themselves do not fully account for segregation processes occurring at both the microscopic and macroscopic scales. In the microsegregation model, two parameters, $[\rho H]$ and $[\rho C]$, were prescribed to capture the effects due to macrosegregation. On the other hand, the inverse segregation model used the limiting Scheil assumption to describe the microsegregation behavior. As noted above, however, the microsegregation model, can be used to represent the solute diffusion behavior in the REV as a whole. In this way we can replace the limiting Scheil assumption with a more complete treatment of the microsegregation. In essence, a dual scale model can be developed in which the macroscopic field values of $[\rho H]$ and $[\rho C]$, obtained from the inverse segregation model, can be used to provide the prescriptions of cooling and mixture solutal density values required by the microsegregation model. In a complimentary fashion the micro domain values of temperature, liquid concentration and liquid fraction can be used in the inverse segregation model.

IMPLEMENTATION

Testing of the proposed dual scale model is carried out by examining the effects of microsegregation behavior on the inverse segregation occurring in the uni-directional casting of an Aluminum-4.1% Copper alloy. Appropriate model data can be obtained from Tables 1 and 2. The governing equations for the dual scale model are the macroscopic equations (Eqs.(3)-(5)) and microscopic equation (Eq.(20)) along with their respective boundary conditions. The numerical solution

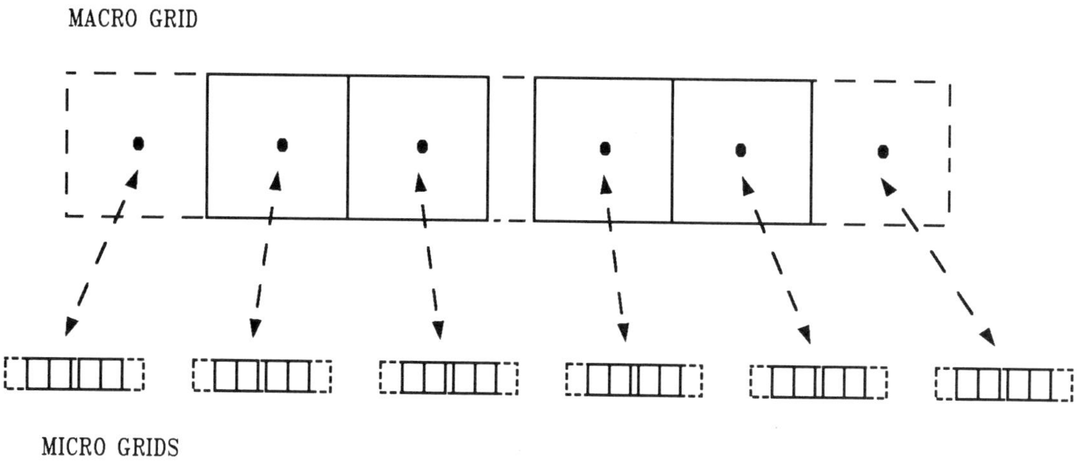

Figure 7. The dual scale grid

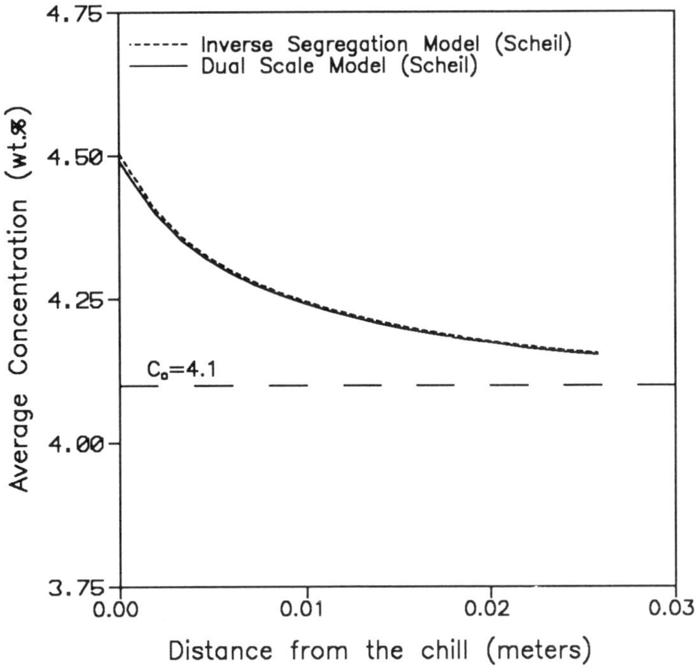

Figure 8. Comparison of dual scale and inverse segregation predictions

of these equations is based on a dual macro-, micro-scale grid, illustrated in Figure 7. Each node point in the macro-grid, used in solving the inverse segregation equations, is associated with a micro-grid on which the microsegregation model is implemented. The basic concept is that the microsegregation and microstructure at each macroscopic node point is representative of the microsegregation and microstructure in the macro control volume as a whole. This is consistent with the well accepted view point that, for example, the macroscopic nodal temperature is the representative temperature in the associated control volume. The solution procedure employed at each time step on the dual scale grid is almost identical to the procedure used in the 'stand alone' inverse segregation model. The main differences are: (i) the temperature T is calculated by rewriting the first term on the LHS of Eq.(3) as

$$\frac{\partial[\rho H]}{\partial t} = C^{APP}\left(\frac{\partial T}{\partial t}\right) \tag{25}$$

where $C^{APP}=(\partial[\rho H]/\partial T)$ is an apparent heat capacity, and (ii) at each macro node point, the non-linear equation solver, used in the 'stand alone' model, is replaced by a solution of the microsegregation model. Note that, in this case the microsegregation model returns the nodal values of C_l, $[\rho]$ and $[\rho H]$ required for the next time step calculation. In the current implementation a time step of 0.9 times the explicit criteria limit and a dual grid of 100 macroscopic node points, each associated with a microscopic grid of 100 nodes, is used. This provides grid independent solutions requiring 15 minutes on a Silicon Graphics R4000 work station for complete solidification of the first 20 macroscopic node points.

Validation

The mechanisms in the numerical solution of the dual scale model can be validated on setting the microsegregation parameters, i.e., partition coefficient, coarsening and back diffusion in the dual scale model to simulate the Scheil assumption used in the 'stand alone' inverse segregation model. Figure 8 compares the inverse segregation predictions of the 'stand alone' model with the dual scale model; in the case of no coarsening (X(t)=23 microns), a close to zero back diffusion ($D_s=10^{-20}$) and constant partition coefficient (k_o=0.172). The agreement between the two models is excellent thereby validating the proposed solution approach used in the dual scale model.

Effect of Microsegregation on Inverse Segregation

The dual scale model can be used to investigate the effect of the local scale phenomena on the predictions of the macroscopic inverse segregation profile; in particular, effects of coarsening and finite back diffusion. Figure 9 shows dual scale predictions for the case of close to zero back diffusion ($D_s=10^{-20}$), when coarsening and a variable k_o are used. On comparison with the results obtained with a constant k_o and fixed arm spacing, we see a decrease in the inverse segregation. Since, the constant partition coefficient (k_o=0.172) is chosen to be representative of the non-linear phase diagram we attribute the difference in macrosegregation predictions to arm coarsening. In effect the material entering the micro domain during coarsening dilutes the liquid and reduced the amount of eutectic which in turn leads to a decreases in the flow and ultimately a decrease in the inverse segregation.

Figure 10 shows the effect of back diffusion on the inverse segregation predictions. Three separate back diffusion predictions are shown corresponding to: (i) close to zero back diffusion ($D_s=10^{-20}$), (ii) realistic back diffusion (D_s in Table 2), and (iii) large back diffusion ($D_s=10^{-9}$). In all these cases, a variable partition coefficient and coarsening were used in the micro component of the model. As a reference point the macrosegregation profile (drawn as a solid line) corresponding to the case of close to zero back diffusion, constant partition coefficient and fixed arm spacing is also shown in Figure 10. There is a large difference between the back diffusion predictions; principally driven by the differences in the eutectic fractions predicted by the microsegregation model. Recall that, with the chosen density model, the major solidification shrinkage occurs at the eutectic formation and that an increase in the level of back diffusion will lead to smaller eutectic fractions. Often in the analysis of Aluminum-Copper systems, in order to simplify the modeling, the assumption of close to zero back diffusion, constant partition coefficient and fixed arm spacing, is used (i.e., the Scheil approximation). On comparing the solid line with the broken lines, however, the results in Figure 10 indicate that using a Scheil approximation may not always be sound. Another interesting feature to note in Figure 10 is that the lever rule approximation predicts 'negative' inverse segregation. This is a function of the density model used in this study, which when used in conjunction with the lever rule approximation can lead to solidification 'expansion' and a flow away from the chill face. Use of an alternative density model will lead to different predictions. In particular, a choice of constant solid and liquid densities (ρ_s=2580 kg/m^3 and ρ_l=2438 kg/m^3) leads to dual model predictions which are much less sensitive to the choice of back diffusion and show no negative segregation, see Figure 11. The reason is due to the fact that, in the constant density model, the eutectic fraction has no impact on the shrinkage.

COMPUTATIONAL ASPECTS

The dual scale modeling approach can be applied to multi-dimensional problems. In doing so, potential problems are the CPU and storage requirements. Note, however, that the macro node microsegregation calculations are independent of each other. Hence, implementation on a parallel architecture will dramatically cut down the CPU time. The storage requirement may become a problem in extending to multi-dimensions. However, in our one-dimensional problem

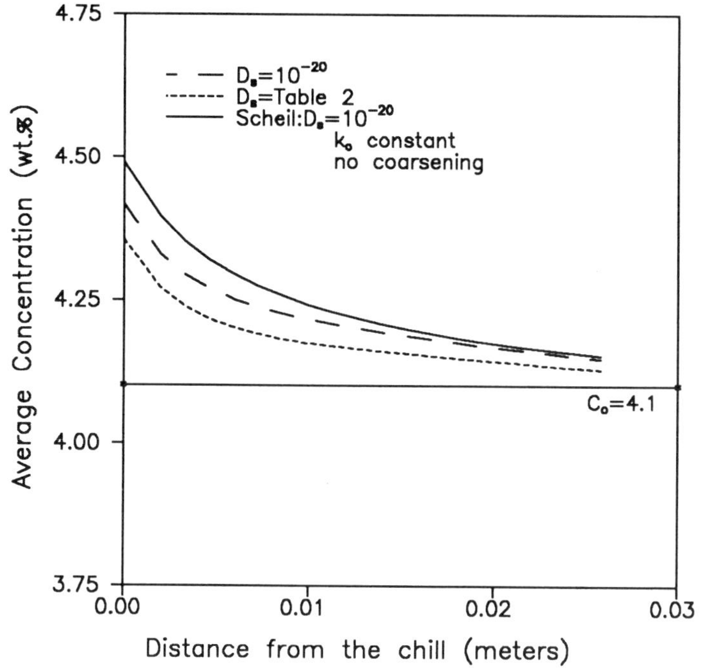

Figure 9. Effects of coarsening and back diffusion

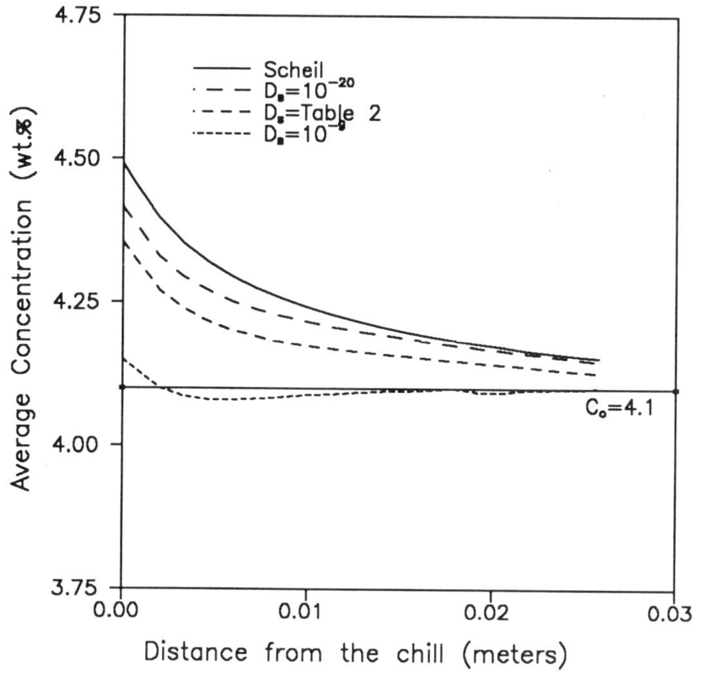

Figure 10. Effect of Back diffusion

nearly all the variables are only stored at the macro nodes. Hence, these variables will only require one-dimensional arrays. The only exception is the variable, V, which requires a two-dimensional array with dimensions (Macro nodes x Micro nodes).

CONCLUSIONS

Two separate models, focussed on a macrosegregation process and a microsegregation process, respectively, have been presented. On using a dual scale numerical grid these models have been coupled to provide a complete description of the segregation processes occurring in the directional solidification of an Aluminum-Copper alloy. A number of conclusions can be drawn from this study.

1. A more exact accounting of the microsegregation process does influence the inverse segregation profile, i.e. the micro scale will influence the macro scale.
2. The amount of eutectic formed, which needs to be predicted by a microsegregation model, takes a key role in determining the solidification shrinkage and ultimately the inverse segregation.
3. If the microsegregation is modeled correctly, the choice of density model will influence the predicted levels of inverse segregation.
4. Choice of a lever rule approximation in shrinkage driven macrosegregation processes in Aluminum-Copper systems is inappropriate. Close comparisons with experiments can be obtained with a lever approximation but it requires the choice of inappropriate density values.
5. On the negative side, use of a complete microsegregation treatment over a Scheil treatment has resulted in a poorer comparison with experiments. The discrepancy could be due to: (i) experimental errors, (ii) inappropriate density values and (iii) missing phenomena. In further work we will investigate the last of two of these factors, in particular, the phenomena of surface exudation.

ACKNOWLEDGEMENTS

The authors would like to acknowledge the Minnesota Supercomputer Institute for furnishing a computer resources grant.

REFERENCES

Amberg,G., 1991, "Computation of Macrosegregation in an Iron-Carbon Cast", Int. J. Heat and Mass Transfer, Vol. 34, pp. 217-227.

Battle,T.P., and Pehlke,R.D., 1990, "Mathematical Modeling of Microsegregation in Binary Metallic Alloys", Metall. Trans. B, Vol. 21, pp. 357-375.

Beckermann,C., and Viskanta,R., 1988, "Double-Diffusive Convection during Dendritic Solidification of a Binary Mixture", Physico. Chem. Hydrodyn., Vol. 10, pp. 195-213

Bennon,W.D., and Incropera,F.P, 1987, "The Evolution of Macro-segregation in Statically Cast Binary Ingots", Metall. Trans. B, Vol. 18, pp. 611-616.

Diao,Q.Z., and Tsai, H.L., 1993, "Modeling of Solute Redistribution in the Mushy Zone during Solidification of Aluminum-Copper Alloys", Metall. Trans. A, vol. 24, pp. 963-973.

Ganesan,S., and Poirier,D.R., 1987, "Densities of Aluminum-rich Aluminum-Copper Alloys during Solidification", Metall. Trans. A, Vol. 18, pp. 721-723.

Kato,H. and Cahoon,J.R., 1985, "Inverse Segregation in Directionally Solidified Al-Cu-Ti Alloys with Equiaxed Grains", Metall. Trans. A, Vol. 16, pp.579-587.

Ni,J., and Beckermann,C., 1991 "A Volume Averaged Two-Phase Model for Transport Phenomena during Solidification", Metall. Trans. B, Vol. 22, pp. 349-361.

Rappaz,M., and Voller,V.R., 1990, "Modeling of Micro-Macrosegregation in Solidification Processes", Metall. Trans. A, Vol. 21, pp. 749-753.

Roosz,A., Halder,E., and Exner,H.E., 1986, "Numerical Calculation of Microsegregation in Coarsened Dendritic Microstructures", Mat. Sci. and Tech., Vol. 2, pp. 1149-1155.

Sarreal,J.A., and Abbaschian,G.J., 1985,"The Effect of Solidification Rate on Microsegregation", Metall. Trans. A, Vol. 17, pp. 2063-2073.

Sundarraj,S. and Voller,V.R. 1992, "Development of a Microsegregation Model for Application in a Micro-Macro Model", in "Micro/Macro Scale Phenomena in Solidification" (Eds. Beckermann,C. et al.,) HTD-218/AMD 139, pp. 35-42.

Sundarraj,S., and Voller,V.R., 1994, "Effect of Macro Scale Phenomena on Microsegregation", International Communications in Heat and Mass Transfer, Vol. 21, pp. 189-197.

Voller,V.R., and Sundarraj,S., 1994 "A Model of Inverse Segregation in a Binary Alloy", submitted to the Int. J. Heat and Mass Transfer.

Voller,V.R. and Sundarraj,S., 1993, "Modelling of Microsegregation", Mat. Sci. and Tech., Vol. 9, pp. 474-481.

Voller,V.R., Brent, A.D., and Prakash, C., 1989, "The Modelling of Heat, Mass and Solute Transport in Solidification Systems", Int. J. of Heat and Mass transfer, Vol. 32, pp. 1719-1731.

HTD-Vol. 284/AMD-Vol. 182, Transport Phenomena in Solidification
ASME 1994

SIMULATION OF THE SOLIDIFICATION OF A LEAD-TIN ALLOY WITH CONSIDERATION OF MICROSEGREGATION AND CONTRACTION DRIVEN FLOW

M. C. Schneider and C. Beckermann
Department of Mechanical Engineering
University of Iowa
Iowa City, Iowa

ABSTRACT

This study reports on simulations of the columnar dendritic solidification of a Pb-Sn alloy in a square cavity cooled from one side, and fed by a rectangular riser. Assuming stationary solid phases, local thermodynamic equilibrium and complete local mixing of solute in the liquid, the macroscopic conservation equations for the liquid, α- and γ-phase solids are derived using the techniques of volume averaging. Emphasis is placed on comparing the model predictions for two limiting cases of solid microsegregation (no local solute diffusion and complete local solute diffusion). The combined effects of buoyancy driven flow, shrinkage driven flow and species diffusion in the liquid are also investigated. The overall macrosegregation patterns for the two microsegregation models are found to be similar, with slightly more severe segregation predicted for the case with complete local solute diffusion in the solid. The amount of eutectic solid formed is significantly higher when no local diffusion of solute in the solid is considered. While contraction flow causes positive macrosegregation near a cooled boundary (inverse segregation), species diffusion in the liquid is observed to have the opposite effect. Finally, since the choice of microsegregation model affects the predicted local average solid concentration and eutectic fraction, and since the solid density is a function of concentration and the primary and eutectic solids have different densities, the microsegregation model also affects the prediction of contraction driven flow.

NOMENCLATURE

a lattice parameter (m)
A area (m^2)
C concentration (wt.% Sn)
d dendrite arm spacing (m)
D mass diffusivity (m^2/s)
g liquidus curve equation
g acceleration of gravity (m/s^2)
h enthalpy (J/kg)
k thermal conductivity (W/m/K)
$\mathbf{K}^{(2)}$ second-order permeability tensor (m^2)
K permeability (m^2)
ℓ length scale (m)
m_ℓ liquidus curve slope (K/wt.% Sn)
p pressure (N/m^2)
t time (s)
t_f local solidification time (s)
T temperature (K)
U heat transfer coefficient ($W/m^2/K$)
v velocity vector (m/s)
V volume (m^3)

Greek Symbols

Γ Gibbs-Thomson coefficient (mK)
ε volume fraction
φ angle between coordinate system and dendrites (radians)
κ segregation coefficient
μ kinematic viscosity (kg/m/s)
ρ density (kg/m^3)
Ψ a quantity of a phase

Subscripts/Superscripts

i interfacial
j species transfer
k phase k
ℓ liquid
o averaging, initial, constant
Pb pure lead

s	solid
Sn	pure tin
t	transpose of a tensor
α	alpha phase
γ	gamma phase
η	normal to dendrite
ξ	perpendicular to dendrite
1	primary dendrite arm
2	secondary dendrite arm
$\bar{}$	interfacial average

INTRODUCTION

In recent years, much time and effort has been expended trying to develop accurate models, as well as efficient numerical algorithms to solve the model equations, to study the transport phenomena that occur during alloy solidification. The aim of these studies is to develop predictive capabilities that allow for the design of defect free castings. Numerical solutions of the conservation equations in macroscopic alloy solidification models have shown the capabilities of such models to predict the development of an irregular liquidus front, local remelting of solid, the development of flow channels in the mushy zone and the establishment of macrosegregation patterns for the solidification of salt-water solutions (Bennon and Incropera, 1987; Beckermann and Viskanta, 1988; Voller et al., 1989) as well as metal alloys (Amberg, 1991; Felicelli et al., 1991; Prescott and Incropera, 1991; Nielson and Incropera, 1993).

In applying alloy solidification models, several assumptions are typically introduced to simplify the solution of the governing conservation equations. The assumptions include: thermal equilibrium, a well-mixed liquid, and complete (i.e., infinitely fast) species diffusion in the solid within a small volume element; no solid motion and an isotropic permeability in the mushy zone; constant and equal phase densities (i.e., neglecting contraction driven flow) with the Boussinesq approximation used to model buoyancy driven flow; phase enthalpies that are functions of temperature only (i.e., neglecting concentration dependencies) as well as constant specific heats; and a linear phase diagram. In order to better evaluate and understand macroscopic solidification models, the effects of these assumptions on the resulting model predictions need to be investigated. Towards that goal, the objective of this paper is two-fold. First, a comparison is made between macrosegregation and eutectic volume fraction patterns predicted when there is assumed to be complete solute diffusion microscopically in the solid and when there is assumed to be no microscopic solid solute diffusion. Then, the effects of including both buoyancy and contraction driven flow, as well as macroscopic species diffusion in the liquid, in alloy solidification simulations are investigated. The model predictions used in all of the comparisons are for the columnar dendritic solidification of a Pb-20 wt.% Sn alloy in a square cavity cooled from one side.

The assumption of complete (or infinitely fast) solute diffusion in the solid on a microscopic scale can be considered as one limiting case to describe local solid microsegregation. Then, a second limiting case can be described by assuming no (or infinitely slow) microscopic solute diffusion in the solid. In the absence of macroscopic advection and diffusion of solute, these two cases reduce to the familiar lever rule and Scheil models (Flemings, 1974; Rappaz and Voller, 1990). Several studies have employed the assumption of no microscopic solid solute diffusion in calculating macrosegregation during alloy solidification (Voller et al., 1989; Felicelli et al., 1991; Xu and Li, 1991a; Shahani et al., 1992). However, Voller et al. (1989) is the only study that directly compares macrosegregation patterns for these two limiting cases. By simulating the solidification of an NH_4Cl-H_2O mixture, it was determined that the general behavior for the two cases was qualitatively similar, but that the predicted macrosegregation for the case of no solute diffusion was slightly worse than that for complete solute diffusion. For the diffusion-dominated solidification of a Pb-Sn alloy, the movement of the liquidus isotherm for the two cases was also shown to differ only slightly (Schneider and Beckermann, 1991; Poirier et al., 1991). However, those results also show that the volume fraction of eutectic in the final solid can be quite different for the two cases (Poirier et al., 1991). One objective of the present study is to further investigate differences in the predictions of macrosegregation and eutectic volume fraction for these two limiting cases. The model used here is particularly suitable for making such comparisons since the conservation equations are written in a general form that easily accommodates both the assumptions of infinitely fast and no solute diffusion in the solid microscopically. The model also explicitly accounts for the presence of both primary solid phases in the eutectic solid. A separate volume fraction is calculated for each primary phase and the thermophysical properties of the solid phases are assumed to be unequal. This is important since the properties of the two solid phases can be quite different. For Pb-Sn alloys, for instance, the primary solid phase specific heats differ by 45% and their densities differ by 28% at the eutectic point (Poirier and Nandapurkar, 1988; Poirier, 1988). Such a detailed consideration of the eutectic reaction has not been included in previous alloy solidification simulations, and can be particularly important for the prediction of shrinkage driven flow.

Including contraction driven flow, in addition to buoyancy driven flow, in single-domain alloy solidification simulations has also received attention recently. Chiang and Tsai (1992a and 1992b) investigated flow patterns caused by shrinkage driven flow, as well as the interaction of buoyancy and shrinkage driven flow during the solidification of a 1% Cr-steel. However, species conservation was not considered and the solid volume fraction in the mushy zone was assumed to vary linearly with temperature in that study. Tsai and co-workers (Chen and Tsai, 1993; Diao and Tsai, 1993a and 1993b) obtained good agreement between predicted and measured inverse segregation profiles for unidirectionally solidified Al-Cu alloys. Since those studies focused on the upward solidification of an Al-4.1 wt.% Cu alloy, where the heavier copper is rejected in the mushy zone, stable thermal and solutal gradients reduced thermosolutal buoyancy driven flow so that the segregation was primarily due to contraction driven flow. In addition, the phase densities were assumed constant, and complete microscopic solid solute diffusion was assumed so that no eutectic formation was predicted. Xu and Li (1991a and 1991b) solved the complete set of conservation equations with both buoyancy and contraction driven flow for the solidification of an Al-Cu alloy. The computational grid used in the simulations, however, was too coarse to capture double-diffusive layering and local remelting of solid. While no effort was made to examine the effects of the combined flow on the final macrosegregation patterns, good agreement with experimental results was obtained (Xu et al., 1991). The model and solution procedure used in the present study is also capable of predicting fluid flow, and the resulting macrosegregation, due to both buoyancy and shrinkage driven flow. By comparing macrosegregation patterns caused solely by contraction driven flow and those caused by combined contraction and buoyancy driven flow, this study provides a basis for judging the importance of including shrinkage flow in solidification modeling. In addition, the choice of microsegregation model can affect the prediction of contraction driven flow since the predicted eutectic fraction for the two limiting cases of microsegregation are quite different, and the densities of the primary and eutectic solids are different. The two microsegregation models will also predict different (average) solid and liquid concentrations, and if the densities are functions of concentration, this too can lead to differences in the prediction of contraction driven flow. It will also be shown here that there is a coupling between species diffusion in the liquid and contraction driven flow near cooled boundaries. In these regions, the contraction flow serves to increase the local concentration (inverse segregation), while species diffusion produces the opposite effect. Finally, some interesting observations can be made about the interactions between the flow in a riser used to feed the solidification shrinkage and the flow in the remainder of the casting.

MODEL DESCRIPTION

The Pb-Sn phase diagram shown in Figure 1 is typical of the binary alloy systems for which the present model is applicable. This figure shows that the model should account for at most three phases: liquid (denoted here by a subscript ℓ), alpha-phase solid (subscript α) and gamma-phase solid (subscript γ). The model is, in essence, a generalization of the model used by Beckermann and Viskanta (1988), and a detailed description of the derivation of the model equations is available elsewhere (Schneider, 1991; Beckermann and Viskanta, 1993; Schneider and Beckermann, 1993) so that only a brief discussion is included here.

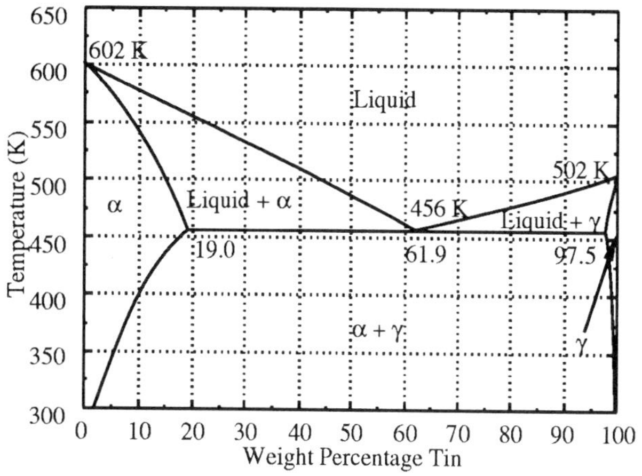

FIG. 1 EQUILIBRIUM PHASE DIAGRAM OF THE LEAD-TIN SYSTEM.

The macroscopic conservation equations in the model can be directly obtained from the volume-averaged two-phase model of alloy solidification presented by Ni and Beckermann (1991). Mixture mass, energy and species conservation equations are obtained by summing the conservation equations for each phase and using interfacial balance requirements. The solid species conservation equations are considered separately to retain the ability to model both infinitely fast and no solid microsegregation. The liquid momentum equation is also considered separately so that the interfacial momentum transfer due to friction in the mushy zone is properly accounted for, and the intrinsic volume average velocity (i.e., $\langle \mathbf{v}_\ell \rangle^\ell$) rather than the volume average (pore) velocity (i.e., $\langle \mathbf{v}_\ell \rangle = \varepsilon_\ell \langle \mathbf{v}_\ell \rangle^\ell$) has been chosen as the dependent variable. In all of the macroscopic conservation equations, $\langle \Psi_k \rangle^k$ indicates the intrinsic volume average of a quantity Ψ of phase k, and $\overline{\Psi}_{ki}$ indicates an average of a quantity Ψ of phase k over the interfacial area of phase k in the averaging volume.

A number of assumptions are also made to simplify the governing equations. They include:

- The solid phases are attached to the mold wall and are rigid so that

$$\langle \mathbf{v}_\alpha \rangle^\alpha = \langle \mathbf{v}_\gamma \rangle^\gamma = 0 \tag{1}$$

- All of the phases within an averaging volume are in thermal equilibrium, i.e.,

$$\langle T_\alpha \rangle^\alpha = \langle T_\gamma \rangle^\gamma = \langle T_\ell \rangle^\ell = T \tag{2}$$

- The liquid within an averaging volume is considered to be solutally well mixed so that the interfacial average and volume average concentrations are equal, i.e.,

$$\langle C_\ell \rangle^\ell = \overline{C}_{\ell i} \tag{3}$$

- Microscopic species diffusion in the solid phases is assumed to take one of two limiting cases: complete diffusion, where the interfacial average and volume average concentrations are equal, i.e.,

$$\overline{C}_{si} = \langle C_s \rangle^s \qquad s = \alpha, \gamma \tag{4}$$

or no diffusion, where there is a microscopic solute profile in the solid, i.e.,

$$\overline{C}_{si} \neq \langle C_s \rangle^s \qquad s = \alpha, \gamma \tag{5}$$

- All macroscopic solid species fluxes are assumed to be negligible, while finite-rate macroscopic liquid species diffusion is included. Also, all macroscopic species diffusion terms appearing in the mixture energy equation have been assumed to be small in comparison with the Fourier heat flux.
- Thermodynamic equilibrium is assumed to exist at the solid-liquid interfaces so that the interfacial temperature and concentrations can be related through the phase diagram, i.e.,

$$T = g(\langle C_\ell \rangle^\ell) \tag{6}$$

$$\overline{C}_{si} / \langle C_\ell \rangle^\ell = \kappa_s(\langle C_\ell \rangle^\ell) \qquad s = \alpha, \gamma \tag{7}$$

where g is an equation describing the liquidus curve, and κ_s is the equation for the segregation coefficient of solid phase s.
- Gravity has been assumed to be the only body force, the interfacial momentum transfer due to density change upon phase change is assumed negligible and the viscous stresses are assumed to be proportional to the rates of deformation.
- The flow through the porous matrix of columnar dendrites in the mushy zone is modeled using the mushy zone permeability in analogy with Darcy's law. The permeability in the mushy zone will, in general, be anisotropic (Poirier, 1987) so the permeability tensor in the momentum conservation equations becomes

$$\mathbf{K}^{(2)} = \begin{bmatrix} \cos^2\phi K_{\xi\xi} + \sin^2\phi K_{\eta\eta} & \sin\phi\cos\phi(K_{\xi\xi} - K_{\eta\eta}) \\ \sin\phi\cos\phi(K_{\xi\xi} - K_{\eta\eta}) & \sin^2\phi K_{\xi\xi} + \cos^2\phi K_{\eta\eta} \end{bmatrix} \tag{8}$$

where $K_{\xi\xi}$ is the permeability along the primary dendrite arms, $K_{\eta\eta}$ is the permeability perpendicular to the primary arms, and φ is the angle between the primary arms and the x-coordinate direction. The dendrites are assumed to grow opposite the flow of heat so that this angle can be determined from

$$\varphi = \tan^{-1}\left(\frac{\partial T}{\partial y} \Big/ \frac{\partial T}{\partial x}\right) \tag{9}$$

In addition, $K_{\xi\xi}$ and $K_{\eta\eta}$ are functions of the primary and secondary dendrite arm spacings, as well as the liquid volume fraction.
- The effective phase diffusion coefficients (i.e., mass diffusivity, thermal conductivity and viscosity) that appear in the conservation equations have been set equal to their microscopic counterparts. In addition, the phase enthalpies are assumed to vary with both temperature and concentration.

The assumptions given by equations (2) through (5) are illustrated in Figure 2, and the macroscopic conservation equations are summarized in Table 1. Before continuing, a few comments on these equations are necessary.

Microscopic Solid Species Diffusion

The term $(A_{si}/V_o)(\rho_s D_s/\ell_s^j)[\overline{C}_{si} - \langle C_s \rangle^s]$ in the solid species conservation equations in Table 1 physically represents the transfer of species at the solid/liquid interface, A_{si}, in an averaging volume due to microscopic species concentration gradients within the solid (Ni and Beckermann, 1991). This interfacial species transfer can be modeled as the product of the interfacial area concentration, A_{si}/V_o, and a mean interfacial species flux, $\rho_s D_s[\overline{C}_{si} - \langle C_s \rangle^s]/\ell_s^j$. In this case, the interfacial species flux is assumed to be proportional to the difference in the interfacial average and volume average solid species concentrations, with the constant of proportionality calculated from a solid species diffusion length, ℓ_s^j, as well as the solid density and mass diffusivity. The diffusion length and the interfacial area concentration are, in general, complicated functions of the solid microstructure, the phase volume fractions, and other conditions within the averaging volume (Wang and Beckermann, 1993). Since the quantity $[(A_{si}/V_o)/\ell_s^j]^{1/2}$ can be considered a characteristic length for the local solid microstructure, and if t_f denotes the local solidification time, the quantity $(A_{si}/V_o)(D_s/\ell_s^j)t_f$ is a dimensionless diffusion time (Fourier number). Then, two limiting cases of microscopic solid species diffusion can be considered (Kurz and Fisher, 1989):

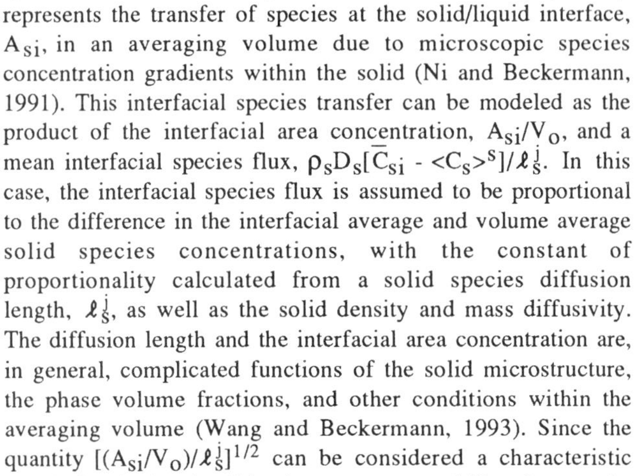

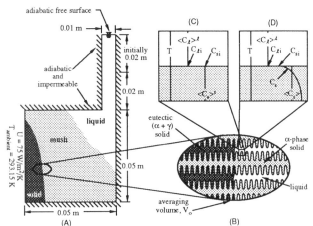

FIG. 2 SCHEMATIC ILLUSTRATIONS OF: (A) THE DOMAIN AND BOUNDARY CONDITIONS USED IN THE SIMULATIONS. (B) A TYPICAL AVERAGING VOLUME THAT INCLUDES α-PHASE SOLID, EUTECTIC (α + γ) SOLID, AND LIQUID. THE ASSUMED MICROSCOPIC TEMPERATURE AND CONCENTRATION PROFILES FOR (C) INFINITELY FAST MICROSCOPIC SOLID SOLUTE DIFFUSION. (D) NO MICROSCOPIC SOLID SOLUTE DIFFUSION.

TABLE 1. SUMMARY OF THE MACROSCOPIC CONSERVATION EQUATIONS.

Mixture Mass Conservation

$$\frac{\partial}{\partial t}(\varepsilon_\ell \rho_\ell) + \nabla\cdot(\varepsilon_\ell\rho_\ell \langle v_\ell\rangle^\ell) = -\frac{\partial}{\partial t}(\varepsilon_\alpha\rho_\alpha) - \frac{\partial}{\partial t}(\varepsilon_\gamma\rho_\gamma)$$

Liquid Species Conservation

$$\varepsilon_\ell\rho_\ell \frac{\partial \langle C_\ell\rangle^\ell}{\partial t} + \varepsilon_\ell\rho_\ell \langle v_\ell\rangle^\ell\cdot\nabla\langle C_\ell\rangle^\ell = \nabla\cdot(\varepsilon_\ell\rho_\ell D_\ell \nabla\langle C_\ell\rangle^\ell)$$

$$- \varepsilon_\alpha\rho_\alpha\frac{\partial\langle C_\alpha\rangle^\alpha}{\partial t} - \varepsilon_\gamma\rho_\gamma \frac{\partial \langle C_\gamma\rangle^\gamma}{\partial t}$$

$$+ [\langle C_\ell\rangle^\ell - \langle C_\alpha\rangle^\alpha]\frac{\partial}{\partial t}(\varepsilon_\alpha\rho_\alpha) + [\langle C_\ell\rangle^\ell - \langle C_\gamma\rangle^\gamma]\frac{\partial}{\partial t}(\varepsilon_\gamma\rho_\gamma)$$

Solid Species Conservation ($s = \alpha, \gamma$)

$$\varepsilon_s\rho_s \frac{\partial\langle C_s\rangle^s}{\partial t} = [\bar{C}_{si} - \langle C_s\rangle^s]\left\{\frac{\partial}{\partial t}(\varepsilon_s\rho_s) + \left(\frac{A_{si}}{V_o}\right)\frac{\rho_s D_s}{\ell_s^j}\right\}$$

Mixture Energy Conservation

$$\varepsilon_\ell\rho_\ell \left.\frac{\partial\langle h_\ell\rangle^\ell}{\partial T}\right|_{\langle C_\ell\rangle^\ell}\frac{\partial T}{\partial t} + \varepsilon_\ell\rho_\ell \left.\frac{\partial\langle h_\ell\rangle^\ell}{\partial T}\right|_{\langle C_\ell\rangle^\ell}\langle v_\ell\rangle^\ell\cdot\nabla T = \nabla\cdot\{(\varepsilon_\ell k_\ell + \varepsilon_s k_s)\nabla T\}$$

$$- \left[\varepsilon_\alpha\rho_\alpha \left.\frac{\partial\langle h_\alpha\rangle^\alpha}{\partial T}\right|_{\langle C_\alpha\rangle^\alpha} + \varepsilon_\gamma\rho_\gamma \left.\frac{\partial\langle h_\gamma\rangle^\gamma}{\partial T}\right|_{\langle C_\gamma\rangle^\gamma}\right]\frac{\partial T}{\partial t}$$

$$- \varepsilon_\ell\rho_\ell \left.\frac{\partial\langle h_\ell\rangle^\ell}{\partial\langle C_\ell\rangle^\ell}\right|_T \frac{\partial\langle C_\ell\rangle^\ell}{\partial t} - \varepsilon_\alpha\rho_\alpha \left.\frac{\partial\langle h_\alpha\rangle^\alpha}{\partial\langle C_\alpha\rangle^\alpha}\right|_T \frac{\partial\langle C_\alpha\rangle^\alpha}{\partial t} - \varepsilon_\gamma\rho_\gamma \left.\frac{\partial\langle h_\gamma\rangle^\gamma}{\partial\langle C_\gamma\rangle^\gamma}\right|_T \frac{\partial\langle C_\gamma\rangle^\gamma}{\partial t}$$

$$+ \left.\frac{\partial\langle h_\ell\rangle^\ell}{\partial\langle C_\ell\rangle^\ell}\right|_T \left\{\varepsilon_\ell\rho_\ell\frac{\partial\langle C_\ell\rangle^\ell}{\partial t} + \varepsilon_\alpha\rho_\alpha\frac{\partial\langle C_\alpha\rangle^\alpha}{\partial t} + \varepsilon_\gamma\rho_\gamma\frac{\partial\langle C_\gamma\rangle^\gamma}{\partial t}\right.$$

$$\left. - [\langle C_\ell\rangle^\ell - \langle C_\alpha\rangle^\alpha]\frac{\partial}{\partial t}(\varepsilon_\alpha\rho_\alpha) - [\langle C_\ell\rangle^\ell - \langle C_\gamma\rangle^\gamma]\frac{\partial}{\partial t}(\varepsilon_\gamma\rho_\gamma)\right\}$$

$$+ [\langle h_\ell\rangle^\ell - \langle h_\alpha\rangle^\alpha]\frac{\partial}{\partial t}(\varepsilon_\alpha\rho_\alpha) + [\langle h_\ell\rangle^\ell - \langle h_\gamma\rangle^\gamma]\frac{\partial}{\partial t}(\varepsilon_\gamma\rho_\gamma)$$

Liquid Momentum Conservation

$$\varepsilon_\ell\rho_\ell\frac{\partial\langle v_\ell\rangle^\ell}{\partial t} + \varepsilon_\ell\rho_\ell\langle v_\ell\rangle^\ell\cdot\nabla\langle v_\ell\rangle^\ell = -\varepsilon_\ell\nabla\langle p_\ell\rangle^\ell + \nabla\cdot(\varepsilon_\ell\mu_\ell\nabla\langle v_\ell\rangle^\ell)$$

$$+ \nabla\cdot\{\varepsilon_\ell\mu_\ell[\nabla\langle v_\ell\rangle^\ell]^t + \mu_\ell[\langle v_\ell\rangle^\ell\nabla\varepsilon_\ell + \nabla\varepsilon_\ell\langle v_\ell\rangle^\ell]\}$$

$$+ \langle v_\ell\rangle^\ell\left[\frac{\partial}{\partial t}(\varepsilon_\alpha\rho_\alpha) + \frac{\partial}{\partial t}(\varepsilon_\gamma\rho_\gamma)\right] - \varepsilon_\ell^2\mu_\ell K^{(2)^{-1}}\langle v_\ell\rangle^\ell + \varepsilon_\ell\rho_\ell g$$

$$\left(\frac{A_{si}}{V_o}\right)\frac{D_s}{\ell_s^j}t_f \gg 1 \qquad s = \alpha, \gamma \qquad (10)$$

or

$$\left(\frac{A_{si}}{V_o}\right)\frac{D_s}{\ell_s^j}t_f \ll 1 \qquad s = \alpha, \gamma \qquad (11)$$

Equation (10) implies that the time required for species diffusion in the solid on a microscopic scale is short in comparison with the local solidification time. Then, an order of magnitude analysis of the solid species conservation equations in Table 1 reveals that the volume average solid concentrations will be equal to the average interfacial solid concentrations, i.e., the solid phases will be solutally well mixed and equation (4) will be satisfied. In numerically solving the conservation equations, this can be accomplished by setting $(A_{si}/V_o)(\rho_s D_s/\ell_s^j)$ to a suitably large number. Conversely, equation (11) means that the time required for microscopic species diffusion in the solid is much longer than the local solidification time, and an order of magnitude analysis of the solid species conservation equations shows that there will be a microscopic concentration profile within the solid in an averaging volume as noted by equation (5). In other words, the solid will have "layers" of different compositions, with the concentration of each layer uniquely related to the concentration of the liquid from which it formed. Numerically, this is accomplished by setting $(A_{si}/V_o)(\rho_s D_s/\ell_s^i)$ equal to zero. As mentioned previously, one objective of the present work is to further investigate the differences in macroscopic model predictions using these two limiting cases to describe microscopic solid species diffusion in metal alloys.

During the solidification process, there is the possibility of local remelting of some of the solid that has formed. Since the solid is assumed to be solutally well mixed on a microscopic scale when using equation (10), this presents no difficulty. When using equation (11), however, the presence of a microscopic concentration profile in the solid creates problems during remelting (Rappaz and Voller, 1990; Poirier et al., 1991). In this case, the manner in which the average solid concentration varies during remelting depends on the concentration of the solid that is melting. During a solidification simulation, one could record the interfacial solid concentration at all times during solidification, back up along this profile during remelting, and calculate the average solid concentration by integrating over the profile. However, this would be a computationally time and space consuming process, and it can be argued that remelting is not the exact reverse of solidification as different parts of the solid could remelt at different rates. To avoid these difficulties, here it is assumed that during remelting the average solid concentration remains constant, i.e.,

$$\langle C_s \rangle^s = \text{constant during remelting} \qquad s = \alpha, \gamma \qquad (12)$$

Careful experimentation would be necessary to obtain a more accurate and realistic model of remelting.

Contraction Driven Flow

As shown in Table 2, the densities of the liquid and solid (both α and γ) phases will, in general, be unequal as well as functions of both temperature and concentration (Poirier, 1987). Hence, bulk liquid motion in the melt is necessary to account for the volume contraction, or shrinkage, that accompanies solid/liquid phase change. In deriving the equations in Table 1, no assumption has been made about the phase densities being constant or constant and equal. Therefore, the model is capable of predicting this contraction driven flow. For the Pb-Sn alloy under consideration here, the solid densities are larger than the liquid density, so that a riser has been attached to the square cavity to feed the solidification shrinkage (as shown in Figure 2). However, surface tension effects on the free surface at the top of the riser are neglected. The method used to handle the movement of the free surface during solidification is discussed in the section *Numerical Implementation*.

Initial Conditions, Boundary Conditions and Thermophysical Properties

Because of the relative abundance of available data for the thermophysical properties, mushy zone permeabilities, dendrite arm spacings and phase diagram parameters for Pb-Sn alloys, this system was chosen for study. These properties are summarized in Tables 2 and 3, while Figure 2 shows the size of the domain and the boundary conditions used to obtain the results in this paper. The initial condition for all of the simulations was a quiescent fluid at a uniform temperature of 576 K (25 K superheat) and a uniform concentration of Pb-20 wt.% Sn.

NUMERICAL IMPLEMENTATION

Since the conservation equations presented in the previous section are equally valid in the fully solid, mushy and bulk liquid regions, they can be solved using a fixed-grid, single-domain numerical solution procedure. For the results presented in this paper, an implicit, control-volume based finite difference scheme has been used to discretize the conservation equations, and a power law scheme used to evaluate the finite difference coefficients. The velocity-pressure coupling in the momentum equations was handled using the SIMPLER algorithm (Patankar, 1980).

The coupling of the energy and species conservation equations in the mushy zone through the phase diagram provides a method for calculating the solid volume fractions (Prakash and Voller, 1989). Briefly, the following steps outline the procedure to calculate ε_α or ε_γ before the eutectic point is reached (with a detailed description found in Schneider and Beckermann, 1993):

- The temperatures and concentrations (and, therefore, the phase enthalpies) in the energy equation are assumed known, and the discretized form of this equation is solved for the appropriate solid fraction, ε_α or ε_γ.
- The species conservation equations are solved for the respective average concentrations, using the most recent known values for the volume fractions and solid interfacial concentrations.
- The temperature for each location in the mushy zone is updated based on the liquidus temperature corresponding to the most recent value of the average liquid concentration.

This procedure is repeated within each time step until convergence of the temperature, concentration and volume fraction fields is achieved. Once the eutectic point is reached, both the α- and γ-phase solids form simultaneously while the temperature and concentrations remain fixed at the values given by the phase diagram. Then, the total $(\varepsilon_\alpha + \varepsilon_\gamma)$ solid fraction can be calculated from the energy equation, and the α- and γ-phase solid fractions calculated from the liquid species conservation equation.

To account for the movement of the free surface in the riser, the height of the upper most control volumes in the domain, i.e., those at the top of the riser in Figure 2, was changed at each time step to assure global mass conservation. One can

TABLE 2. PHASE DIAGRAM RELATIONS AND THERMOPHSYSICAL PROPERTIES FOR THE LEAD-TIN SYSTEM.

Liquidus Curve (K) (Poirier, 1988)

$$T = \begin{cases} 600.8 - 2.8290C_\ell + 2.5088\times10^{-2}C_\ell^2 - 2.7597\times10^{-4}C_\ell^3 & \text{for } C_\ell \le 61.9 \\ 229.4 + 7.7091C_\ell - 0.091235C_\ell^2 + 4.1752\times10^{-4}C_\ell^3 & \text{for } C_\ell > 61.9 \end{cases}$$

Segregation Coefficients (wt.% Sn/wt.% Sn) (Poirier, 1988)

$$\kappa_\alpha = 0.8273 - 4.2208\times10^{-2}C_\ell + 1.9680\times10^{-3}C_\ell^2 - 5.1866\times10^{-5}C_\ell^3 + 6.8075\times10^{-7}C_\ell^4 + 3.4568\times10^{-9}C_\ell^5;$$

$$\kappa_\gamma = 85.83/C_\ell + 0.33878 - 4.4858\times10^{-3}C_\ell + 2.0146\times10^{-5}C_\ell^2$$

Phase Enthalpies (J/kg) (Poirier and Nandapurkar, 1988)

$$h_\ell = [0.079393C_\ell + 156.81]T - 7.452\times10^{-5}(100 - C_\ell)T^2 - 25490C_\ell T^{-1} + 228.122C_\ell + 53769C_\ell(100-C_\ell)/(11869+88.51C_\ell) - 978.2C_\ell(100-C_\ell)(325.89C_\ell - 11869)/(11869+88.51C_\ell)^2 - 27747.9;$$

$$h_\alpha = [113.678+0.682376C_\alpha]T + [2.3507\times10^{-2} + 5.2996\times10^{-5}C_\alpha]T^2 + 214.25C_\alpha + 47590C_\alpha(100-C_\alpha)/(11869+88.51C_\alpha) - 22930C_\alpha(100-C_\alpha)(325.89C_\alpha - 11869)/(11869+88.51C_\alpha)^2 - 36028;$$

$$h_\gamma = [113.678+0.682376C_\alpha]T + [2.3507\times10^{-2}+5.2996\times10^{-5}C_\alpha]T^2 - 273.6C_\gamma + 196930C_\gamma(100-C_\gamma)/(11869+88.51C_\gamma) - 33670$$

Phase Densities (kg/m³) (Poirier, 1988)

$$\rho_\ell = \{(1.9095\times10^{16} + 3.3211\times10^{14}C_\ell + 9.014\times10^{11}C_\ell^2 + 4.0665\times10^{9}C_\ell^3) - (2.1363\times10^{12} + 3.9986\times10^{10}C_\ell - 1.6899\times10^{8}C_\ell^2 + 1.8477\times10^{6}C_\ell^3)\,T\}/(88.51C_\ell + 11869)^3;$$

$$\rho_\alpha = 1.6334\times10^{-20}/(88.51C_\alpha + 11869)\,a_\alpha^{-3} \quad \text{where} \quad a_\alpha = 4.8910\times10^{-10} + 1.9625\times10^{-14}\,T - \frac{2.9328\times10^{-9}C_\alpha}{88.51C_\alpha + 11869};$$

$$\rho_\gamma = 2.9940\times10^{-20}/(88.51C_\gamma + 11869)\,a_\gamma^{-3} \quad \text{where} \quad a_\gamma = \frac{1.1305\times10^{-8}}{(6.724\times10^{-5}\,T^2 + 0.1270\,T + 7262)^{1/3}} - \frac{1.6795\times10^{-8}(100-C_\gamma)}{88.51C_\gamma + 11869}$$

Phase Thermal Conductivities (W/m/K) (Felicelli et al., 1991; Touloukian et al, 1970; Metals Handbook, 1979; Schneider and Beckermann, 1992)

$$\ln(k_\ell) = \frac{C_\ell}{100}\ln(k_\ell^{Sn}) + \frac{100 - C_\ell}{100}\ln(k_\ell^{Pb}) \quad \text{where} \quad \ln(k_\ell^{Sn}) = 0.85337 + 0.4109\ln(T) \quad \text{and} \quad \ln(k_\ell^{Pb}) = -2.0725 + 0.7521\ln(T);$$

$$\ln(k_s) = \frac{C_s}{100}\ln(k_s^{Sn}) + \frac{100 - C_s}{100}\ln(k_s^{Pb}) \quad \text{where} \quad \ln(k_s^{Sn}) = 4.5422 - 0.1708\ln(T) \quad \text{and} \quad \ln(k_s^{Pb}) = 3.7507 - 0.1708\ln(T)$$

$$\text{and} \quad C_s = (\varepsilon_\alpha\rho_\alpha C_\alpha + \varepsilon_\gamma\rho_\gamma C_\gamma)/(\varepsilon_\alpha\rho_\alpha + \varepsilon_\gamma\rho_\gamma)$$

Viscosity (kg/m/s) (Thresh and Crawley, 1970)

$$\mu_\ell = (118.69C_\ell\,\mu_\ell^{Sn} + 207.2C_\ell\,\mu_\ell^{Pb})/(88.51C_\ell + 11869)$$

$$\text{where} \quad \mu_\ell^{Sn} = 2.75\times10^{-5}\,(\rho_\ell^{Sn})^{1/3}\exp\{0.0885\rho_\ell^{Sn}/T\}$$

$$\text{and} \quad \mu_\ell^{Pb} = 2.54\times10^{-5}\,(\rho_\ell^{Pb})^{1/3}\exp\{0.0863\rho_\ell^{Pb}/T\}$$

Liquid Mass Diffusivity (m²/s) (Streat and Weinberg, 1974)

$$D_\ell = 3.0\times10^{-9}$$

TABLE 3. MUSHY ZONE PERMEABILITIES AND DENDRITE ARM SPACINGS USED IN CACLUATIONS

Permeability (m^2):

Parallel to Primary Dendrite Arms (Porier, 1987; Felicelli et al., 1991)

$$K_{\xi\xi} = \begin{cases} \left[4.53\times10^{-4} + 4.02\times10^{-6}(\varepsilon_\ell + 0.1)^{-5}\right] \dfrac{d_1^2\varepsilon_\ell^3}{(1-\varepsilon_\ell)} & \text{for } \varepsilon_\ell < 0.7 \\ 0.07425\, d_1^2 \left[-\ln(1-\varepsilon_\ell) - 1.487 + 2(1-\varepsilon_\ell) - 0.5(1-\varepsilon_\ell)^2\right] & \text{for } \varepsilon_\ell \geq 0.7 \end{cases}$$

Perpendicular to Primary Dendrite Arms (m^2) (Poirier, 1987; Felicelli et al., 1991; Sangani and Acrivos, 1982)

$$K_{\eta\eta} = \begin{cases} \left[1.73\times10^{-3}\left(\dfrac{d_1}{d_2}\right)^{1.09}\right] \dfrac{d_2^2\varepsilon_\ell^3}{(1-\varepsilon_\ell)^{0.749}} & \text{for } \varepsilon_\ell < 0.7 \\ K_{\eta\eta} = 0.03979 d_1^2 \left[-\ln(1-\varepsilon_\ell) - 1.476 + 2(1-\varepsilon_\ell) - 1.774(1-\varepsilon_\ell)^2 + 4.076(1-\varepsilon_\ell)^3\right] & \text{for } \varepsilon_\ell \geq 0.7 \end{cases}$$

Dendrite Arm Spacings (m):

Primary (Klaren et al., 1980; Tewari and Shaw, 1991)

$$d_1 = 325.1\times10^{-6} C_0^{0.25} \left[\left(\frac{\partial T}{\partial x}\right)^2 + \left(\frac{\partial T}{\partial y}\right)^2\right]^{-0.25} \left(\frac{\partial T}{\partial t}\right)^{-0.25}$$

Secondary (Roosz et al., 1986)

$$d_2(t_f) = \left[d_2(0)^3 + \int_0^{t_f} \frac{\Gamma D_\ell}{m_\ell(\kappa_s - 1)C_\ell}\, dt \right]^{1/3}$$

where m_ℓ = slope of the liquidus curve

$\Gamma = 1.0\times10^{-7}$ J/m^2 and $d_2(0) = 15\times10^{-6}$ m

imagine this process as approximating the regression of the liquid surface down the riser. To be completely rigorous, the movement of the control volume faces should be accounted for in the discretization of the conservation equations. For simplicity that has not been done, but in the simulations presented here the volume change during any one time step was less than 0.005% so that this procedure is not expected to have a significant effect on the model predictions. In addition, the solid densities were not allowed to vary with temperature in those control volumes that were completely solid. This is required to satisfy the assumption of no solid movement as given by equation (1).

Effort has been made to assure that the model and solution procedure are sound. Comparison between predictions of the model for diffusion dominated (i.e., no fluid flow) solidification, the Neumann solution for isothermal phase change, and a semi-analytic solution for alloy solidification (Voller, 1989) showed good agreement. In addition, agreement was obtained between predictions of inverse segregation using the present model and results presented by Diao and Tsai (1993) for the solidification of an Al-4.1 wt.% Cu alloy cooled from below. Finally, the computations were performed on a grid that had 50 control volumes in the horizontal direction, 65 control volumes in the vertical direction, and was biased near the walls. A time step of 0.1 seconds was used in obtaining all the results. Based on previous experience with similar simulations, this grid and time step are fine enough to capture all of the fundamental transport phenomena while allowing for reasonable computational costs. Calculations have been successfully performed separately on Apollo DN10000, IBM 3090 and HP 715/50 computers. When using constant properties and a linear phase diagram, 1 second of simulation time required approximately 220 seconds of cpu time on an HP 715/50 workstation. For the variable properties and non-linear phase diagram used here, computational times were considerably longer.

RESULTS AND DISCUSSION

The results of three different simulations are described:

- Case S1 (Scheil 1) assumes that there is no microscopic solid solute diffusion, i.e., equation (10) holds, and includes both buoyancy and contraction driven flow.
- Case S2 (Scheil 2) is also the same as Case S1, but includes only contraction driven flow.
- Case L1 (Lever 1) assumes complete microscopic solid solute diffusion, i.e., equation (11) holds, and includes both buoyancy and contraction driven flow.

In order to illustrate the general phenomena that occur in Cases S1 and L1, detailed results from Case S1 will be presented. Results from Case L1 will be presented in parallel with those results at appropriate points to facilitate comparison between the predictions when the two limiting microsegregation models are used. Comparison of the final results of Cases S1 and L1 with those of Case S2 allows for an evaluation of the effects of contraction driven flow on macrosegregation.

In the plots used to illustrate the simulation results, the velocity vectors represent the actual liquid velocity, $\langle v_\ell \rangle^\ell$, not the pore velocity, $\langle v_\ell \rangle = \varepsilon_\ell \langle v_\ell \rangle^\ell$, and a velocity scale is shown in the upper left of the plots. Superimposed on the vector plots are solid volume fraction isopleths in 10 % increments, with the location of the liquidus and solidus/eutectic fronts shown in bold. The shaded macrosegregation plots are of the mixture concentration, i.e., $C_{mixture}$ =

$$\frac{\varepsilon_{\ell}\rho_{\ell}<C_{\ell}>^{\ell} + \varepsilon_{\alpha}\rho_{\alpha}<C_{\alpha}>^{\alpha} + \varepsilon_{\gamma}\rho_{\gamma}<C_{\gamma}>^{\gamma}}{\varepsilon_{\ell}\rho_{\ell} + \varepsilon_{\alpha}\rho_{\alpha} + \varepsilon_{\gamma}\rho_{\gamma}} \quad (14)$$

with a scale provided in the figures. Finally, the shaded eutectic fraction plots are of the total solid fraction ($\varepsilon_{\alpha} + \varepsilon_{\gamma}$) formed during the eutectic reaction, with a scale also provided in the figures.

Early Stages of Solidification

After cooling is begun at the left wall, thermal buoyancy forces establish a counter-clockwise natural convection cell in the melt for Cases S1 and L1. This cell serves to reduce the melt superheat and the onset of solidification is delayed when compared to Case S2 where only contraction driven flow is considered. For Case S2 the first solid begins to form after about 35 seconds of cooling. For the cases that include buoyancy driven flow, the first α-phase solid begins to form at the bottom of the cooled wall after about 80 seconds, and as time progresses, the mushy zone grows upward along the cooled wall and into the melt. After 150 seconds of cooling the mushy zone occupies approximately one-third of the cavity, and there are no completely solid regions. Figure 3 shows isotherm and liquid concentration isopleths for Case S1 after 150, 250 and 400 seconds of cooling. Due to the different solubilities of tin in the α-phase solid and the liquid, the formation of solid is accompanied by the enrichment of the interdendritic liquid with tin. Since the density of tin is smaller than that of lead, this enrichment induces solutal buoyancy forces that oppose the thermal buoyancy forces induced by the temperature gradients shown in Figure 3(a). The density of the solute enriched liquid is significantly less than the density of the liquid of the initial composition, and, therefore, solutal buoyancy forces dominate in the mushy zone. As shown in Figure 3(d), the flow driven by these buoyancy forces carries the enriched liquid to the top of the cavity and into the bottom of the riser. The enriched liquid is prevented from moving farther up the riser by convective flow in the riser due to both thermal buoyancy and feeding due to solid/liquid density differences.

Figure 4 shows velocity vector, solid fraction isopleth and macrosegregation plots for Cases S1 and L1 after 250 seconds of cooling. Figure 4(a) shows that for Case S1 the mushy zone occupies approximately one-half of the cavity. By this time the flow is dominated by solutal buoyancy forces, the exceptions being a very small thermally driven cell in the lower right corner of the cavity and the combined effects of buoyancy and contraction flow in the riser. Again, the upward flow in the mushy zone lifts the tin-rich interdendritic liquid to the top of the cavity where, as shown in Figures 3(e) and 4(c), it collects to form a thin layer. The liquidus temperature in this layer is depressed significantly by the high tin concentration so that the mushy zone is confined to a small region near the cooled wall.

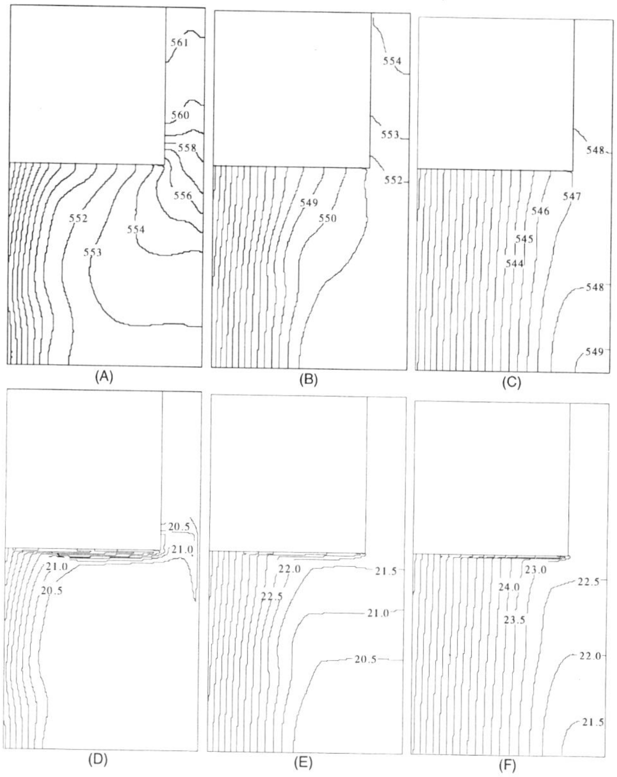

FIG. 3 ISOTHERMS AND LIQUID CONCENTRATION ISOPLETHS FOR CASE S1: (A) 150 s, T_{max} = 561.2, T_{min} = 542.0 K, (B) 250 s, T_{max} = 554.1, T_{min} = 536.7 K, (C) 400 s, T_{max} = 549.2, T_{min} = 529.7 K, (D) 150 s, C_{max}= 24.7, C_{min} = 20.0 wt.% Sn, (E) 250 s, C_{max}= 27.2, C_{min} = 20.1 wt.% Sn, AND (F) 400 s, C_{max}= 25.4, C_{min} = 16.9 wt.% Sn.

The velocity vectors and solid fraction isopleths for Case S1 show that the strong flow from the riser into the cavity warms some of the tin-rich fluid at the top of the cavity (as determined from Figure 3(b)) and draws it back into the upper-right portion of the mushy zone. As shown in Figure 4(a), the result of this interaction is the formation of a channel in the mushy zone. The presence of tin-rich liquid in the channel serves to lower the liquidus temperature, and the advection of warm fluid into the region causes both remelting and the delayed formation of solid. The channel provides a preferred path for the upward flow of the tin-rich interdendritic liquid and, as seen in Figure 4(c), it contains a higher concentration of tin than the surrounding regions.

The predictions for Case S1 (Figures 4(a) and (c)) and Case L1 (Figures 4(b) and (d)) after 250 seconds of cooling are remarkably similar. Even the distribution of the solid fraction across the mushy zone is nearly the same. This is somewhat surprising since Case S1 assumes that there is no solute

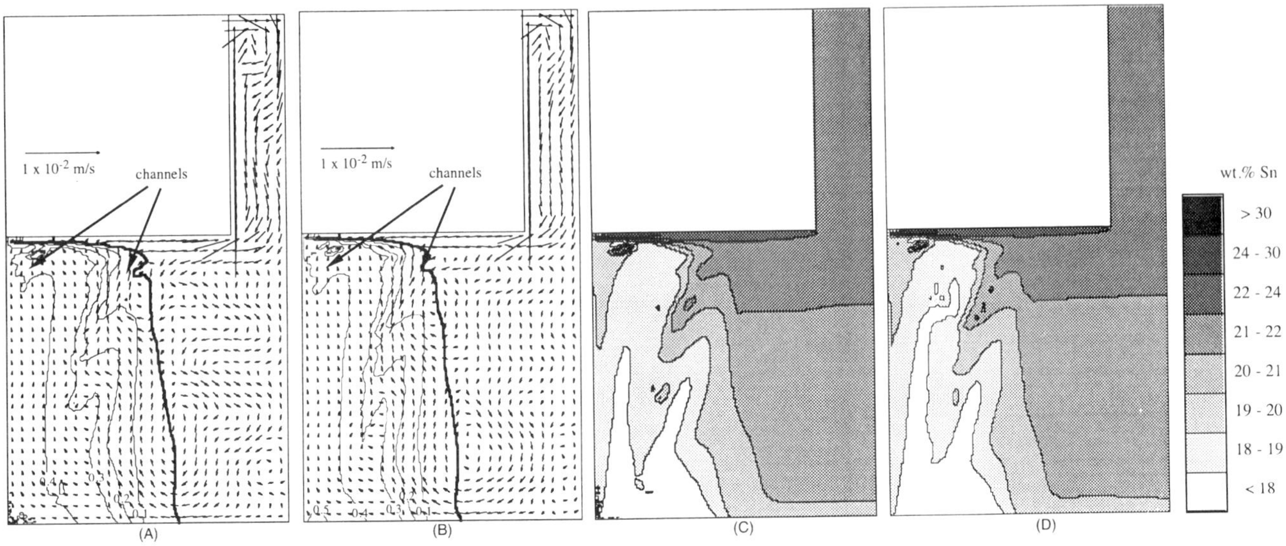

FIG. 4 VELOCITY FIELD, SOLID FRACTION ISOPLETHS AND MACROSEGREGATION PATTERNS AT 250 s: (A) CASE S1, ε_{max} = 0.801, ε_{min} = 0.0, (B) CASE L1, ε_{max} = 0.521 AND ε_{min} = 0.0, (C) CASE S1, C_{max} = 25.8, C_{min} = 15.7 wt.% Sn AND (D) CASE L1, C_{max} = 36.0, C_{min} = 16.7 wt.% Sn.

diffusion microscopically in the solid while Case L1 assumes that the solid is microscopically well mixed. The discussion in the section *Final Eutectic Volume Fractions* will show that the primary difference between the predictions of the two cases is in the amount of eutectic formed, and this leads to differences in the prediction of shrinkage driven flow, as discussed in the section *Final Stages of Solidification*.

Intermediate Stages of Solidification

After 400 seconds of cooling in Case S1, Figure 5(a) shows that the mushy zone occupies about three-fourths of the cavity. The strongest buoyancy driven flow is limited to the pure liquid region and the portion of the mushy zone where the liquid fraction is relatively high. In the remainder of the mushy zone there is a combination of flow toward the cooled wall and toward the top of the cavity. This flow is slow enough that, as seen in Figure 3(c), energy transport through this portion of the mushy zone is nearly conduction dominated. As detailed in Figure 5(a), a second less severely segregated channel has begun to form in the upper right portion of the mushy zone. The tin rich liquid at the top of the cavity, shown in Figures 3(f) and 5(b), has kept the liquidus temperature low enough that the mushy zone is still confined to a small region near the cooled wall. Were it not for the fact that much of the tin-rich liquid has been transported to the riser (as shown in Figure 5(b)) it is expected that the tin rich layer at the top of the cavity would be much thicker and more severely segregated.

By 800 seconds after the initiation of cooling for Case S1, heat transfer across the cavity is conduction dominated. Figure 5(c) shows that the mushy zone occupies nearly all of the cavity (except for part of the thin tin-rich layer at the top) and two-thirds of the riser. A small solutally driven convection cell is contained in the top one-third of the riser, while the flow through the cavity is of a much smaller magnitude and is towards the cooled wall and the top of the cavity. The macrosegregation plot in Figure 5(d) clearly shows the segregation in the two channels that have formed in the mushy zone, as well as the small tin-rich layer that extends from the top of the cavity along the left and into the top of the riser. There is also a very large tin-deficient region at the bottom of the cavity.

Final Stages of Solidification

At about 1700 seconds after the initiation of cooling for Case S1, the liquid near the cooled wall approaches the eutectic temperature and concentration, and the formation of eutectic solid (both α- and γ-phase solid) commences. Since by this time the energy transport across the cavity is conduction dominated, the eutectic front (i.e., the eutectic isotherm) remains nearly straight and vertical as it moves across the cavity. Figure 6(a) shows that after 1800 seconds the eutectic front has progressed to approximately the midpoint of the cavity, and the rest of the domain is occupied by mush. This figure also shows that the flow is dominated by the solid/liquid density change on solidification. For this case solidification of the cavity was completed after 2050 seconds.

Figure 6(b) shows the velocity field and the position of the solidus/eutectic front for Case L1 after 2050 seconds of

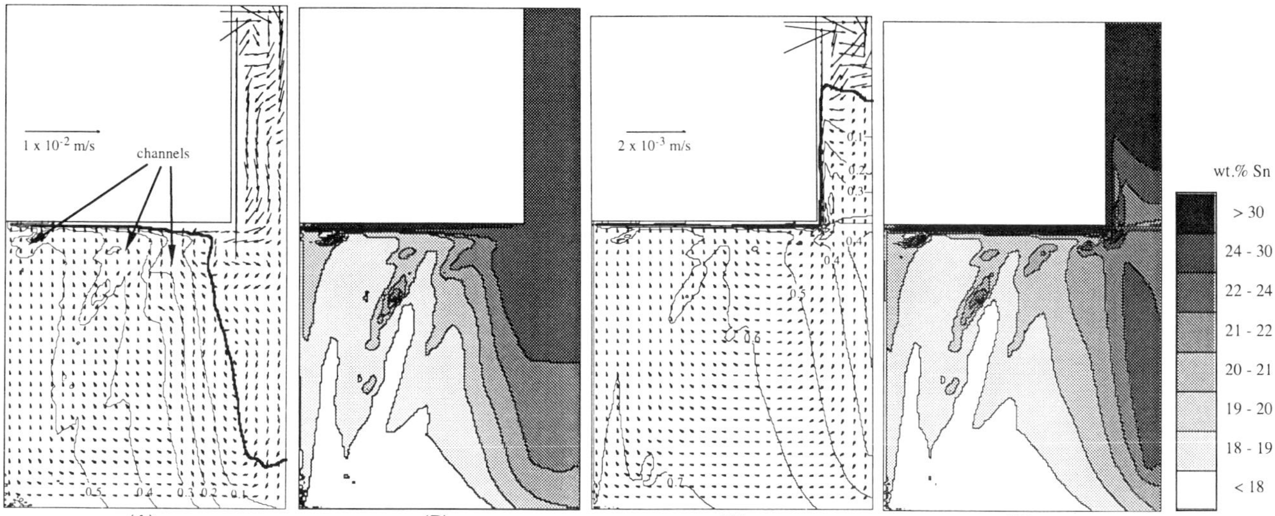

FIG. 5 VELOCITY FIELD, SOLID FRACTION ISOPLETHS AND MACROSEGREGATION PATTERNS FOR CASE S1: (A) 400 s, $\varepsilon_{max} = 0.839$, $\varepsilon_{min} = 0.0$, (B) 400 s, $C_{max} = 29.0$, $C_{min} = 15.7$ wt.% Sn, (C) 800 s, $\varepsilon_{max} = 0.891$, $\varepsilon_{min} = 0.0$, AND (D) 800 s, $C_{max} = 35.8$, $C_{min} = 15.6$ wt.% Sn.

cooling, and indicates that the final stages of solidification for this case are quite different from Case S1. Similar to that case, the first completely solid regions began to form after about 1700 seconds, but in Case L1 the solid was in the tin-poor area at the bottom of the cavity (not at the cooled wall) and contained only α-phase (no eutectic) solid. In fact, no eutectic solid was formed until after 2000 seconds. Figure 6(b) shows that by 2050 seconds approximately one-half of the cavity is

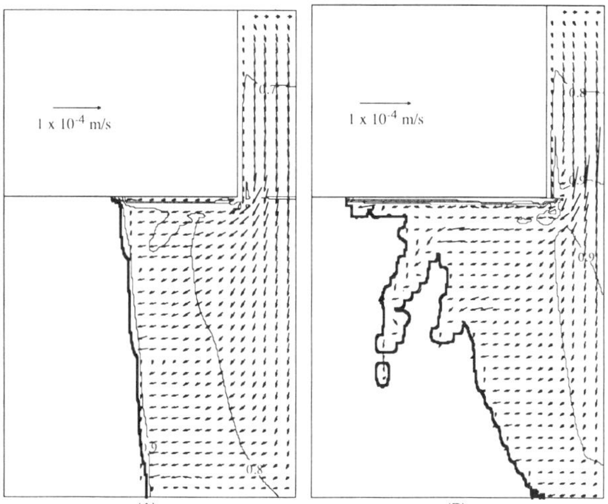

FIG. 6 VELOCITY FIELD, SOLID FRACTION ISOPLETHS AND EUTECTIC/SOLIDUS FRONT NEAR THE END OF SOLIDIFICATION: (A) CASE S1, 1800 s, $\varepsilon_{min} = 0.499$ AND (B) CASE L1, 2050 s, $\varepsilon_{min} = 0.563$.

completely solid. Since much of the solid region contains no eutectic, at this time the boundary between the mushy and solid regions is not the eutectic isotherm. Comparison of Figures 6(a) and (b) shows that the height of the liquid in the riser in Case L1 is 1.5 mm higher than that in Case S1. This is due to the fact that in Case S1 the local average α-phase solid concentrations are, in general, less than those in Case L1. The solid density is a function of concentration, and since tin is lighter than lead, higher concentration solid will be less dense. Therefore, in Case S1 the density difference between the α-phase solid and liquid is greater than that in Case L1. Close inspection of Figures 6(a) and (b) shows that the magnitude of the flow (especially in the riser) is slightly larger in Case L1 than in Case S1. This is due to the fact that in Case L1 mostly α-phase solid is forming while in Case S1 eutectic solid is forming. The eutectic density (8455 kg/m^3) is less than that of the α-phase solid (10003 kg/m^3) so that more flow is needed to feed the solidification shrinkage in Case L1. Both of these points illustrate the way the choice of a microsegregation model can affect the prediction of contraction driven flow. For Case L1, after about 2100 seconds the remaining liquid has a high enough liquid composition that eutectic solid forms from it, and the cavity was completely solidified after 2190 seconds of cooling.

Final Macrosegregation Distributions

Figure 7 shows the final macrosegregation patterns for all of the cases (S1, S2 and L1). It is interesting to first compare the macrosegregation plots for Case S1 after 800 seconds (Figure 5(d)) and 2050 seconds (Figure 7(a)). While the segregated

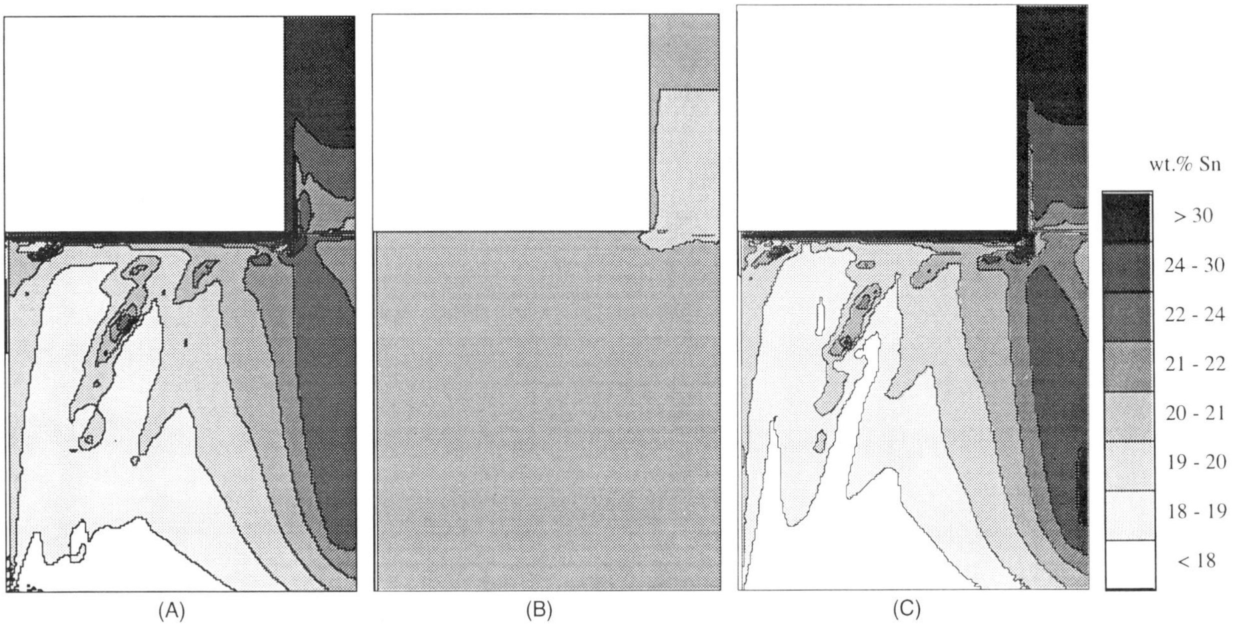

FIG. 7 FINAL MACROSEGREGATION PATTERNS: (A) CASE S1, 2050 s, C_{max} = 37.8, C_{min} = 16.1 wt.% Sn, (B) CASE S2, 2070 s, C_{max} = 20.7, C_{min} = 17.8 wt.% Sn, AND (C) CASE L1, 2190 s, C_{max} = 36.0, C_{min} = 16.7 wt.% Sn.

channels appear in both figures, there are some important differences, such as the change in the size of the tin-poor region at the bottom of the cavity. Close examination reveals that the size of all the tin deficient regions has decreased. The explanation for this behavior is the continuous drawing of tin-rich liquid from the top of the cavity and the riser into the rest of the cavity by contraction driven flow during the later stages of solidification.

Figure 7(b) shows that in comparison with the cases that include buoyancy driven flow, the magnitude of segregation for Case S2 was very small. A comparison of the plots in Figures 7(a) and (c) shows that the final macrosegregation patterns for Cases S1 and L1 are again very similar. Closer examination reveals that the extent of macrosegregation is slightly worse for Case L1. This is seen, for instance, in the size of the tin-poor (less than 18 wt.% Sn) region at the bottom of the cavity and in the presence of a small tin-rich area (between 24 and 30 wt.% Sn) at the lower right wall. In comparing predictions of macrosegregation for the solidification of an NH_4Cl-H_2O solution, Voller et al. (1987) observed that the opposite was true, i.e., segregation was more severe when there was assumed to be no microscopic solid solute diffusion (S1) rather than no microscopic solute diffusion (L1). Swaminathan (1994), on the other hand, observed large macrosegregation differences for the two microsegregation models when simulating the solidification of an Al-Cu alloy with both shrinkage and buoyancy driven flow.

To further illustrate the differences in macrosegregation predicted by the different cases, Figure 8 shows the final macrosegregation profiles along the horizontal and vertical midsections of the cavity, with the behavior at the left wall and top of the cavity shown in more detail in Figures 8(a) and (d), respectively. The first observation that can be made from Figure 8(a) is that all of the cases, even Case S2 where only contraction driven flow is considered, predict a large degree of negative segregation near the cooled wall. Previous investigations of contraction driven flow and macrosegregation have shown only positive (inverse) segregation near the cooled boundary (Chen and Tsai, 1993; Diao and Tsai, 1993a and 1993b). To explain why the contraction driven flow case considered here indicates negative segregation near the wall, Figure 9 shows the macrosegregation profiles predicted by the present model when the same alloy is solidified unidirectionally, using the same initial and boundary conditions, and the assumption of no species diffusion microscopically in the solid. The curves shown in Figure 9 correspond to three different cases: the full model (i.e., as used in the two-dimensional simulations) with no buoyancy driven flow; the full model with no buoyancy driven flow and no macroscopic species diffusion in the liquid; and the full model with the solid and liquid densities equal, i.e., no buoyancy or contraction driven flow. Figure 9(b) shows that for the two cases that include contraction driven flow the model does predict the type of inverse segregation observed in previous studies, and as expected, the case with no flow shows a nearly uniform mixture concentration across most of the casting. Figure 9(a), however, shows that for the two cases where species diffusion in the liquid is considered, there is a small negatively segregated region very near the chill that is

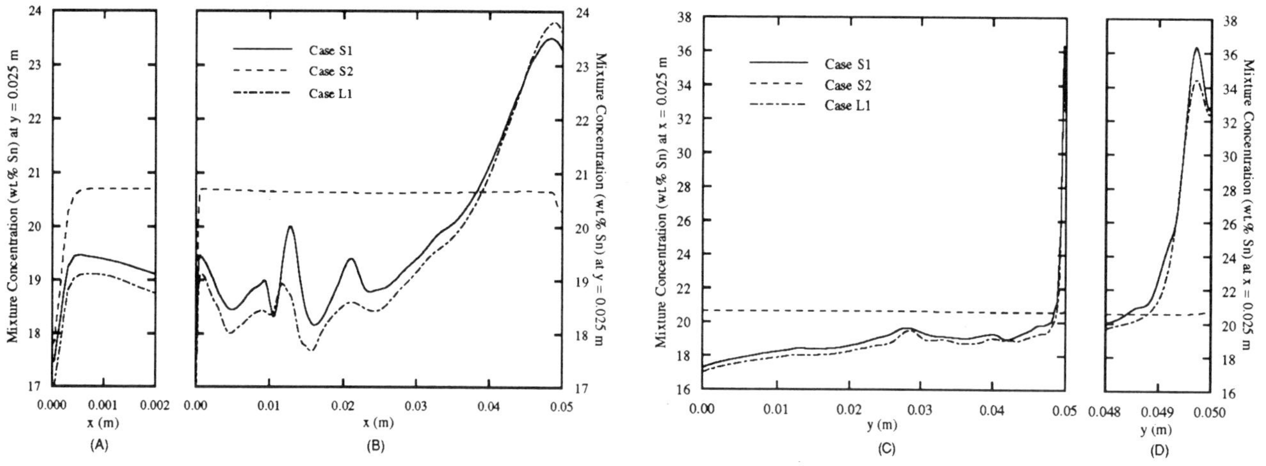

FIG. 8 FINAL MACROSEGREGATION PROFILES: (A) AND (B) ALONG y = 0.025 m, (C) AND (D) ALONG x = 0.025 m.

not present when species diffusion in the liquid is neglected. The cause of this behavior is diffusion of species away from the wall due to the concentration gradient in the liquid formed by the rejection of tin into the liquid during solidification. Based on these results, the negative segregation observed near the cooled wall in Figure 8(a) must be attributed to macroscopic species diffusion in the liquid.

Returning to the two-dimensional simulations, Figure 8(b) shows that, in general, the two cases that involve buoyancy flow (S1 and L1) predict similar macrosegregation distributions (i.e., negative segregation up to $x \approx 0.035$ m and positive segregation from that point to the right wall), and the variations in macrosegregation for these cases are much larger than those predicted using only contraction driven flow (S2).

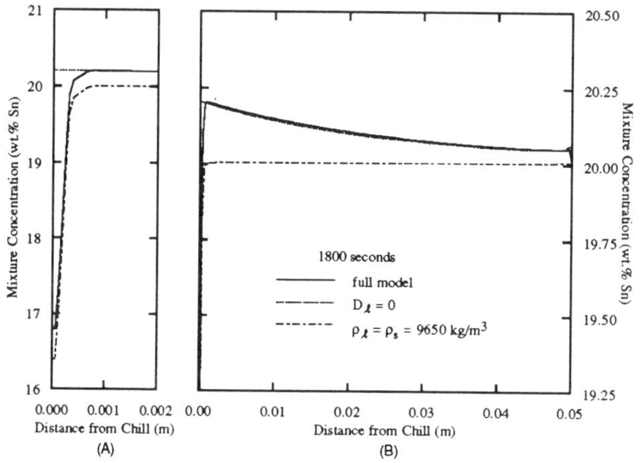

FIG. 9 MACROSEGREGATION PROFILES FOR UNIDIRECTIONAL SOLIDIFICATION WITH NO BUOYANCY DRIVEN FLOW: (A) NEAR THE CHILL AND (B) THROUGHOUT THE CASTING.

Case S1 shows the largest jump in the mixture concentration across the cavity, and this corresponds to one of the channels seen in the previous macrosegregation plots. Finally, Figure 8(b) indicates that, at least along the horizontal centerline of the cavity, Case L1 predicts the most severe segregation (both positive and negative). Comparing this case with Case S1, one sees that although the macrosegregation patterns for the two microscopic solid species diffusion models (no diffusion and complete diffusion) are similar, the extent of macrosegregation predicted by the models is slightly different.

Examining Figures 8(c) and (d) shows that the extent of macrosegregation along the vertical centerline of the cavity is nearly the same for the two cases with buoyancy flow, and as expected, there is little variation in the profile for the contraction flow case. As in the previous graphs, Case L1 shows the most severe negative segregation. Figure 8(d) shows the extremely high positive segregation found at the top of the cavity for the cases with buoyancy driven flow. If some of the tin-rich fluid had not been allowed to escape into the riser, one would expect that this layer would be much thicker and more severely segregated.

Final Eutectic Fraction Distributions

Figure 10 contains shade plots that show the final eutectic volume fractions predicted for Cases S1, S2 and L1. Comparing Figure 10(a) with Figure 7(a) shows that for Case S1 the final macrosegregation and eutectic fraction patterns are very similar, with more eutectic formed where positive segregation is largest, e.g., in the channels and at the top of the cavity. It is important to note that for this case there is no fully solid region that contains less than 5 % eutectic by volume. Figure 10(c), however, shows something completely different for Case L1. In this case, a large portion of the solid in the cavity contains little or no eutectic. The Scheil and lever rule models (along with approximate properties for the Pb-Sn

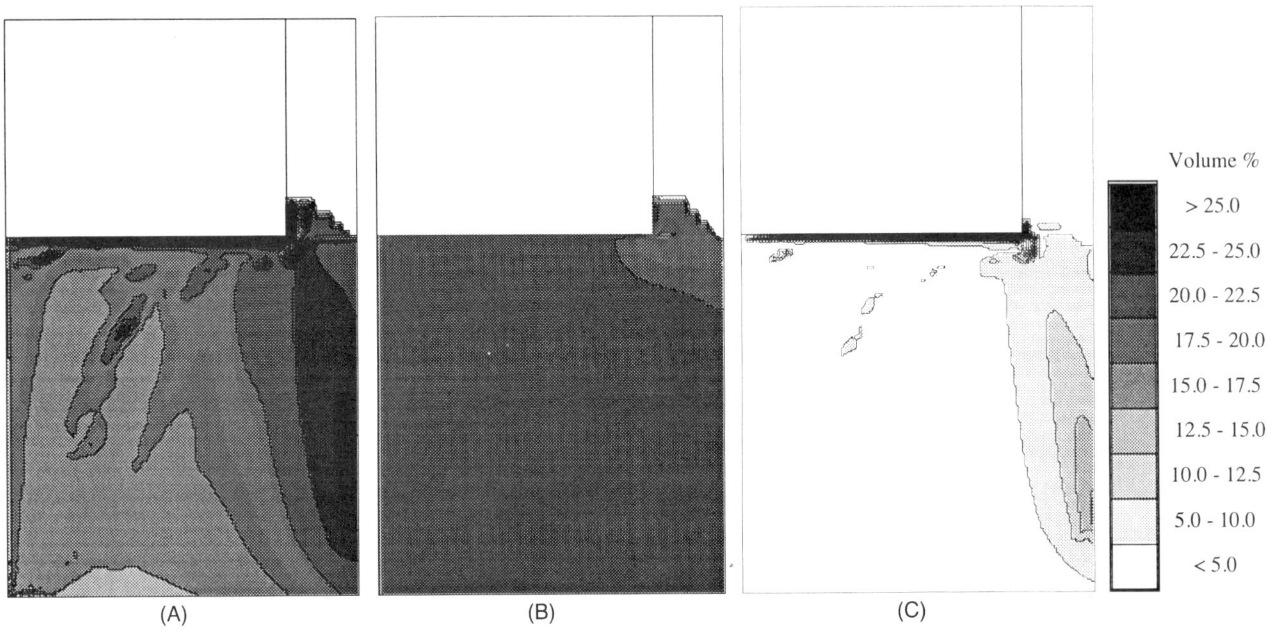

FIG. 10 FINAL EUTECTIC VOLUME FRACTION DISTRIBUTIONS: (A) CASE S1, 2050 s, ε_{max} = 52.5 %, (B) CASE S2, 2070 s, ε_{max} = 20.7 % (C) CASE L1, 2190 s, ε_{max} = 43.7 %.

system) would predict eutectic volume fractions of about 25 % and 5 %, respectively. Since Cases S1 and L1 would reduce to those two models if macroscopic species transport was neglected, the differences between Figures 10(a) and (c) are not surprising. These results are also consistent with the observations of Poirier et al. (1991) for diffusion dominated solidification. Finally, as mentioned in the discussion of Figure 6, note the difference in the height of fluid in the risers in Cases S1 and L1. Again, this can be attributed to the differences in the solid densities caused by the differences in the average solid concentrations and the amount of eutectic formed when using the different microsegregation models.

To further illustrate the differences in eutectic fraction predicted by the cases, Figure 11 shows the final eutectic fraction distribution along the horizontal and vertical midsections of the cavity. As for the mixture concentration, the variations in Case S2 are small compared to those where buoyancy driven flow is included. As was seen in the shaded eutectic fraction plots, the case where no microscopic solid solute diffusion was assumed (S1) has variations in the prediction of eutectic fraction similar to those seen in the macrosegregation graphs in Figure 8 (i.e., higher eutectic fractions where segregation is higher). As observed in the shade plots, Case L1 predicts quite different behavior. Figures 11(a) and (b) shows that there is essentially no eutectic formed along the horizontal centerline of the cavity up to $x \approx 0.03$ m. From there to the right cavity wall there is a slow increase in the eutectic fraction up to a maximum of about 13 % by volume. Case S1, by comparison, has a maximum of about 25 % eutectic. Figures 11(c) and (d) show similar behavior along the vertical centerline of the cavity. Along this section Case L1 predicts little or no eutectic across most of the cavity. In the tin-rich layer at the cavity top, however, this case shows a sudden increase in eutectic fraction up to a maximum of about 40 %. Case S1 also shows a much higher eutectic fraction in the tin-rich layer, but has a relatively uniform eutectic fraction across the rest of the centerline.

CONCLUSIONS

In order to better understand macroscopic solidification models, the combined effects of microsegregation and contraction driven flow on the prediction of macrosegregation and eutectic fraction during the solidification of a Pb-Sn alloy have been evaluated. To investigate the sensitivity of macroscopic solidification simulations to the choice of solid microsegregation model, two limiting cases were compared: no microscopic solid species diffusion or infinitely fast microscopic solid species diffusion. For the Pb-Sn alloy and geometry considered here, assuming infinitely fast solute diffusion resulted in the prediction of slightly more severe macrosegregation. Simulation of the solidification of an NH_4-Cl mixture (Voller et al., 1987) and an Al-Cu alloy (Swaminathan, 1994) showed slightly worse macrosegregation for no solid solute diffusion and a large difference in macrosegregation for the two microsegregation models, respectively. These differences in model predictions indicates a need for continued investigation into the effects of solid microsegregation on macrosegregation. In the present results, the most significant difference in the predictions for

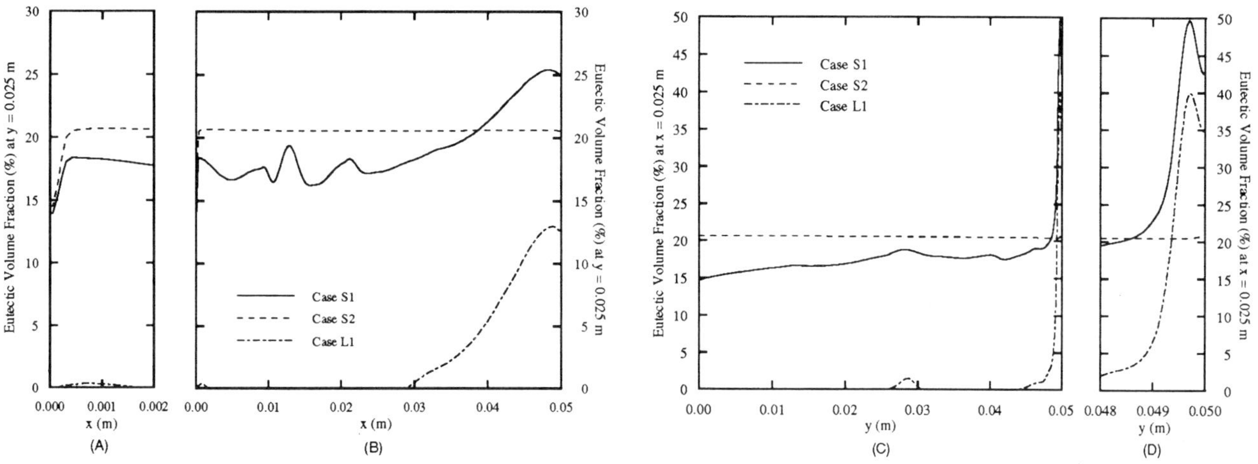

FIG. 11 FINAL EUTECTIC VOLUME FRACTION PROFILES: (A) AND(B) ALONG y = 0.025 m, (C) AND (D) ALONG x = 0.025 m.

the two solid microsegregation models was in the amount of eutectic solid formed. While the assumption of no microscopic solid species diffusion resulted in the prediction of the formation of a significant amount of eutectic throughout the casting, the assumption of infinitely fast diffusion led to the prediction of the formation of a small amount eutectic only in the portion of the casting where there was severe positive segregation. The present results suggest that it may not be necessary to use more complicated microsegregation models (e.g., including finite rate solute diffusion in the solid microscopically or more carefully incorporating coarsening effects) if one is solely interested in predicting macrosegregation. However, these results also suggest that such complicated microsegregation models are probably necessary to accurately predict eutectic formation. Since the solid density is a function of concentration, and since the eutectic and primary solid phases have different densities, the choice of microsegregation model can also have an effect on the prediction of contraction driven flow, due to differences in the prediction of the solid concentrations and eutectic fractions. Finally, it would be interesting to compare experimentally measured eutectic fractions, in addition to macrosegregation, against the corresponding predictions when the two microsegregation models are used.

The degree of macrosegregation due solely to contraction driven flow was seen to be small in comparison with macrosegregation due to combined contraction and buoyancy driven flow. The effects of species diffusion macroscopically in the liquid appears to be important, at least near cooled boundaries. While contraction driven flow serves to increase the mixture concentration near these boundaries (i.e., causes inverse macrosegregation), species diffusion causes the opposite effect (i.e., it serves to cause negative segregation). It would be interesting to investigate what effect different cooling rates have on the formation of this negative segregation, whether it is predicted for other alloy systems, and if it can be measured experimentally.

Acknowledgments

This work was supported by the National Science Foundation under Grant No. CTS-8957149.

REFERENCES

Amberg, G., 1991, "Computation of Macrosegregation in an Iron-Carbon Cast," *Int. J. Heat Mass Transfer*, Vol. 34, pp. 217-227.

Beckermann, C. and Viskanta, R., 1988, "Double-Diffusive Convection during Dendritic Solidification of a Binary Mixture," *PhysicoChem. Hydrodyn.*, Vol. 10, 195-213.

Beckermann, C. and Viskanta, R., 1993, "*Mathematical Modeling of Transport Phenomena during Alloy Solidification*," Applied Mechanics Reviews, Vol. 46, pp. 1-27.

Bennon, W.D. and Incropera, F.P., 1987, "The Evolution of Macrosegregation in Statically Cast Binary Ingots," *Metall. Trans. B.*, Vol. 18B, pp. 611-616.

Chen, J.H. and Tsai, H.L., 1993, "Inverse Segregation for a Unidirectional Solidification of Aluminum-Copper Alloys," *Int. J. Heat Mass Transfer*, Vol. 36, pp. 3069-3075.

Chiang, K.C. and Tsai, H.L., 1992a, "Shrinkage-Induced Fluid Flow and Domain Change in Two-Dimensional Alloy Solidification," *Int. J. Heat Mass Transfer*, Vol. 35, pp. 1763-1770.

Chiang, K.C. and Tsai, H.L., 1992b, "Interaction between Shrinkage-Induced Fluid Flow and Natural Convection during Alloy Solidification," *Int. J. Heat Mass Transfer*, Vol. 35, pp. 1771-1778.

Diao, Q.Z., and Tsai, H.L., 1993a, "Modeling of Solute Redistribution in the Mushy Zone during Solidification of Aluminum-Copper Alloys," *Metall. Trans. A*, Vol. 24A, pp. 963-973.

Diao, Q.Z., and Tsai, H.L., 1993b, "The Formation of Negative and Positive Segregated Bands during Solidification of Aluminum-Copper Alloys," *Int. J. Heat Mass Transfer*, Vol. 36, pp. 4299-4305.

Felicelli, S.D., Heinrich, F.C. and Poirier, D.R., 1991, "Simulation of Freckles during Vertical Solidification of Binary Alloys," *Metall. Trans. B*, Vol. 22B, pp. 847-859.

Flemings, M.C., 1974, *Solidification Processing*, McGraw-Hill, New York.

Klaren, C.M., Verhoeven, J.D. and Trivedi, R., 1980, "Primary Dendrite Spacing of Lead Dendrites in Pb-Sn and Pb-Au Alloys," *Metall. Trans. A*, Vol. 11A, pp. 1853-1861.

Metals Handbook, 1948, T. Lyman, ed., ASM.

Ni, J. and Beckermann, C., 1990, A Two-Phase Model for Mass, Momentum, Heat and Species Transport during Solidification, *Metall. Trans. B*, Vol. 22B, pp. 349-361.

Nielson, D.G. and Incropera, F.P., 1993, "Effect of Rotation on Fluid Motion and Channel Formation during Unidirectional Solidification of a Binary Alloy," *Int. J. Heat Mass Transfer*, Vol. 36, pp. 489-503.

Patankar, S.V., 1980, *Numerical Heat Transfer and Fluid Flow*, McGraw-Hill, New York.

Poirier, D.R., 1987, "Permeability for Flow of Interdendritic Liquid in Columnar-Dendritic Alloys," *Metall. Trans. B*, Vol. 18B, pp. 245-255.

Poirier, D.R., 1988, "Densities of Pb-Sn Alloys during Solidification," *Metall. Trans.*, Vol. 19A, pp. 2349-2354.

Poirier, D.R. and Nandapurkar, P.J., 1988, "Enthalpies of a Binary Alloy during Solidification," *Metall. Trans. A*, Vol. 19A, pp. 3057-3061.

Poirier, D.R., Nandapurkar, P.J. and Ganesan, S., 1991, "Then Energy and Solute Conservation Equations for Dendritic Solidification," *Metall. Trans. B*, Vol. 22B, pp. 889-900.

Prakash, C. and Voller, V., 1989, "On the Numerical Solution of Continuum Mixture Model Equations Describing Binary Solid Liquid Phase Change," *Numer. Heat Transfer*, Vol. 15, pp. 171-189.

Prescott, P.J. and Incropera, F.P., 1991, "Numerical Simulation of a Solidifying Pb-Sn Alloy: The Effects of Cooling Rate on Thermosolutal Convection and Macrosegregation," *Metall. Trans. B*, Vol. 22B, pp. 529-540.

Rappaz, M. and Voller, V.R., 1990, "Modeling of Micro-Macrosegregation in Solidification Processes," *Metall. Trans. A*, Vol. 21A, pp. 749-753.

Roosz, A., Halder, E. and Exner, H.E., 1986, "Numerical Calculation of Microsegregation in Coarsened Dendritic Microstructures," *Mat. Sci. and Tech.*, Vol. 2, pp. 1149-1155.

Sangani, A.S. and Acrivos, A., 1982, "Slow Flow past Periodic Arrays of Cylinders with Application to Heat Transfer," *Int. J. Multiphase Flow*, Vol. 8, pp. 193-206.

Schneider, M.C., 1991, *Modeling the Columnar Dendritic Solidification of Lead-Tin Alloys*, M.S. Thesis, The University of Iowa.

Schneider, M.C. and Beckermann, C., 1991, "Effects of Simplified Enthalpy Relations on the Prediction of Heat Transfer during Solidification of a Lead-Tin Alloy," *Appl. Math. Modelling*, Vol. 15, pp. 596-605.

Schneider, M.C. and Beckermann, C., 1993, "Summary of a Method for Numerically Simulating the Columnar Dendritic Solidification of Binary Alloys," *Technical Report UIME-CB01-1993*, Dept. of Mechanical Engineering, The University of Iowa, Iowa City, IA.

Shahani, H., Amberg, G. and Fredriksson, H., 1992, "On the Formation of Macrosegregations in Unidirectionally Solidified Sn-Pb and Pb-Sn Alloys," *Metall. Trans. A*, Vol. 23A, pp. 2301-2311.

Streat, N. and Weinberg, F., 1974, "Macrosegregation during Solidification resulting from Density Differences in the Liquid," *Metall. Trans.*, Vol. 5, pp. 2539-2548.

Swaminathan, C.R., 1994, "Numerical Modeling of Filling and Solidification in Casting Processes," Ph.D. Thesis, The University of Minnesota, Minneapolis, MN.

Tewari, S.N and Shah, R., 1992, "Thermosolutal Convection during Dendritic Growth and its Effect on Macrosegregation," *Micro-Macro Scale Phenomena in Solidification*, C. Beckermann, L.A. Bertram, S.J. Pien and R.E. Smelser, eds., ASME-HTD, 9-16.

Thresh, H.R., and Crawley, A.F., 1970, "The Viscosities of Lead, Tin and Pb-Sn Alloys," *Metall. Trans.*, Vol. 1, pp. 1531-1535.

Touloukain, Y.S., Powell, R.W., Ho, C.Y. and Klemens, P.G., 1970, *Thermophysical Properties of Matter*, Vol. 1, IFI/Plenum, New York.

Voller, V.R., 1989, "Development and Application of a Heat Balance Integral Method for Analysis of Metallurgical Solidification", *Appl Math. Modelling*, Vol. 13, pp. 3-11.

Voller, V.R., 1990, "Fast Implicit Finite-Difference Method for the Analysis of Phase-Change Problems", *Numer. Heat Transfer, Part B*, Vol. 17, pp. 155-169.

Voller, V.R., Brent, A.D. and Prakash, C., 1989, "The Modelling of Heat, Mass and Solute Transport in Solidification Systems," *Int. J. Heat Mass Transfer*, Vol. 32, pp. 1719-1731.

Wang, C.Y. and Beckermann, C., 1993, "A Multiphase Solute Diffusion Model for Dendritic Alloy Solidification," *Met Trans. A*, Vol. 24A, pp. 2787-2802.

Xu, D. and Li, Q., 1991a, "Numerical Method for Solution of Strongly Coupled Binary Alloy Solidification Problems," *Numer. Heat Transfer A*, Vol. 20A, pp. 181-201.

Xu, D. and Li, Q., 1991b, "Gravity- and Solidification-Shrinkage-Induced Liquid Flow in a Horizontally Solidified Alloy Ingot," *Numer. Heat Transfer A*, Vol. 20A, pp. 203-221.

Xu, D., Li, Q. and Pehlke, R.D., 1991, "Computer Simulation of Al-Cu Alloy Solidification using a Continuum Model, *AFS Trans.*, Vol. 91, pp. 737-745.

HTD-Vol. 284/AMD-Vol. 182, Transport Phenomena in Solidification
ASME 1994

STEREOLOGY-BASED MODELING OF EQUIAXED SOLIDIFICATION

S. P. Marsh
Naval Research Laboratory
Washington, D.C.

D. Banerjee
UES, Incorporated
Annapolis, Maryland

ABSTRACT

A stereology-based formalism has been developed to smoothly integrate macroscale numerical computations with microstructural dynamics in the simulation of casting processes. This approach uses morphology-independent stereological parameters to quantify the geometric characteristics of the developing microstructure. Incorporating this approach into numerical schemes allows for the modeling of a wide variety of morphologies with minimal changes in the basic computer code, as well as great flexibility in coupling phenomena between the microscopic and macroscopic regimes. Transitioning between various micromodels is also greatly simplified. The stereological approach has been used to model the various stages of equiaxed solidification of binary alloys. This modeling effort expresses lengthscale evolution through the specific surface area parameter, S_V, and demonstrates the technique of combining models of basic mechanisms to describe the overall microstructure development.

NOMENCLATURE

A interfacial area
A^I area associated with tip-region dendrite solidification
A^{II} area associated with epitaxial solidification
C_∞ equilibrium solute concentration at a flat interface
D solute diffusion coefficient
K surface-area coarsening rate constant
N^u number of dendrite branch units
N_v number (of nuclei) per unit volume
Pe Péclet number
R radius
$\mathbf{R}$ gas constant
R^c radius of the equivalent cylinder
$\bar{R}_g$ final average radius of the equiaxed grains
S_v Surface area per unit volume
T temperature
V_e fraction of solid within the grain envelope
V^I volume associated with tip-region dendrite solidification
V^{II} volume associated with epitaxial solidification
V_m molar volume
V_v Volume fraction of a phase
Z reciprocal of the Péclet number
t time

Greek Symbols

α, β phases α and β, respectively
γ interfacial free energy
λ lamellar thickness
λ_s secondary dendrite sidebranch spacing
λ^α lamellar thickness of phase α
λ^β lamellar thickness of phase β
Ω supersaturation of solute
φ parent phase of the lamellar eutectic

Subscripts

g dendritic grain envelope
e per unit volume of the grain envelope
tip tip region of a growing dendrite
v per unit volume of microstructure

Superscripts

I associated with tip-region solidification
II associated with epitaxial (uniform) solidification
c cylinder (part of a dendritic branch unit)
u a dendritic branch unit (defined in the Appendix)
α, β phases α and β, respectively

INTRODUCTION

One of the key objectives of solidification modeling is the optimization of material properties in castings through control of microstructure. The physical processes that occur during solidification span a wide range of lengthscales, from microscopic (interatomic) and mesoscopic (microstructural) scales to macroscopic distances comparable to the size of the casting itself. Much research has been directed toward development of modeling equations to describe the microscopic processes that occur below the resolution of numerical techniques. These micromodels, which may be analytical or empirical in form, are then incorporated into computer codes that simulate the macroscopic processes of heat transfer and fluid flow. The ability to incorporate micromodels into this calculational scheme is complicated by the wide variety of morphology-specific micromodels that exist, and the need to incorporate multiple models describing various processes that occur during solidification of a single casting. Combining micromodels with numerical computer codes thus requires extensive programming to merge the detailed solidification behavior of a specific alloy with the more general modeling equations for heat, mass, and momentum flow. Physical consistency between the microscopic and macroscopic model equations must also be addressed, and can be difficult to attain uniformly through the variety of forms that micromodels are expressed in.

Reviews of the various thermophysical phenomena and computational factors that are relevant to micro/macro-modeling of solidification processes are provided in the literature by Rappaz (1989) and Tseng *et al.* (1992). The major considerations on the micro- and macroscales will be reviewed here briefly. Macroscopically, the solidification process is limited by the rate of heat flow from the alloy through the mold wall. Another important effect that occurs over these lengthscales is convective flow of the melt within the casting. The fluid flow affects both the heat transfer characteristics and the redistribution of species within multicomponent materials. The simulation of these phenomena involves calculation of transport equations over a discretized mesh using a finite-element method (FEM) or finite-difference method (FDM). The scale of the discretization represents a compromise between the spatial resolution required to represent the geometry of the casting and simulate the continuum transport processes accurately, and the computational resources required to simulate the entire solidification and cooling process in a reasonable amount of time. Numerical simulations generally have a spatial resolution on the order of millimeters to centimeters, and it is at this level that the process variables, such as temperature and composition, are tracked directly.

The size scales of microstructural features that are present during solidification are on the approximate order of micrometers. The formation and evolution of these features are determined by thermophysical phenomena such as interface attachment kinetics and capillary effects. It is clearly not feasible to simulate the geometry of such processes in detail throughout the casting and carry the effects up to the macroscopic scale. Furthermore, details of microstructural features such as the shapes of individual dendrite arms and precipitates are not needed to predict and correlate the mechanical properties that are observed macroscopically. The as-cast structure results from the continuous interaction of the microscopic and macroscopic processes as the casting solidifies and cools, and both regimes must be addressed to obtain useful structural information from solidification simulations.

The purpose of this paper is to outline a general and robust basis for incorporating micromodels into numerical simulation codes. The approach is based on the use of fundamental stereological variables to describe the microstructure quantitatively. The micromodels serve as evolution equations for these variables, which are tracked in the macroscopic simulation code. This approach leads to a computational algorithm that can accommodate the various phases and structures that appear during solidification, and provides a consistent framework in which to couple the microscopic and macroscopic phenomena. The incorporation of new micromodels and modification of existing ones can be done with a minimum of reprogramming, simplifying the development of useful simulations considerably. This approach may also be extended to incorporate such phenomena as porosity formation and stress effects.

STEREOLOGY

The science of stereology deals with the precise definition of quantitative geometric parameters that describe three-dimensional structures, and determination or estimation of their values from measurements made in planar cross-sections. A thorough discussion of stereological concepts can be found in the book by Underwood (1970). A review of the techniques and mathematical background will not be presented here. Instead, we focus on two primary stereological parameters, volume fraction and specific surface area, that have direct relevance to the quantitative description and dynamical modeling of microstructures.

Global Properties

A key concept in stereology is that of a global property, which is a density term that expresses the total amount of a geometric feature per unit amount of another parameter. In physical materials, global properties are often defined with respect to a unit volume of the system of interest. The unit volume is generally chosen large enough to contain a representative sample of the structure, rather than portions of individual features. The global properties thus defined are morphology-independent. In principle, any defined geometrical parameter can be totalled in a unit volume regardless of the particular shape, dispersion or topology of the structural features.

The two primary stereological parameters that will be used to characterize microstructures are the volume fraction, V_V, and the specific surface area, S_V. The volume fraction represents the total volume of a particular phase, V, per unit volume of the material considered, v. Note that the volume fraction is a dimensionless quantity having a value between zero and unity. Also, the sum of the volume fractions of all phases present must, by definition, be equal to unity. The volume fraction is defined for each phase present, and thus is used in conjunction with the component concentrations in the phases to specify the mass balances.

The specific surface area, S_V, defines an unambiguous, physically relevant size scale of the microstructure. Although a variety of lineal parameters, or metrics, have been used to specify the size of features observed in different morphologies, they are generally shape-dependent. Such metrics include the average particle "size" (radius or diameter) for dispersed phases, lamellar spacings that occur in layered structures, and secondary arm spacings of dendritic structures that commonly appear during alloy solidification. The global property S_V is well-defined for any morphology, and is simply the total interfacial area separating two phases of interest, S, per unit volume of the structure, v. S_V has units of reciprocal length, so that large values of S_V correspond to fine-featured or highly dispersed structures, and vice-versa. This parameter is physically significant because it represents the total interfacial area across which the transport processes and phase transformations occur during microstructural evolution. There are other stereological parameters that provide additional geometrical information about the microstructure morphology, including contiguity (Underwood, 1970) and integral mean curvature (DeHoff and Iswaran, 1982). These can be introduced as needed to provide more detailed geometric characterization of structures. In the micro/macro integration scheme presented here, we use S_V alone to provide a single characteristic size scale of the various microstructures.

Definition of the Unit Volume

The fundamental connection between micromodels and discrete macroscopic simulations lies in the definition of the unit volume of the micromodel. The simulations on the macroscale are performed on a discrete mesh that is adapted to the shape of the casting geometry and is generally fixed in time (Rappaz, 1989). The unit volume associated with a mesh point is defined to be the locus of points that lie closer to the mesh point of interest than to any neighboring point. The detailed shape of the unit volumes is not required for the incorporation of micromodels into simulations. Only the volume associated with each mesh point is needed as a weighting factor for the global properties to determine the total amount of the geometric quantities associated with each point.

This approach toward micro/macro modeling suggests that the resolution on the macroscopic level should be determined primarily through considerations of stability and convergence of the macroscopic transport equations. The features that lie below the resolution of the mesh can be specified and tracked through the global property parameters. The delineation of macroscopic features that span many mesh points (such as large voids) is achieved by setting the volume fraction of the included points equal to unity, and the volume fraction at points along the boundary equal to some fractional value. Adjacency information among node points can be analyzed at the macroscopic scale to determine the extent of these larger features.

Formulation and Adaptation of Micromodels

Micromodels describe both the formation of new phases from existing ones and the structural changes that occur within a given phase mixture. It is often necessary to incorporate a variety of micromodels to account for all of the significant phase transformations that occur during a single casting operation. This is simplified greatly if all of the micromodels are formulated in terms of a common set of geometric parameters, S_V and V_V. These can be related to the specific geometry of any particular model by using a geometric construction that relates the volumes and surface areas through a single lengthscale. Examples of this appear in the equiaxed model that is developed in the following section.

In the numerical simulations, state variables such as temperature and concentration evolve through the macroscopic field equations. In the micromodels, these same parameters represent average conditions on the local unit volume of microstructure at each node point over a timestep. This approach is physically consistent with the spatial resolution of the simulations as defined by the finite element mesh. One advantage of this formalism is that it allows for the smooth transition between micromodels when an appropriate physical limit is reached in the process. The parameter values at the end of one micromodel become the initial conditions for the new micromodel. Although the morphology specific to the two models may change, the interfacial areas and phase volumes vary smoothly and conservation laws are easily tracked in a consistent manner.

MODELING OF EQUIAXED SOLIDIFICATION

The solidification of many alloys begins with the nucleation process in undercooled melts, which produces a dispersion of microscopic solid-phase particles. These nuclei proceed to grow dendritically, with the principal growth occurring in the six orthogonal crystallographic directions of cubic materials. The dendritic structure forms an envelope defined by the spherical volume centered around the nucleus and containing the tips of the primary dendrites. The growth rate of the dendrites within the envelope is generally limited by diffusion of solute to the envelope from the surrounding liquid matrix. The equiaxed grains continue to grow until impingement of neighboring grains occurs. At this point, the rapid primary growth of the dendrites ceases and subsequent solidification is dominated by the temperature-dependent phase fractions as specified by the phase diagram. Once the temperature falls below the eutectic temperature, the remaining liquid generally forms a finely interspersed two-phase eutectic structure.

In this section, a model of equiaxed dendritic solidification describing the above phenomena is developed in terms of stereological parameters. This process is separated into the following four major steps: nucleation of the primary solid phase from the melt, growth of the equiaxed dendritic grains, further solidification of the primary phase, and formation of a eutectic solid from the remaining interdendritic liquid (Kurz and Fisher, 1985). The focus of this model is on the stereological representation of the appropriate models, and on the sequential and simultaneous combination of specific micromodels to describe the overall process.

Nucleation

The primary result of the nucleation process is the determination of the local density of nuclei, N_V. Many nucleation models are continuous in nature (Thevoz *et al.*, 1989), and allow nuclei to continue forming over time. In the micro/macro approach presented in this paper, an instantaneous nucleation model is more appropriate. Nucleation is assumed to occur at a single time and temperature. The nuclei formed in the volume around a single node point are thus equivalent, and a single "characteristic" dendritic envelope describes the average local grain behavior. The results of an instantaneous nucleation model will vary with local cooling rate and other variables at each node point (Stefanescu *et al.*, 1990), thus allowing for variations in nucleation at the same scale as the resolution of the numerical grid.

The stereological parameter N_v, which specifies the local density of nuclei, also determines the local average size of the equiaxed grains. The average volume of an equiaxed grain at impingement is equal to $1/N_v$, and thus the average radius of the nearly spherical grains, R_g, may be found from the expression

$$N_v^{-1} = \frac{4}{3}\pi R_g^3 \ . \tag{1}$$

A useful result of this approach is the ability to refine nucleation models by combining simulation and physical analysis of actual castings. The measured grain sizes may be used to express N_v in terms of the relevant cooling conditions obtained by simulating the thermal conditions at the onset of nucleation.

Equiaxed Growth

To describe the equiaxed dendritic growth of the nucleated grains, we begin by adopting the analytical model developed by Rappaz and Thévoz (1987a). This model describes the kinetics of the solute diffusion-limited growth process using a boundary layer around each equiaxed grain envelope. This envelope is a spherical domain containing the tips of the growing dendrite branches. Although there are some gaps in the dendritic structure between the six orthogonal branches, the model consistently accounts for the net rate-limiting diffusion of solute from the entire dendritic structure within the grain to the surrounding matrix. The Rappaz-Thévoz model describes the solidification of a single equiaxed grain. The salient results of this model will be presented here, and more details are available in the original reference. In the current stereological approach, this grain represents the average behavior of all grains within the local volume associated with a single node point in the macroscopic mesh. We then proceed to modify this growth model to incorporate the development of lengthscales in the solidifying structure.

The growth rate of the grain envelope radius, dR_g/dt, is exactly equal to the tip velocity of the dendrite arms, v_{tip}, that delineate the envelope boundary. This velocity is related to the square of the supersaturation of solute in the liquid matrix (Kurz and Fisher, 1985). The volume fraction occupied by the grain envelopes, $V_{v,g}$, is given by the expression

$$V_{v,g} = N_v \frac{4}{3}\pi R_g^3 \ , \tag{2}$$

which is the total current volume of N_v grains per unit volume of material.

Solid-Phase Growth. The fraction of solid within the grain envelope, V_e (denoted as f_i in the original paper), is given by the Rappaz-Thévoz model as

$$V_e = \Omega\left(1 + \frac{3}{2}Z + Z^2 + \frac{1}{4}Z^3\right), \tag{3}$$

where Ω is the local supersaturation. Z is the reciprocal of the Péclet number of the grain envelope, Pe, and is defined as

$$Z = \frac{2D}{v_{tip} \cdot R_g} = \frac{1}{Pe} \ . \tag{4}$$

In this expression, D is the solute diffusion coefficient, and the dendrite tip velocity, v_{tip}, also represents the velocity of the envelope surface. The fraction of solid within the grain envelope, V_e, is related to the overall volume fraction of solid, V_v, through the volume fraction of the grain envelopes, $V_{v,g}$ (2) as

$$V_v = V_e \cdot V_{v,g} \ . \tag{5}$$

Tracking two of these volume fractions is necessary because both the Rappaz-Thévoz model and the lengthscale model developed in this paper address the structure within the grain envelope, whereas the mass and energy balances in the unit volume at a node point require the overall compositions and volume fractions. The grain envelope is treated as a "phase" in the present formalism, and growth of this phase is tracked through its volume fraction, $V_{v,g}$. This volume fraction relates all stereological parameters based on the grain volume to those based on the overall unit volume at each node.

Lengthscale Evolution. A model for the formation and evolution of lengthscales within the equiaxed dendritic structure will now be developed. The lengthscales in this model are expressed in terms of surface areas. This allows different simultaneously operating mechanisms to be combined smoothly. It also permits the conversion of resulting values to more conventional measures, such as dendrite arm spacings, through the dendritic geometry.

We assume that there are three principle mechanisms that contribute to the observed lengthscales in the equiaxed grains. The first is the creation of area (and fine lengthscales) in the tip region of the growing dendrites. Second is the creation of area and thickening of the dendritic features within the envelope arising from the net additional solidification that occurs during equiaxed growth. Finally, there is the capillary-driven coarsening phenomenon that reduces the surface area (and increases the characteristic lengthscales) with no change in the net volume of solid. These mechanisms are assumed to operate independently, and will be addressed individually in the following sections.

Dendrite tip growth. The essentially unconstrained growth of the dendrite tips into the surrounding melt produces features on the order of the tip radius, R_{tip} (Kurz and Fisher, 1985). To describe this quantitatively, we use a construction that approximates the average geometry of the dendrite in the tip region. The construction (Appendix A) represents a segment of the main dendrite branch in the tip region containing four orthogonal side branches. This unit may be repeated end-to-end to approximate the size and shape relationships in the vicinity of the growing tip.

The length of this repeating branch unit is $4R_{tip}$. Thus, the rate at which these units are formed along a single growing main branch, dN^u/dt, is related to the tip velocity as

$$\frac{dN^u}{dt} = \frac{v_{tip}}{4\,R_{tip}} . \tag{6}$$

The solid that forms due to the tip-region solidification in an equiaxed grain is denoted as V^I. The rate at which this volume increases from the growth of the six dendrite tips, dV^I/dt, is equal to the volume of a single dendrite unit, V^u, multiplied by the total rate of formation of such units in the grain. This may be written, using dN^u/dt from (6) and V^u from (A1) as

$$\frac{dV^I}{dt} = 6\,\frac{v_{tip}}{4\,R_{tip}} \cdot 336\,R_{tip}^3 = 504\,v_{tip} \cdot R_{tip}^2 . \tag{7}$$

The interfacial area created in the tip region, A^I, is determined in a similar manner as the area of a single dendrite unit multiplied by the rate at which such units are being formed. Thus, using (6) and (A2), we have

$$\frac{dA^I}{dt} = 6\,\frac{v_{tip}}{4\,R_{tip}} \cdot 384\,R_{tip}^2 = 576\,v_{tip} \cdot R_{tip} . \tag{8}$$

These two equations represent the approximate rate at which area and volume are being created due to growth of the six dendrite tips from an equiaxed grain. Note that these are net values, and must be normalized per unit volume (i.e., must be multiplied by N_v) to represent the variation in the global properties $d\,V_v^I$ and $d\,S_v^I$.

Epitaxial growth. The diffusion-limited solidification of the dendritic grain, as described by the model of Rappaz and Thévoz (1987a), includes both solidification at the tips and epitaxial solidification of the existing dendrite structure. To model the epitaxial solidification, we assume that it occurs uniformly over the existing dendritic structure within the grain envelope. A coarsening term will be introduced to describe the rearrangement of this solid arising from capillary effects.

The amount of solid that forms on the existing dendritic structure over a timestep is denoted by dV^{II}. This is simply the total change in solid volume, dV, over a timestep (given by the Rappaz-Thévoz model), less the increase in volume associated with growth at the dendrite tips, dV^I. The dendritic structure contains complex branching patterns, but is predominantly cylindrical in nature. Although there is a distribution of sidebranch sizes, we use the stereological parameters of the structure to characterize the average growth behavior of the dendrites. For epitaxial solidification, we define a characteristic cylinder that has the same area/volume ratio as the overall structure. Ignoring the ends of such a cylinder, the characteristic radius of such a cylinder, R^C, is given by the equation

$$R^c = 2\frac{V_v}{S_v} = 2\frac{V_e}{S_e} . \tag{9}$$

Both fractions in this equation represent the solid-phase volume/area ratio, because the normalizing volume at the node point or of the grain envelope cancels. The factor of 2 appears because the V/A ratio of a cylinder is R/2.

The differential ratio of area to volume change for a cylinder of radius R, dA/dV, is 1/R. The rate of area increase, dA^{II}, arising from the epitaxial solidification is determined by using dV^{II} for the increase in solid-phase volume and R^C as the effective radius of curvature for the entire dendritic structure. This leads to the expression

$$dA^{II} = \frac{1}{R^c}\,dV^{II} = \frac{S_v}{2V_v}\,dV^{II} . \tag{10}$$

Equation (10) represents the increase in area (thickening) of the dendritic structure within the grain envelope arising from the net epitaxial solidification, dV^{II}. Both dA^{II} and dV^{II} are then normalized by appropriate volume terms to yield the change in the stereological parameters associated with the epitaxial component of the net solidification. Using the stereological formalism and a geometrical model, the progress of this morphologically complex mechanism is expressed in a simple form that contains the relevant geometric factors.

Coarsening. In addition to the increase in area due to solidification, there is also a capillarity-driven coarsening process by which the interfacial area decreases with no change in the total solid-phase volume. The coarsening process is often quantified in the literature by specifying the growth of a characteristic lengthscale with time. However, the driving force for the local diffusion that leads to coarsening is the excess interfacial energy associated with a ramified or dispersed structure (Voorhees, 1985). Thus the coarsening process may also be described as the diffusion-limited reduction of interfacial area, where the total area of a structure is proportional to the excess interfacial energy present through the specific surface energy, γ. The rate of coarsening has been observed to increase with the volume fraction of the coarsening phase. This is mainly due to a proximity effect, whereby the chemical potential (and concentration) gradients within the structure increase as the distances between the curved interfaces causing the local capillary shifts decrease. The morphology of the coarsening structure has been shown to have a lesser effect on coarsening rates (Marsh *et al.*, 1988), as the process is characterized statistically by the diffusion among curved interfaces through the embedding matrix volume. The detailed shape of the interfaces in such a process is less important than the areal distribution of curvature.

A statistical theory of coarsening has been developed that shows good agreement with experimental results on the volume-fraction dependence of the coarsening rate (Marsh, 1989, and Glicksman *et al.*, 1992). This theory specifies the coarsening rate over a wide range of volume fractions, and is expressed in terms of the appropriate material constants and a dimensionless volume fraction-dependent rate constant, K. The kinetic expression for the decay of S_V may be written as

$$\frac{dS_v^{-3}}{dt} = K^{-3} M , \tag{11}$$

where K is the dimensionless rate constant originally defined as $dS_v/d(t^{-1/3})$. M is the group of material parameters that dimensionalizes the rate expression with the appropriate capillary length and diffusion timescale (Voorhees, 1985), and may be written for solute diffusion as

$$M = \frac{\gamma V_m^2 D C_\infty}{RT} . \tag{12}$$

In this expression, γ is the surface energy, V_m is the molar volume, D is the solute diffusion coefficient, C_∞ is the equilibrium solute concentration in the liquid at a flat interface, R is the gas constant, and T is the local temperature. Equation (11) expresses the well-known scaling law for diffusion-limited coarsening that the cube of any characteristic lengthscale in the structure (such as average radius) grows linearly with time (Voorhees, 1985). The value of K over a wide range of volume fractions is given in Table 1 (Marsh, 1989). For calculational purposes, these values may be interpolated for intermediate volume fractions.

To apply (11) to coarsening within the dendritic envelope, S_V and the V_V value used to determine K refer to the area and volume of the solid phase per unit volume of the grain envelope, respectively. This expression is applied at the beginning of a timestep to calculate the change in S_e over the timestep. Once this is done, (3), (7), (8) and (10) are used to calculate the other volume and area changes over the timestep. Over time, this general coarsening equation accounts for such phenomena as the shrinking, coalescence and disappearance of dendrite arms.

Late-Stage Solidification

The equiaxed grains continue to grow into the surrounding melt until their volume fraction, $V_{V,g}$ approaches unity. The solute rejected from the envelope by the growing dendrites increases the mean concentration in the surrounding liquid, which slows down the growth of the dendrite tips (Rappaz and Thévoz, 1987). When the concentration is high enough, the interdendritic liquid approaches the limit of complete mixing, and solute diffusion from the grain envelope no longer limits the equiaxed growth. At this stage, the rate of further solidification is determined primarily by the local temperature, as specified by the phase diagram. If back-diffusion in the solid is neglected, the solidification rate is well-represented by the Scheil equation (Kurz and Fisher, 1985). At this stage, the grain fraction $V_{V,g}$ is essentially unity and need not be tracked further. The dendritic structure fills the available volume, and is characterized by the global properties S_V and V_V.

In this late-stage solidification, the terms that contribute to further lengthscale evolution are the epitaxial growth term (10) and the coarsening expression (11). The volume growth term dV^{II} in (10) represents the total temperature-dependent solidification rate as determined by the Scheil equation. This solidification continues until the eutectic temperature is reached, at which point the remaining liquid generally solidifies to form a finely-divided two-phase eutectic.

TABLE 1 – DIMENSIONLESS SURFACE AREA COARSENING RATE, K,(V_V), USED IN EQUATION (11) OF THE TEXT. [FROM MARSH, 1989]

V_V	K
0	0
0.01	0.026
0.02	0.050
0.03	0.072
0.04	0.095
0.05	0.117
0.10	0.221
0.15	0.317
0.20	0.406
0.25	0.489
0.30	0.567
0.35	0.638
0.40	0.703
0.45	0.760
0.50	0.813
0.55	0.858
0.60	0.894
0.65	0.922
0.70	0.938
0.75	0.942
0.80	0.929
0.85	0.893
0.90	0.824
0.95	0.690

Dendrite Arm Spacing

At the end of the dendritic solidification phase, when the eutectic begins to form, the dendritic structure is characterized by V_V and S_V values that result from the various mechanisms discussed in this section. These parameters can be measured directly from cross-sections of cast materials using standard stereological methods (Underwood, 1970). This permits direct comparison between simulations and the actual processes, and provides an easy method for refinement of micromodel parameters to obtain better simulation results. However, the average sidebranch spacing, λ_s, is commonly used in the literature to characterize dendritic structures. This linear metric can be recovered from the stereological parameters by considering the typical dendritic geometry shown in Figure 1 of the Appendix. In this construction, the center-to-center branch spacing is 4R and the solid-phase volume/area ratio is 7R/8, as given by Eq. (A3). Equating this to the overall stereological volume/area ratio, V_V/S_V, and solving for R leads to a simple expression for the average sidebranch spacing, λ_s, as

$$\lambda_s = \frac{32}{7}\frac{V_v}{S_v} \;. \tag{13}$$

This expression is a valid approximation if there is a recognizable branched structure at the end of the solidification process. Under some conditions, there may be extensive coarsening of the dendritic phase, resulting in an irregular or spheroidal morphology. In these cases the stereological parameters may be used directly to characterize the observed structure.

Eutectic Growth

There are many models in the literature that describe eutectic solidification. The particular form of the eutectic phases results from an interaction of the local mass balance, diffusion, and capillary terms that dominate the process (Kurz and Fisher, 1985). In normal binary eutectics, solidification leads to the formation of a lamellar structure. These lamellae have the form of thin plate-like sheets. The relative thickness of the lamellae of the α and β phases is determined by the relative amounts of these phases formed from liquid having the eutectic composition.

The relationship between the lamellar thicknesses λ^{α} and λ^{β} and the stereological parameters describing the eutectic phase, V_V and S_V, are derived in the Appendix. For lamellar eutectics, S_V refers only to the interfacial area between the α and β phases, and specifies the size scale within the eutectic mixture itself. The characteristic wavelength of the periodic structure, λ, is simply the sum of the widths of the alternating layers, λ^{α} and λ^{β} . The relationship between V_V, S_V, and λ for a lamellar structure is

$$\lambda = 2\frac{V_v}{S_v} \;. \tag{14}$$

An outline and analysis of the factors that determine the value of λ and the growth front velocity, v, in terms of the solidification conditions and material properties is presented by Kurz and Fisher (1985). However, the conditions governing eutectic solidification in the volume around a node point can change during the process. This complication in applying eutectic models can be overcome through the use of the stereological formalism.

The appropriate eutectic model and local solidification conditions determine the instantaneous value of λ. This parameter is then used as the differential coefficient that relates the increase in interfacial area to that of the volume of eutectic as solidification proceeds. The differential relationship between the area and volume changes is derived from (14) as

$$dS_v = \frac{2}{\lambda}\, dV_v \;. \tag{15}$$

At the end of the eutectic solidification, the resulting values of V_V and S_V can be inserted into (14) to obtain the average lamellar thickness, λ. This average value of λ represents the integrated effect of the various mechanisms throughout the eutectic solidification process in the small volume associated with each node point.

SUMMARY

A general formalism is described that allows for the coupling of microstructural models with macroscopic transport calculations in casting simulations. A unit volume of microstructure is associated with each grid point in the macroscopic numerical mesh. The state variables at each point represent the average conditions within the unit volume of microstructure over a computational timestep. This permits a physically consistent coupling of the macroscopic and microscopic regimes, with the mesh spacing setting the spatial resolution of both the macroscopic field variables and the local microstructural characteristics.

An important feature of this approach is the use of morphology-independent stereological parameters to characterize the various microstructural features. The two parameters employed in the equiaxed solidification model, volume fraction and specific surface area, together specify the relative amounts and the lengthscales of the various phases that are present. Appropriate geometric models can be used to relate these parameters to more conventional metrics that many existing micromodels are based on. Examples of this for dendritic and lamellar morphologies are presented in the Appendix.

An additional benefit of using stereological parameters is the ease with which micromodels describing different physical mechanisms can be combined. Models for dendrite tip growth, epitaxial growth, and coarsening were used together to determine the overall evolution of lengthscales during equiaxed growth. Switching among micromodels as appropriate physical limits are reached is also accomplished in a straightforward manner. Furthermore, the stereological approach requires minimal adaptation of the simulation code for different micromodels. The micromodels serve as evolution equations for a consistent parameter set that is morphology-independent.

ACKNOWLEDGEMENT

The authors gratefully acknowledge support for this research by ARPA through the Investment Casting Cooperative Agreement (ICCA).

REFERENCES

DeHoff, R.T., and Iswaran, C.V., 1982, "The Usefulness of Integral Mean Curvature Measurements in the Study of the Kinetics of Coarsening," *Metallurgical Transactions A*, Vol. 13A, pp. 1389-1395.

Glicksman, M.E., Smith, R.N., Marsh, S.P. and Kuklinski, R., 1992, "Mushy Zone Modeling With Microstructural Coarsening Kinetics," *Metallurgical Transactions A*, Vol. 23A, pp. 659-667.

Kurz, W., and Fisher, D., 1985, *Fundamentals of Solidification*, TransTech Publications, Aedermannsdorf, Switzerland.

Marsh, S.P., 1989, "Kinetics of Diffusion-Limited Microstructural Coarsening," Ph.D. Thesis, Rensselaer Polytechnic Institute, Troy, NY.

Marsh, S.P., Glicksman, M.E., and Zwillinger, D.I., 1988, "Statistical Mechanics of Mushy Zones," *Modeling and Control of Casting and Welding Processes IV*, A.F. Giamei and G.J. Abbaschian, ed., The Metallurgical Society, Warrendale, Pa., pp. 921-928.

Rappaz, M., 1989, "Modelling of Microstructure Formation in Solidification Processes," *International Materials Reviews*, Vol. 34, pp. 93-123.

Rappaz, M., and Thévoz, P., 1987a, "Solute Diffusion Model for Equiaxed Dendritic Growth: Analytical Solution," *Acta Metallurgica*, Vol. 35, No. 12, pp. 2929-2933.

Rappaz, M., and Thévoz, P., 1987b, "Solute Diffusion Model for Equiaxed Dendritic Growth," *Acta Metallurgica*, Vol. 35, No. 7, pp. 1487-1497.

Stefanescu, D.M., Upadhya, G., and Bandyopadhyay, D., 1990, "Heat Transfer-Solidification Kinetics Modeling of Solidification of Castings," *Metallurgical Transactions A*, Vol. 21A, pp. 997-1005.

Thévoz, P., Desboilles, J.L., and Rappaz, M., 1989, "Modeling of Equiaxed Microstructure Formation in Casting," *Metallurgical Transactions A*, Vol. 20A, pp. 311-322.

Tseng, A.A., Zou, J., Wang, H.P., and Hoole, S.R.H., 1992, "Numerical Modeling of Macro and Micro Behaviors of Materials in Processing: A Review," *Journal of Computational Physics*, Vol. 102, pp. 1-17.

Underwood, E.E., 1970, *Quantitative Stereology*, Addison-Wesley Publishing Company, Inc., Reading, Mass.

Voorhees, P.W., 1985, "The Theory of Ostwald Ripening," *Journal of Statistical Physics*, Vol. 38, Nos. 1/2, pp. 231-252.

APPENDIX

Dendrite Geometry Model

In this section, an approximate model of the branched dendritic geometry is formulated. This model has two primary uses. First, it relates the volumes and areas of the newly-formed dendrite branches in the tip region to the size scale of the tip radius, R_{tip}, which can be determined from the growth conditions. This allows a physically consistent introduction of the fine structure in the tip region to the growth model. Second, the geometric model allows estimation of the secondary sidebranch spacing, λ_S, from the S_V and V_V values of the solid dendritic phase. This can be done because the S_V term has lengthscale information, and when divided by V_V it yields the area/volume ratio of the solid dendritic phase. This ratio can then be compared to that for a typical dendritic geometry to get the corresponding average sidebranch spacing.

The dendritic geometry that we model is that which forms from a typical material with cubic crystallographic symmetry. There is a main branch with periodic, evenly-spaced sidebranches that project from it at right angles. The sidebranches are fourfold and orthogonal to each other. The basic repeating unit of this structure is a short segment of the main branch containing four sidebranches (shown in bold outline in Figure 1), with endpoints that lie halfway between consecutive sidebranches along the main branch.

The geometric ratios used are ones that approximate the relative sizes in a typical dendritic structure (Kurz and Fisher, 1985). R_{tip} is the radius of curvature of the tip itself. The main branch thickens behind the tip, so an average main branch radius of $4{\cdot}R_{tip}$ is assumed. The sidebranch spacing is about half the diameter of the main branch, or $4{\cdot}R_{tip}$. The branch diameters are about one-half of the branch spacings, so the radii of the sidebranches are about equal to R_{tip}. Finally, the length of the sidebranches behind the tip are about 1.5 times the main branch diameter, or about $12{\cdot}R_{tip}$. These ratios are shown in Figure 1, along with the characteristic structure that results from repeating them end-to-end.

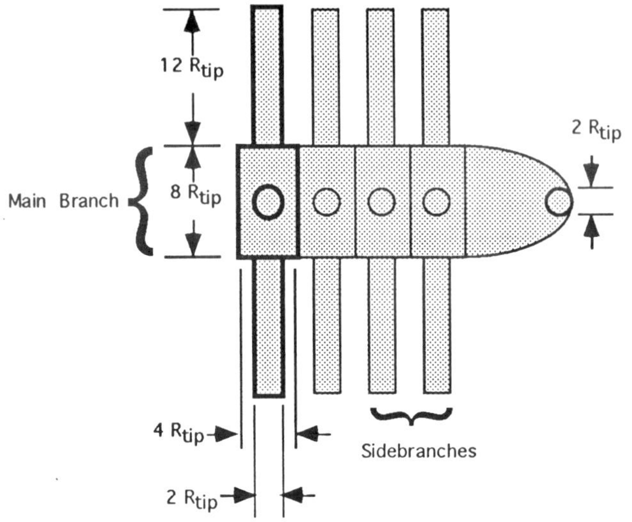

FIGURE 1 – SCHEMATIC DRAWING OF THE DENDRITE GEOMETRY USED TO APPROXIMATE VOLUME AND SURFACE AREA RELATIONSHIPS. ALL BRANCHES ARE CYLINDRICAL, AND A SINGLE REPEATING BRANCHED "UNIT" IS OUTLINED IN BOLD.

The volume and area associated with the dendrite sidebranch unit, V^u and A^u, are calculated by assuming that all branches are cylinders. Minor contributions to these quantities, such as the ends of the sidebranches, the portions of the main branch covered by the bases of sidebranches, and the slightly ellipsoidal shape of the sidebranches are ignored. The intent here is to get a reasonable relationship among lengthscales in the dendrite, and not to formulate an exact geometric model.

The volume of the dendrite unit, V^u, is simply the sum of the volumes of the main branch cylinder and the four sidebranch cylinders. Approximating π as 3, consistent with the level of approximation in this model, we have

$$V^u = 3\cdot(4R_{tip})^2\cdot 4R_{tip} + 4\left[3\cdot R_{tip}^2\cdot 12R_{tip}\right] = 336\,R_{tip}^3\ . \qquad \text{(A1)}$$

In a similar fashion, the total surface area of the five cylinders, A^u, is give by

$$A^u = 3 \cdot 8 R_{tip} \cdot 4R_{tip} + 4\left[3 \cdot 2R_{tip} \cdot 12R_{tip}\right] = 384\, R_{tip}^2 \,. \qquad (A2)$$

Finally, the volume/area ratio for this dendritic model is given by the ratio of the above results as

$$\frac{V^u}{A^u} = \frac{336\, R_{tip}^3}{384\, R_{tip}^2} = \frac{7}{8} R_{tip} \,. \qquad (A3)$$

Eutectic Geometry Model

A simple geometric model is used to provide a stereological description of a lamellar eutectic structure consisting of two phases, α and β. The lamellar structure is approximated by alternating planar layers of the phases having average thicknesses λ^α and λ^β (see Figure 2). The ratio of the layer thicknesses, $\lambda^\alpha / \lambda^\beta$, is equal to the volume fraction ratio of the phases, V_v^α / V_v^β. The overall volume fraction of the lamellar eutectic is simply $V_v^\alpha + V_v^\beta$.

We first calculate parameters describing the lamellae by assuming that the entire unit volume consists only of the eutectic phases α and β. The results are then normalized by the volume fraction of the eutectic mixture present relative to the other phases present (denoted by φ in Figure 2). These other phases may include both the primary dendritic solid that has formed, if any, and the eutectic liquid parent phase. Per unit area of cross-section, A, the total interfacial area between the eutectic phases is 2nA, where n is the number of α–β layer pairs. The total volume is equal to $nA(\lambda^\alpha + \lambda^\beta)$. Taking the ratio of these quantities gives the value of S_V as $2/(\lambda^\alpha + \lambda^\beta)$. Substituting the ratio of the volume fractions for the ratio of the layer thicknesses and rearranging yields the lamellar thickness λ^α as $2/[S_V(1 + V_v^\alpha / V_v^\beta)]$. Normalizing this result to account for the presence of the parent phase γ yields the average lamellar thickness of the α phase as

$$\lambda^\alpha = \frac{2\,(V_v^\alpha + V_v^\beta)}{S_v^{\alpha\beta}\left[1 + \frac{V_v^\beta}{V_v^\alpha}\right]} = \frac{2\,V_v^\alpha}{S_v^{\alpha\beta}} \,. \qquad (A4)$$

The analogous equation for λ^β is $2\,V_v^\beta / S_v^{\alpha\beta}$. The characteristic wavelength for the eutectic structure is the repeat distance λ, equal to $\lambda^\alpha + \lambda^\beta$, and is given by

$$\lambda = \lambda^\alpha + \lambda^\beta = \frac{2\,(V_v^\alpha + V_v^\beta)}{S_v^{\alpha\beta}} . \qquad (A5)$$

Note that the numerator of this expression for λ, $V_v^\alpha + V_v^\beta$, is simply the volume fraction of the eutectic mixture.

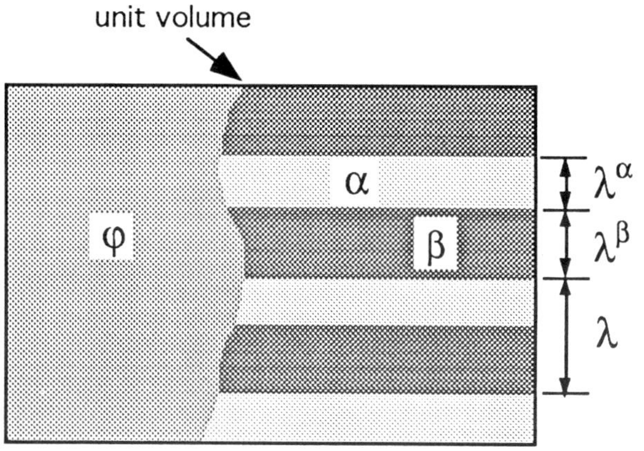

FIGURE 2 – SCHEMATIC ILLUSTRATION OF THE LAMELLAR EUTECTIC STRUCTURE MODELED IN THE APPENDIX. THE VOLUME OF MICROSTRUCTURE EXTENDS UNIT DEPTH INTO THE PAGE.

HTD-Vol. 284/AMD-Vol. 182, Transport Phenomena in Solidification
ASME 1994

A DETERMINISTIC NUCLEATION MODEL FOR EQUIAXED SOLIDIFICATION

Ingo Steinbach and Robert Prieler
ACCESS e.V.
Aachen, Germany

Abstract

Several approaches to model nucleation in dendritic-equiaxed solidification have been made [1-4]. The most recent model by Rappaz and Gandin [4] relates the grain diameter to dendritic growth velocity and thereby to cooling rate and undercooling. The individual grain grows until it reaches the next nucleation site. Within this work a deterministic δ-like nucleation density is examined. The model describes the propagation of a front of equiaxed grains into the liquid. Due to recalescence the temperature of the front oscillates with the frequency of the nucleation rate, which determines the final grain density. The model is applied to Al-Si-casting. The calculated grain densities are compared with experimental data given in literature. The columnar to equiaxed transition is discussed with reference to its dependencies on growth velocity and temperature gradient in the liquid.

1. Introduction

The grain density greatly influences the mechanical properties of all equiaxed casting. In Al-Si alloys inoculation with Ti is commonly used to reach a fine and homogeneous grain structure.

For low inoculation, the grain density varies monotonously with the density of inoculant, while it reaches saturation above 0.6 m% inoculant [6]. In this range the statistical distribution of the nucleation sites playes a minor role, while deterministic laws control the nucleation. Possible mechanisms are the agglomeration of inoculants or the suppression of nucleation within the thermal or solutal diffusive field around a growing grain.

Both mechanisms become active if the mean distance of inoculating particles decreases below the dominant interaction length which is then comparable to the average grain size of the casting.

Within this work, the thermal and solutal diffusion in front of a growing grain will be examined numerically in respect to its limiting behaviour on the nucleation in a highly inoculated Al-Si alloy, i.e. extinction of nucleation sites. The model uses existing theories of growth of individual equiaxed particles [7,8] and the velocity of dendrite tips [9]. Nucleation occures instantanously at a given undercooling. The simulation includes nucleation and growth of individual particles as well as the interaction of different particles.

2. Model description

The model describes the propagation of a columnar front as well as the front of equiaxed grains into the liquid, like in the model presented by Flood & Hunt [10]. The temperature field is assumed to be 1–dimensional and directed by the heat flux towards the mould.

The casting may be divided into 3 topological different regions as indicated in fig. 1.

Region I is the solid or mushy material near thermodynamic equilibrium. The temperature gradient is approximately constant throughout the solid or in the mush, monotonously decreasing towards the liquid and a smooth function in time.

Region II contains the solidification front. In case of equiaxed solidification the temperature oscillates due to nucleation of new grains and recalescence. One individual grain grows until the maximum undercooling in front of the tips reaches the critical nucleation temperature giving birth to a new grain.

Region III contains the melt. Due to the heat flux to the mould, the temperature gradient in the melt is always positive and the melt temperature is always above the mean temperature of region II.

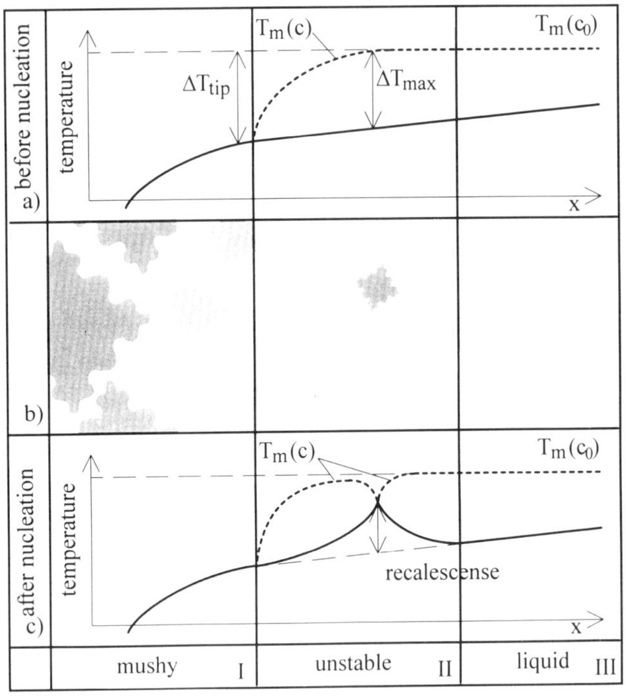

Fig. 1: Scheme of the temperature distribution at the equiaxed front. Nucleation and recalescence occurs within the unstable region II

The governing equations are for the leading degrees of freedom temperature T, liquid constitution c and fraction solid f_s:

thermal diffusion: $$\rho c_p \dot{T} = \frac{\partial}{\partial x}\lambda\frac{\partial}{\partial x}T + L\cdot \dot{f}_s$$

solutal diffusion: $$\dot{c} = \frac{\partial}{\partial x}D\frac{\partial}{\partial x}c + \frac{c(1-k)\dot{f}_s}{(1-f_s)}$$

thermosolutal equilibrium in the mush:

$$T = T_m(c) = T^0 + m\cdot c$$

The fraction solid in the mush is given implicit by the solution of these three equations.

c_p: specific heat
λ: thermal conductivity
L: latent heat of fusion
D: liquid diffusion coefficient
K: segregation coefficient
T^0: Melting point of pure substance
m: slope of liquidus isotherm

The solid constitution c_s can be deduced by integrating the solute ballance equation

$$\dot{c}_s = c(1-k)\frac{\dot{f}_s}{1-f_s}$$

2.1 Growth

In equiaxed solidification the growth velocity $\bar{v}_g$ of the system is no longer given by the growth velocity of the dendrite tips, but rather by the nucleation rate $\dot{n}$ and the average grain size $\bar{r}$

$$\bar{v}_g = \bar{r}\cdot\dot{n}$$

Thermodynamically it is controlled by the cooling condition in the liquid

$$\bar{v}_g = \frac{\dot{T}}{G_{liq}}$$

$\dot{T}$ ist the cooling rate, G_{liq} the thermal gradient in the liquid.

In order to allow equiaxed growth, the growth rate of the tips of the equiaxed grains v_t must be smaller than the average growth velocity $\bar{v}_g$. By that, the growth of the dendrite tips of the equiaxed grains does not produce enough heat of fusion to keep its interface temperature constant. The undercooling of the liquid in front of the envelope of the equiaxed grains increases until the maximum undercooling reaches the critical undercooling for nucleation, as sketched in fig. 1c. The front now jumps to the new position outside the solutal diffusion field of the grains considered before and shows a microscopic recalescence due to the approximately undisturbed constitution of the alloy at the new nucleation site.

The new grain will grow during the time $T_g = \frac{1}{\dot{n}}$, until the heat of recalescence is removed. This time interval T_g and not the growth velocity of the tip defines the average grain size for a given thermodynamic growth velocity, though both quantities are coupled through the release of latent heat during grain growth.

2.2 Nucleation

Commonly used micromodels for equiaxed solidification need a finite nucleation density as an input [1...4]. This density is deduced from experiments or assumed. In this work, a steep increase of nucleation is assumed if the temperature falls below the nucleation temperature, as proposed in the basic theory presented by Turnbull & Fisher [11]. The extinction of nucleation sites and therefore the final grain density is given by the mechanism described before.

In the numerical model the maximum nucleation density is restricted by the discretisation which therefore has to be choosen small to the average grain size. At an individual volume point in the numerical grid nucleation occurs if the local undercooling of this point exceeds the critical nucleation undercooling. The local undercooling $\Delta T(c)$ is defined as the difference of the local temperature to the constitution dependent melting temperature. The undercooling in respect to the bulk composition $\Delta T(c_0)$ may, due to the positive temperature gradient in the liquid, exceed the nucleation undercooling, as indicated in fig. 1a.

2.3 Numerical Model

The numerical model used within this work uses a 1-D discretisation of the region II in fig. 1. The discretisation is 10 µm for a typical grain size $\overline{R} > 100\,\mu m$. The range is taken from 100 cells behind to 150 cells in front of the actual front position. The time stepping is explicit with a discretisation of 10^{-6} s. The calculation is started with a constant temperature gradient throughout the specimen. About $2\cdot 10^7$ time steps were needed to get quasi stable conditions for each set of boundary conditions.
The thermophysical data of Ref. [12 / Table 1] were used for the Al-Si7 alloy.

Local degrees of freedom are the temperature, constitution in the liquid, fraction of solid and fraction of grain. The latter is used according to the definition of Dustin & Kurz [7] in the notation of Rappaz & Thévoz [8] to describe the fraction of a grain within one numerical cell. The fraction of one cell that corresponds to the local fraction of grain is considered to be in thermal equilibrium. The interdendritic liquid is assumed to be completely mixed. Solutal diffusion between cells in the solid and the mush is neglected.

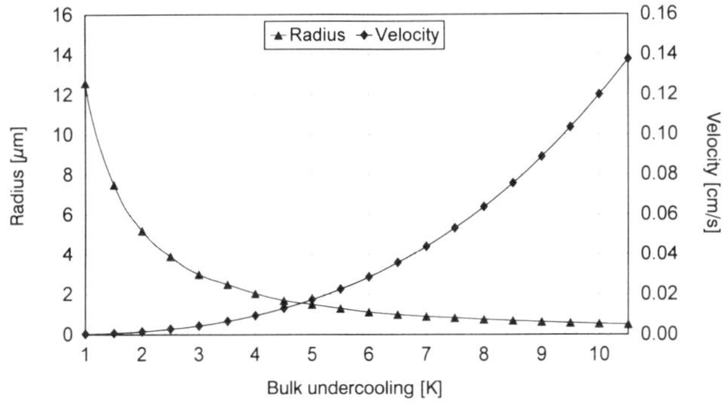

Fig. 2: Dendrite tip velocity and tip radius versus bulk undercooling

The release of latent heat and solute redistribution is calculated implicit according to the thermal and solutal balance from the equilibrium phase diagram (constant liquidus slope). Eutectic solidification could be treated within the model, but does not occure within the considered range. In order to calculate the fraction grain in one cell, the position of the envelope of the dendritic network has to be tracked. This is done by integrating the tip velocity over time. The velocity of the dendrite tips is calculated after the model of Lipton et al. [9]. Fig. 2 shows the calculated velocities and corresponding tip radius, using a Gibbs-Thompson coefficient of $1.35\cdot 10^{-7}$ Km and the data from Ref. 12. The tip radii at an undercooling ranging from 1K to 4K are small compared to the final grain size(>100 µm). Therefore the incubation time until to which the dendritic structure of the grain envolves can be neglected. In the calculation, a quadratic function for the tip velocity was used.

$$v_{tip} = 0.0012(\Delta T)^2 \left[\frac{cm}{sK^2}\right]$$

It must be noted, that the undercooling in respect of the bulk-liquid concentration $\Delta T(c_0)$ has to be applied.

This assumption produces an inconsistency in the solute diffusion. On the one hand, an analytical Ivantsov solution for solute diffusion around a single tip is used. The diffusion length is of the order of the tip radius (2 µm at 4K undercooling). On the other hand in the 1-dimensional model diffusion ahead of the envelope of the dendritic network is used. This is assumed planar because the grain radius is small compared to the discretisation. The diffusion length in this case is of the order of 10 µm. In order to resolve this inconsistency a coupled analysis of diffusion controled growth of a dendritic network has to be performed. This exceeds the scope of this work.

The boundary conditions of the simulation are a given temperature gradient in the liquid and a given cooling rate in the mush. These data can be deduced from measurements or from a macro simulation of the process. Micro-macro coupling is not necessary as long as the boundary conditions of the micro simulation can be deduced in regions of thermodynamic equilibrium.

The range under consideration is according to the experimental setup given in Ref. [12, fig. 5]

G_{liq} : [1K/cm ....20K/cm]

$\dot{T}$: [0.1 ......0.5K/s]

The cooling rate must be defined at the end of the calculation regime, 1 mm behind the actual front position.

3. Results

The scenario of oscillating equiaxed growth, as sketched in the model description, was examined in the direct computer simulation. Fig. 3 shows the calculated temperature profile in the unstable region around the equiaxed front. The solid line at t = 3.198 s shows the temperature profile immediately before nucleation. The temperature is nearly linear. The nucleation site is at position 10 [100 µm]. This graph corresponds to the scheme in fig. 1a. 0.002 s after nucleation the temperature shows a steep peak of recalescence. The new grain now grows in a negative temperature gradient, but with a low undercooling. The recalescence peak is removed until t = 3.212 s. The subsequent curves show the final cooling of the front, until at t = 3.664 s the conditions for new nucleation are reached. The last curve at t = 3.664 s is identical to the first at t = 3.1198 s, but translated to the new nucleation position. The boundary conditions in this simulation are G_{liq} = 3 K/cm, $\dot{T}$ = 0,2 K/s, ΔT_{nuk} = 4K.

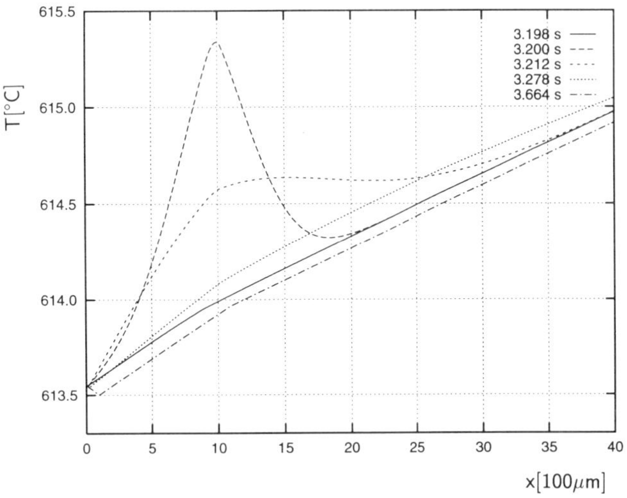

Fig. 3: Calculated temperature distribution during recalescence.

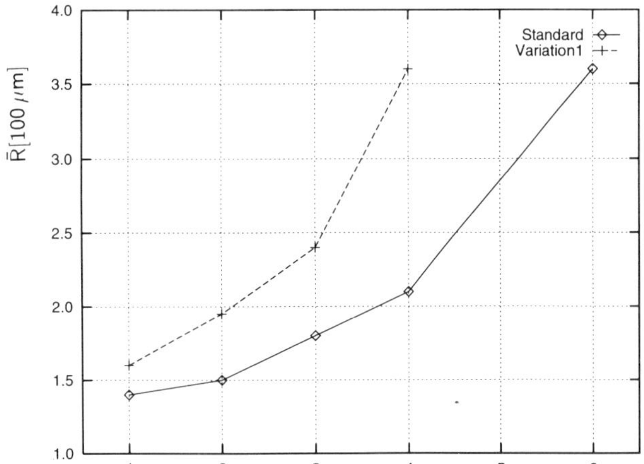

Fig. 4: Calculated average grain radius for two different functions of tip velocity

The microscopic recalescence in this calculation is 1.5 K. The time between individual nucleation events is 0.44 s and the maximum distance the grain has grown within this time in one direction is 70 μm, which is 40 % of the final grain size.

The thermodynamic growth velocity, i.e. the distance of nucleation sites multiplied with the nucleation rate is 0.04 cm/s and much faster than the maximum tip velocity at maximum undercooling of 0.02 cm/s.

The simulation confirms qualitatively the theoretical model. In order to test the sensitivity of the simulation on the thermophysical data, the solidification velocities and the critical nucleation temperature are varied.

Fig. 4 shows the average grain size for different gradients in the liquid. The solid line is the standard calculation with a solidification velocity as plotted in fig.2. The darked line gives the results, calculated with enhanced tip velocity.

$$v_{tip} = 0.0017(\Delta T)^2 \left[\frac{cm}{sK^2}\right]$$

This corresponds to a Gibbs Thompson coefficient of $0.946 \cdot 10^{-7}$ Km; the remaining data stay unchanged. Obviously, the grain radius is quite sensitive on the tip velocity. The deviation of both curves increases, as the gradients approach the Columnar-Equiaxed Transition (CET, see below). This transition is reached for the enhanced velocity at lower gradients than for the standard one.

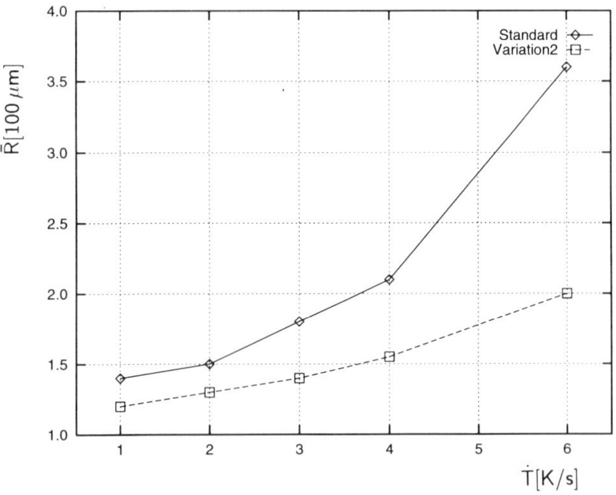

Fig. 5: Calculated average grain radius for different nucleation undercooling

The sensitivity of the system on the nucleation undercooling ΔT_n = 3 K is shown in fig. 5. For lower nucleation undercooling the average grain size decreases, since the influence of recalescence on the thermal evolution of the system is less important in this case compared to a higher nucleation undercooling.

In order to compare the model to experimental data, both the temperature gradient in the liquid and the cooling rate are varied. Table 1 shows the calculated grain size depending on cooling rate and temperature gradient. The tendency is that the grain size increases with increasing temperature gradient and decreases with decreasing cooling rate.

The experimental data from Thévoz & Rappaz [12] for a 10 cm Al-Si7 casting with directed heat flow to the chill show an increase of grain size from 200 μm to 400 μm during the first 6 cm of the casting. This can be explained quantitatively by considering that the cooling rate decreases during the time of solidification and with the enlarging of the mushy zone while the temperature gradient in the liquid is approximately constant.

At the end of the casting however the superheat of the melt is removed and the temperature gradient tends to zero due to the isolation condition. Here the grain size decreases to approximately 200 μm.

near the mould

$\dot{T}$ [K/s]										
	0.5	11.0 .021	2.40 .029	1.85 .032	1.20 .039	1.10 .055	1.10 .065	1.15 .073	1.00 .077	R[100μm] v[cm/s]
	0.3	c	c	8.15 .022	2.90 .028	1.75 .038	1.40 .052	1.30 .058	1.30 .068	-
	0.2	c	c	c	c	3.60 .019	2.10 .035	1.80 .042	1.50 .052	1.40 .061
	0.1	c	c	c	c	c	c	6.20 .023	3.50 .030	2.15 .042
	G_{liq} [K/cm]	21	15	12	9	6	4	3	2	1

center of casting

Table 1: Calculated average grain radius and corresponding growth velocities for different cooling rates and gradients in the liquid. The 'c' indicates conditions for columnar growth. The shaded path corresponds to typical conditions in the experimental setup used by Thévoz et al. [12].

The shaded line in table 1 shows a path through the map of boundary conditions of the simulation, that gives the measured nucleation densities. This is in reasonable agreement with the measurements of Thévoz & Rappaz as far as it can be compared by using their publicated cooling curves.

As pointed out before, the condition for equiaxed nucleation is given only if the dendrite tip velocity is below the thermodynamik growth velocity. At the columnar equiaxed transition the thermodynamic growth velocity matches the dendrite tip velocity at maximum undercooling. The critical velocity is 0.02 cm/s at an undercooling of 4 K.

Fig. 6 shows the calculated critical gradients in the liquid for different cooling rates. While the critical velocity is nearly constant, the gradient increases nearly linear. The critical G/v for the columnar equiaxed transition is therefore not a constant. The model proposes instead of G/v the critical velocity to control the CE-transition.

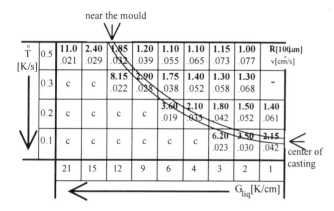

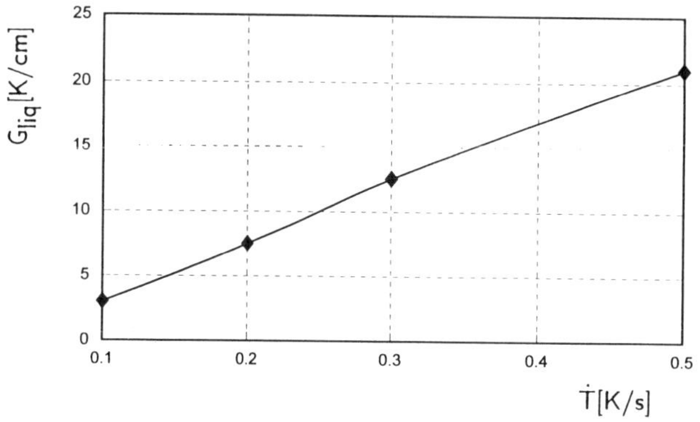

Fig. 6: Calculated critical gradients in the liquid and the corresponding growth velocities

4. Conclusion

A new model is proposed that calculates the grain density in equiaxed solidification by considering thermal and solutal diffusion in front of a growing grain.

The front of equiaxed grains grows by subsequent nucleation of grains at the position of maximum undercooling. Microscopic recalescence and the time needed to remove the heat of recalescence determines the nucleation rate. The model is restricted to highly inoculated alloys, where the assumption of a sharply defined nucleation temperature is valid. The exaggeration to a broad, but limited distribution of nucleation sites is straight forward. Convection in the melt is neglected.

The model explains quantitatively the dependence of nucleation density on the gradient in the liquid and the cooling rate in the mush, requiring the nucleation temperature and thermophysical data of the metal as the only input.

The critical gradient and growth velocity for the columnar to equiaxed transition can be deduced quantitatively. Under the assumption of the model, the nucleation is limited to small layer of undercooled liquid in front of the solutal diffusion field of growing grains. Recalescence is therefore a phenomenon of individual grains and not of a large area of bulk liquid. Macroscopically, recalescence is only detectable in two cases.

i) the individual grains are large compared to the thermocouple tip and the time of microscopic recalescence (i.e. the reciprocal of nucleation rate) is comparable to the response time of the thermocouple

ii) the nucleated grains are rapidly washed out by convection into an undercooled melt region so that the recalescence of individual grains cannot impede subsequent nucleation. The whole region now shows a common and very broad recalescence, what can usually be observed in the center of the casting.

5. Acknowledgement

The work was supported by the "Ministerium für Forschung und Technologie, NRW-Germany", Förderkennzeichen IV A-213 029 93

6. References

1 M. Rappaz, Int. Mat. Rev. 34,3 (1989) 93 and Ref. therein
2 D.M. Stefanescu, Met. Trans. A 21 (1990) 997
3 J. A. Spittle S.G.R. Brown, Acta Met 37 (1989) 1803
4 M. Rappaz, Ch-A Gandin, Acta Met 41 (1993) 345
5 W. Kurz et al.; Acta Met 34, Nr 5 (1986) 823
6 A. Banerij et al; Metall 45, Nr 12 (1991) 1232
7 I. Dustin, W. Kurz; Z. Metallk. 77 Nr 5 (1986) 265
8 M. Rappaz, Ph. Thévoz; Acta Met 35 Nr 7 (1987) 1487
9 J. Lipton et al; Met. Trans. 18A (1987) 341
10 S.C. Flood; J.D. Hunt; J. Cryst. Growth 82 (1987) 543
11 D. Turnbull, J.C. Fisher; J. Chem. Phys 17 (1949) 71
12 Ph. Thévoz et al. Met. trans. 20 A (1989) 311

HTD-Vol. 284/AMD-Vol. 182, Transport Phenomena in Solidification
ASME 1994

MULTI-SCALE/-PHASE MODELING OF DENDRITIC ALLOY SOLIDIFICATION

C. Y. Wang and C. Beckermann
Department of Mechanical Engineering
University of Iowa
Iowa City, Iowa

ABSTRACT

A multiphase model is proposed to predict compositional and structural evolutions in dendritic alloy solidification. The model accounts for the transport phenomena occurring on the macroscopic (system) scale, as well as the grain nucleation and growth over various microscopic length scales. The present model generalizes a previous multi-scale/-phase model (Metall. Trans., Vol.24A, pp.2787-2802, 1993) by including liquid melt convection and solid phase transport. The macroscopic transport equations for the solid, and the interdendritic and extradendritic liquid phases are derived using the volume averaging technique. The resulting model equations are supplemented by constitutive relations for the interfacial transfer terms. Finally, the model is applied to investigate equiaxed dendritic solidification of an Al-4wt% Cu alloy in a rectangular cavity. For the first time, quantitative results for the dendritic microstructure evolution in the presence of melt convection and solid movement are obtained. The effects of crystal sedimentation on macrosegregation as well as the grain size distribution are illustrated.

NOMENCLATURE

A	interfacial surface area
A_s	area of the solid/interdendritic liquid interface
A_e	area of the dendrite envelope
C	concentration of a chemical species
c_p	specific heat
C_ε	settling ratio
C_p	shape factor function
d_s	mean characteristic length or diameter of the solid phase
d_e	mean characteristic diameter of the dendrite envelope
D	mass diffusion coefficient
G	temperature gradient
h	chill heat transfer coefficient or enthalpy
Iv	Ivantsov function
j	species diffusion flux
J	interfacial species transfer rate per unit of volume
k	thermal conductivity
l	species diffusion length
m_l	liquidus line slope
$\mathbf{M}_s^d$	solid/liquid interfacial drag
n	equiaxed nuclei density
n	outwardly directed unit normal vector
Pe_ε	multiphase Pelcet number, $\varepsilon_l\lvert\mathbf{v}_l - \mathbf{v}_s\rvert d_e/D_l$
Pe_t	solutal Peclet number at the dendrite tip, $V_tR_t/2D_l$
Pe_∞	ambient Pelcet number for dendrite tips, $\lvert\mathbf{v}_l - \mathbf{v}_s\rvert R_t/D_l$
S	interfacial area concentration
t	time
T	temperature
$\dot{T}$	cooling rate, $\partial T/\partial t$
v	velocity
V_k	volume of phase k
V_o	averaging volume
V_t	dendrite tip velocity
w	interface velocity

Greek Symbols

β	dimensionless parameter, Eq.(11)
Γ	interfacial phase change rate or Gibbs-Thomson coefficient
Δh	latent heat of phase change
ε	volume fraction
ε_{si}	internal solid fraction, $\varepsilon_s/(\varepsilon_s + \varepsilon_d)$
κ	partition coefficient
κ_v	flow partition coefficient
λ	dendrite arm spacing
λ_p	slip coefficient for solid
ϕ	shape factor

ρ density
μ viscosity
σ^* stability constant
Φ a general transfer
Ψ a field property
Ω solutal supersaturation

Subscripts

d interdendritic liquid
e dendrite envelope
E eutectic point
f total liquid phase (d+l)
g grain
j phase j
k phase k
kj pertinent to phase k on the k-j interface
l extradendritic liquid
L liquidus
ld extradendritic-interdendritic liquid interface
m melting point of pure metals
n normal direction
N nucleation
o initial state
s solid
sd solid-interdendritic liquid interface
t dendrite tip or tangential
w wall
1 primary
2 secondary

Superscripts

c critical
j due to species gradients
t macroscopic dispersion
Γ due to interface movement
\- interfacial area-averaged
* effective

1. INTRODUCTION

Toward predicting both compositional and structural features in alloy castings, this paper presents a general framework of modeling the microstructure evolution during dendritic alloy solidification. The modeling task is to incorporate descriptions of fundamental microscopic phenomena, such as nucleation, undercooling and grain growth kinetics, into macroscopic heat and fluid flow calculations. An extensive review of the micro-macroscopic modeling approach has been provided by Rappaz (1989) and Thevoz et al. (1989), and recent developments have been reported in conference proceedings (Voller et al., 1991; Piwonka et al., 1993). Two most recent approaches include the probablistic modeling proposed by Brown and Spittle (1989), Zhu and Smith (1992), and Rappaz and Gandin (1993), and the multi-scale/-phase model developed by Wang and Beckermann (1993a, 1993b, 1994). However, all these previous models have not considered melt convection and solid transport occurring during solidification, thereby greatly limiting their utility in practice. The present work is intended to extend the multiphase model of Wang and Beckermann (1993a) by accounting for melt convection and solid transport.

The present work is also a continuation of Ni and Beckermann's two-phase model (1991, 1993) which deals with globulitic solidification and represents the only study available in the literature to account for melt convection and solid transport.

The general multi-scale/-phase modeling framework is first introduced in Section 2. A specific model obtained using this general modeling approach is then presented in Section 3, where all the necessary supplementary relations are also supplied to complete the mathematical system. In Section 4, calculations for two-dimensional equiaxed dendritic solidification of an Al-4wt% Cu alloy are carried out using the multiphase model. Finally, a variety of fundamental features as related to macrosegregation, channel formation, grain size redistribution and dendritic structure during equiaxed dendritic solidification are discussed in Section 5.

2. MULTI-SCALE/-PHASE MODELING

In this section, a micro-macroscopic model of dendritic alloy solidification is rigorously formulated by utilizing a multiphase approach and volume averaging. After explaining the basic approach in Section 2.1, Section 2.2 briefly summarizes the resulting macroscopic equations. The detailed derivation using the volume averaging technique can be found in Wang (1994) and is not repeated here for brevity. Section 2.3 presents the general form of the constitutive relations for the phase interaction terms.

2.1 Multiphase Approach

Consider a small volume element that contains several equiaxed or columnar dendritic crystals, as schematically illustrated in Fig.1, in which two different interfacial length scales can be distinguished. In the equiaxed case, the solid crystal and the interdendritic liquid share a common interfacial structure of the order of 10^{-5} to 10^{-4} m, whereas the interface between the liquid outside the grains and the interdendritic liquid has a higher length scale (of the order of 10^{-4} to 10^{-3} m). The same is true for the columnar case, if one notes the difference between the primary and secondary arm spacings (see Fig.1b). The size of the volume element is chosen such that it is much larger than all interfacial length scales, but small compared to the system scale (of the order of 10^{-1} to 10^{0} m). Hence, a proper volume element could have a radius between 10^{-3} and 10^{-2} m, about the same size as a typical computational element used in numerical analyses.

The hypothetical interface between the interdendritic liquid and the liquid outside the crystals is referred to as the dendrite envelope. The specification of this envelope is somewhat subjective. However, a reasonable choice appears to be a smooth surface connecting the primary and secondary dendrite arm tips, as shown by the interrupted line in Fig.1. More

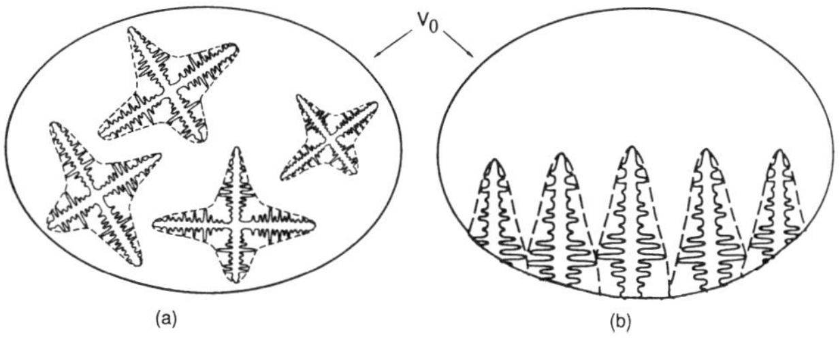

FIG.1 SCHEMATIC ILLUSTRATION OF THE AVERAGING VOLUME AND THE DENDRITE ENVELOPES FOR: (a) EQUIAXED GROWTH, AND (b) COLUMNAR GROWTH.

discussion on the envelope topology can be found in Wang and Beckermann (1993a).

Now, the volume element can be considered to consist of three different phases: the solid phase and the two liquid phases. The two liquid phases separated by the dendrite envelope are distinguished by their different interfacial length scales. Separate macroscopic conservation equations can then be formulated for each phase. These macroscopic equations are linked through interfacial transfer terms, which reflect the microscopic transport phenomena present at the interfaces. The new interface between the two liquid phases (i.e., the envelope), thus, provides an opportunity to incorporate additional microscopic phenomena in the model and transmit information from the two different length scales into the macroscopic equations.

Based on the multiphase approach, the macroscopic conservation equations can be derived using the volume averaging technique, as described in Ni and Beckermann (1991), and Wang and Beckermann (1993a).

2.2 Macroscopic Equations

Application of certain averaging theorems to the microscopic (exact) conservation equations shown in the first column of Table 1 results in the macroscopic mass, momentum, energy, and species conservation equations for a phase k. They are also summarized in Table 1. The numerous symbols in Table 1 are defined in the Nomenclature.

Several features can be observed with regard to the averaged equations in Table 1: (1) they contain the phase volume fraction, ε_k; (2) there arise integrals over the interfacial areas that account for the interactions of phase k with all other phases due to relative movement of interfaces (e.g., phase change) and interfacial transport (e.g., diffusion/convection); (3) they contain dispersive fluxes which reflect the effects of microscopic fluctuations of a property within a phase on the macroscopic transport (such terms are of key importance in turbulence modeling), and (4) an interfacial balance requires that the interfacial fluxes are equal on both sides of the interface. Since in the present model phases may be simply distinguished by their interfacial length scales, several interfacial integrals appear, through which information from each microscopic level is passed to the macroscopic level.

2.3 Constitutive Relations

The interfacial or phase interaction terms as well as the dispersive fluxes require further modeling, since the microscopic variables on which they are based are not known from the solution of the macroscopic equations. This information has been lost in the averaging process. The modeling of these terms for solidification systems requires (1) postulation of constitutive relations and (2) formal microscopic analyses for the system in question.

2.3.1 Interfacial Transfers due to Interfacial Movement.

Interfacial movement can be due to phase change at the solid/liquid interface or dendrite tip advancement at the dendrite envelope. The exact expressions for the interfacial transfers of mass, momentum, heat and species due to this movement are provided in Table 1. Physically, these terms represent advection of an interfacial quantity of phase k due to the relative motion of the interface. In view of the mean value theorem for integrals, the terms can be modeled as the product of an interfacial area concentration and a mean interfacial flux. Hence, at the k-j interface the interfacial mass transfer rate becomes

$$\Gamma_{kj} = S_{kj}\rho_k \bar{w}_{nkj} \tag{1}$$

where $\bar{w}_{nkj}$ represents the average normal velocity of the interface kj relative to phase k.

In like manner, a general transfer Φ_{kj}^{Γ} corresponding to the property Ψ at the k-j interface due to interfacial movement can be expressed as

$$\Phi_{kj}^{\Gamma} = \bar{\Psi}_{kj}\,\Gamma_{kj} \tag{2}$$

where the overbar together with the subscript kj denotes an average over the interfacial area A_{kj} in V_o. The term Φ_{kj}^{Γ} stands for the momentum transfer M_{kj}^{Γ}, heat transfer Q_{kj}^{Γ}, and species transfer J_{kj}^{Γ}, if Ψ corresponds to the velocity, enthalpy, and concentration, respectively. Note that Eq.(2) introduces interfacial quantities, $\bar{\Psi}_{kj}$, into the macroscopic conservation equations that are usually distinct from their volume averaged counterparts, $<\Psi_k>^k$.

2.3.2 Interfacial Transfers due to Diffusion/Convection.

The exact expressions for the interfacial stress, M_{kj}^{d}, heat transfer, Q_{kj}^{d}, and species transfer, J_{kj}^{d}, due to diffusion/convection are also given in Table 1. Physically, these terms represent the transport phenomena among the phases within V_o and are caused by microscopic velocity, temperature, and species concentration gradients, respectively, on each side of the interface A_{kj}. Similar to the interfacial transfers due to interfacial movement, they can

Table 1. Summary of microscopic and macroscopic conservation equations

	Microscopic conservation equations	Macroscopic conservation equations	Interfacial balances	Dispersive fluxes
Mass	$\frac{\partial}{\partial t}\rho_k + \nabla\cdot(\rho_k \mathbf{v}_k) = 0$	$\frac{\partial}{\partial t}(\varepsilon_k\rho_k) + \nabla\cdot(\varepsilon_k\rho_k\langle \mathbf{v}_k\rangle^k) = \sum_{j,j\neq k}\Gamma_{kj}$	$\Gamma_{kj} + \Gamma_{jk} = 0$	—
Momentum	$\frac{\partial}{\partial t}(\rho_k \mathbf{v}_k) + \nabla\cdot(\rho_k \mathbf{v}_k \mathbf{v}_k) =$	$\frac{\partial}{\partial t}(\varepsilon_k\rho_k\langle \mathbf{v}_k\rangle^k) + \nabla\cdot(\varepsilon_k\rho_k\langle \mathbf{v}_k\rangle^k\langle \mathbf{v}_k\rangle^k) =$	$\mathbf{M}_{kj} + \mathbf{M}_{jk} = 0$	$\langle \tau_k^t\rangle = -\langle \rho_k\hat{\mathbf{v}}_k\hat{\mathbf{v}}_k\rangle$
	$-\nabla p_k + \nabla\cdot\tau_k + \mathbf{b}_k$	$-\varepsilon_k\nabla\langle p_k\rangle^k + \nabla\cdot(\langle\tau_k\rangle + \langle\tau_k^t\rangle) + \sum_{j,j\neq k}\mathbf{M}_{kj} + \varepsilon_k\langle \mathbf{b}_k\rangle^k$		
Energy	$\frac{\partial}{\partial t}(\rho_k h_k) + \nabla\cdot(\rho_k h_k \mathbf{v}_k) =$	$\frac{\partial}{\partial t}(\varepsilon_k\rho_k\langle h_k\rangle^k) + \nabla\cdot(\varepsilon_k\rho_k\langle h_k\rangle^k\langle \mathbf{v}_k\rangle^k) =$	$Q_{kj} + Q_{jk} = 0$	$\langle \mathbf{q}_k^t\rangle = \langle \rho_k\hat{h}_k\hat{\mathbf{v}}_k\rangle$
	$-\nabla\cdot\mathbf{q}_k$	$-\nabla\cdot(\langle \mathbf{q}_k\rangle + \langle \mathbf{q}_k^t\rangle) + \sum_{j,j\neq k} Q_{kj}$		
Species	$\frac{\partial}{\partial t}(\rho_k C_k) + \nabla\cdot(\rho_k C_k \mathbf{v}_k) =$	$\frac{\partial}{\partial t}(\varepsilon_k\rho_k\langle C_k\rangle^k) + \nabla\cdot(\varepsilon_k\rho_k\langle C_k\rangle^k\langle \mathbf{v}_k\rangle^k) =$	$J_{kj} + J_{jk} = 0$	$\langle \mathbf{j}_k^t\rangle = \langle \rho_k\hat{C}_k\hat{\mathbf{v}}_k\rangle$
	$-\nabla\cdot\mathbf{j}_k$	$-\nabla\cdot(\langle \mathbf{j}_k\rangle + \langle \mathbf{j}_k^t\rangle) + \sum_{j,j\neq k} J_{kj}$		

	Total interfacial transfers	Interfacial transfers due to phase change	Interfacial stress and transfers due to diffusion/convectiomn
Mass	Γ_{kj}	$\Gamma_{kj} = -\frac{1}{V_o}\int_{A_{kj}} \rho_k(\mathbf{v}_k - \mathbf{w}_k)\cdot\mathbf{n}_k\, dA$	---
Momentum	$\mathbf{M}_{kj} = \mathbf{M}_{kj}^{\Gamma} + \mathbf{M}_{kj}^{d}$	$\mathbf{M}_{kj}^{\Gamma} = -\frac{1}{V_o}\int_{A_{kj}} \rho_k\mathbf{v}_k(\mathbf{v}_k - \mathbf{w}_k)\cdot\mathbf{n}_k\, dA$	$\mathbf{M}_{kj}^{d} = \frac{1}{V_o}\int_{A_{kj}} \tau_k\cdot\mathbf{n}_k\, dA$
Energy	$Q_{kj} = Q_{kj}^{\Gamma} + Q_{kj}^{d}$	$Q_{kj}^{\Gamma} = -\frac{1}{V_o}\int_{A_{kj}} \rho_k h_k(\mathbf{v}_k - \mathbf{w}_k)\cdot\mathbf{n}_k\, dA$	$Q_{kj}^{d} = -\frac{1}{V_o}\int_{A_{kj}} \mathbf{q}_k\cdot\mathbf{n}_k\, dA$
Species	$J_{kj} = J_{kj}^{\Gamma} + J_{kj}^{d}$	$J_{kj}^{\Gamma} = -\frac{1}{V_o}\int_{A_{kj}} \rho_k C_k(\mathbf{v}_k - \mathbf{w}_k)\cdot\mathbf{n}_k\, dA$	$J_{kj}^{d} = -\frac{1}{V_o}\int_{A_{kj}} \mathbf{j}_k\cdot\mathbf{n}_k\, dA$

generally be modeled as the product of the interfacial area concentration S_{kj} and a mean interfacial flux. It can further be assumed that the mean interfacial flux is, in turn, linearly proportional to the difference between the interfacial average and the intrinsic volume average of a quantity of phase k, i.e., $\bar{\Psi}_{kj} - \langle\Psi_k\rangle^k$. In other words, this difference is assumed to be the driving force for the interfacial flux. Hence, the interfacial mass transfer at the k-j interface due to diffusion/convection in phase k can be expressed as

$$J_{kj}^{d} = S_s \frac{D_k}{l_{kj}}(\bar{C}_{kj} - \langle C_k\rangle^k) \tag{3}$$

where l is called the diffusion length which characterizes the resistance to diffusion/convection (Wang and Beckermann, 1993a). The diffusion length is generally a complicated function of the microscopic phenomena, and its determination requires a formal microscopic analysis of diffusion processes (see Section 3.3.6 for more detail).

2.3.3 Modeling of Macroscopic Fluxes. The macroscopic fluxes include the viscous stress $\langle\tau_k\rangle$, heat flux $\langle \mathbf{q}_k\rangle$ and species flux $\langle \mathbf{j}_k\rangle$, as well as their dispersive counterparts, $\langle\tau_k^t\rangle$, $\langle \mathbf{q}_k^t\rangle$ and $\langle \mathbf{j}_k^t\rangle$. These fluxes are typically modeled by introducing effective transport properties, so that

$$\langle\Phi_k\rangle + \langle\Phi_k^t\rangle = -\Gamma_k^* \varepsilon_k \nabla\langle\Psi_k\rangle^k \tag{4}$$

where Γ_k^* represents an overall macroscopic transport property, which is a function of not only the microscopic transport property but also the microstructure as well as microscopic flow fields. For multiphase flows, evaluation of these effective transport properties is an area of considerable research and controversy.

3. A MULTIPHASE MODEL

The full form of the macroscopic conservation equations together with the constitutive relations has been presented in the preceding section. These governing equations can be considerably simplified for specific systems by making certain assumptions. Various limiting cases as well as simplified model equations for diffusion-controlled solidification have been extensively discussed in Wang and Beckermann (1993a). In the present study, emphasis is placed on a three-phase system consisting of the solid (k=s), the interdendritic liquid (k=d), and the extradendritic liquid outside the dendrite envelope (k=l), so that $\varepsilon_s + \varepsilon_d + \varepsilon_l = 1$. An internal solid fraction can be defined as $\varepsilon_{si}=\varepsilon_s/(\varepsilon_s+\varepsilon_d)$, and the grain fraction is given by $\varepsilon_g=\varepsilon_s+\varepsilon_d$. It is further assumed that the solid (s) has only pointwise contact with the liquid (l) outside the dendrite envelope (see Fig.1), so that

$$A_{sd} = A_{ds} = A_s,\ A_{dl} = A_{ld} = A_e,\ \text{and}\ A_{sl} = A_{ls} = 0 \tag{5}$$

These geometrical relationships imply that there exists no direct coupling between phases (s) and (l), while phase (d) interacts with both phases (s) and (l). More model assumptions are made in the next subsection. Also, in the remainder of this paper, the averaging symbols are dropped for convenience, namely $\langle\Phi_k\rangle^k=\Phi_k$, whereas an interfacial quantity is still denoted by an overbar, so as to distinguish it from its volume-averaged counterpart.

3.1 Model Assumptions

The model equations presented below are based on the following assumptions:

(1) Mechanical equilibrium exists, i.e., $p_s = p_d = p_l = p$.

(2) The momentum exchange due to interfacial movement is neglected.

(3) A certain flow partitioning between the inter- and extra-dendritic regions is assumed. As schematically shown in Fig.2 for the equiaxed system, the liquid may flow either through the inter- or the extra-dendritic region. The relative portions can be quantified by introducing a flow partition tensor, κ_v, which is defined as the ratio of the liquid mass flux through the porous dendrites to the total liquid mass flux; i.e.,

$$\varepsilon_d\rho_d(\mathbf{v}_d - \mathbf{v}_s) = \kappa_v\, \varepsilon_f\rho_f(\mathbf{v}_f - \mathbf{v}_s) \tag{6}$$

and

$$\varepsilon_l\rho_l(\mathbf{v}_l - \mathbf{v}_s) = (1 - \kappa_v)\varepsilon_f\rho_f(\mathbf{v}_f - \mathbf{v}_s) \tag{7}$$

where ε_f and $\mathbf{v}_f$ stand for the total liquid fraction, consisting of both the interdendritic and extradendritic phases, and the mixture velocity vector for both phases, respectively: $\varepsilon_f = \varepsilon_d + \varepsilon_l$, and $\varepsilon_f\rho_f\mathbf{v}_f = \varepsilon_d\rho_d\mathbf{v}_d + \varepsilon_l\rho_l\mathbf{v}_l$. Note that when $\kappa_v=\rho_d\varepsilon_d/(\rho_f\varepsilon_f)$, a uniform flow distribution results; i.e., $\mathbf{v}_d = \mathbf{v}_l = \mathbf{v}_f$. The coefficient κ_v is also called the fluid collection efficiency of porous aggregates in chemical engineering (Adler, 1981). A correlation for κ_v is developed in a later section. The concept of flow partitioning between the inter- and extra-dendritic regions is introduced to simplify the solution of the momentum equations in the proposed multiphase model. Once κ_v is calculated, only the momentum equation for the total liquid phase needs to be solved, and the individual liquid velocity fields, $\mathbf{v}_d$ and $\mathbf{v}_l$, can be algebraically obtained from Eqs.(6) and (7).

(4) Local thermal equilibrium exists, i.e., $T_k = \overline{T}_{kj} = T$. The assumption can safely be made under normal solidification conditions because of the large value of the Lewis number of metal alloys, so that heat transfer at an interface is fast enough to reach local thermal equilibrium.

(5) The interdendritic liquid is well mixed so that $\overline{C}_{ds} = \overline{C}_{dl} = \overline{C}_{ld} = C_d = \overline{C}_e$. The validity of this assumption has been discussed in Wang and Beckermann (1993a).

(6) The dendrite envelope is spherical.

(7) Thermophysical properties are the same for the interdendritic and extradendritic liquid phases.

As discussed in Assumption 3, only the solid and the total liquid phases require principal consideration. The distinction between the variables pertinent to the inter- and extra-dendritic liquids can be made algebraically after the primary variables pertinent to the total liquid phase (f) are obtained. The primary variables pertinent to the total liquid phase are defined by the rule-of-mixtures, i.e.,

volume fraction	$\varepsilon_f = \varepsilon_d + \varepsilon_l$	(8)
density	$\rho_f\varepsilon_f = \rho_d\varepsilon_d + \rho_l\varepsilon_l$	(9)
viscosity	$\rho_f\varepsilon_f\mu_f^* = \rho_d\varepsilon_d\mu_d^* + \rho_l\varepsilon_l\mu_l^*$	(10)
mass diffusivity	$\rho_f\varepsilon_f D_f^* = \rho_d\varepsilon_d D_d^* + \rho_l\varepsilon_l D_l^*$	(11)
thermal conductivity	$\varepsilon_f k_f^* = \varepsilon_d k_d^* + \varepsilon_l k_l^*$	(12)
specific heat	$\rho_f\varepsilon_f c_f = \rho_d\varepsilon_d c_d + \rho_l\varepsilon_l c_l$	(13)
concentration	$\rho_f\varepsilon_f C_f = \rho_d\varepsilon_d C_d + \rho_l\varepsilon_l C_l$	(14)
velocity	$\rho_f\varepsilon_f\mathbf{v}_f = \rho_d\varepsilon_d\mathbf{v}_d + \rho_l\varepsilon_l\mathbf{v}_l$	(15)

3.2 Model Equations

With the assumptions stated above, a reduced set of model equations can be derived from the general formulation presented in Table 1 and the constitutive relations developed in the preceding section. These equations are summarized in Table 2. Some details of their derivations are provided in the following subsections.

3.2.1 Calculation of Phase Change Rate. As a critical parameter in solidification processes, the phase change rate Γ_s may be determined from the species balance in the interdendritic liquid phase (extracted from Table 1):

$$\frac{\partial}{\partial t}(\rho_d\varepsilon_d C_d) + \nabla\cdot(\rho_d\varepsilon_d\mathbf{v}_d C_d) = \nabla\cdot(\rho_d\varepsilon_d D_d^*\nabla C_d) - \left[\, \overline{C}_{sd}\Gamma_s + \frac{\rho_s S_s D_s}{l_{sd}}(\overline{C}_{sd} - C_s)\right] + \left[\, \overline{C}_e\Gamma_e - \frac{\rho_l S_e D_l}{l_{ld}}(\overline{C}_e - C_l)\right] \tag{16}$$

where the interfacial species fluxes on the RHS have been replaced by their counterparts on the other sides of the interfaces, because the former become indeterminate under Assumption 5.

Eliminating Γ_e in Eq.(16) using the mass conservation equation for phase (d) and noting that $C_d= \overline{C}_e$ (Assumption 5), it follows that

Table 2 Summary of a multiphase model

CONTINUITY EQUATIONS

Solid Phase

$$\frac{\partial}{\partial t}(\rho_s \varepsilon_s) + \nabla \cdot (\rho_s \varepsilon_s \mathbf{v}_s) = \Gamma_s$$

Total Liquid Phase

$$\frac{\partial}{\partial t}(\rho_f \varepsilon_f) + \nabla \cdot (\rho_f \varepsilon_f \mathbf{v}_f) = - \Gamma_s$$

INTERFACIAL SPECIES BALANCE

(for Calculating Phase Change Rate)

$$(\bar{C}_e - \bar{C}_{sd})\Gamma_s = \frac{\rho_s S_s D_s}{l_{sd}}(\bar{C}_{sd} - C_s) + \frac{\rho_l S_e D_l}{l_{ld}}(\bar{C}_e - C_l) + [\rho_d \varepsilon_d \frac{\partial \bar{C}_e}{\partial t} + \rho_d \varepsilon_d \mathbf{v}_d \cdot \nabla \bar{C}_e - \nabla \cdot (\rho_d \varepsilon_d D_d^* \nabla \bar{C}_e)]$$

MOMENTUM EQUATIONS

Solid Phase

$$\frac{\partial}{\partial t}(\rho_s \varepsilon_s \mathbf{v}_s) + \nabla \cdot (\rho_s \varepsilon_s \mathbf{v}_s \mathbf{v}_s) = -\varepsilon_s \nabla p + \nabla \cdot (\mu_s^* \varepsilon_s \nabla \mathbf{v}_s) + \mathbf{M}_s^d + \rho_s \varepsilon_s \mathbf{g}$$

Total Liquid Phase

$$\frac{\partial}{\partial t}(\rho_f \varepsilon_f \mathbf{v}_f) + \nabla \cdot (\rho_f \varepsilon_f \mathbf{v}_f \mathbf{v}_f) = -\varepsilon_f \nabla p + \nabla \cdot (\mu_f^* \varepsilon_f \nabla \mathbf{v}_f) - \mathbf{M}_s^d + \varepsilon_f \rho_f \mathbf{g} + \nabla \cdot [\gamma \rho_f \varepsilon_f (\mathbf{v}_f - \mathbf{v}_s)(\mathbf{v}_f - \mathbf{v}_s)]$$

SPECIES EQUATIONS

Solid Phase

$$\frac{\partial}{\partial t}(\rho_s \varepsilon_s C_s) + \nabla \cdot (\rho_s \varepsilon_s \mathbf{v}_s C_s) = \nabla \cdot (\rho_s \varepsilon_s D_s^* \nabla C_s) + \bar{C}_{sd}\Gamma_s + \frac{\rho_s S_s D_s}{l_{sd}}(\bar{C}_{sd} - C_s)$$

Total Liquid Phase

$$\frac{\partial}{\partial t}(\rho_f \varepsilon_f C_f) + \nabla \cdot (\rho_f \varepsilon_f \mathbf{v}_f C_f) = \nabla \cdot (\rho_f \varepsilon_f D_f^* \nabla C_f) - [\bar{C}_{sd}\Gamma_s + \frac{\rho_s S_s D_s}{l_{sd}}(\bar{C}_{sd} - C_s)] + \nabla \cdot \{\rho_f \varepsilon_f (\mathbf{v}_f - \mathbf{v}_s)[C_f - \kappa_v C_d - (1-\kappa_v) C_l]\}$$

MIXTURE ENERGY EQUATION

$$\frac{\partial}{\partial t}[(\rho_s \varepsilon_s c_s + \rho_f \varepsilon_f c_f)T] + \nabla \cdot [(\rho_s \varepsilon_s c_s \mathbf{v}_s + \rho_f \varepsilon_f c_f \mathbf{v}_f)T] = \nabla \cdot [(\varepsilon_s k_s^* + \varepsilon_f k_f^*)\nabla T] + \Gamma_s[\Delta h + (c_s - c_l)T_E]$$

AUXILIARY RELATIONS FOR SECONDARY VARIABLES

Interdendritic Liquid Fraction

$$\frac{\partial}{\partial t}(\rho_d \varepsilon_d) + \nabla \cdot (\rho_d \varepsilon_d \mathbf{v}_d) = S_e \rho_l \bar{w}_{ne} - \Gamma_s$$

Extradendritic Liquid Fraction

$$\varepsilon_l = \varepsilon_f - \varepsilon_d$$

Extradendritic Liquid Concentration

$$C_l = (\rho_f \varepsilon_f C_f - \rho_d \varepsilon_d \bar{C}_e)/(\rho_l \varepsilon_l)$$

Inter- and Extra-dendritic Liquid Velocities

$$\mathbf{v}_d = \mathbf{v}_s + \kappa_v \frac{\rho_f \varepsilon_f}{\rho_d \varepsilon_d}(\mathbf{v}_f - \mathbf{v}_s); \quad \mathbf{v}_l = \mathbf{v}_s + (1-\kappa_v)\frac{\rho_f \varepsilon_f}{\rho_l \varepsilon_l}(\mathbf{v}_f - \mathbf{v}_s)$$

$$(\bar{C}_e - \bar{C}_{sd})\Gamma_s = \frac{\rho_s S_s D_s}{l_{sd}}(\bar{C}_{sd} - C_s) + \frac{\rho_l S_e D_l}{l_{ld}}(\bar{C}_e - C_l) + [\rho_d \varepsilon_d \frac{\partial \bar{C}_e}{\partial t} + \rho_d \varepsilon_d \mathbf{v}_d \cdot \nabla \bar{C}_e - \nabla \cdot (\rho_d \varepsilon_d D_d^* \nabla \bar{C}_e)] \tag{17}$$

Physically, this equation implies that the species flux rejected into the interdendritic liquid due to phase change (LHS) is either diffused into the solid and extradendritic liquid through interphase exchanges within the control volume (the 1st and 2nd terms on the RHS), or stored in the interdendritic region (3rd term on the RHS), or advected and diffused out of the control volume (4th and 5th terms on the RHS). Equation (17) is used to calculate the phase change rate, Γ_s.

3.2.2 Momentum Conservation. The momentum equation for phase (f) listed in Table 2 is obtained by summing up the momentum conservation equations for phases (d) and (l) as listed in Table 1. The viscous terms are linear so that they are additive, whereas the summation of the nonlinear advective terms results in an additional term (the last term on the RHS), where γ is called the momentum dispersion coefficient and is given by

$$\gamma = 1 - \rho_f \varepsilon_f \left[\frac{\kappa_v^2}{\rho_d \varepsilon_d} + \frac{(1-\kappa_v)^2}{\rho_l \varepsilon_l} \right] \tag{18}$$

When $\kappa_v = \rho_d \varepsilon_d / \rho_f \varepsilon_f$ (i.e., uniform flow through the inter- and extra-dendritic regions), $\gamma = 0$ so that the last term in the momentum equation for phase (f) vanishes. This is why γ is called the dispersion coefficient.

The solid/liquid interfacial drag, $\mathbf{M}_s^d$, in the two momentum equations listed in Table 2 is modeled in Section 3.3.4.

3.2.3 Species Conservation. The species conservation equations for the solid and total liquid phases can be derived in a similar fashion. These equations contain interfacial species transfer terms that are inversely proportional to the solid and liquid diffusion lengths l_{sd} and l_{ld}, respectively. These diffusion lengths are modeled in Section 3.3.6. Notice again that when $\kappa_v = \varepsilon_d \rho_d / (\varepsilon_f \rho_f)$ (uniform flow), the last term in the species conservation equation for the total liquid phase drops out.

3.2.4 Energy Conservation. In deriving the energy equation for the multiphase mixture, the macroscopic enthalpies of the various phases are expressed as linear functions of temperature:

$$h_s = c_s T \tag{19}$$

$$h_d = c_d T + (c_s - c_d)T_E + \Delta h \tag{20}$$

and

$$h_l = c_l T + (c_s - c_l)T_E + \Delta h \tag{21}$$

where Δh_E is the latent heat of fusion at the eutectic temperature, T_E; i.e.,

$$\Delta h = (h_l - h_s)|_{T=TE} \tag{22}$$

The last term on the RHS of the energy equation listed in Table 2 represents the latent heat release due to solidification.

3.2.5 Secondary Variables. The model equations listed in Table 2 constitute a complete mathematical formulation for eight primary variables: ε_s, Γ_s, $\mathbf{v}_s$, $\mathbf{v}_f$, p, C_s, C_f and T, while the total liquid fraction, ε_f, can be obtained from the constraint: $\varepsilon_s+\varepsilon_f=1$. All quantities pertinent to the interdendritic and extradendritic liquid phases, are classified as secondary variables whose determination from the above primary variables is explained below.

To distinguish the interdendritic and extradendritic liquid fractions from the total liquid fraction ε_f, one can resort to the following mass conservation equation for the interdendritic liquid phase:

$$\frac{\partial}{\partial t}(\rho_d\varepsilon_d) + \nabla\cdot(\rho_d\varepsilon_d\mathbf{v}_d) = \Gamma_e - \Gamma_s \tag{23}$$

where Γ_e is related to the growth velocity of the dendrite envelope via Eq.(1):

$$\Gamma_e = S_e\rho_l\,\bar{w}_{ne} \tag{24}$$

Hence, the quantity Γ_e can be calculated from the growth model for the dendrite envelope, which is provided in Section 3.3.3. Once ε_d is obtained, the extradendritic liquid fraction is simply equal to $(\varepsilon_f-\varepsilon_d)$.

By definition, the extradendritic liquid concentration can be calculated, once C_f is available, from

$$C_l = (\rho_f\varepsilon_f C_f - \rho_d\varepsilon_d\,\bar{C}_e)/(\rho_l\varepsilon_l) \tag{25}$$

where the relation $C_d=\bar{C}_e$ has been used due to the assumption that the interdendritic liquid is well mixed.

Likewise, the liquid velocities in the inter- and extra-dendritic regions are obtained, respectively, from the definition of the flow partition coefficient:

$$\mathbf{v}_d = \mathbf{v}_s + \kappa_v\frac{\rho_f\varepsilon_f}{\rho_d\varepsilon_d}(\mathbf{v}_f - \mathbf{v}_s) \tag{26}$$

$$\mathbf{v}_l = \mathbf{v}_s + (1-\kappa_v)\frac{\rho_f\varepsilon_f}{\rho_l\varepsilon_l}(\mathbf{v}_f - \mathbf{v}_s) \tag{27}$$

in which κ_v is calculated as shown in Section 3.3.4.

The above auxiliary relations for calculating the secondary variables from the primary variables are also summarized in Table 2. To complete the mathematical system, supplementary relations are, however, needed for the interfacial area concentrations, S_s and S_e, the growth velocity of dendrite envelope $\bar{w}_{ne}$, the solid/liquid interfacial drag, $\mathbf{M}_s^d$, the flow partition coefficient κ_v, the interfacial diffusion lengths, l_{sd} and l_{ld}, and the macroscopic transport properties as well. These additional inputs to the multiphase model are provided in the following subsections. It should also be mentioned that the relations for the solid/liquid interfacial drag, $\mathbf{M}_s^d$, the flow partition coefficient κ_v, and the interfacial diffusion lengths, l_{sd} and l_{ld}, are presented only for equiaxed dendritic solidification in this article.

3.3 Supplementary Relations

3.3.1 Morphological Relations. The interfacial area concentrations, S_s and S_e, characterize the topology of the interfacial structures and are thus related to complex microscopic phenomena, such as the growth of various solid microstructures, impingement of interfaces, and coarsening of dendrite arms. The area concentrations also play important roles in the modeling of the interfacial transfer terms, as shown above. For completeness, the morphological relations derived by Wang and Beckermann (1993a) are included in Table 3. The interfacial area concentrations in Table 3 are expressed as functions of the traditionally employed dendrite arm spacings and grain densities. The interfacial area concentration, S, is related to the specific area, S_v, by $S=S_v(1-\varepsilon)$, where ε is the volume fraction of the microstructure under consideration.

Table 3 Summary of morphological relations

Quantity	Equiaxed growth	Columnar growth
Mean diameter of the solid phase, d_s	$\frac{\varepsilon_s\lambda_2}{1-\varepsilon_l}$	
Mean diameter of the dendrite envelope, d_e	$\left(\frac{6(1-\varepsilon_l)}{n\pi}\right)^{1/3}$	$\left(\frac{4(1-\varepsilon_l)}{\pi}\right)^{1/2}\lambda_1$
Solid/liquid interfacial area concentration, S_s	$\frac{2}{\lambda_2}$	
Envelope area concentration, S_e	$\frac{1}{\phi_e}(36\pi)^{1/3}n^{1/3}(1-\varepsilon_l)^{2/3}$	$\frac{1}{\phi_e}(4\pi)^{1/2}(1-\varepsilon_l)^{1/2}\frac{1}{\lambda_1}$

3.3.2 Grain Nucleation. As an important microstructural parameter, the grain density is needed for the evaluation of certain geometrical quantities listed in Table 3. Due to solid motion in the equiaxed case, this grain density, n, is not only determined by nucleation mechanisms but also modified by the flow field during solidification, according to the following conservation equation (Ni and Beckermann, 1991):

$$\frac{\partial n}{\partial t} + \nabla\cdot(\mathbf{v}_s n) = \dot{n} \tag{28}$$

where the second term on the LHS is the flux of grains due to a finite solid velocity, $\mathbf{v}_s$. The term $\dot{n}$ is the net nucleation rate accounting for both the birth and death of grains due to heterogeneous nucleation, remelting, dendrite arm pinch-off, agglomeration and other effects. Although a number of semi-empirical nucleation models are available, they do not explicitly account for fragmentation and agglomeration effects in the presence of convection. The realistic modeling of grain structure formation on the macroscopic scale will largely depend on resolving these issues. Careful experimentation coupled with solutions of the present model equations may help in this respect.

In the present work, the simplest nucleation model, namely the instantaneous nucleation law proposed by Stefanescu et al. (1990), is employed. In this model, it is assumed that a certain number of nuclei instantaneously appear as soon as the temperature of the liquid melt falls below the nucleation temperature, T_N; i.e., $\dot{n} = n_o\delta(T - T_N)$, where n_o is a constant and δ is the Dirac delta function. Moreover, nucleation can only occur if the local grain density before nucleation is equal to zero. This implies that no new grains will nucleate in the immediate neighborhood of existing grains. In the presence of solid movement, grains may be advected into regions of higher temperature and remelt to a sufficiently small diameter d_{si}. In this case, death of the grains takes place, and the present nucleation model instantaneously resets the local grain density to zero. The control volume in question is then allowed to re-nucleate later when the conditions are right. Grains may exist in regions of superheated melt as long as their diameter is above d_{si}.

3.3.3 Grain Growth. The dendrite envelope motion is governed by the growth of dendrite tips. The growth model for dendrite tips can be obtained by connecting two phenomena: solute transport near the tip and tip stability. Assuming no back diffusion in the solid and using the common marginal stability condition for tip growth as proposed by Lipton et al. (1984), it can be shown that (Wang and Beckermann, 1992)

$$\bar{w}_{ne} = \frac{4\sigma^* D_l m(\kappa-1)\bar{C}_e}{\Gamma} Pe_t^2 \tag{29}$$

where σ^* is the stability constant ($\approx 1/4\pi^2$ in the pure diffusion limit) and Γ is the Gibbs-Thomson coefficient. The tip Peclet number, Pe_t, is related to the dimensionless solutal undercooling, Ω:

$$\Omega = \frac{\bar{C}_e - C_l}{\bar{C}_e(1 - \kappa)} \tag{30}$$

via the solution of the solute transport problem near the tip. Coupling such a solution with Eq.(29) yields a growth model that relates $\bar{w}_{ne}$ directly to the solutal undercooling Ω. Equation (29) is generic, in that all the effects of the assumed dendrite tip shape and flow conditions around the tips are incorporated in the stability constant σ^* and the relation between the tip Peclet number Pe_t and undercooling Ω. Below, diffusion- and convection-dominated cases are considered, separately.

For diffusion-dominated growth, the exact Ivantsov function is given by

$$Iv(Pe_t) = Pe_t \exp(Pe_t)\, E_1(Pe_t) = \Omega \tag{31}$$

where $E_1(Pe_t)$ is the exponential integral function. For computational convenience, the inverse Ivantsov function can be approximated by (Wang and Beckermann, 1993b):

$$Pe_t = Iv^{-1}(\Omega) = a\left(\frac{\Omega}{1-\Omega}\right)^b \tag{32}$$

where a=0.4567 and b=1.195 give the best fit. Substitution of Eq.(32) into Eq.(29) and insertion of $\sigma^*=1/4\pi^2$ yield a growth model for diffusion-dominated dendrite tip growth. This model has been used in Wang and Beckermann (1993a; 1994) for diffusion-dominated solidification.

For convection-dominated growth, there is ample experimental evidence showing that both the stability criterion and the species gradients are affected by the flow field around dendrite tips. A reliable and accurate model accounting for these convection effects is, however, not yet available. To a first approximation, one can assume a negligible influence of convection on the stability criterion, and thus the focus is first placed on the fluid flow effect on the species transport field around dendrite tips.

Considerable research has been conducted in order to find analytical solutions of the species transport around dendrite tips in the presence of convection. A summary has been given by Ananth and Gill (1991). It was found that the Stokes approximation of the Navier-Stokes equations for convection in a subcooled melt yields an exact solution for shape preserving growth of a parabolic dendrite. The solution was also found to be in good agreement with the available experimental data of Huang and Glicksman (1981). In terms of the tip Peclet number Pe_t and the dimensionless undercooling Ω, this solution can be written as

$$\Omega = 2Pe_t \left(\int_1^\infty \frac{\exp[-\int_1^\eta (f/\eta)d\eta]}{\eta} d\eta \right) \tag{33}$$

where the function $f(\eta)$ is given by

$$f(\eta) = 2Pe_t\, \eta^2 + \frac{2Pe_\infty}{E_1[(Pe_\infty + 2Pe_t)/Sc]} [\, \eta^2(2\ln \eta - 1) + 1] \tag{34}$$

and the ambient Peclet number is based on the relative velocity between the liquid and the solid dendrite; i.e.,

$$Pe_\infty = |v_l - v_s|\, R_t/D_l \tag{35}$$

When Pe_∞=0, which implies no convection, Eq.(34) yields $f(\eta)=2Pe_t\eta^2$ and Eq.(33) reduces to the Ivantsov solution for pure diffusion as given in Eq.(31).

Again, for computational efficiency, the inverse of the solution to Eqs.(33-34) for convection-dominated dendrite tip growth can be curvefitted using the same form as Eq.(32):

$$a = 0.4567 + 0.173\, Pe_\infty^{0.55} \tag{36a}$$

$$b = 1.195 - 0.145\, Pe_\infty^{0.16} \tag{36b}$$

Figure 3 shows a comparison of the present correlation consisting of Eqs.(32) and (36) with the Stokes solution given by Eqs.(33) and (34) for various values of Pe_∞. It can be seen that the present correlation adequately matches with the analytical results.

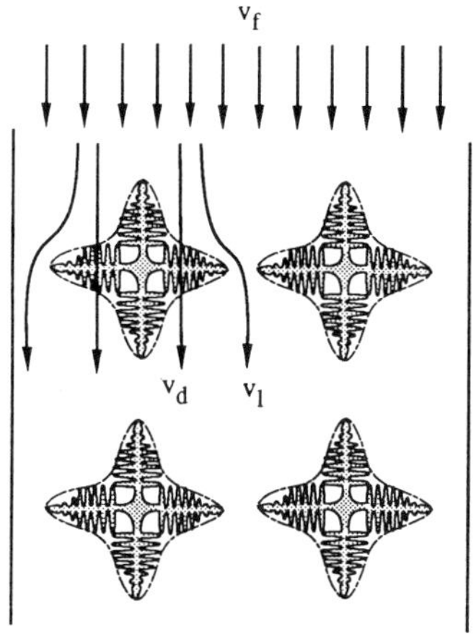

FIG.2 SCHEMATIC OF THE PARTITIONING OF THE LIQUID FLOW THROUGH THE INTER-DENDRITIC AND EXTRADENDRITIC REGIONS IN EQUIAXED SOLIDIFICATION

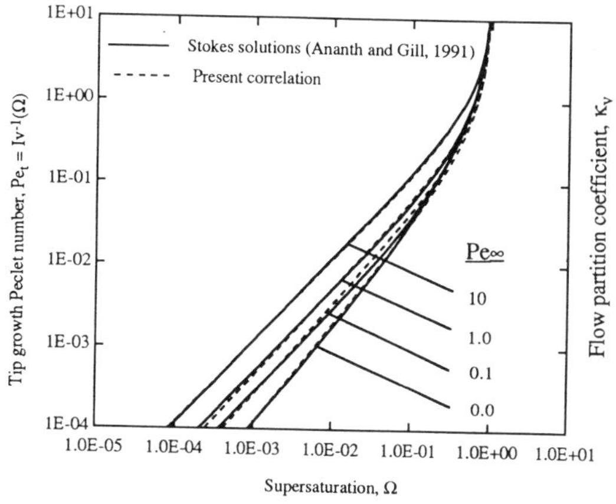

FIG.3 COMPARISON OF THE STOKES SOLUTION OF Ananth AND Gill (1991) WITH THE PRESENT CORRELATION, Eqs.(32) AND (36), FOR DENDRITE TIP GROWTH.

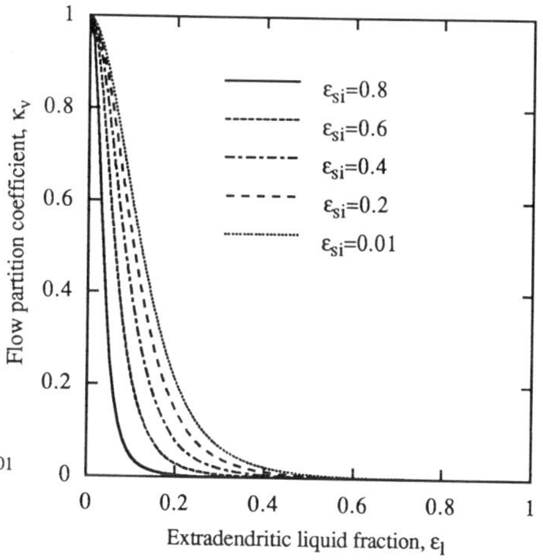

FIG.4 FLOW PARTITION COEFFICIENT AS FUNCTIONS OF THE EXTRADENDRITIC LIQUID FRACTION AND INTERNAL SOLID FRACTION FOR S_s/S_e=0.1.

3.3.4 Solid/Liquid Interfacial Drag. The dissipative interfacial stress in a multiparticle system has traditionally been modeled using various approaches. For high solid fractions (i.e., the packed bed regime), the porous medium approach is often adopted, with the permeability representing a key parameter (Carman, 1956; Flemings, 1974); while at low solid fractions (i.e., the free particle regime), the submerged object model is more frequently used (Happel and Brenner, 1976) in which the drag coefficient is important. Recently, both approaches have been unified by Wang et al. (1994) for the multiparticle system of equiaxed solidification, and a general correlation (valid for all solid fractions ranging from zero to unity) for the dissipative interfacial stress, $\mathbf{M}_s^d$, on the solid crystals has been obtained; i.e.,

$$\mathbf{M}_s^d = \varepsilon_f\, \beta^2 \frac{\mu_f}{R_e^2}\, \varepsilon_f(\mathbf{v}_f - \mathbf{v}_s) \qquad (37)$$

where β is a dimensionless parameter which is only a function of the particle volume fraction and its morphology and R_e is the envelope radius. The expression for β is given by

$$\beta = \frac{\beta_d}{[(1 - \varepsilon_l)^n + (\beta_d/\beta_l)^{2n}]^{1/2n}} \qquad (38)$$

where

$$\beta_d = \frac{3\sqrt{5}}{(1 - \varepsilon_{si})^{3/2}} \frac{S_s}{\phi_e S_e} \qquad (39)$$

$$\beta_l = \left\{\frac{9}{2}(1 - \varepsilon_l)\, \frac{2 + 4/3\eta^5}{2 - 3\eta + 3\eta^5 - 2\eta^6}\, \frac{1}{C_p(\phi_e)} \times \frac{2\beta_d^2 (1 - tanh\, \beta_d/\beta_d)}{2\beta_d^2 + 3(1 - tanh\, \beta_d/\beta_d)}\right\}^{1/2} \qquad (40)$$

$$n = 0.176 log\, \beta_d + 0.275 \qquad (41)$$

The function $C_p(\phi_e)$ accounts for the effect of an aspherical dendrite envelope, with ϕ_e being the sphericity of the dendrite envelope (de Groh et al., 1993; Wang and Beckermann, 1993a). The following expression for $C_p(\phi_e)$ has been proposed by Wang et al. (1994):

$$C_p(\phi_e) = \begin{cases} \phi_e^2 & \text{for } 0.7>\varepsilon_l>0.0 \\ 1.26 log_{10}(\frac{\phi_e}{0.163}) & \text{for } 1>\varepsilon_l>0.7 \end{cases} \qquad (42)$$

While other details on the drag model are available elsewhere (Wang et al., 1994), several salient features of the model are outlined here. First, note that this drag model accounts for the multiple length scales present in a dendritic structure, namely S_s and S_e (or R_e). Secondly, the drag model encompasses many important limiting cases, which include the single equiaxed dendrite (Ahuja, 1992; de Groh et al., 1993), and packed beds of impermeable and permeable spheres. Thirdly, the model has been validated against various experimental data available in the literature for both globular and dendritic crystals (Wang et al., 1994). In particular, it was found that this model improves the prediction of permeabilities of equiaxed dendritic structures due to its explicit consideration of multiple length scales. For spherical solid particles, this drag model reduces identically to the well known Stokes law for the drag coefficient in the free particle regime (Happel and Brenner, 1976), while it coincides with the Kozeny-Carman permeability relation in the packed bed regime.

3.3.5 Flow Partitioning between Inter- and Extra-dendritic Regions. In equiaxed solidification, it can be assumed that the flow partition coefficient is isotropic, so that only a single value of κ_v is required. It has been shown by Wang et al. (1994) that

$$\kappa_v = (1 - \varepsilon_l)(\beta/\beta_d)^2 \qquad (43)$$

where β and β_d are given by Eqs.(38) and (39). Figure 4 illustrates the effects of the extradendritic liquid fraction, ε_l, and internal solid fraction, ε_{si} (i.e., the ratio of the solid fraction to the grain fraction), on the flow partition coefficient in an equiaxed dendritic system with S_s/S_e=0.1. As can be seen, the portion of the flow through the dendrites approaches zero in the free particle regime (i.e. higher ε_l). On the other hand, in the packed bed regime, the flow partition coefficient quickly increases as ε_l decreases and reaches unity at ε_l=0, at which point all flow must be through the interdendritic spaces.

3.3.6 Interfacial Mass Transfer. By considering the diffusion process in the solid and the moving solid/liquid interface due to phase change, it has been shown by Wang and Beckermann (1993a) that the solid diffusion length l_{sd} in dendritic solidification is given by

$$l_{sd} = d_s/6 \qquad (44)$$

where the mean diameter of the solid phase, d_s, can be related to the secondary dendrite arm spacing, λ_2, and the volume fraction ε_s (see Table 3).

In the presence of convection, the diffusion length ahead of the dendrite envelope in equiaxed solidification can be expressed as (Wang, 1994):

$$\frac{d_e}{l_{ld}} = 2 + 0.865\left(\frac{C_\varepsilon}{\varepsilon_l}\right)^{1/3} Pe_\varepsilon^{1/3} \qquad (45)$$

where

$$Pe_\varepsilon = \frac{\varepsilon_l |v_l - v_s| d_e}{D_l} \qquad (46)$$

and

$$C_\varepsilon = \frac{2 + \frac{4}{3}(1-\varepsilon_l)^{5/3}}{2 - 3(1-\varepsilon_l)^{1/3} + 3(1-\varepsilon_l)^{5/3} - 2(1-\varepsilon_l)^2} \qquad (47)$$

This correlation is based on the momentum-mass transfer analogy, and is derived along the same lines as the interfacial drag expressions given by Eqs.(37-42). A comparison between this correlation and Agarwal's formula (1988), which was employed previously by Ni and Beckermann (1993), indicated a discrepancy of less than 20 percent for all solid fractions (Wang, 1994). In addition, it should be mentioned that the correlation given by Eqs.(45-47) neglects the effect of interfacial movement. This can be justified by the fact that in the presence of convection, the convection effect overrides that of interfacial movement in determining mass transfer rates.

3.3.7 Macroscopic Transport Properties. The effective macroscopic viscosities μ_s^* and μ_l^* represent the rheological behavior of a multiphase mixture. They are dependent on the viscous properties and deformations of the phases, the flow field, and the distribution and geometry of the dispersed or suspended phase. To a first approximation, the liquid macroscopic viscosity can be taken to be equal to its microscopic counterpart; i.e.,

$$\mu_l^* = \mu_l \qquad (48)$$

Modeling of the solid macroscopic viscosity is required only for equiaxed solidification systems, since in columnar solidification the solid crystals are attached to the wall and thus remain stationary. In the equiaxed situation, the packing limit must be taken into account where the grains impinge upon each other (i.e., when $\varepsilon_g=\varepsilon_g^c$) and form a coherent and rigid solid structure. In this limit, μ_s^* must approach an infinite value so that the macroscopic velocity gradients of the solid phase vanish. If the rigid solid is fixed to a wall, the solid velocity will then be uniformly equal to the velocity of the wall (which may be zero).

In the other extreme where $\varepsilon_g \to 0$, the seminal theory of Einstein predicts that $\mu_s^*=3.5\mu_l$ (Davis, 1993). In solidification systems where the grain fraction may vary anywhere from zero to unity, a smooth transition between these two limits is necessary. Like Ni and Beckermann (1993), we use the following formula for μ_s^*:

$$\mu_s^* = \frac{\mu_l}{\varepsilon_g}\left[(1 - \varepsilon_g/\varepsilon_g^c)^{-2.5\varepsilon_g^c} - (1 - \varepsilon_g)\right] \qquad (49)$$

Note that the right hand side of Eq.(49) reduces to 3.5 μ_l for $\varepsilon_g \to 0$ and to an infinite value for $\varepsilon_g \geq \varepsilon_g^c$. It should also be emphasized that for dendritic structures, the solid viscosity is not directly dependent on the solid fraction but rather on the grain fraction. In other words, as soon as the grain fraction reaches the packing limit (ε_g^c is about 0.637), the solid microstructure will already become rigid, even though the solid fraction may be much lower than ε_g^c. There has been ample experimental evidence to support this hypothesis. For example, experimental data for different alloys (Flemings, 1991; Arnberg et al., 1993) indicated that the packing limit could be reached at solid fractions between 0.1 and 0.3 in a large-grained casting where the grain fraction is much higher than the solid fraction. In contrast, in well-grain-refined castings, packing of dendrites was found to occur at much higher solid fractions between 0.5 and 0.65. This is because the grain fraction is nearly equal to the solid fraction for small grains.

As a first approximation, the macroscopic thermal conductivity and mass diffusivity are taken to be equal to their microscopic counterparts:

$$k_k^* = k_k\,; \quad D_k^* = D_k \qquad (50)$$

3.3.8 Thermodynamic Relations. Under the assumption of interfacial thermodynamic equilibrium, the following conditions are valid at the solid/interdendritic liquid interface:

$$\bar{C}_e = \frac{T - T_m}{m_l} \tag{51}$$

and

$$\bar{C}_{sd} = \begin{cases} \kappa\, \bar{C}_e & \text{during primary solidification} \\ C_s & \text{during remelting} \end{cases} \tag{52}$$

where it has been assumed that the remelting solid has a composition equal to the average concentration of the solid phase. The reader is urged to consult Wang (1994) for a more detailed discussion of remelting.

4. APPLICATION TO EQUIAXED DENDRITIC SOLIDIFICATION

In recent years, modeling of equiaxed dendritic solidification without convection has experienced considerable progress (Rappaz, 1989; Thevoz et al., 1989). Nucleation and growth kinetic laws have been coupled with transient heat conduction calculations to determine the solidification microstructure. However, modeling of equiaxed dendritic solidification with melt convection and solid movement has not been attempted largely because of the complications associated with the transport of free equiaxed crystals in the melt. The gravity-induced settling or floating of free crystals is fundamental to the development and extent of the equiaxed zone and also greatly affects the columnar to equiaxed transition (CET). Another possible effect of crystal sedimentation or floatation is to cause severe macrosegregation as well as structural inhomogeneities. The only study available in the literature that accounts for both liquid convection and solid transport is by Ni and Beckermann (1993) but deals with globulitic structures (as opposed to dendritic).

This section describes a first attempt towards predicting equiaxed dendritic microstructure in the presence of melt convection and solid movement using the foregoing model. The microstructural features of particular interest include the grain size and the internal solid fraction which is an index measuring how dendritic the grains are. In addition to this main objective, equiaxed dendritic solidification also represents a particularly useful case to fully demonstrate the predictive capabilities of the multiphase model proposed in Section 3. This is because in equiaxed solidification, grain nucleation and growth are strongly coupled to the macroscopic transport phenomena, including the crystal movement, and both have to be considered simultaneously.

4.1 System Description

The physical system considered in this illustrative application deals with solidification of an Al-4wt% Cu alloy in a two-dimensional rectangular cavity of width of 0.05 m and of height of 0.1 m, as shown in Fig.5. The melt has an initial temperature of 930 K (the superheat is about 10 K) and initial concentration of 4 percent of copper in weight. The walls are impermeable and adiabatic, except for the west wall which is subject to convective cooling for t>0. The coolant temperature is fixed at 293 K and the convective heat transfer coefficient between the coolant and the mold wall is chosen as 250 W/m^2K in all the simulations presented below. This set of parameters is representative of practical casting conditions, and falls into the range of equiaxed dendritic solidification in the diagram of Kurz and Fisher (1989).

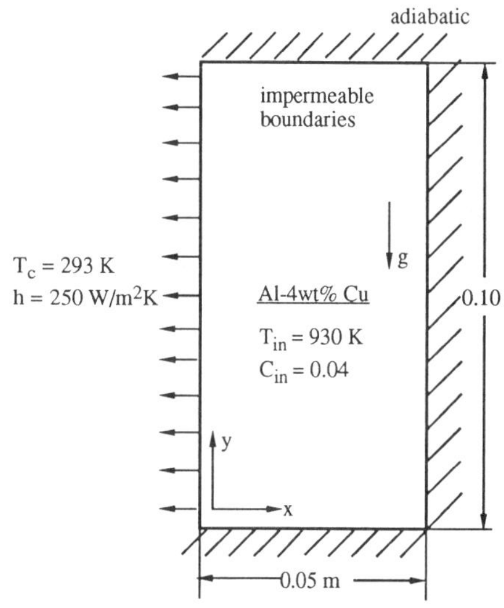

FIG.5 SCHEMATIC OF THE PHYSICAL SYSTEM.

The model equations together with the supplementary relations have been presented in Section 3. For the calculations presented in this section, it is further assumed that the densities of the solid and liquid phases are equal and constant, except for the ones in the buoyancy terms. Hence, volume contraction or expansion during solidification is neglected. For the buoyancy term in the liquid momentum equation, the liquid density is allowed to vary with the liquid temperature and species concentration, so that thermosolutal convection is fully considered. The relation between density, temperature and concentration for the liquid phase is taken from Ganesan and Poirier (1987), i.e.,

$$\rho_f = 1000\left[0.397 - 4.522\times10^{-3}C_f + 4.0924\times10^{-5}T + 1.1078\times10^{-6}C_fT + 2.7475\times10^{-5}C_f^2\right]^{-1} \tag{53}$$

where the temperature T is in °C and the concentration C_f in wt%, respectively. From Eq.(53), the ratio of solutal to thermal buoyancy can be estimated to be approximately 30. The positive value indicates that the solutal and thermal buoyancy forces in and near the mushy zone augment each other. The fact that the ratio is much larger than unity implies that the solutal buoyancy forces are dominant.

The solid density is approximately constant at a value of 2558 kg/m^3 (Ganesan and Poirier, 1987), which is larger than the liquid density at the initial composition. Hence, crystal sedimentation is expected during solidification.

The physical properties and empirical constants used in all simulations are summarized in Table 4, and the relevant metallurgical relations are shown in Table 5. Two very different nucleation rates (i.e., $n_o=10^9$ and 10^{11} m^{-3}) are chosen to cover a wide range of the resulting grain size as well as to examine various multiphase flow patterns. In the case of the low nucleation rate (i.e., $n_o=10^9$ m^{-3}), the grown crystals are large enough to cause significant relative motion between the liquid and solid. In the other extreme, the high nucleation rate (resulting in small crystals) leads to a highly dispersed flow of the solid.

Table 4 Thermophysical properties and empirical constants for Al-4wt% Cu alloy

Property data	
Density of the liquid phase, ρ_f (kg/m^3) (except in buoyancy term)	2450
Density of the solid phase, ρ_s (kg/m^3) (except in buoyancy term)	2450
Density of the solid phase in buoyancy term, (kg/m^3)	2558
Dynamic viscosity of the liquid phase μ_f ($N\text{-}s/m^2$)	0.0012
Thermal conductivity of the liquid phase, k_f (W/m-K)	77
Thermal conductivity of the solid phase, k_s (W/m-K)	153
Specific heat of the liquid phase, c_f (J/kg-K)	1179
Specific heat of the solid phase, c_s (J/kg-K)	766
Latent heat of fusion at T_E, Δh (J/kg)	3.97×10^5
Mass diffusivity of the liquid phase, D_l (m^2/s)	5.0×10^{-9}
Mass diffusivity of the solid phase, D_s (m^2/s)	8.0×10^{-13}
Segregation coefficient, κ	0.173
Eutectic temperature, T_E (K)	821.2
Eutectic concentration, C_E (wt% of Cu)	0.327
Melting temperature of Al, T_m (K)	933.5
Gibbs-Thomson coefficient, Γ (mK)	2.41×10^{-7}
Empirical Constants	
Maximum solid packing fraction, ε_g^c	0.637
Initial grain diameter, d_{si} (m)	10^{-6}
Dendrite sphericity, ϕ_e	1.0

The velocity boundary conditions are as follows. Because all walls are impermeable, the normal velocities of both the solid and liquid are equal to zero. The no-slip condition applies for the liquid tangential velocity. However, partial slip may occur for the solid at the wall if the diameter of the solid particles is larger than the length scale of the surface roughness (Ding and Gidaspow, 1990). Eldighidy et al. (1977) argued that the tangential velocity of the solid is proportional to its normal gradient at the wall; i.e.,

$$(v_s)_t|_w = -\lambda_p \frac{\partial (v_s)_t}{\partial n}|_w \tag{54}$$

where λ_p is the mean distance between particles. Ding and Gidaspow (1990) estimated λ_p by assuming that the particles are packed in a simple cubic structure. Hence

$$\lambda_p = \frac{d_e}{\varepsilon_g^{1/3}} \tag{55}$$

where d_e and ε_g are the grain diameter and grain fraction, respectively. Note that for small d_e, the slip coefficient λ_p approaches zero so that a no-slip condition for the grains results.

Table 5 Metallurgical relations used in simulations

Nucleation Model (see Section 3.3.2):

$\dot{n} = n_o\delta(T - T_N)$, where $T_N=T_L(C_f)$;

$n_o= 10^9$ (m^{-3}) in Cases I-III and 10^{11} (m^{-3}) in Case IV.

Grain Growth Model (see Section 3.3.3):

$$Pe_t = Iv^{-1}(\Omega) = a\left(\frac{\Omega}{1-\Omega}\right)^b$$

where

$a = 0.4567 + 0.173\ Pe_\infty^{0.55}$

$b= 1.195 - 0.145\ Pe_\infty^{0.16}$

Primary Dendrite Arm Spacing (Hunt, 1979):

$\lambda_1 = \{64\Gamma D_l m_l(1-\kappa)C_o\}^{1/4}G^{-1/2}V_t^{-1/4}$

Secondary Dendrite Arm Spacing (Jones, 1984):

$\lambda_2 = a\dot{T}^{-1/3}$, where $a = 50\ \mu m(K/s)^{1/3}$

4.2 Numerical Implementation

A control-volume based finite-difference method is employed to discretize the model equations presented in Table 2. In particular, a fully implicit multiple timestep scheme is employed to enable accurate simulation of both macroscopic transport behaviors and microstructural evolution, since they are associated with widely disparate time scales (Wang and Beckermann, 1994). Integration of the scheme into the control-volume method provides an efficient and stable numerical procedure. During the eutectic reaction, the temperature is fixed at the eutectic value, undercooling is neglected, and the solid fraction is backed out from the mixture energy equation. Other details of the numerical implementation of the multiphase model and several validation studies can be found in Wang (1994).

The computational domain is divided into a 40x40 grid. This mesh was selected based on a compromise between accuracy and computational time. Several preliminary calculations conducted for different meshes indicated that the 40x40 grid system is able to capture all solidification features at a reasonable computational cost, whereas coarser meshes were unable to reveal certain localized phenomena such as the formation of channel segregates. A uniform grid was chosen because the locations of strong gradients in the macroscopic variables are not known *a priori* .

Different time steps were used for various simulations to ensure that the sensitivity of the results to the time step is minimized in each case. In the first two cases to be described in the next section, a time step of 0.05 seconds was used although the time step for the first diffusion case could be larger. In the last two cases, a time step of 0.025 seconds was employed in the first half and doubled in the second half of the simulations. Iterations performed within each time step were terminated when changes in the overall species and energy balances fell below 0.001%. The calculations were performed on HP 715/50 and IBM 3090 computers, and each 1 s of real-time simulation required approximately 30, 360, 720 and 720 CPU seconds on the IBM 3090 computer for the first, second, third, and fourth cases, respectively.

5. RESULTS AND DISCUSSION

A total of four different simualtions were performed. With the same nucleation rate of $n_o=10^9$ m^{-3}, the first three cases examine the effects of melt convection and solid transport. In Case I, both melt convection and solid movement are neglected so that solidification is controlled solely by diffusion. In contrast, the second case includes the influence of melt convection while assuming a stationary solid, while the third case considers both melt convection and solid transport. Otherwise identical to Case III, the last case features a higher nucleation rate of $n_o=10^{11}$ m^{-3}. This case can be viewed to correspond to a grain-refined casting.

5.1 Case I: Diffusion-Controlled Solidification

This is a base case for all the following simulations including convection. In addition, this case is representative of a microgravity environment, where both liquid flow and solid movement diminish.

In the absence of flow, solidification occurs in a one-dimensional manner. The cooling curves and the solid and grain fraction evolutions at five different locations inside the casting are shown in Figs.6a and 6b, respectively. The x- and y-coordinates of the five locations are given in the figure captions. It can be seen from the inset of Fig.6a that the first cooling curve in the immediate neighborhood of the mold wall undergoes a marked recalescence period which is characteristic of equiaxed solidification. The other cooling curves corresponding to the interior of the casting, however, exhibit thermal plateaus because of decreased cooling rates. Between t=395 s and 402 s, the eutectic reaction occurs in the first computational cell. The simulation is terminated at t=402 s, since no interesting phenomena follow.

As can be seen from Fig.6b, the grain growth is rapid in the cell nearest to the cold wall where the cooling rate is the highest, but becomes slower inside the domain because of the lower cooling rates. Except for the first location, the grain fraction curves (dashed lines) merge to the solid fraction curves (solid lines) at certain intermediate times, implying that the grain growth thereafter occurs in a globulitic manner. This is because the extradendritic liquid is continuously enriched by the solute rejected during solidification, and consequently the undercooling, which drives the grain growth, diminishes.

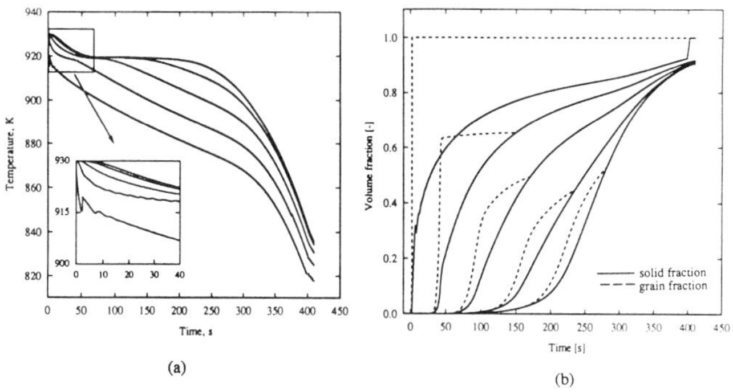

FIG.6 (a) COOLING CURVES AND (b) SOLID AND GRAIN FRACTION EVOLUTIONS IN DIFFUSION-CONTROLLED EQUIAXED DENDRITIC SOLIDIFICATION (Case I). THE CURVES FROM LEFT TO RIGHT CORRESPOND TO FIVE INTERIOR LOCATIONS OF THE CASTING WITH THE (x,y) COORDINATES BEING: (0.0625,1.25), (11.825,23.75), (24.375,48.75), (36.875,73.75) and (49.375,98.75) IN UNITS OF MM.

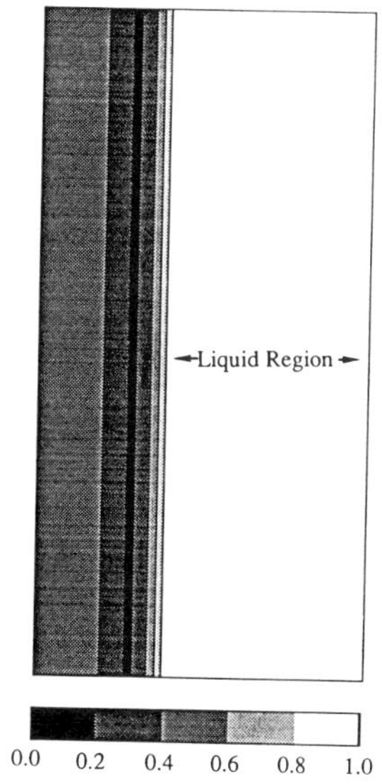

FIG.7 INTERNAL SOLID FRACTION DISTRIBUTION AT t=50 s FOR Case I.

For brevity, no distributions of temperature and solid fraction are presented here, except that Figure 7 illustrates the internal solid fraction distribution at t=50 s. The internal solid fraction is defined as the ratio of the solid fraction to the grain fraction and is thus a direct measure of the dendritic structure of the crystals. The lower the internal solid fraction, the more dendritic the equiaxed crystals are. An internal solid fraction of unity corresponds to a globulitic crystal. It can be found that the structure is most dendritic just behind the liquidus isotherm. This is because the mean concentration in the extradendritic liquid is still close to the initial concentration in that region, so that the undercooling in front of the dendrite tips is large. At the edge of the mushy zone, the tiny nuclei appear in a globulitic form so that the internal solid fraction is equal to unity. Deep within the mushy zone, significant solidification inside the grains results in a less dendritic structure, causing the internal solid fraction to approach unity.

5.2 Case II: Solidification with Melt Convection

In this case, the solid is still not allowed to move, implying that the equiaxed grains are fixed in space as soon as they nucleate. However, thermosolutal convection in the liquid melt is fully considered. For the alloy under consideration, the heavier copper is rejected during solidification, so that both solutal and thermal buoyancy forces cause a downward flow near the cold wall.

Figures 8a and 8b illustrate the cooling curves and solid and grain fraction evolutions at the same locations as in Case I. Again, a recalescence is clearly seen in the first cooling curve of Fig.8a for the same reason as explained earlier. Overall, the cooling curves are qualitatively similar to the ones in diffusion-dominated solidification, although the temperatures are different in magnitude. From Fig.8b, it can be seen that the equiaxed grains in the first cell undergo free growth, while the grain growth at the four internal locations slows down due to the increase in the concentration of the extradendritic liquid as solute-rich fluid is advected into these regions. Consequently, the grain fractions during solidification are lower in the interior of the casting.

The detailed time evolutions of the solidification and transport behaviors are documented in Wang (1994) and are not presented here for brevity. Only the final compositional and structural features of Case II are briefly discussed below. The shaded final macrosegregation plots shown in Fig.9 are of the mixture concentration, i.e.,

$$C_{mix} = \varepsilon_s C_s + \varepsilon_f C_f \tag{56}$$

with a single scale applied to all figures. The physical cause of macrosegregation is the movement of liquid relative to the solid phase during solidification.

Overall, the final macrosegregation shown in Fig.9a for Case II indicates positive segregation at the bottom of the cavity. This is at the expense of negatively segregated regions at the top and in the middle so that the global species balance is maintained. Several channel segregates can be observed. The solute-enriched fluid feeding a channel depresses the local liquidus temperature, thereby reducing the solidification rate and/or causing partial remelting. The channel in turn provides a preferred path for the downward flow of the solute-rich liquid. The presence of more solute-rich liquid in the channel reduces solidification further. The outcome of this runaway phenomenon is the formation of a channel segregate.

The present type of channel segregates has been previously observed in laboratory experiments using Al-Cu alloys (Mehrabian et al., 1970). A similar type, oriented in the

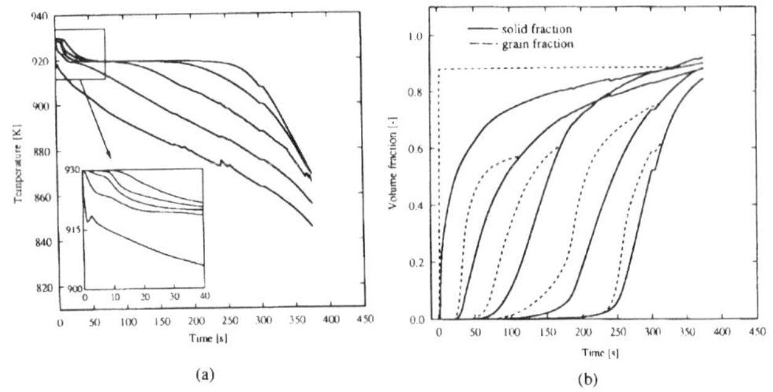

FIG.8 (a) COOLING CURVES AND (b) SOLID AND GRAIN FRACTION EVOLUTIONS IN EQUIAXED DENDRITIC SOLIDIFICATION WITH A STATIONARY SOLID (Case II) FOR THE SAME FIVE INTERIOR LOCATIONS AS IN FIG.6.

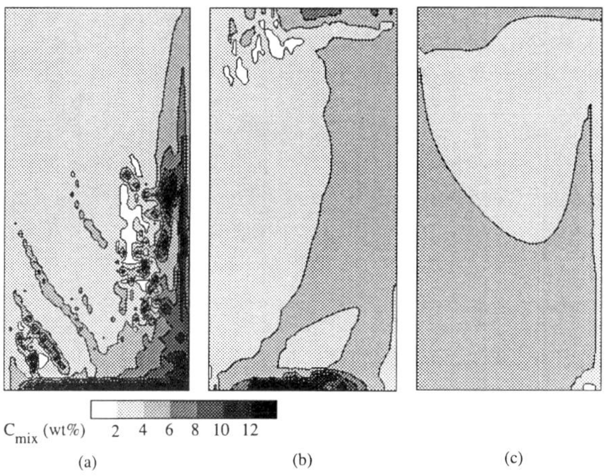

FIG.9 FINAL MACROSEGREGATION PATTERNS FOR Cases II-IV: (a) Case II (STATIONARY SOLID, $n_o=10^9$ m^{-3}), (b) Case III (MOVING SOLID, $n_o=10^9$ m^{-3}), and (c) Case IV (MOVING SOLID, $n_o=10^{11}$ m^{-3}).

opposite direction, located at the top of a casting, and called "A" segregates, has been widely predicted for other alloy systems (Bennon and Incropera, 1987; Fellicelli et al., 1991; Schneider and Beckermann, 1994). It is well established by experiments (e.g., Shaw et al., 1986) that the direction of channel segregates depends on the sign of the density change and hence the flow direction. In an alloy such as Al-4wt% Cu, the liquid flow is downwards and, hence, the positively segregated channels turn downwards, as predicted in the present study. In other systems such as H_2O-NH_4Cl and Pb-Sn alloys where the flow is upwards, the usual "A" segregates appear. Both types of segregates can be attributed to the same physical mechanisms. It must be cautioned that channels are three-dimensional in nature. Therefore, two-dimensional simulations may not be realistic.

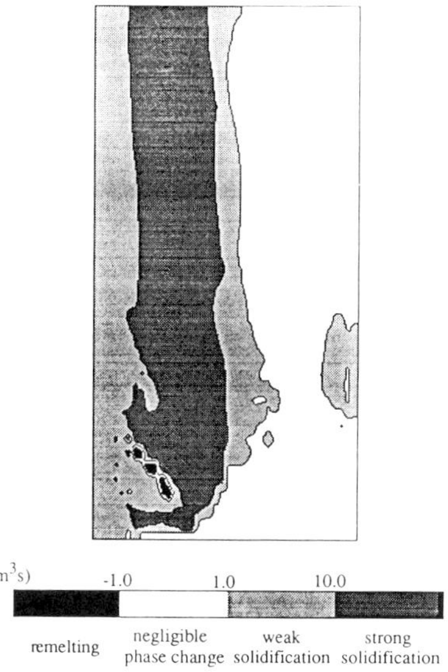

FIG.10 PREDICTED PHASE CHANGE RATE FOR Case II AT t=90 s SHOWING REMELTING INSIDE A SEGREGATED CHANNEL.

To understand the formation of channel segregates, much research has been conducted in the past three decades (Hellawell et al., 1993). Most previous work speculates that localized remelting is a major mechanism for channel formation. However, conclusive experimental evidence for metal alloys is still lacking due to the extreme difficulty in forecasting the channel locations, arranging proper measurements before the channels start to develop, and finally determining the phase change rate inside these tiny channels. In order to study the channel formation in more detail, Fig.10 shows the phase change rate at t=90 s. It can be seen that remelting occurs nowhere but inside the second channel from the bottom (corresponding to Fig.9a). This evidence indicates, at least theoretically, that the formation of channel segregates is accompanied by localized remelting. Nonetheless, remelting may not be a necessary condition for the initiation of channel segregates. It would be of interest to see whether remelting also occurs in the channel segregates predicted elsewhere (Bennon and Incropera, 1987; Felicelli et al., 1991; Schneider and Beckermann, 1994).

In the absence of solid transport, the final grain size distribution in Case II is determined solely by nucleation, and hence remains uniform at a radius of 0.62 mm corresponding to $n_o=10^9$ (m^{-3}).

5.3 Case III: Solidification with Melt Convection and Solid Movement

This case features both liquid and solid motion, thus requiring the full multiphase model proposed in the preceding section. The predicted cooling curves and the solid and grain fraction evolutions are shown in Figs.11a and 11b, respectively. They should be compared to Figs.6a and 6b for the diffusion case and Figs.8a and 8b for the case with a stationary solid. While the cooling curves strongly resemble those for Cases I and II, the solid and grain fraction evolutions have a distinctive feature: oscillating solid and grain fractions occur at certain times at the internal locations. Furthermore, it can be noticed that both fractions oscillate in phase. This is obviously due to the grain movement, and no oscillations appear after the grain fraction reaches the packing limit.

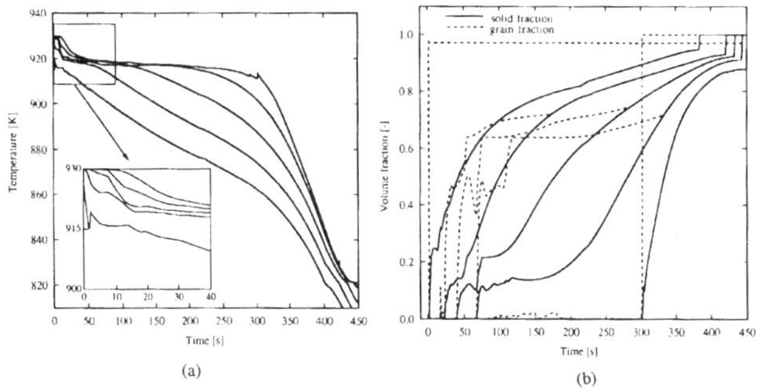

FIG.11 (a) COOLING CURVES AND (b) SOLID AND GRAIN FRACTION EVOLUTIONS IN EQUIAXED DENDRITIC SOLIDIFICATION WITH MELT CONVECTION AND SOLID MOVEMENT (Case III) FOR THE SAME INTERIOR LOCATIONS AS IN FIG.6.

Figures 12 to 15 show the solidification and transport behaviors at times t=10, 50, 150 and 350 s, respectively. These figures include the solid fraction, liquid velocity, mixture concentration, temperature, and relative velocity distributions. The liquid velocity vector plots are superimposed on the solid fraction images, with a velocity scale shown below each plot. For clarity, the velocity vectors are interpolated to a coarser grid than used in the computations. The solid fraction images are produced using a continuous spectrum of gray scales. The isotherms are in equal increments. The relative velocity vectors, $\mathbf{v}_f - \mathbf{v}_s$, are also displayed to illustrate the movement of the liquid relative to the solid. Note that for a stationary solid (i.e., $\mathbf{v}_s=0$), the relative velocity simply represents the liquid velocity through the packed crystal bed.

5.3.1 Early Stages of Solidification. At an early stage of solidification (i.e., t=10 s), the liquid flow field (Fig.12a) consists of a single counterclockwise rotating convection cell. The liquid flow in this case is not only driven by thermosolutal convection but also by the sedimentation of the forming solid. The downward flow of the solid adjacent to the cold wall, due to its higher density than the liquid, exerts a large interfacial drag on the liquid and pulls the liquid

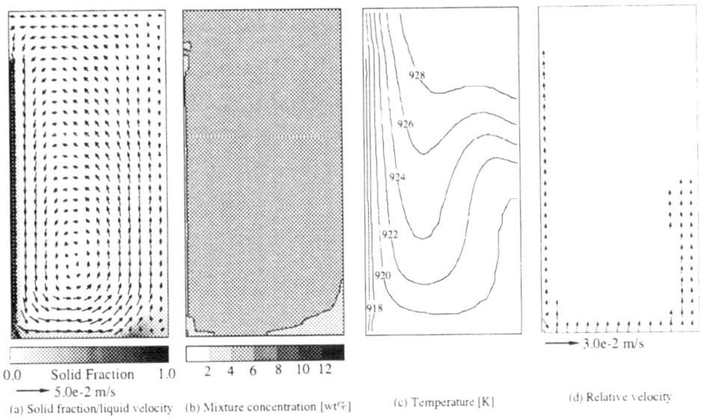

FIG.12 RESULTS FOR Case III AT t=10 s: (a) sOLID FRACTION AND LIQUID VELOCITY VECTORS; (b) MIXTURE CONCENTRATION; (c) ISOTHERMS, AND (d) RELATIVE VELOCITY VECTORS ($\mathbf{v}_f$ - $\mathbf{v}_s$).

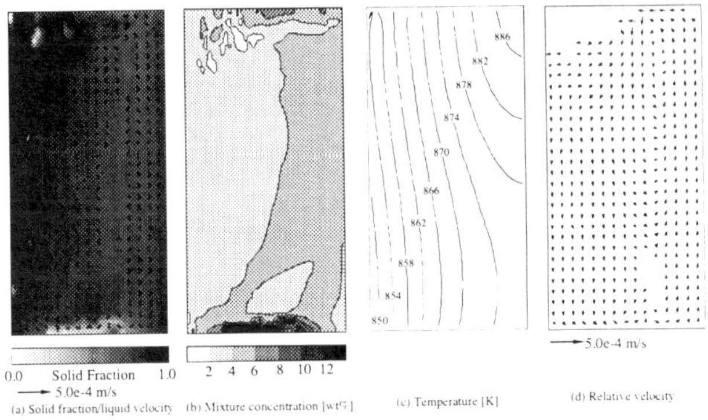

FIG.15 RESULTS FOR Case III AT t=350 s: (a) SOLID FRACTION AND LIQUID VELOCITY VECTORS; (b) MIXTURE CONCENTRATION; (c) ISOTHERMS, AND (d) RELATIVE VELOCITY VECTORS ($\mathbf{v}_f$ - $\mathbf{v}_s$).

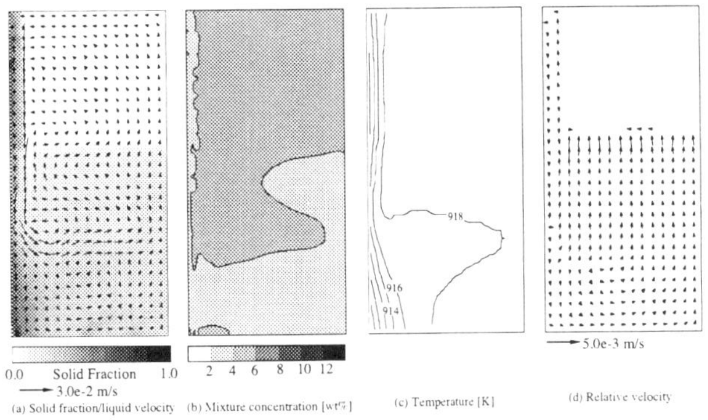

FIG.13 RESULTS FOR Case III AT t=50 s: (a) SOLID FRACTION AND LIQUID VELOCITY VECTORS; (b) MIXTURE CONCENTRATION; (c) ISOTHERMS, AND (d) RELATIVE VELOCITY VECTORS ($\mathbf{v}_f$ - $\mathbf{v}_s$).

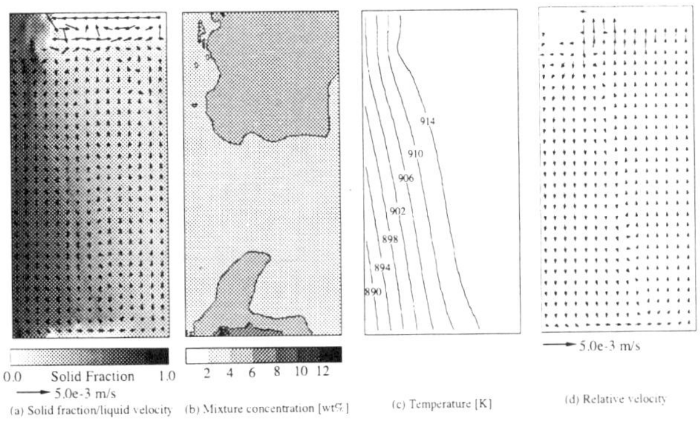

FIG.14 RESULTS FOR Case III AT t=150 s: (a) SOLID FRACTION AND LIQUID VELOCITY VECTORS; (b) MIXTURE CONCENTRATION; (c) ISOTHERMS, AND (d) RELATIVE VELOCITY VECTORS ($\mathbf{v}_f$ - $\mathbf{v}_s$).

downwards. This sedimentation-driven liquid flow further augments the thermal and solutal buoyancy forces in the liquid. Convection driven by sedimentation has been little researched in the thermo/fluids area and deserves more attention.

The solid fraction distribution shown in Fig.12a indicates that some solid crystals, that nucleated and grew along the left cold wall, are swept by the liquid flow into the superheated region near the right wall. The mixture concentration plot shown in Fig.12b also illustrates this trend, since negative segregation associated with the initially forming solid appears in the lower-right corner. The isotherms shown in Fig.12c greatly deviate from the vertical due to convection effects.

The relative velocities shown in Fig.12d are mostly upward, demonstrating that the downward component of the solid velocity is larger than the one of the liquid. This is a direct evidence of crystal sedimentation. In the bulk liquid region, the small nuclei cause such a large interfacial drag that the relative velocity vanishes.

Results at t=50 s (Fig.13) show an extensive mushy zone forming in the lower portion of the cavity. A crystal sediment bed appears, implying that sedimentation is a dominant phenomenon in equiaxed solidification, especially for the low grain density (i.e., $n_o=10^9$ m^{-3}) and, hence, large crystal sizes in the present case. In the bottom fourth of the cavity, a coherent and dense network of dendrites forms, which forces the liquid flow to bypass it. Above this bottom packed bed, the multiphase flow in the mushy zone and the pure liquid flow near the top strongly interact with each other.

The region of negative segregation further penetrates into the domain in the direction of the solid motion, as can be seen from Fig.13b. The negative segregation is strongest at the bottom where the solute-poor crystals have settled. The isotherm plot in Fig.13c shows an interesting feature: the lower-right corner below the 918 K isotherm is as warm as the upper portion of the cavity. This is a direct consequence of solid motion, which shifts the locations where solidification occurs. With a high solidification rate in the lower portion as a result of crystal sedimentation, a significant amount of latent heat is released keeping the local temperature high.

The relative velocities shown in Fig.13d are still mostly upward, particularly in the regions above the bottom packed bed. Inside the packed bed, where the grain fraction is greater than the packing limit, the crystals do not move, and thus the relative velocity vectors reflect the liquid velocity only. A weak liquid recirculation is seen inside this packed bed.

5.3.2 Intermediate Stages of Solidification. Simulation results at an intermediate stage of solidification are shown in Fig.14 for t=150 s. Figure 14a shows that only a thin liquid layer exists in the upper-right-hand corner. However, at the bottom of the cavity, a small region with a lower gray level can be observed, implying that the solid fraction there has decreased. The cause of this remelting phenomenon can be inferred from Fig.14b which shows a high copper concentration at the same location. Even after the formation of the packed bed, the solute-rich liquid continues to flow downwards and collect at the bottom due to its high density. This liquid greatly depresses the liquidus temperature and even causes remelting of the solid that settled there at an earlier time.

The isotherms bend towards the right side on the bottom (Fig.14c). The relative velocity distribution shown in Fig.14d has a qualitatively similar pattern as before.

5.3.3 Later Stages of Solidification. At a later stage of solidification (t=350 s, Fig.15), the bottom remelt zone is still visible despite the fact that it has begun to resolidify. In addition, the upper thin liquid layer has solidified appreciably. Overall, higher solid fractions prevail throughout the mushy zone, so that the liquid velocity is drastically reduced. Although the convection is weakened at this stage of solidification, the isotherms remain curved (Fig.15c). The relative velocity distribution shown in Fig.15d indicates no significant sedimentation of crystals occurring at this stage of solidification.

The macrosegregation pattern remains almost unchanged (Fig.15b). Negative segregation appears in the left half of the cavity where solidification is the fastest. The right half of the cavity is more positively segregated due to the advection of solute-rich liquid into this region. Another striking pattern is the bottom positive segregation, which is caused by the deposition of solute-rich liquid at the bottom, as discussed earlier.

5.3.4 Final Macrosegregation and Eutectic Distribution. As compared to the macrosegregation pattern shown in Fig.9a for Case II, the final macrosegregation pattern shown in Fig.9b for Case III has several distinctive features. First, macrosegregation is overall less severe. This is because the solute-rich liquid and the solute-poor solid flow simultaneously downwards. Hence the macrosegregation due to relative phase motion is reduced. Secondly, no channel segregates are observed in Case III. This can also be attributed to solid movement, since the nonuniformities in the solid fraction associated with such channels are readily equalized by the mobile crystals.

It should be cautioned however that solid movement does not always result in a more uniform composition on the system scale. Other alloy systems exist, in which the solute-rich liquid flows upwards and the solid settles down, so that the solute-rich liquid will be separated from the solute-poor solid. This would cause very severe macrosegregation. More simulations should be conducted to capture these and other macrosegregation patterns.

Consistent with the macrosegregation pattern, the final eutectic fraction distribution displayed in Fig.16a for Case III indicates a significant amount of eutectic at the bottom, whereas nearly no eutectic phase is present in the upper-left corner.

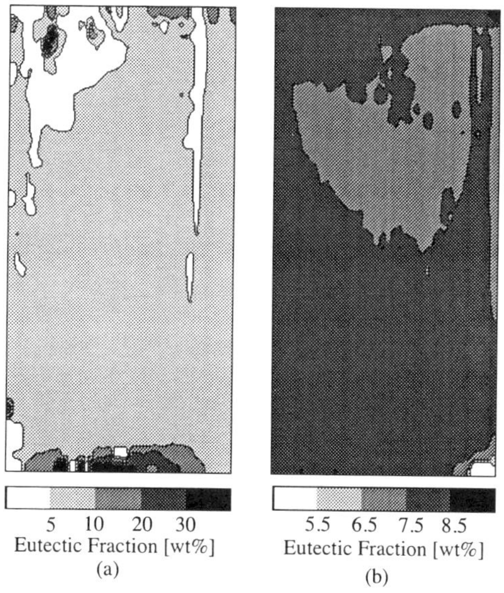

FIG.16 EUTECTIC FRACTION DISTRIBUTIONS IN: (a) Case III AND (b) Case IV.

5.3.5 Microstructure. The nature of the dendritic structure of the equiaxed crystals evolving during solidification can be deduced from Fig.17, where the internal solid fraction distribution is plotted for different times. Similar to diffusion-dominated solidification, highly dendritic structures always appear just behind the liquidus front where equiaxed crystals undergo free growth (Fig.17a). After the grains grow to a sufficiently large size, they impinge upon each other, whereas the dendrite arms keep thickening due to solidification. Therefore, the internal solid fraction is close to unity near the cold wall (Fig.17b). At t = 250 s, isolated

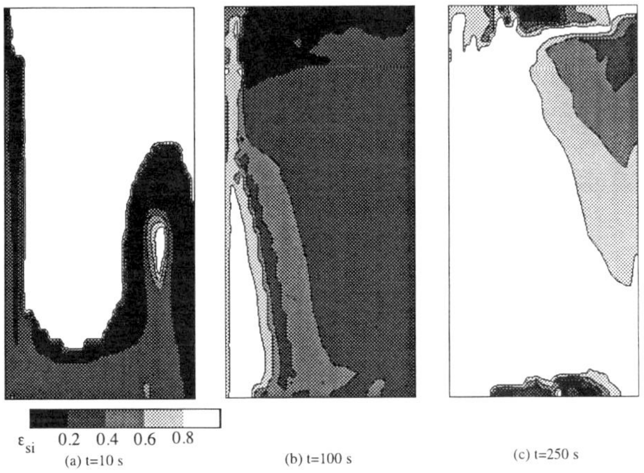

FIG.17 PREDICTED INTERNAL SOLID FRACTION FOR Case III AT: (a) t=10 s; (b) t=100 s, AND (c) t=250 s.

highly dendritic structures can be observed both at the very top and bottom of the cavity, as shown in Fig.17c.

Another interesting microstructural parameter is the grain density, or equivalently, grain size. In Case III, the local grain density is not only determined by the nucleation rate, but also influenced by the solid motion during solidification. The advection of solid will cause a redistribution of the grains, in addition to influencing the nucleation process itself.

Figure 18 illustrates the evolution of the grain density. It can be seen from Fig.18a that a stream of highly concentrated nuclei is swept into the central part of the cavity. Notice that at this time (i.e., t=10 s), the solid motion is extremely strong due to the small size of the nuclei and the vigorous liquid flow. At t=30 s (Fig.18b), the crystals lifted by the liquid flow along the right wall begin to re-settle along the left wall. In addition, a central region of lower grain density appears. This is because the crystals in this region grew to such a large size that they settled down. The grains present in the upper region of the cavity are, however, too small to settle, so that the grain density remains high. This effect becomes more evident in Fig.18c, which shows that the relatively sharp and horizontal interface between the regions of high and low grain densities coincides with the interface between the crystal sediment bed and the nearly solid-free liquid region (see Fig.13a). At t=100 s (Fig.18d), the zone of low grain density is shifted upwards as the sediment bed increased in height.

The grain density ceases to evolve at about 350 seconds, Fig.18e. At this time, the nucleation process is completed throughout the domain and solid movement is absent as the grains impinge upon one another. The top zone of low grain density can be attributed to the sedimentation effect. In addition, it can be seen that a small region at the bottom appears where the grain density is also low. This is mainly caused by the remelting phenomenon explained earlier, which kills a number of grains in this region.

The corresponding final grain size distribution for Case III is shown in Fig.19a. Fine grains of about 0.62 mm in size (i.e., radius) are found mostly in the lower-middle portion of the cavity. Crystals with a size larger than 2 mm are located at the top of the cavity, due to crystal sedimentation, as well as at the very bottom as a result of remelting.

5.4 Case IV: Solidification with a High Nucleation Rate

Based on Case III, it is of interest to further explore the solidification and transport behaviors when the nucleation rate is raised from 10^9 to 10^{11} (m^{-3}). Two significant consequences are associated with higher nucleation rates and therefore smaller grains: (i) the equiaxed crystals tend to grow in a more globulitic fashion, and (ii) there is less relative motion between the solid and liquid phases due to the larger interfacial drag.

The first consequence can readily be seen from Fig.20. The grain fractions at some internal locations evolve closely with the solid fractions, implying that the internal solid fraction is closer to unity when compared to Cases II and III (compare Figs.20b, 8b and 11b). This is a clear indication of globulitic solidification, as maybe expected in grain-refined castings. The oscillations in the solid and grain fractions for Case IV are similar to Case III, again because of solid motion. Another fact noticed in Fig.20b is that crystal impingement (where ε_g=0.637) is significantly delayed in solidification with a high nucleation rate (Case IV) when compared to solidification with a low nucleation rate (Case III). This has a profound effect on the multiphase flow patterns during solidification. The recalescence shown in the inset of Fig.20a is also less pronounced than in Figs.8a and 11a for Cases II and III, respectively.

The reduced slip velocity between the liquid and solid phases in Case IV can be observed by comparing the magnitudes of the relative velocity. In Case III, the difference between the solid and liquid velocities is of the order of 5 mm/s, whereas in Case IV this value is reduced to 1 mm/s. The lower settling velocity of the solid combined with the delayed packing in Case IV promotes vigorous advection of the solid inside the cavity. Ultimately, this leads to much more homogeneous compositional and structural distributions in the final casting. Figure 9c demonstrates a relatively uniform final macrosegregation pattern, and Fig.16b accordingly shows a more uniform distribution of the eutectic phase. To help in understanding how a homogeneous grain size distribution results from the highly dispersed flow of the solid crystals, Fig.21 displays the evolution of the grain density in Case IV. At t=10 s (Fig.21a), a stream of high nuclei density, originating near the cold left wall, is circulating into the center of the cavity. This stream of nuclei is seen to descend along the left wall and arrive at the bottom at t=30 s (Fig.21b).

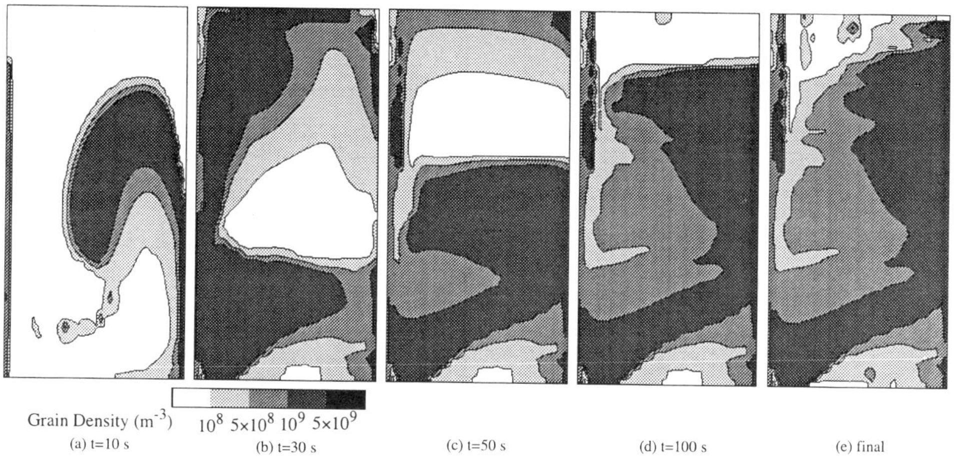

FIG.18 EVOLUTION OF THE GRAIN DENSITY FOR Case III AT: (a) t=10 s; (b) t=30 s; (c) t=50 s; (d) t=100 s, AND (e) FINAL.

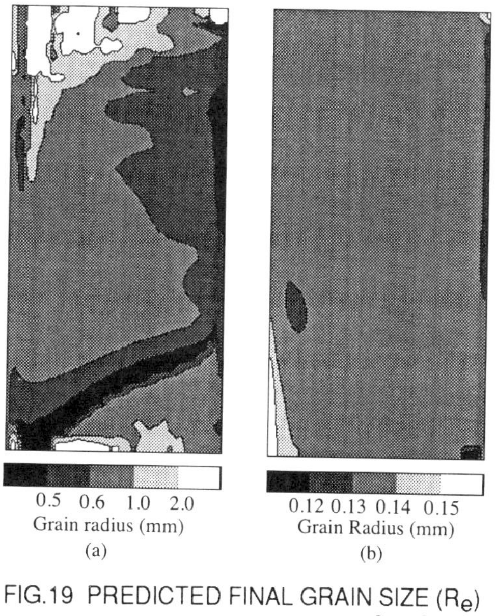

FIG.19 PREDICTED FINAL GRAIN SIZE (R_e) DISTRIBUTION FOR (a) Case III: $n_o=10^9$ m^{-3}, AND (b) Case IV: $n_o=10^{11}$ m^{-3}.

Because the small size of the crystals prevents their deposition at the bottom, the circulation of the solid inside the cavity continues (Figs.21c and 21d). At about t=350 s (Fig.21e), the final grain density pattern is reached. The grain density throughout most of the cavity varies only over a narrow range (between 0.75 and 1.25×10^{11} m^{-3}). The corresponding final grain size distribution is also uniform over the entire cavity, as shown in Fig.19b.

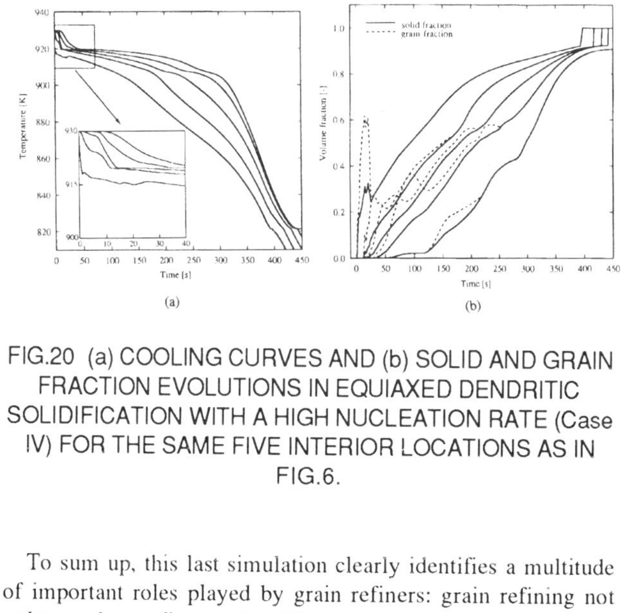

FIG.20 (a) COOLING CURVES AND (b) SOLID AND GRAIN FRACTION EVOLUTIONS IN EQUIAXED DENDRITIC SOLIDIFICATION WITH A HIGH NUCLEATION RATE (Case IV) FOR THE SAME FIVE INTERIOR LOCATIONS AS IN FIG.6.

To sum up, this last simulation clearly identifies a multitude of important roles played by grain refiners: grain refining not only produces fine and uniform grain structures, but also reduces the severity of the macrosegregation by promoting solid motion together with melt convection during most of the solidification process.

6. CONCLUSIONS

A multi-scale/-phase approach to the modeling of dendritic alloy solidification is proposed in this article. The macroscopic transport equations are developed separately for the solid, the interdendritic and extradendritic liquid phases

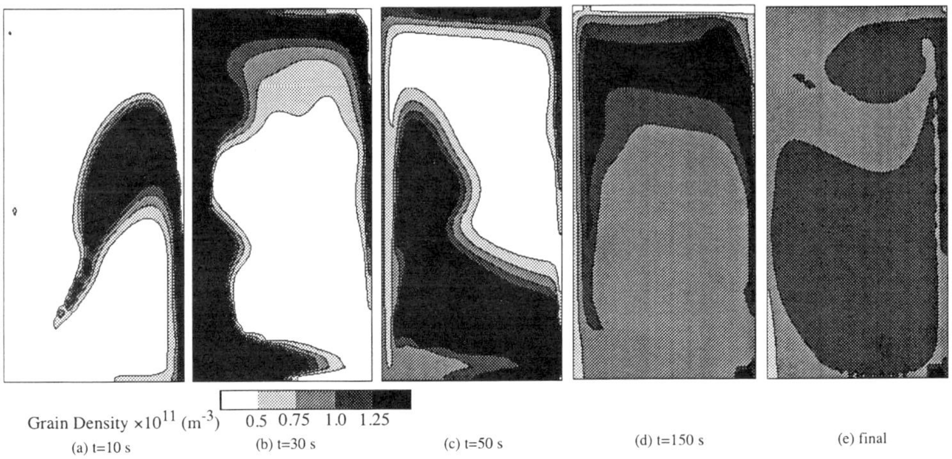

FIG.21 EVOLUTION OF THE GRAIN DENSITY FOR Case IV AT: (a) t=10 s; (b) t=30 s; (c) t=50 s; (d) t=150 s, AND (e) FINAL.

using the technique of volume averaging. The model distinguishes different microscopic length scales present in a dendritic structure, and rigorously links the microscopic phenomena occurring on each length scale to the heat flow, solute redistribution, melt convection, and solid movement taking place on the macroscopic (system) scale. In particular, the model incorporates grain nucleation and growth, as well as accounts for dendrite geometry, coarsening and finite-rate solute diffusion in the solid. The model is capable of predicting compositional and structural features on the system scale. A detailed numerical study of two-dimensional equiaxed dendritic solidification of an Al-4wt% Cu alloy revealed the following:

(1) Through comparisons among four different cases, it is shown how severe compositional and structural inhomogeneities in a casting can be caused by gravity-induced melt convection and solid movement.

(2) As demonstrated in Case II, channel segregates may arise from thermosolutal convection within a stationary mushy zone. In the Al-Cu alloy, the channels are oriented downwards as observed previously in laboratory experiments. This study also provides evidence that remelting is associated with the formation of channel segregates.

(3) As shown in Case III, solid movement reduces macrosegregation. This is because of the co-current flow of solute-rich liquid and solute-poor solid in the present system. The effect of solid transport becomes even more obvious in Case IV where the small crystals closely follow the liquid flow. However, to fully assess the effect of solid transport on macrosegregation, future research is needed to study other alloy systems in which the solute-rich liquid tends to separate from the solute-poor solid (i.e., counter-current liquid-solid flow).

(4) The predicted grain size distributions for Cases III and IV clearly demonstrate that there exists no one-to-one correspondence between the nucleation rate and the local grain size whenever solid motion is present. Hence, the final grain size, which is routinely measured from micrographs of solidified materials, cannot be directly used to infer the nucleation rate, because the grain density distribution may be altered by flow during solidification. However, the knowledge of the measured final grain size, combined with the prediction of solid transport as shown in this study, would enable the development of a realistic nucleation model. Herein lies an important practical significance of the present numerical study.

(5) Promotion of solid motion together with liquid flow is shown to provide an effective means of controlling the structure and chemical homogeneity of a casting. Although this is a well-known fact in practice, the present model simulations reveal for the first time the detailed transport mechanisms responsible for the formation of a variety of inhomogeneities. Nonetheless, thorough experimental validation is required before the model can be applied with confidence.

ACKNOWLEDGEMENTS

This work was supported by the National Aeronautics and Space Administration under Grant No. NCC3-290 and the ALCOA Technical Center, Alcoa Center, PA. The authors would like to thank Mr. C. Fan for his help in the numerical simulations.

REFERENCES

Adler, P.M., 1981, "Streamlines in and around Porous Particles," *J. Coll. Int. Sci.*, Vol.81, pp.531-535.

Agarwal, P.K., 1988, "Transport Phenomena in Multi-Particle Systems -- II. Particle-Fluid Heat and Mass Transfer," *Chem. Sci. Eng.*, Vol.43, pp.2501-2510.

Ahuja, S., 1992, "Solid/Liquid Interfacial Drag in Equiaxed Solidification," *M.S.M.E. Thesis*, The University of Iowa, Iowa City.

Ananth, R. and Gill, W.N., 1991, "Self-Consistent Theory of Dendritic Growth with Convection," *J. Crystal Growth*, Vol.108, pp.173-189.

Arnberg, L., Chai, G. and Backerud, L., 1993, "Determination of Dendritic Coherency in Solidifying Melts by Rheological Measurements," *Mat. Sci. Eng.*, Vol.A173, pp.101-103.

Bennon, W.D. and Incropera, F.P., 1987, "The Evolution of Macrosegregation in Statically Cast Binary Ingots," *Metall. Trans. B*, Vol.18B, pp.611-616.

Carman, P.C., 1956, *Flow of Gases through Porous Media*, Butterworth Scientific, London.

Davis, R.H., 1993, "Microhydrodynamics of Particulate Suspensions," *Adv. in Coll. Int. Sci.*, Vol.43, pp.17-50.

de Groh III, H.C., Weidman, P.D., Zakhem, R., Ahuja, S. and Beckermann, C., 1993, "Calculation of Dendrite Settling Velocity Using a Porous Envelope," *Metall. Trans. B*, Vol.24B, pp.749-753.

Ding, J. and Gidaspow, D., 1990, "A Bubble Fluidization Model Using Kinetic Theory of Granular Flow," *AIChE J.*, Vol.36, pp.523-538.

Drew, D.A., 1983, "Mathematical Modeling of Two-Phase Flow," *Ann. Rev. Fluid Mech.*, Vol.15, pp.261-291.

Eldighidy, S.M., Chen, R.Y. and Comparin, R.A., 1977, "Deposition of Suspensions in the Entrance of a Channel," *ASME J. Fluid Eng.*, Vol.99, pp.365-370.

Felicelli, S.D., Heinrich, J.C. and Poirier, D.R., 1991, "Simulation of Freckles during Vertical Solidification of Binary Alloys," *Metall. Trans. B*, Vol.22B, pp.847-859.

Flemings, M.C., 1974, *Solidification Processing*, McGraw-Hill, New York, NY.

Flemings, M.C., 1991, "Behaviors of Metal Alloys in the Semi-Solid State," *Metall. Trans. A*, Vol.22A, pp.957-981.

Ganesan, S. and Poirier, D.R., 1987, "Densities of Aluminum-Rich Aluminum-Copper Alloys during Solidification," *Metall. Trans. A*, Vol.18A, pp.721-723.

Happel, J. and Brenner, H., 1976, *Low Reynolds Number Hydrodynamics*, Noordhoff International Publishing.

Hellawell, A., Sarazin, J.R. and Stuebe, R.S., 1993, "Channel Convection in Partly Solidified Systems," *Phil. Trans. R. Soc. Lond. A*, Vol.345, pp.507-544.

Huang, S.C. and Glicksman, M.E., 1981, "Fundamentals of Dendritic Solidification -- I. Steady-State Tip Growth," *Acta Metall.*, Vol.29, pp.701-715.

Hunt, J.D., 1979, *Solidification and Casting of Metals*, Metal Society, London, pp.1-9.

Jones, H., 1984, "Microstructure of Rapidly Solidified Materials," *Mat. Sci. and Eng.*, Vol.65, pp.145-156.

Kurz, W. and Fisher, D.J., 1989, *Fundamentals of Solidification*, Trans Tech Publications, Aedermannsdorf, Switzerland.

Lipton, J., Glicksman, M.E. and Kurz, W., 1984, "Dendritic Growth into Undercooled Alloy Melts," *Mater. Sci. and Eng.*, Vol.65, pp.57-63.

Mehrabian, R., Keane, M.A. and Flemings, M.C., 1970, "Experiments on Macrosegregation and Freckle Formation," *Metall. Trans.*, Vol.1, pp.3238-3241.

Ni, J. and Beckermann, C., 1991, "A Volume-Averaged Two-Phase Model for Transport Phenomena during Solidification," *Metall. Trans. B*, Vol.22B, pp.349-361.

Ni, J. and Beckermann, C., 1993, "Modeling of Globulitic Alloy Solidification with Convection," *J. Materals Processing & Manufacturing Science*, Vol.2, pp.217-231.

Rappaz, M., 1989, "Modeling of Microstructure Fromation in Solidification Processes," *Int. Mater. Rev.*, Vol.34, pp.93-123.

Piwonka, T.S., Voller, V.R. and Kategerman, L., 1993, *Modeling of Casting, Welding and Advanced Solidification Processes VI*, TMS, Warrendale, Pennsylvania.

Schneider, M.C. and Beckermann, C., 1994, "A Numerical Study of the Combined Effects of Microsegregation, Mushy Zone Permeability, and Contraction Driven Flow on Macrosegregation and Eutectic Formation in Binary Alloy Solidification," *Int. J. Heat Mass Transfer*, submitted for publication.

Shaw, L.H., Beech, J. and Hickley, R.H., 1986, "Channel Segregation in Cast Steel Rolls," *Ironmaking and Steelmaking*, Vol.3, pp.154-160.

Stefanescu, D.M., Upadhya, G. and Bandyopahyoy, D., 1990, "Heat Transfer-Solidification Kinetics Modeling of Solidification of Castings," *Metall. Trans. A*, Vol.21A, pp.997-1005.

Thevoz, Ph., Desbiolles, J.L. and Rappaz, M., 1989, "Modeling of Equiaxed Microstructure Formation in Casting," *Metall. Trans. A*, Vol.20A, pp.311-322.

Voller, V.R., Stachowicz, M.S. and Thomas, B.G., 1991, *Materials Processing in the Computer Age*, Publication of TMS, Warrendale, Pennsylvania.

Wang, C.Y., 1994, "Multi-Scale/-Phase Modeling of Dendritic Alloy Solidification," *Ph.D Thesis*, The University of Iowa, Iowa City.

Wang, C.Y., Ahuja, S., Beckermann, C. and de Groh III, H.C., 1994, "Multiparticle Interfacial Drag in Equiaxed Solidification," *Metall. Mater. Trans. B*, in press.

Wang, C.Y. and Beckermann, C., 1992, "A Multiphase Micro-Macroscopic Model of Solute Diffusion in Dendritic Alloy Solidification," in *Micro/Macro Scale Phenomena in Solidification*, eds. by C. Beckermann et al., ASME HTD-Vol.218/AMD-Vol.139, pp.43-57, ASME, New York.

Wang, C.Y. and Beckermann, C., 1993a, "A Multiphase Solute Diffusion Model for Dendritic Alloy Solidification," *Metall. Trans. A*, Vol.24A, pp.2787-2802.

Wang, C.Y. and Beckermann, C., 1993b, "A Unified Solute Diffusion Model for Columnar and Equiaxed Dendritic Alloy Solidification," *Mater. Sci. and Eng. A*, Vol.A171, pp.199-211.

Wang, C.Y. and Beckermann, C., 1994, "Prediction of Columnar to Equiaxed Transition during Diffusion-Controlled Dendritic Alloy Solidification," *Metall. Mater. Trans. A*, Vol.25A, pp.1081-1093.

HTD-Vol. 284/AMD-Vol. 182, Transport Phenomena in Solidification
ASME 1994

MACRO/MICRO MODELING OF MELT FLOW AND MICROSTRUCTURE FORMATION DURING CONTINUOUS CASTING

Ben Q. Li
Department of Mechanical Engineering
Louisiana State University
Baton Rouge, Louisiana

Prince N. Anyalebechi
Alcoa Technical Center
Alcoa Center, Pennsylvania

ABSTRACT

An integrated approach is presented to model the evolution of fluid flow, temperature distribution and equi-axed grain structure formation in continuous casting of aluminum. In this approach, the dynamic development of fluid flow and thermal fields during the start-up phase of the casting operation is modeled using the deforming finite element method, coupled with an Lagrangian-Eulerian formulation. The micro solidification events, that is, nucleation and grain growth, are modeled by a micro kinetic model. The coupling of the fluid flow and thermal calculations and the micro model is made possible through an iterative micro/macro iterative time step scheme. The model is applied to study the dynamic phenomena during the starting phase of continuous casting. Numerical results for the transient evolution of fluid flow and temperature fields and the average grain size distribution are presented. The results are compared with experimental measurements, and reasonably good agreement is obtained.

NOMENCLATURE

C_p	specific heat
H	latent heat
f	solid fraction
$\vec{g}$	gravity vector
k	thermal conductivity
k_b	Boltzmann constant
K	empirical constant in grain growth rate expression
L(t)	ingot length at time t
L_d	length of the mold
L_r	radius of ingot
n	out normal
N	nucleation rate
N_o	nucleation rate constant
N_{max}	total nucleation sites
ΔG	nucleation energy
p	pressure
r	r coordinate
T	temperature
T_{in}	inlet temperature
T_{bot}	bottom block temperature
T_r	reference temperature
T_{water}	cooling water temperature
ΔT_o	center of Gaussian distribution
ΔT_σ	standard derivation of Gaussian distribution
ΔT	undercooling
t	time
$\vec{u}$	velocity vector
$U_{casting}$	casting speed
U_{in}	inlet velocity
v	grain growth velocity
Y	radius of pouring hole
z	z coordinate
$\hat{z}$	unit vector in z-direction

Greek letters

β	volume expansion coefficient
ρ	density
ψ	impingement factor
ω	free surface motion factor
ν	grain growth velocity

INTRODUCTION

Continuous casting is a major process for ingot production in the metals industry. The process involves complex physical phenomena such as liquid metal flow in the liquid pool, heat and mass transfer as well as thermally induced stresses. An accurate mathematical model of these phenomena can be of great value for both fundamental understanding and practical process design. Because of this importance, numerous models have appeared since the advent of the process, and have resulted in improved process understanding and equipment design. The ever increasing demand on better ingot quality and lower operating cost has provided the thrust for continuous process improvement, which must come from a better understanding of process fundamentals. One area that has been largely neglected in the past and has now become increasingly important is the starting phase of the casting operation. Although only about 10% of the total casting time for an ingot drop, the starting phase can have important implications to the formation of macro casting defects. Experience with aluminum casting has indicated that many defects, such as hot tearing, hot cracking, surface cracking and corner cracking initiate during the starting phase and remain in the products. The formation of these defects is closely related to the liquid metal flow and temperature distribution in the casting system, which are dynamically evolving during the initial phase of the casting operation (Granger and Jensen, 1984). Information on this evolving fluid flow and thermal behavior can be of critical importance in understanding the physics controlling the formation of these defects, thereby providing a rational basis for process design and optimization.

Another important issue that has so far eluded mathematical modeling efforts is the modeling of microstructure formation during continuous casting, especially in combination with the thermal and flow analyses. Traditionally, studies on microstructures formed in ingots fall into the arena of materials science, and the microstructural characteristics of ingots are obtained through metallographic measurements. While these continue to be a major source for understanding of microstructure formation, recent advances in solidification studies have indicated that solidification microstructures may be modeled from first principles, at least semi-quantitatively (Rappaz and Stefanescu, 1988). This modeling effort may be combined with thermal analyses, which provide information on thermal history needed for micro kinetic models for nucleation and grain growth. Such a combined model, often referred to as a micro/macro model, provides a unified approach to study casting processes, allowing the prediction at the same time of both thermal and microstructure information for ingots being cast, and hence can be substantially more useful from the point of view of casting process design and quality control. Indeed, mathematical models that coupled heat transfer with microstructure formation have been developed for simple one-dimensional or zero-dimensional systems. Application of these models to simultaneously predict grain structures and thermal history has met with some success for foundry type casting processes (Rappaz, 1989). To our knowledge, however, few attempts, if any, have been made to develop a model that has a full integration of dynamically evolving flow and thermal phenomena with microstructure formation for continuous casting processes.

This paper presents an integrated model for the simultaneous prediction of transient fluid flow and heat transfer phenomena as well as microstructure formation during continuous casting processes. The model can be used for both fundamental understanding of the starting phase and microstructures formed during continuous casting. To developed such a coupled model, two specific issues must be addressed. First, modeling of the starting phase requires to represent the ingot that is grown at a casting speed. This is further complicated by the fact that the fluid flow and thermal fields are also dynamically evolving in the growing ingot and the whole calculations then become quite nonlinear. In the present study, the problem is treated as a special class of free surface problem, with deforming finite elements used for modeling the dynamic growth of the ingot. The effect of the node movement resulting from the element deformation on the fluid flow and temperature distribution is then accounted for using a mixed Eulerian-Lagrangian transformation. Second, as microstructure formation takes place at a much smaller time scale than the thermal phenomena, an effective coupling strategy must be utilized to integrate the kinetic micro models describing the nucleation and grain growth phenomena with the finite element model representing the transient fluid flow and heat transfer. In the present study, an iterative micro/macro time step scheme is introduced and numerical results indicate that such a scheme can be effectively applied in developing these integrated models.

PROBLEM FORMULATION

Let us consider the continuous casting problem as shown schematically in Figure 1. The coordinate system is cylindrical with axial symmetry, with the x-axis coincident with the casting direction. To start, the bottom block is moved up to form a cavity with the mold. The cooling water is switched on. The molten aluminum is then introduced into the cavity through the top pouring hole, or more often through a nozzle, until the cavity is filled. The molten metal begins to cool down and subsequently solidifies along the surface of the cavity. As the bottom block is pulled away at a controlled speed, the solidifying surface is directly exposed to the cooling water, resulting in more metal being solidified. The solidified metal is being withdrawn while the molten metal is continuously supplied from the top. Eventually, the process reaches a quasi-steady state, and by then the fluid flow and temperature profile with respect to the mold no longer changes with time. Prior to that, however, the fluid flow and temperature distribution in the system undergo drastic changes and evolve as the casting process approaches the steady state.

At the micro-scale level, nucleation and grain growth occur, which contribute to the formation of final microstructures (Kurz and Fisher, 1986). During solidification, nuclei first form because of thermal fluctuations in the liquid metal that is being cooled below a certain temperature. Some nuclei can not continue to exist because their radius is too small to be stable, while others survive to form a stable cluster. As the temperature continues to decrease, the portion of survived nuclei increases. These stable nuclei provide the seeding sites on which further crystal growth takes place.

A. Formulation of Flow and Thermal Phenomena

The transient fluid flow and thermal development discussed above can be described mathematically by a set of time-dependent nonlinear differential equations: the Navier-Stokes equation for fluid flow and thermal balance equation for temperature distribution along with appropriate boundary conditions.

Transient Fluid Flow.

The convective flow in the system described above originates from two sources: one is the momentum of the incoming flow from the nozzle or the pouring hole, and the other from the temperature gradient in the liquid pool. Assuming that the fluid flow is incompressible and the temperature effect can be approximated in line with Boussinesq's assumption, the transient fluid flow phenomena evolving during the process may be represented by the equation of continuity and the equation of momentum balance (Bird, Stewart and Lightfoot, 1960), namely,

Equation of continuity:

$$\nabla \cdot \vec{u} = 0 \qquad (1)$$

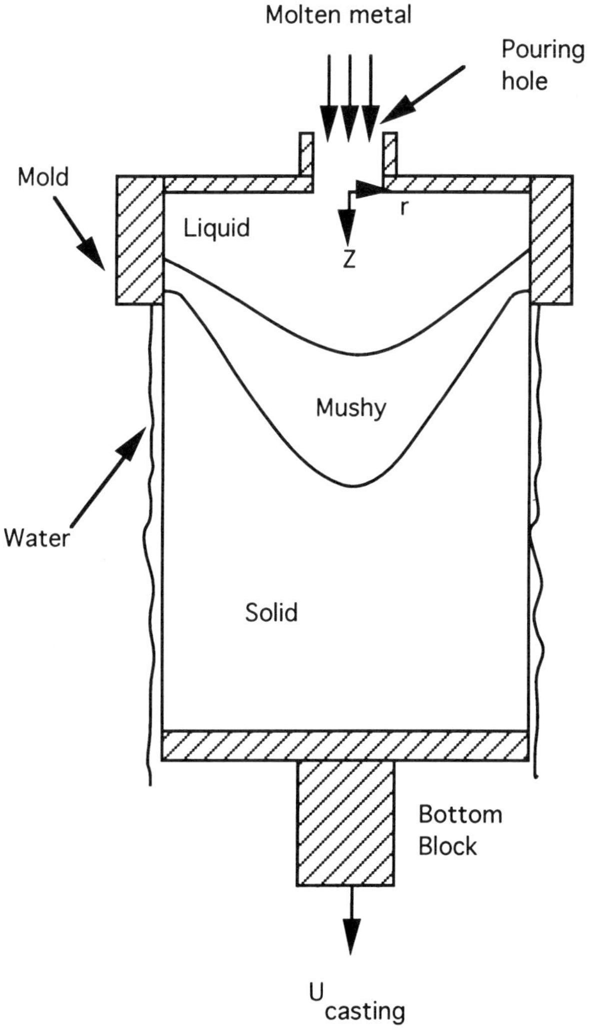

Figure 1. Schematic representation of dynamic aspects of continuous solidification of aluminum alloys.

Equation of momentum balance:

$$\rho \frac{\partial \vec{u}}{\partial t} + \rho \vec{u} \cdot \nabla \vec{u} = -\nabla p + \nabla \cdot \mu \nabla T + \rho\beta\left(T - T_r\right) \qquad (2)$$

In the above equations, the subscript r designates a reference state.

Thermal Energy Balance.

The transient temperature distribution and hence the solidification processes are strongly influenced by the fluid flow field, especially during the starting phase, and are described by the transient thermal balance equation (Bird, Stewart and Lightfoot, 1960). Neglecting the viscous dissipation, which is a rather small fraction of heat generation, the conservation of thermal energy in the process can be expressed in terms of temperature in the form of

$$\rho C_p \frac{\partial T}{\partial t} + \rho C_p \vec{u} \cdot \nabla T = \nabla \cdot k \nabla T + \rho H \frac{df}{dt} \qquad (3)$$

where the last term represents the heat contribution released from solidification. In micro/macro modeling, this term serves as a window through which the micro models for solidification are linked to the fluid and thermal calculations. The physical properties in the above equations are mixture properties of liquid and solid phases and are calculated based on the solid and liquid fractions.

Boundary Conditions.

To obtain information on the transient fluid flow and heat transfer phenomena, the above equations must be solved subject to the physical constraints specific to the system or the boundary conditions. In the present study, the no-slip condition is enforced along the solid and liquid interface for the fluid flow calculations. Thermal boundaries are of the Newton cooling type where the heat transfer coefficient in general is temperature dependent. The coefficient can be a strong function of temperature when the effect of both film and boiling heat transfer is considered along the side interface between the solidifying surface and the cooling water (Weckman and Niessen, 1982). What differentiates this study from other similar studies is perhaps the boundary condition describing the growth of the ingot length as the casting operation proceeds from the beginning. This condition is obtained from the overall mass balance. The inlet flow and thermal conditions are prescribed in accordance with casting conditions. With reference to Figure 1, the boundary conditions needed for the present numerical study can be mathematically stated as below:

(i) at the bottom of the ingot,

$$\frac{dn}{dt} = \vec{u} \cdot n = U_{casting} \quad and$$
$$-kn \cdot \nabla T = h\left(T - T_{bot}\right) \quad at \quad z = L(t) \qquad (4)$$

(ii) on the top of the liquid pool,

$$T = T_{in} \text{ and } \vec{u} = U_{in}(r) \quad at \quad x = 0 \quad and \quad r \le Y \tag{5}$$

$$n \cdot \nabla T = 0 \quad and \quad \vec{u} = 0 \quad at \quad z = 0 \quad and \quad r > Y \tag{6}$$

(iii) along the side of the liquid pool and the solidifying ingot,

$$\vec{u} = 0 \quad and \quad -kn \cdot \nabla T = h\left(T - T_{mold}\right) \quad at \quad z \le L_d \quad and \quad r = L_r \tag{7}$$

$$\vec{u} = (U_{casting}, 0) \quad and \quad -kn \cdot \nabla T = h\left(T - T_{water}\right) \quad at \quad z > L_d \quad and \quad r = L_r \tag{8}$$

B. Formulation of Nucleation and grain growth Phenomena

From the principle of statistical physics, nucleation is a fluctuating phenomenon that comes from the thermal fluctuations in a liquid. At any moment, the number of nuclei in the liquid obeys the Boltzmann distribution (Kittel and Kroemer, 1980), and may be written as below,

$$N = N_o \exp\left(-\frac{\Delta G}{k_b T}\right) \tag{9}$$

Although very simple in form, Eq. (9) poses a problem for computation as the exponential term often leads to an erroneous estimate. To overcome this difficulty, Rappaz (1989) proposed that the number of nuclei formed during solidification may be approximated by a Gaussian distribution,

$$\frac{dN}{d(\Delta T)} = \frac{N_{max}}{\sqrt{2\pi}\Delta T_\sigma} \exp\left(-\frac{\left(\Delta T - \Delta T_\sigma\right)^2}{2\left(\Delta T_\sigma\right)^2}\right) \tag{10}$$

In the case of aluminum casting, grain refiner is added to induce heterogeneous nucleation. Zhou and Rappaz (1991) showed that Eq. (10) is still valid provided that N_{max} is treated as the total density of heterogeneous nucleation sites or grain refining particle density added to the liquid aluminum.

There are many models for grain growth on a nucleus. For a grain refined aluminum melt, the grain growth rate may be described by the following expression (Zhou, Shivkumar, and Apelian, 1991),

$$v = \left(\frac{\Delta T}{K}\right)^2 \tag{11}$$

where K is an empirical constant that can be obtained by fitting the measured cooling curves and final grain sizes. When the grain growth velocity is known, the solid fraction may be calculated as,

$$\frac{\partial f}{\partial t} = 4\pi N(t) R^2(t) v(t) \psi \tag{12}$$

with ψ being the factor accounting for grain impingement. Eqs. (11) and (12) were used in modeling of grain refined aluminum alloy solidification and satisfactory results were obtained (Zhou, Shivkumar, and Apelian, 1991). The present study makes use of the above grain growth model with the same empirical constants K and ψ as reported by Zhou, *et al* (1991).

SOLIDIFICATION MODELING

Two aspects associated with alloy solidification modeling are the drastic change in liquid viscosity and the release of latent heat due to phase transformation. The former affects the fluid flow behavior while the latter the temperature distribution. There exist mainly two approaches to account for the effect of solidification on the liquid flow, and they both are empirical. One is to simulate the mushy zone and solidification effect by introducing a drag function (Voller, Brent and Prakash, 1989) and the other by treating the viscosity of the alloy as a function of temperature (Danzig, 1988). The latter is used in this study as it also helps to stabilize the numerical calculations by the finite element method. The temperature dependency of viscosity used in obtaining the results presented below takes the exponential form determined experimentally by Joly and Mehrabian (1976).

In alloy solidification processes, the latent heat release is closely related to the solid fraction evolution. There are many documented models for calculating solid fraction during solidification. For the coupled micro/macro model presented in this study, the solid fraction evolution during solidification is directly evaluated by Eq. (12), which along with Eq. (11) is applied to predict the grain structure during solidification. These equations may be readily discretized and incorporated into the fluid flow and heat transfer calculations.

NUMERICAL DEVELOPMENT

Detailed finite element formulation of the problem is described elsewhere (Li, Liu and Brock, 1993), and hence only a summary is given below. The approach is akin to that used for free surface flow calculations using the finite element method, originally proposed by Sato and Scriven (1982). To facilitate calculations, the bottom surface of the ingot is considered as a free surface. A group of spines that connect the free surface with a conveniently chosen internal surface fixed as a reference surface are introduced. The nodes, both internal and on the bottom surface, located along each of the spines are made to move in the direction of casting. The nodes on the bottom surface, or free surface, are constrained to move, in the present study, at a speed of casting. The movement of the internal nodes situated at the spines is constrained along the spines, but the speed at which they move is determined in such a way that the relative spacing between the adjacent nodes along the same spine is kept in a predetermined fashion. This allows the deforming of the elements in the spine region to be appropriately controlled so that a desired distribution of the deforming elements is obtained. In the present study, a uniform spacing between the adjacent nodes along a spine is maintained before and after a time step over which free surface nodes move. This way, the elements in the spine region are uniformly deformed.

As a result of node movement, the equations for transport phenomena described in the Eulerian frame must be modified to allow for the effect of the movement. This is done using a mixed Eulerian and Lagrangian transformation, which may be described as follows. In the spine region, the equations are written as a Lagrangian form with the reference frame moving at the node speed. Experience showed that the approach gives reasonably accurate results provided that the time step over which the nodes in the spine region move is small. This time step may not be the same as that for transient flow and temperature calculations. But an appropriate time step may be selected using the automatic predictor-corrector time scheme based on the residuals calculated for each time step, as proposed by Gresho, et al. (1980).

THE ITERATIVE MICRO/MACRO COUPLING SCHEME

Mathematically, the coupling between the micro model and macro model requires the simultaneous solution of Eqs. (3) and (12). The temperature calculated is used to compute nucleation rate, grain size and solid fraction evolved during solidification, and the solid fraction so estimated is then fed back to the momentum and thermal balance equations for updating the temperature distribution. As the time scales are significantly different for nucleation and fluid flow variation, an appropriate time step must be carefully chosen to make the numerical computation possible. A natural choice would be to select the smallest time step for the computation of both microstructure formation and fluid flow. Such an intuitive selection, however, can be too naive for the present modeling effort in that it leads to a prohibitively high computing cost. To overcome this difficulty, we devised the following iterative micro/macro time step scheme, which is then integrated with the conventional implicit time matching algorithm for thermal and flow calculations.

First, an appropriate time step is chosen based purely on the fluid flow and temperature calculations. The selection of the time step may be based on the error estimate, which can be made automatic using the available strategies (Gresho, Lee, and Sani, 1980). The temperature distribution calculated at the node points this way is then used in calculations for microstructure formation. To do so, it is assumed that over a micro time step for microstructure calculation, the fluid flow velocity, temperature distribution and node coordinates are each interpolated as a linear function of time. The solid fraction evolved during solidification is accumulated and is then fed back to re-calculate the temperature and fluid flow field. This micro- and macro-time step iteration then continues for one macro time step until the calculated unknowns for both macro-scale and micro-scale parameters meet the preset convergence criteria. A new macro time step is then selected and another set of micro and macro time step iterations is made. The calculation proceeds in this fashion until the total time period preset for the simulation is reached. This macro and micro coupling scheme is schematically represented in Figure 2.

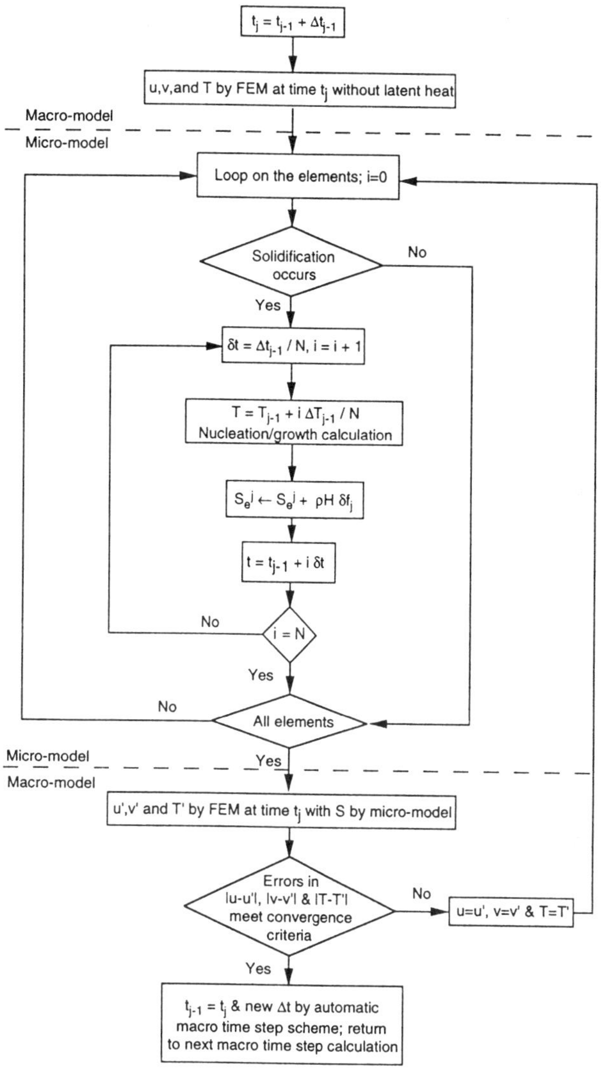

Figure 2. The iterative micro/macro time step scheme for coupling between the macro-scale model and the micro-scale model.

SOLUTION METHOD

The above equation is solved by modifying the general purpose finite element program for fluid flow, FIDAP. The modifications include incorporating the micro model for solidification, the iterative micro/macro time step scheme, the temperature dependent heat transfer coefficients and the temperature dependent viscosity. The results presented below were obtained from the micro/macro model along with the automatic time step control scheme as suggested by Gresho, *et al.* (1980). The calculations used 1575 4-node elements with only a portion of the nodes being allowed to move. A typical calculation for the evolving fluid flow and temperature fields and microstructure formation required about 18 to 34 CPU hours on a single processor Silicon Graphics workstation (Model-380).

COMPUTED RESULTS AND DISCUSSION

The finite element-based integrated modeling methodology presented above permits the prediction of the evolution of the fluid flow field, the temperature field and the formation of solidification microstructure in a solidifying ingot from start-up to steady state during continuous casting operations. Numerical computations start with the filling the molten metal in the cavity formed by lifting the bottom block to level with the water cooled mold. Because of limited space, only a selection of the computed results will be presented below. The results are for a round ingot with a diameter of 0.40 m and for a casting speed of 9.0×10^{-4} m/sec. The condition of axial symmetry was assumed. The physical and thermal property data for the calculations were taken from a report by Bennon (1989).

In simulating the start-up phase of a continuous casting process, both the growing of solidifying ingot length and the transient thermal and flow fields evolving in the ingot must be resolved simultaneously. Figure 3 shows the evolution of the ingot length from the beginning of casting up to a steady state, while Figures 4, 5, 6, and 7 depict the unfolding vector velocity field, streamline profiles, temperature field and liquid-solid transformation as the casting operation proceeds. The pictures shown are oriented such that the casting direction is in the z-direction and the axis of symmetry coincides with the left side of the picture. These figures clearly demonstrate that the large deformation and the accompanying transient fluid flow, thermal and solidification phenomena in the round ingot casting process can be very well simulated by the deforming finite element method described earlier.

Examination of the set of pictures in Figures 4, 5 and 6 reveals the general trend of the dynamic fluid flow and thermal development within the growing, solidifying ingot: there are drastic changes in fluid flow and temperature initially but these changes proceed more slowly as the process approaches a steady state. The flow in the liquid pool is predominantly driven by the temperature gradient and the flow from the inlet has an almost negligible effect on the flow field. Figures 4 and 5 show that the recirculation loop grows quickly initially, but it becomes relatively stable after about 100 seconds. The corresponding evolution of the thermal field follows the same fashion in that the temperature field changes quickly at the start of the operation and the changes slow down afterwards, as illustrated in Figure 8. This dynamic behavior of fluid flow and thermal fields is as expected from first principles and is in general agreement with casting experience. From Figure 4(a), it is evident that cooling first starts along the water cooled mold and the bottom block (Figure 6(a)). At the subsequent stage, more molten metal is poured in from the top, and consequently the thermal energy in the system increases. At the same time more heat is removed from the system as the downward movement of the bottom block exposes more solidifying surface to the cooling water. Since heat is extracted at a slower pace than input from the molten metal, thermal energy builds up in the system, which is evidenced by the larger area of higher temperature (Figure 6(b)). The ensuing temperature field evolves in the same manner but less drastically as the process continues until a steady state is reached and the thermal energy brought in by the incoming metal is balanced by what is extracted from the system. From the last three sets of plots in Figures 4, 5 and 6, it is apparent that the fluid flow field in the liquid pool and the isothermal contours in the region around the mold become almost stationary with respect to the top surface. This suggests that a quasi-thermal-equilibrium has been established. However, in the region below the mold and especially near the bottom, the temperature profiles are still developing but again much more slowly than at the initial stage. From Figure 6(e) as well as those calculated for longer times, it is found that a great portion of the ingot reaches the quasi-steady state except near the bottom block. Thus, it may be reasonable to argue that Figure 6(e) represents approximately the quasi-steady state. The corresponding dynamic solidification behavior in the system also deserves a note. As shown in Figure 7, the mushy zone region quickly expands initially (Figure 7(a) and 7(b)), but the expansion slows down afterwards. It eventually reaches the quasi-steady state after which the mushy zone size no longer changes, as evident in Figure 7(e).

To verify the results computed from the micro/macro model, a set of thermal measurements under a steady state condition was made in a commercial-scale ingot. Figure 8 shows the comparison of the calculated and measured results for the temperature distribution along the center line of the ingot under the steady state condition. It is clear that the prediction is in reasonably good agreement with the measurement. Note also that the steep decrease in temperature after the solidification is completed is also very well predicted by the micro/macro model.

As mentioned earlier, one of the distinct features of the micro/macro model developed in this study is that the mode is capable of predicting the microstructure characteristics for ingots with equi-axed grain structures. The computed results for the average grain size in the ingot under consideration are plotted in Figure 9 as a function of the distance from the ingot surface. The grain size of the ingot can also be determined by metallographic measurements, and the measured results for average grain size, along with the standard variation, are also shown in Figure 9. Inspection of the figure indicates that the calculated grain size distribution agrees with the measured one within the error margins associated with the measurements. Both the predicted and measured results show that the average grain size increases inward from the ingot surface. It is noteworthy that slightly finer grains are predicted by the micro/macro model while a larger grain size is calculated at the center.

As shown above the micro/macro model can be used for continuous casting processes, and predicted results are in reasonably good agreement with measurements. However, the modeling methodology can be extended to other solidification processes as well. Indeed, if appropriate boundary conditions are imposed and casting velocity is set to zero, the model can be directly used to predict the same macro- and micro-scale phenomena in solidification of equi-axed grain structures in other solidification processes, such as investment casting, die casting and mold casting. Moreover, if an appropriate micro kinetic model can be derived for the formation of other solidification structures, a similar micro/macro model can be developed by using the same micro/macro coupling scheme.

It should be pointed out that a micro/macro coupling scheme has also been proposed by Rappaz (1989), but it differs from

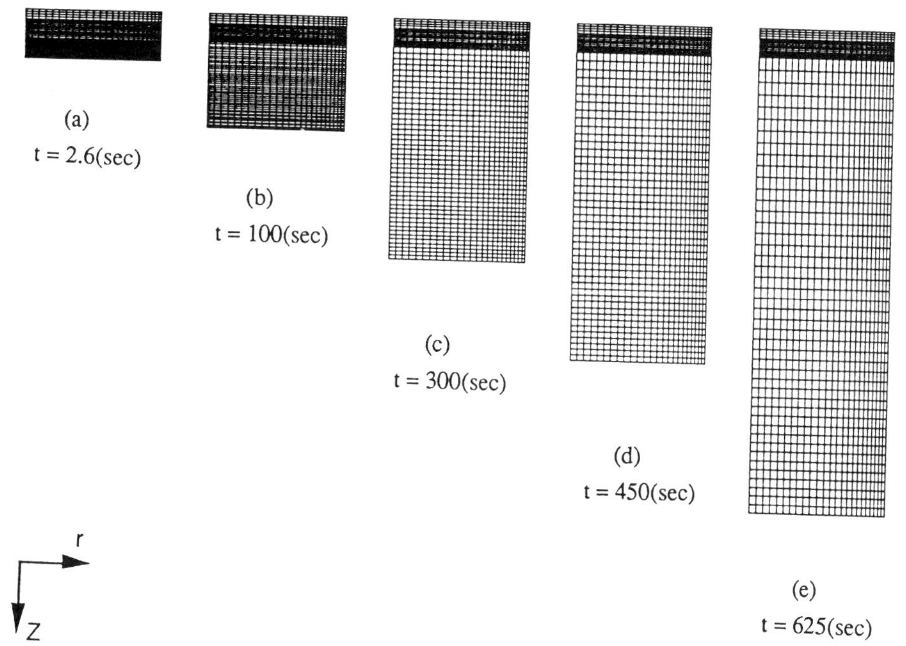

Figure 3. Expansion of finite element grids to simulate the growth of the ingot length during the starting phase of the round ingot casting process.

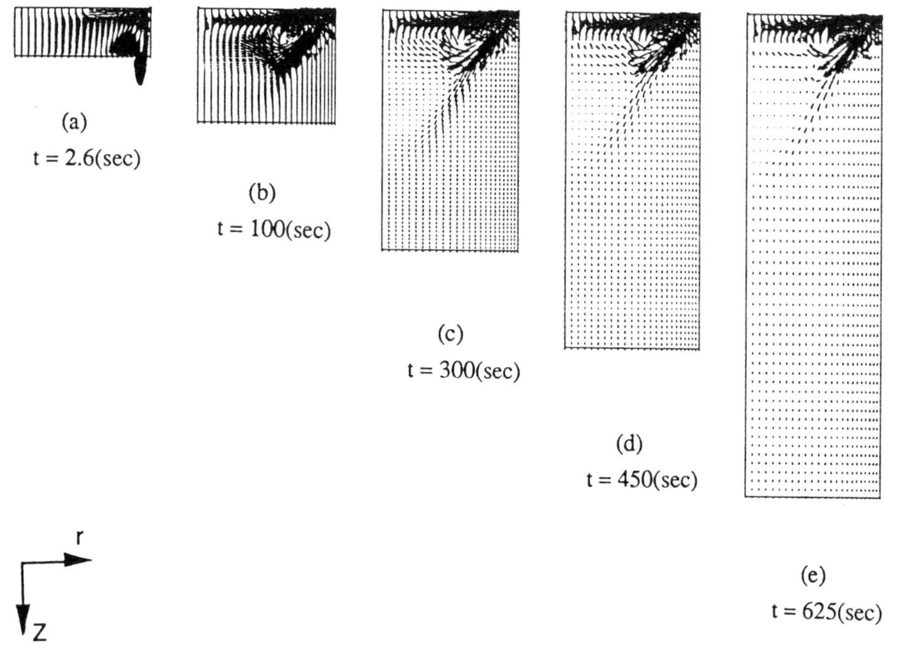

Figure 4. Transient development of the fluid flow field in the growing round ingot during the starting phase. The molten metal inlet velocity is $3.6x\ 10^{-3}$m/sec.

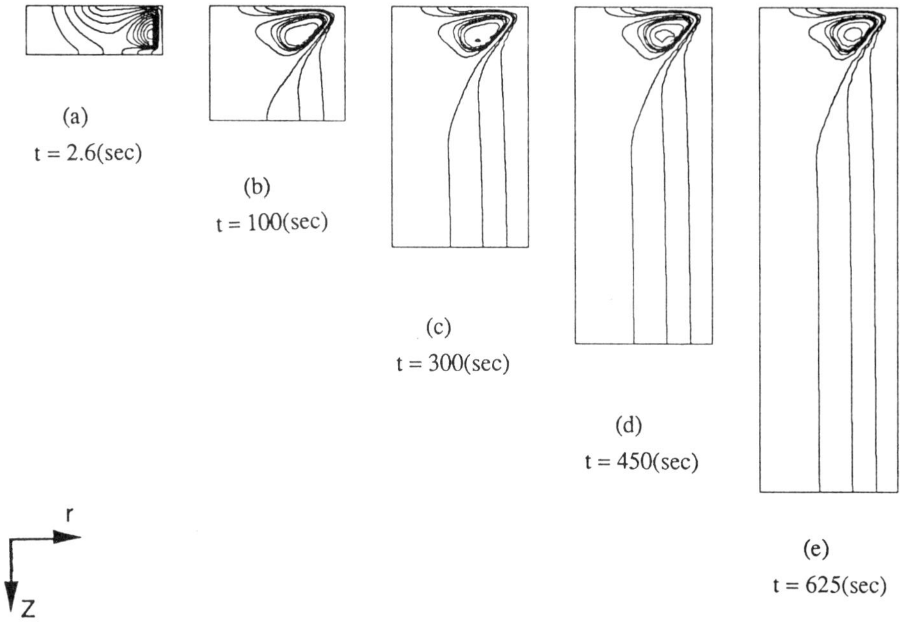

Figure 5. The corresponding stream line profiles of the velocity field shown in Figure 4.

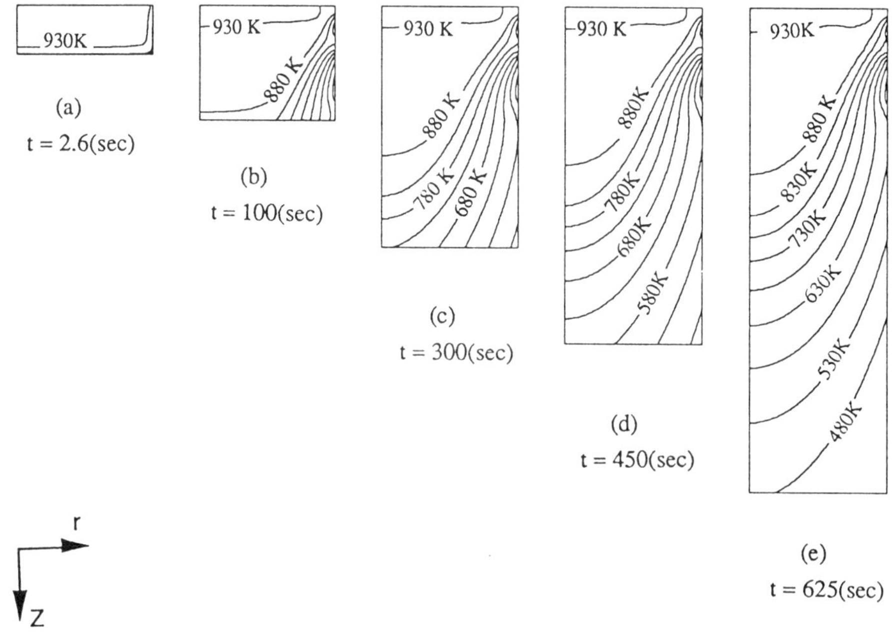

Figure 6. Evolution of temperature distributions in the growing round ingot during the starting phase.

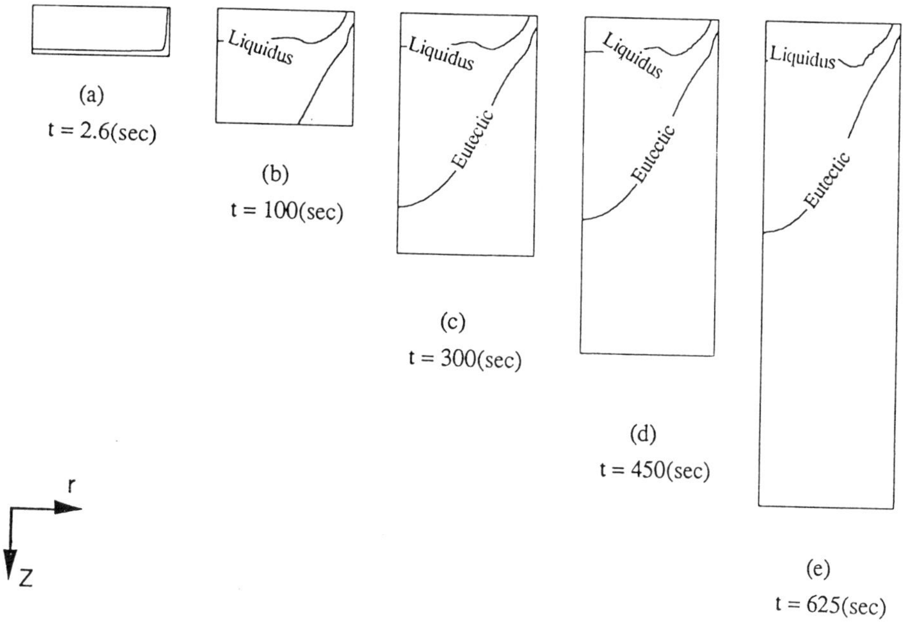

Figure 7 Evolution of mushy zone region in the growing round ingot during the starting phase.

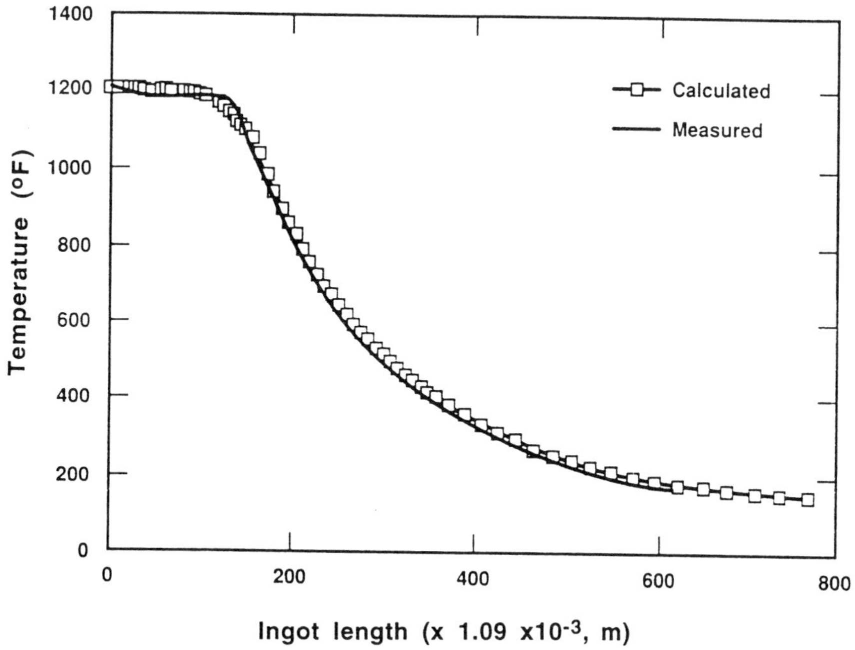

Figure 8 Comparison of computed and measured centerline axial temperature distribution under a steady state condition during continuous casting of aluminum alloys.

the present micro/macro time step coupling algorithm in several aspects. First of all, his scheme has no automatic time step control. While it may be sufficient for simplified solidification systems for a demonstration purpose, it is doubtful that the scheme has an adequate efficiency for more complicated computations. Also, the scheme is linear and it is difficult to be extended to nonlinear fluid flow calculations. Most important of all, according to his scheme the temperature distribution is predicted using the solid fraction calculated from the temperature field at the previous macro time step. Clearly, significant errors may result unless the macro time step is small enough. These errors may propagate and accumulate as time matching calculation continues, thereby having a potential for resulting in incorrect predictions. It should be stressed here that the errors in the estimation of solid fraction still can not be corrected even if an automatic time step control strategy would be applied.

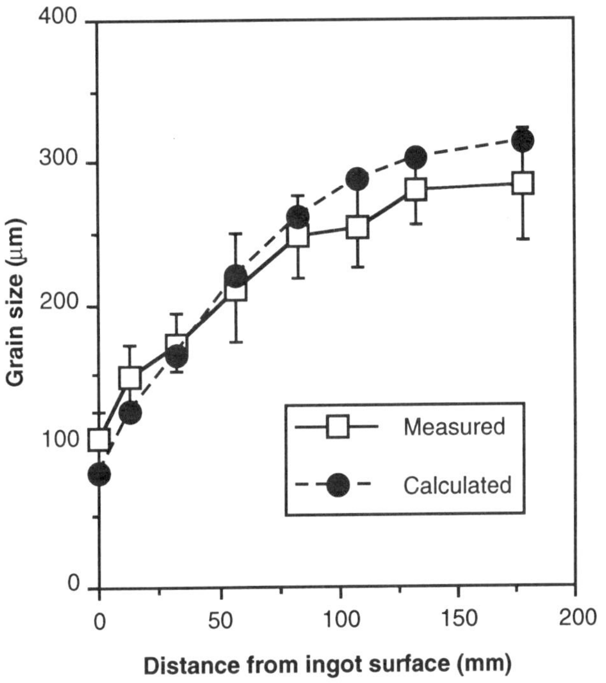

Figure 9 Comparison of calculated and measured average grain size distribution as a function of radial distance from ingot surface in the continuously cast ingot.

In solidification processing of materials, thermal stresses arising due to solidification are often the origin of casting defects, such as hot cracking and hot tearing. In calculating the thermal stresses, information on the history of the temperature distribution and of the particle path in the ingot is needed. The above computational methodology provides a useful means by which the needed thermal information can be calculated and can be readily linked to a thermal stress model, thereby facilitating the development of a combined thermoflow and thermostress model for continuous casting processes. The frequently used mathematical models, developed based on the steady state solidification theory, would not provide the needed information on the evolution of temperature distribution and particle history, and thus would be difficult to be integrated directly with thermal stress models.

While the present micro/macro time step scheme has proved to be very useful for studying fluid flow, temperature distribution and microstructure formation during solidification, it can be computationally intensive and thus may be dispensed with when the microstructure is not a predicted parameter. If, for example, only the thermal and flow fields are of the main concern (Li, Liu and Brock, 1993), as in the case of thermal stress calculations, the micro model can be replaced by much simpler and computational economical models, such as the Scheil model, for solid fraction evolution. Our numerical experiments showed that the solid fraction and temperature profiles are predicted by the micro model (with nucleation and grain growth) and the Scheil model (Kurz and Fisher, 1986) are almost the same, except that the former also gives information on grain size distribution. As the only variable in the Scheil model is temperature, no iterative micro/macro coupling scheme is needed, thereby resulting in substantial savings in computing time (Li, Liu and Brock, 1993).

CONCLUDING REMARKS

This paper has presented a micro/macro modeling methodology for the study of the transient evolution of the fluid flow, heat transfer and microstructure formation during continuous casting processes. The deforming finite element method, in combination with the an Eulerian-Lagrangian formulation, has been used to represent the dynamic development of fluid flow and temperature distribution in a solidifying ingot that itself is grown at a casting speed. The nucleation and equi-axed grain growth phenomena, which lead to the formation of final microtructure in the ingot, have been modeled using a micro kinetic model. An iterative micro/macro time step scheme has been introduced to couple between the microstructure calculations and thermal fluid flow calculations. Numerical results for continuous casting of a round ingot have been presented, and good agreement is obtained between the computed results and experimental measurements for temperature distribution in the caster. The results showed that the fluid flow and temperature distribution change rapidly at the initial stage but the change slows down later in the process. The average grain size distribution predicted by the micro/macro model agreed reasonably well with the measured results. Both measured and computed results showed that the average grain size decreases with distance from the ingot surface, which is as expected from the theory of solidification processing.

ACKNOWLEDGMENT

The work was supported in part by Alcoa's Transport and Solidification Process Design Science Program.

REFERENCES

Becker, E. B., Carey, G. F. and Oden, J. T., 1981, *Finite Elements, An Introduction,* Vol. 1, Prentice-Hall, Englewood Cliffs, New Jersey.

Bennon, W. D., 1989, "The Prediction of Macrosegregation in Continuously Cast DC Ingot," Alcoa Report, Alcoa Center, PA.
Bird, R. B., Stewart, W. E., and Lightfoot, E. N., 1960, *Transport Phenomena,* John Wiley & Sons, New York.
Danzig, J. A., 1988, "Modeling Liquid-Solid Phase Changes with Melt Convection," in *Second FIDAP Users' Conference*, The Fluid Dynamics International, Evanston, IL.
Grange, D. A. and Jensen, C. L., 1984, "Role of Ingot Structure in Structural Streaking," Light Metals, TMS/AIME, pp.1249-1263.
Gresho, P. M., Lee, R. L. and Sani, R. L., 1980, "On the Time Dependent Solution of the Incompressible Navier-Stokes Equations in Two and Three Dimensions," in *Recent Advances in Numerical Methods in Fluids*, Pineriadge Press, Swansea, U.K.
Joly, A. and Mehrabian, R., 1976, "The Rheology of a Partially Solid Alloy," *Journal of Materials Science*, 11, 1393-1418.
Kattel, C. and Kroemer, H., 1980, *Thermal Physics*, 2nd Ed, W. H. Freeman and Company, San Francisco, CA.
Kurz, W. and Fisher, D. J., 1986, *Fundamentals of Solidification*, Trans. Tech. Pub., Aedermannsdorf, Switzerland.
Li, B. Q., Liu, J. C. and Brock, J. A., 1993, "Numerical Simulation of Transient Fluid Flow and Solidification Phenomena During Continuous Casting of Aluminum," in *Materials Processing/EPD Congress*, Ed. J. P. Hager, 841-857, TMS/AIME, Pennsylvania.
Rappaz, M., 1989, "Modeling of Microstructure Formation in Solidification Processes," *International Materials Review*, Vol. 34, No. 3, 93-123.
Rappaz, M. and Stefanescu, D. M., 1988, "Modeling of Microstructure Evolution," in *Metals Handbook*, 9th Edition, Vol. 15, Casting, 883-892.
Saito, H. and Scriven, L. E., 1981, "Studying of Coating Flow by the Finite Element Method," *J. Comp. Phys.*, Vol 42, 53-60.
Voller, V. R., Brent, A. D., and Prakash, C., 1989, "The Modeling of Heat, Mass and Solute Transport in Solidification Systems," *Int. J. Heat Mass Transfer,* 32(9), 1719-1731.
Weckman, D. C. and Niessen, P., 1982, "A Numerical Simulation of the D.C. Continuous Casting Process Including Nucleate Boiling Heat Transfer," *Metall. Trans. B*, Vol. 13B, 593-602.
Zhou, J. and Rappaz, M ., 1991, "Experiment and Modeling of Gray Cast Iron Solidification," in *Materials Processing in the Computer Age*, Ed. V. R. Voller, M. S. Stachowicz and B. G. Brian, TMS/AIME, 335-348.
Zhou, J., Shivkumar, S., and Apelian, D., 1991, "Modeling of Porosity Formation in Grain Refined Aluminum Castings," in *Materials Processing in the Computer Age*, Ed. V. R. Voller, M. S. Stachowicz and B. G. Brian, TMS/AIME, 389-401.

HTD-Vol. 284/AMD-Vol. 182, Transport Phenomena in Solidification
ASME 1994

NUMERICAL SOLUTION OF MOVING BOUNDARY PROBLEMS USING INTEGRAL EQUATIONS

S. Nair
Department of Mechanical and Aerospace Engineering
Illinois Institute of Technology
Chicago, Illinois

ABSTRACT

The one-dimensional Stefan problem in a finite domain is formulated as a set of three integral equations. The specific problem considered is that of the freezing of a liquid with the interface moving from left to right. Using Boley's embedded domain approach, the above problem is viewed as a combination of two problems: a frozen domain with unknown right boundary condition and a liquid domain with unknown left boundary condition. These boundary conditions and the interface location form the three unknown functions in the integral equations. Results are obtained for the interface location with unsteady boundary conditions and non-uniform initial conditions with the right boundary insulated.

INTRODUCTION

Moving boundary problems arise naturally in many physical phenomena. A classical example is the freezing of water (or melting of ice) where the interface separating the two phases is a moving boundary. The presence of such interfaces renders, otherwise linear heat conduction problem nonlinear. Some other examples of moving boundary problems are sublimation and evaporation of matter in chemistry, crystal growth in solid state physics, formation of alloys in metallurgy, freezing and thawing of soils in civil engineering, bubble growth in chemical engineering, contact of deformable bodies in elasticity, grinding wheel wear in manufacturing, and break down in nuclear reactors.

Probably the most studied problem in the above group is the freezing problem first considered by Neumann in his unpublished lecture notes (*circa* 1860). He found exact solutions for a frozen front moving into a semi-infinite domain due to an applied sub-zero temperature at the origin, using a similarity variable. On the basis of a special case of the Neumann solution published by Stefan previously, this class of problems are known as *Stefan problems* in the literature (Carslaw and Jaeger (1959)). Analytical solutions for the semi-infinite domain with arbitrary initial and boundary conditions were unavailable for the Stefan problem for over a hundred years until the series solutions due to Tao (1978, 79a, 79b, 79c, 80, 81).

Meanwhile, a host of approximate methods have been proposed to solve the one dimensional Stefan problem. The approximate methods may be classified as analytic, numerical or mixed. The solutions of finite domain melting problems using the perturbation method, due to Weinbaum and Jiji (1977) and Charach and Zoglin (1985) fall under the first group. As in all perturbation solutions the need for a small parameter limits the applicability of these solutions. Finite difference and finite element methods form the bulk of numerical methods. Detailed appraisals of these methods have been published by Crank (1984), Rubinstein (1971), Ockendon and Hodgkins (1975), Wilson, Solomon and Boggs (1978) and Fukusako and Seki (1987). Under mixed methods comes the use of a sequence of global approximating functions for the temperature or enthalpy distibution. The heat balance integral method due to Goodman (1958) is an example of this.

The main difficulty with the existing numerical

and mixed methods is that the singularities inherent in the moving problems are ignored or smoothed out. A recent mixed method due to Dursunkaya and Nair (1990), using spectral methods on a tranformed problem overcomes this difficulty. The transformation needed to fix the interface is not apparent in multi-dimensional cases.

Another class of mixed methods stem from the integral equation formulation of moving boundary problems by Kolodner (1956), Boley (1961) and Tao (1986). The formulations by Kolodner and Tao employ the Green's functions of moving heat sources at the interface while Boley uses overlapping extended frozen and liquid domains with variable boundary temperatures to satisfy the interface conditions.

In what follows, we consider Boley's method in a numerical setting. The nonlinear integral equation obtained in Boley's formulation is solved numerically to obtain the location of the interface. The convergence of the method with respect to step size in the time dimension is established and the results are also compared with the existing solution due to Dursunkaya and Nair (1990). The problem of freezing in one dimension with finite length is taken as the model problem. Unsteady boundary conditions and non-uniform initial conditions are also examined.

FORMULATION

With s representing the interface location at time t, the temperature T_1 in the frozen domain and T_2 in the liquid domain are governed by the differential equations,

$$\alpha_1 \frac{\partial^2 T_1}{\partial x^2} - \frac{\partial T_1}{\partial t} = 0, \qquad 0 < x < s \tag{1}$$

$$\alpha_2 \frac{\partial^2 T_2}{\partial x^2} - \frac{\partial T_2}{\partial t} = 0, \qquad s < x < l \tag{2}$$

where $\alpha_i (i = 1, 2)$ are the diffusivities and l is the length of the one-dimensional domain.

The initial and boundary conditions are given by

$$T_2(x, 0) = V(x) > T_m \tag{3}$$

$$T_1(0, t) = U(t) < T_m \tag{4}$$

$$\frac{\partial T_2}{\partial x}(l, t) = 0 \tag{5}$$

where T_m is the melting temperature and V and U are given analytical functions of their respective variables.

The interface conditions are

$$T_1(s, t) = T_2(s, t) = T_m \tag{6}$$

$$k_1 \frac{\partial T_1}{\partial x} - k_2 \frac{\partial T_2}{\partial x} = \rho L \frac{ds}{dt} \tag{7}$$

where $k_i (i = 1, 2)$ are conductivities, ρ the density and L is the latent heat of solidification.

Using the non-dimensional variables

$$\xi = x/l, \qquad \sigma = s/l, \qquad \tau = \alpha_1 t / l^2,$$

$$\psi_1 = T_1/T_m, \qquad \psi_2 = T_2/T_m,$$

$$S_1 = k_1 T_m/\alpha_1 \rho L, \qquad S_2 = k_2 T_m / \alpha_2 \rho L, \qquad \alpha = \alpha_1/\alpha_2, \tag{8}$$

with $S_i (i = 1, 2)$ being the Stefan numbers, we obtain the governing partial differential equations in the form,

$$\psi_1'' - \dot{\psi}_1 = 0, \qquad 0 < \xi < \sigma \tag{9}$$

$$\alpha \psi_2'' - \dot{\psi}_2 = 0, \qquad \sigma < \xi < 1 \tag{10}$$

the initial and boundary conditions,

$$\psi_2(\xi, 0) = v(\xi) > 1 \tag{11}$$

$$\psi_1(0, \tau) = u(\tau) < 1 \tag{12}$$

$$\psi_2'(1, \tau) = 0 \tag{13}$$

and the interface conditions,

$$\psi_1(\sigma, \tau) = \psi_2(\sigma, \tau) = 1 \tag{14}$$

$$\dot{\sigma} = S_1 \psi_1' - \alpha S_2 \psi_2' \tag{15}$$

where $(\ )' = \partial(\ )/\partial\xi$, $\dot{(\ )} = \partial(\ )/\partial\tau$, $v = V/T_m$ and $u = U/T_m$.

Following the embedding method introduced by Boley (1961) we assume extended domains for the frozen phase and liquid phase and rewrite the equations (9-13) as two uncoupled systems as

$$\psi_1'' - \dot{\psi}_1 = 0, \qquad 0 < \xi < 1 \tag{16}$$

$$\psi_1(\xi, 0) = w_1(0), \quad \psi_1(1, \tau) = w_1(\tau), \quad \psi_1(0, \tau) = u(\tau) \tag{17}$$

$$\alpha \psi_2'' - \dot{\psi}_2 = 0, \qquad 0 < \xi < 1 \tag{18}$$

$$\psi_2(\xi, 0) = v(\xi), \quad \psi_2'(1, \tau) = 0, \quad \psi_2(0, \tau) = w_2(\tau) \tag{19}$$

where $w_i (i = 1, 2)$ are yet unknown.

The system of equations (16-19) will be first solved for arbitrary functions w_i and then the interface conditions (14-15) will be used to obtain the three unknown functions, $w_1(\tau), w_2(\tau)$ and $\sigma(\tau)$.

Solutions of equations (16-19) can be expressed as

$$\psi_1(\xi,\tau) = [E_{11}(\xi,\tau) + E_{12}(\xi,\tau)]w_1(0)$$

$$- \int_0^{\tau} [\dot{E}_{12}(\xi,\eta)w_1(\tau-\eta) + \dot{E}_{11}(\xi,\eta)u(\tau-\eta)]\, d\eta \quad (20)$$

$$\psi_2(\xi,\tau) = E_{21}(\xi,\tau)v_0 - \int_0^{\tau} \dot{E}_{22}(\xi,\eta)w_2(\tau-\eta)\, d\eta \quad (21)$$

where the Green's functions E_{ij} are given by the series

$$\begin{aligned}
E_{11} &= \sum_{n=1}^{\infty} \frac{2}{n\pi} e^{-n^2\pi^2\tau} \sin n\pi\xi \\
E_{12} &= \sum_{n=1}^{\infty} \frac{2}{n\pi} (-1)^{n+1} e^{-n^2\pi^2\tau} \sin n\pi\xi \\
E_{21} &= \frac{2}{v_0} \sum_{n=1}^{\infty} e^{-\alpha n'^2\pi^2\tau} \sin n'\pi\xi \int_0^1 v(\xi') \sin n'\pi\xi' d\xi' \\
E_{22} &= \sum_{n=1}^{\infty} \frac{2}{n'\pi} e^{-\alpha n'^2\pi^2\tau} \sin n'\pi\xi
\end{aligned} \quad (22)$$

with v_0 being a normalizing constant and $n' = n - 1/2$.

The interface conditions (14-15) give the following system of integro-differential equations:

$$[E_{11}(\sigma,\tau) + E_{12}(\sigma,\tau)]w_1(0)$$

$$- \int_0^{\tau} [\dot{E}_{12}(\sigma,\eta)w_1(\tau-\eta) + \dot{E}_{11}(\sigma,\eta)u(\tau-\eta)]\, d\eta = 1 \quad (23)$$

$$E_{21}(\sigma,\tau)v_0 - \int_0^{\tau} \dot{E}_{22}(\sigma,\eta)w_2(\tau-\eta)\, d\eta = 1 \quad (24)$$

$$\dot{\sigma} = S_1\Big\{[E'_{11}(\sigma,\tau) + E'_{12}(\sigma,\tau)]w_1(0)$$

$$- \int_0^{\tau} [\dot{E}'_{12}(\sigma,\eta)w_1(\tau-\eta) + \dot{E}'_{11}(\sigma,\eta)u(\tau-\eta)]\, d\eta\Big\}$$

$$-\alpha S_2\Big\{E'_{21}(\sigma,\tau)v_0 - \int_0^{\tau} \dot{E}'_{22}(\sigma,\eta)w_2(\tau-\eta)\, d\eta\Big\} \quad (25)$$

The above equations will be solved numerically to obtain the unknown functions $w_1(\tau)$, $w_2(\tau)$ and $\sigma(\tau)$. Once these are known, the temperature distribution at any time can be evaluated using equations (20) and (21).

In equations (23-25) the time derivatives $\dot{E}_{ij}$ are singular at $\eta = 0$. It is numerically advantageous to integrate the terms involving these derivatives by parts in the form,

$$\int_0^{\tau} \dot{E}_{ij}(\sigma,\eta)w(\tau-\eta)\, d\eta = E_{ij}(\sigma,\tau)w(0) - E_{ij}(\sigma,0)w(\tau)$$

$$+ \int_0^{\tau} E_{ij}(\sigma,\eta)\dot{w}(\tau-\eta)\, d\eta \quad (26)$$

The following asymptotic results for the kernels E_{ij} when $\tau \ll 1$ and $\xi < 1/2$ will be of use in evaluating the short-time behavior of the integro-differential equations (23-25):

$$E_{11}(\xi,\tau) \sim \text{erf}(\frac{\xi}{2\sqrt{\tau}}) - \xi \quad (27)$$

$$E_{22}(\xi,\tau) \sim \text{erf}(\frac{\xi}{2\sqrt{\alpha\tau}}) \quad (28)$$

$$E_{12}(\xi,\tau) \sim \xi \quad (29)$$

Using equations (26-29) the integro-differential equations can be written in the form

$$w_1(\tau) = \frac{1}{\sigma}\Big\{1 - E_{11}(\sigma,\tau)[w_1(0) - u(0)] - (1-\sigma)u(\tau)$$

$$+ \int_0^{\tau} [E_{12}(\sigma,\eta)\dot{w}_1(\tau-\eta) + E_{11}(\sigma,\eta)\dot{u}(\tau-\eta)]\, d\eta\Big\} \quad (30)$$

$$w_2(\tau) = 1 - E_{21}(\sigma,\tau)v_0 + E_{22}(\sigma,\tau)w_2(0)$$

$$+ \int_0^{\tau} E_{22}(\sigma,\eta)\dot{w}_2(\tau-\eta)\, d\eta \quad (31)$$

$$\dot{\sigma} = S_1\Big\{[E'_{11}(\sigma,\tau)[w_1(0) - u(0)] + w_1(\tau) - u(\tau)$$

$$- \int_0^{\tau} [E'_{12}(\sigma,\eta)\dot{w}_1(\tau-\eta) + E'_{11}(\sigma,\eta)\dot{u}(\tau-\eta)]\, d\eta\Big\}$$

$$-\alpha S_2\Big\{E'_{21}(\sigma,\tau)v_0 - E'_{22}(\sigma,\tau)w_2(0)$$

$$- \int_0^{\tau} E'_{22}(\sigma,\eta)\dot{w}_2(\tau-\eta)\, d\eta\Big\} \quad (32)$$

In what follows, to obtain the short term behavior of the solutions we set $v(\xi) = v_0$, a constant. With this, E_{21} becomes identical to E_{22}. Furthermore, we let $u(\tau) = 0$. It is convenient to follow Neumann's approach and let the interface velocity constant

$$\lambda = \sigma/2\sqrt{\tau} \quad (33)$$

Using the asymptotic results and neglecting the integrals in equations (30-31) we obtain

$$w_1(0) = \frac{1}{\text{erf}(\lambda)} \qquad w_2(0) = \frac{1 - v_0\text{erf}(\lambda/\sqrt{\alpha})}{\text{erfc}(\lambda/\sqrt{\alpha})} \quad (34)$$

The interface velocity equation (32) gives the transcendental equation for λ,

$$\sqrt{\pi}\lambda = \frac{S_1}{\text{erf}(\lambda)}e^{-\lambda^2} - \sqrt{\alpha}\frac{S_2(v_0 - 1)}{\text{erfc}(\lambda/\sqrt{\alpha})}e^{-\lambda^2/\alpha} \quad (35)$$

NUMERICAL SOLUTION

The solution of equations (30-32) was carried out in discrete time steps of duration h. The initial values of the two unknown functions $w_1(\tau)$ and $w_2(\tau)$ were obtained from equation (34) after solving the transcendental equation (35) for λ. In the examples given below, we use the Neumann solution, $\sigma_N = 2\lambda\sqrt{\tau}$ to propagate the interface for five time steps. The values of $w_1(\tau)$ and $w_2(\tau)$ for these time steps were obtained from equations (30) and (31), neglecting the integral terms. In this range $w_1(\tau)$ and $w_2(\tau)$ remain almost constant as shown in Table 1 and the omission of the integrals involving time derivatives causes negligible error.

TABLE 1. HISTORIES OF INTERFACE LOCATION AND THE EXTENDED DOMAIN WALL TEMPERATURES WHEN S_1=10.0, S_2=10.0, α = 1.0, h = 0.001

τ	σ_N	σ	w_1	w_2
0.0000	0.00000	0.00000	2.05212	0.04953
0.0200	0.04140	0.04140	2.05212	0.04953
0.0300	0.05071	0.05071	2.05212	0.04953
0.0400	0.05855	0.05855	2.05212	0.04953
0.0500	0.06546	0.06546	2.05212	0.04953
0.0610	0.22868	0.22868	2.05229	0.04943
0.1210	0.32204	0.32261	2.02911	0.04917
0.1810	0.39387	0.39925	1.87556	0.06000
0.2410	0.45449	0.47328	1.66887	0.09979
0.3010	0.50792	0.55594	1.47193	0.15730
0.3610	0.55625	0.65539	1.29965	0.23749
0.4210	0.60070	0.77912	1.15512	0.35681
0.4810	0.64208	0.93404	1.03749	0.53982
0.5020	0.65595	0.99760	1.00071	0.62188

From the sixth step onwards the effect of the integrals are added to $w_1(\tau)$ and $w_2(\tau)$ and σ by evaluating the integrals using the simple trapezoidal rule with the time derivatives evaluated using the backward difference relation. The derivatives involved in the convolution have significant effect at the end point $\eta = 0$ and approximate values for $w_1(\tau)$ and $w_2(\tau)$ obtained by neglecting the integral terms are used for computing these derivatives. Equation (32) is solved using the Euler method. Overall the integral equation method appears to be sufficiently robust and no recourse for sophisticated multi-step methods is warranted during the time stepping. The Green's functions E_{ij} had to be recalculated at all causal times when the interface is located at σ. A substantial portion of the total computational time is spent on evaluating these functions. In order to speed up this effort, the $\sin n\pi\xi$ and $\cos n\pi\xi$ terms are expressed in terms of the Chebyshev polynomials T_n and U_n and their recursion relation, as follows:

$$\cos n\pi\xi = T_n(y), \quad \sin n\pi\xi = \sqrt{1-y^2}U_{n-1}(y)$$

$$y = \cos \pi\xi \quad (36)$$

$$T_{n+1} = 2yT_n - T_{n-1}, \quad (1-y^2)U_{n-1} = T_{n-1} - yT_n \quad (37)$$

The recursion relations are used in conjunction with

$$T_0 = 1, \quad T_1 = y \quad (38)$$

The computations were carried out using two FORTRAN programs. The first program solves the transcendental equation (35) to obtain the value of λ. The second program computes the discretized values of $w_1(\tau)$, $w_2(\tau)$ and σ. The material parameters, step size and total estimated duration of interface motion are input to the program.

RESULTS AND DISCUSSION

The programs were run for the Stefan numbers $S_1 = 0.1$, $S_2 = 0.1$, $v_0 = 2.0$, $u(\tau) = 0$ and $\alpha = 1.0$ to study the convergence of the method with respect to the step size h. The time taken by the interface to traverse the finite one dimensional medium was computed for each time step selection. Table 2. shows the effect of step size on the time for the total freezing of the domain.

TABLE 2. EFFECT OF STEP SIZE ON THE TIME FOR TOTAL FREEZING

h	τ
0.5000	5.5000
0.1000	5.3000
0.0500	5.3000
0.0100	5.3600
0.0075	5.3625
0.0050	5.3650

A comparison with the solution obtained by Dursunkaya and Nair (1990) shows excellent agreement for the interface location. Figure 1 shows a plot of σ against τ when $S_1 = 0.1$, $S_2 = 0.1$, and $\alpha = 1.0$. The interface location for the Neumann solution is also plotted for comparison. Figure 2 shows the interface locations for $\alpha = 10$ with the remaining parameters the same as before. Again $h = 0.01$ appears to be sufficient for an accuracy of 3 significant digits.

In Figure 3, the effect of the interface velocity constant λ is examined. According to the Neumann solution $\lambda = 0.1891$ which is shown by the middle curve. Underestimating the starting value appears to have negligible effect in computing the total time for freezing. The computation has a certain amount of self-correction. The value $\lambda = 0.5$, inspite of the initial self-correction does not fully converge to the true solution in the available time.

The unsteady boundary conditions and non-uniform initial conditions are studied in the parametric form

$$u(\tau) = \beta\tau, \quad v(\xi) = v_0(1 + \gamma\xi) \tag{39}$$

where β and γ describe the slopes of the temporal and spatial distributions of temperautures.

Figure 4 shows, as expected, if the left boundary temperature is gradually increased the interface motion slows down. If this temperature is decreased the interface accelerates. The possibility of a second melting front is not considered in this formulation and β has to be restricted by an upper bound.

In Figure 5, the gradient of the initial temperature is included using γ. For a negative gradient the interface speeds up and for a positive gradient it slows down. In Figures 3, 4, and 5 the other parameters are $S_1 = 0.1$, $S_2 = 0.1$ and $\alpha = 1.0$.

The feasibility of using the integral equation approach has been clearly illustrated in the examples shown here.

Acknowledgement

The author is indebted to Professor L. N. Tao for numerous discussions on the Stefan problem. An ERIF grant from the Illinois Institute of Technology is acknowledged.

REFERENCES

Boley, B. A., 1961, "A Method of Heat Conduction Analysis of Melting and Solidification Problems," J. Math. Phys., Vol. 40, pp. 300–313.

Carslaw, H. S. and Jaeger, J. C., 1959, *Conduction of Heat in Solids*, Oxford University Press, UK.

Charach, Ch. and Zoglin, P., 1985, "Solidification in a Finite Initially Overheated Slab," International Journal of Heat and Mass Transfer, Vol. 28, pp. 2261–2268.

Crank, J., 1984, *Free and Moving Boundary Problems*, Clarendon Press, UK.

Dursunkaya, Z. and Nair, S., 1990, "A Moving Boundary Problem in a Finite Domain," J. Appl. Mechanics, Vol. 57, pp. 50–56.

Fukusako, S. and Seki, N., 1987, "Fundamental Aspects of Analytical and Numerical Methods on Freezing and Melting Heat Transfer Problems," Annual Review of Numerical Fluid Mechanics and Heat Transfer (T. C. Chawla, editor) Vol. 1, pp. 351–402.

Goodman, T. R., 1958, "The Heat Balance Integral and its Applications to Problems Involving a Change of Phase," Journal of Heat Transfer, Vol. 80, pp. 335–341.

Kolodner, I. I., 1956, "Free Boundary Problem for the Heat Equation with Applications to Problems of Change of Phase," Comm. Pure and Appl. Math. Vol. 9, pp. 1-31.

Ockendon, J. R. and Hodgkins, W. R., 1975, "*Moving Boundary Problems in Heat Flow and Diffusion*, Clarendon Press, UK.

Rubinstein, L. I., 1971, *The Stefan Problem*, American Mathematical Society, Providence, RI.

Tao, L. N., 1978, "The Stefan Problem with Arbitrary Initial and Boundary Conditions," Quart. Appl. Math., Vol. 36, pp. 223–233.

Tao, L. N., 1979a, "On Free Boundary Problems with Arbitrary Initial and Flux Conditions," Z. Angew. Math. Phys., Vol. 30, pp. 416–426.

Tao, L. N., 1979b, "Free Boundary Problems with Radiation Boundary Conditions," Quart. Appl. Math. Vol. 37, pp. 1-10.

Tao, L. N., 1979c, "On Solidification Problems including the Density Jump at the Moving Boundary,"

Quart. J. Mech. Appl. Math., Vol. 32, pp. 175–185.
Tao, L. N., 1980, "The Analyticity of Solutions of the Stefan Problem," Arch. Rational Mech. and Anal., Vol. 72, pp. 285–301.
Tao, L. N., 1981, "The Exact Solutions of Some Stefan Problems with Prescribed Heat Flux," J. Appl. Mech., Vol. 48, pp. 732–736.
Tao, L. N., 1986, "A Method for Solving Moving Boundary Problems," SIAM J. Appl. Math., Vol. 46, pp. 254–264.
Weinbaum, S. and Jiji, L. M., 1977, "Singular Perturbation Theory for Melting or Freezing in Finite Domains Initially not at the Fusion Temperature," J. Appl. Mech. Vol. 44, pp. 25–30.
Wilson, D. G., Solomon, A. D., and Boggs, P. T., 1978, *Moving Boundary Problems*, Academic Press, New York.

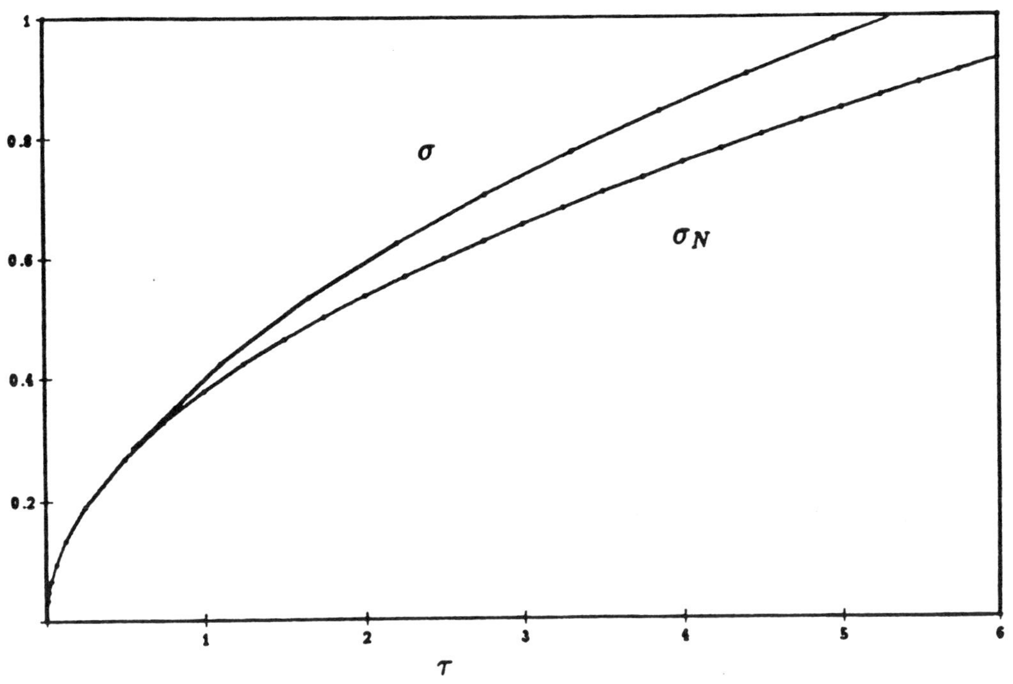

Fig. 1 Location of the interface σ when $S_1 = 0.1$, $S_2 = 0.1$, $\alpha = 1.$ as compared to the Neumann solution σ_N.

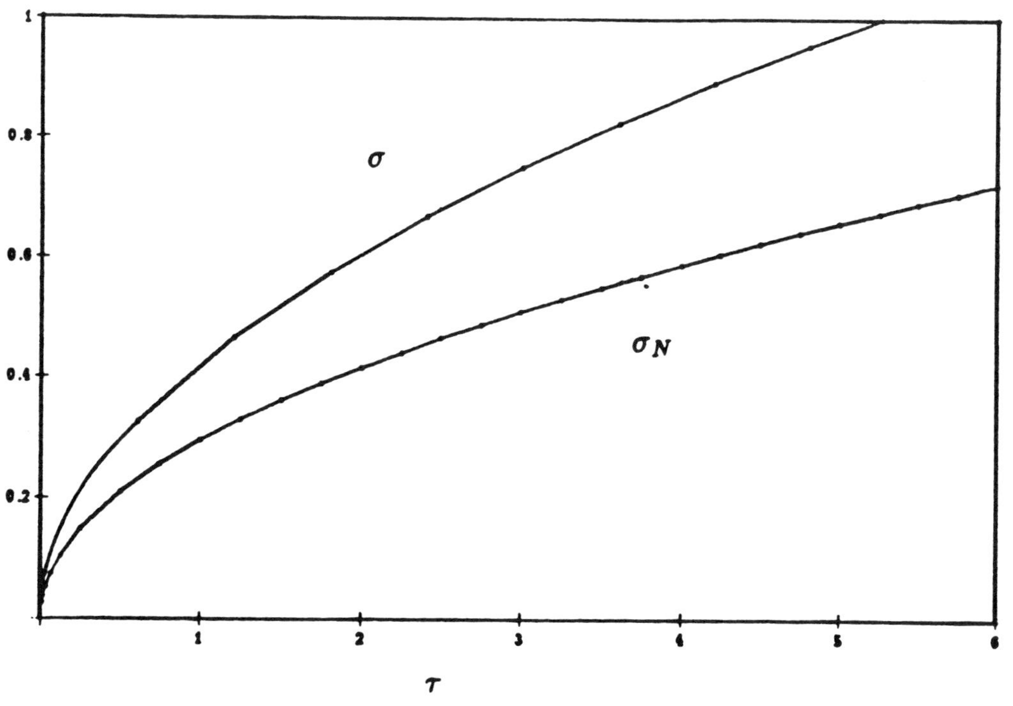

Fig. 2 Location of the interface σ when $S_1 = 0.1$, $S_2 = 0.1$, $\alpha = 10.$ as compared to the Neumann solution σ_N.

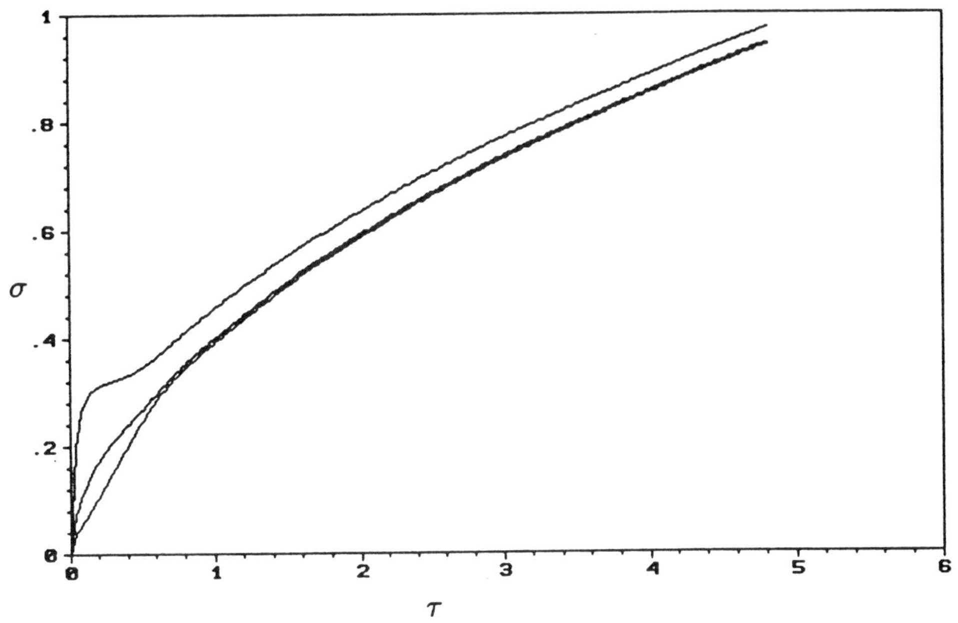

Fig. 3 Effect of initial interface velocity constant λ.
The upper and lower curves represent $\lambda = 0.5$ and $\lambda = 0.1$, respectively. The middle curve is for the exact Neumann solution $\lambda = 0.1891$ for $S_1 = 0.1$, $S_2 = 0.1$ and $\alpha = 1.0$.

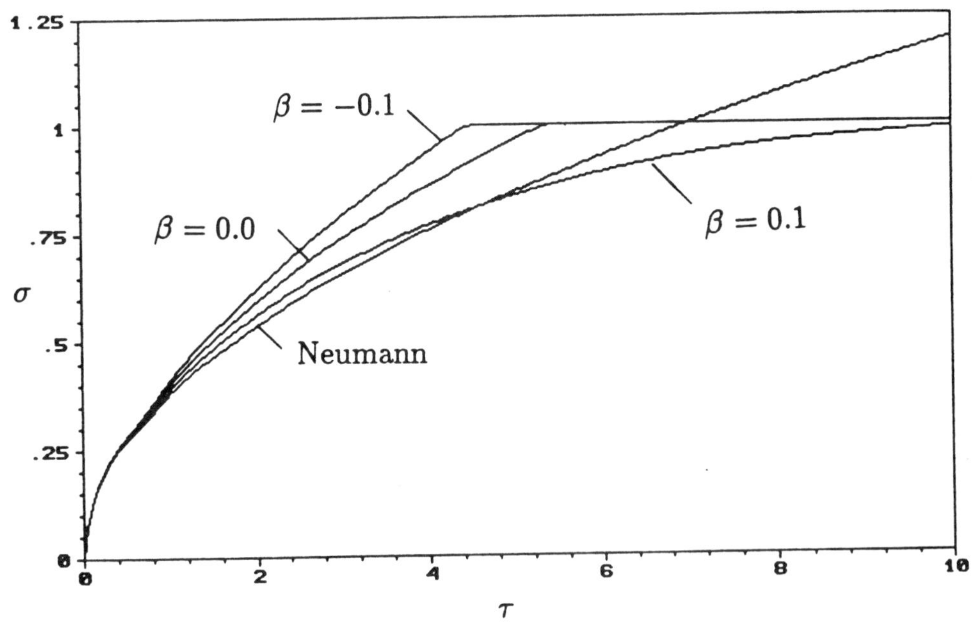

Fig. 4 Interface history with unsteady boundary condition.

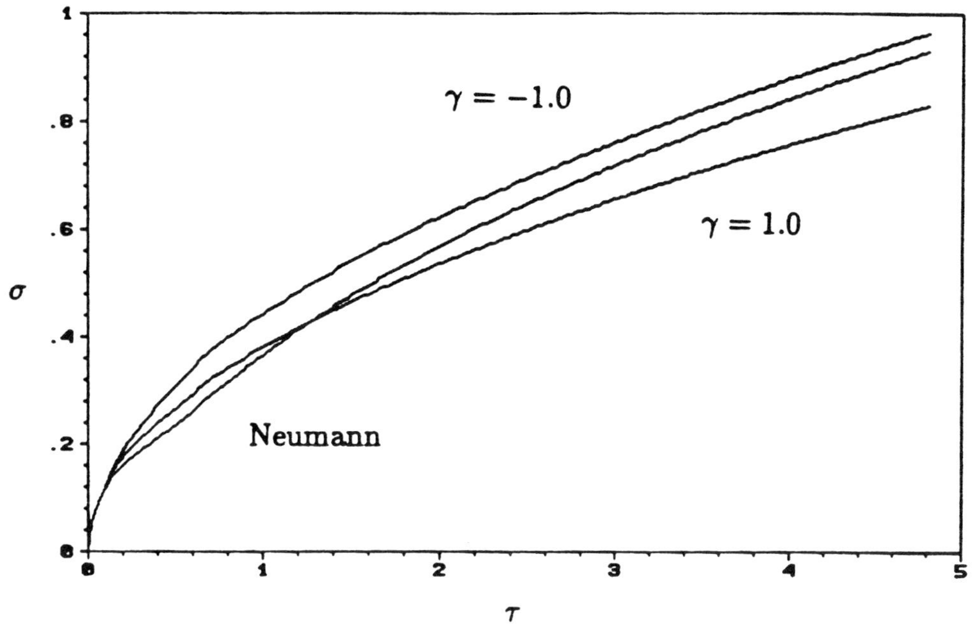

Fig. 5 Interface history with non-uniform initial condition.

HTD-Vol. 284/AMD-Vol. 182, Transport Phenomena in Solidification
ASME 1994

SOLIDIFICATION BY CONVECTIVE COOLING WITH VOID FORMATION

Z. Yang, M. Sen, and S. Paolucci
Department of Aerospace and Mechanical Engineering
University of Notre Dame
Notre Dame, Indiana

ABSTRACT

Solidification of a one-dimensional finite slab of a pure substance subjected to convective cooling is studied. The liquid is initially above its freezing temperature. A void is formed at the cooled surface due to shrinkage of the material during solidification. The interface position is found as a function of time for small Stefan numbers ϵ. The order of magnitude of the Biot number at the cold end determines the nature of the solution. Regular and multiple-scale perturbation solutions are obtained for Biot numbers $\sim O(\epsilon^{-1/2})$ and $\sim O(1)$, respectively, covering a wide range of possible Biot numbers. The analytical results agree well with numerical solutions obtained using the enthalpy method.

NOMENCLATURE

Bi	Biot number
c	specific heat
h	heat transfer coefficient
k	thermal conductivity
l	thickness of slab
l	subscript for liquid
L	latent heat of solidification
s	solid-liquid interface location
s	subscript for solid
t	time
t^*	time solidification begins
T	temperature in the slab
T_0	temperature at $x = 0$
T_i	initial temperature in liquid
T_f	freezing temperature
x	position along the slab
α	thermal diffusivity
γ	shrinkage factor
ϵ	Stefan number
ζ	nondimensional coordinate for numerical method
η	nondimensional coordinate in liquid
θ	nondimensional temperature in solid
θ^*	nondimensional cooling temperature
λ	ratio of liquid to solid thermal conductivity
μ	ratio of liquid to solid thermal diffusivity
ξ	nondimensional coordinate in solid
ρ	density
σ	nondimensional interface position
τ	nondimensional time scaled by diffusion time
τ^*	nondimensional time at beginning of solidification
ϕ	nondimensional temperature in liquid

INTRODUCTION

Heat transfer problems involving phase change are of great practical importance (see, for example, Carslaw and Jaeger, 1959). The mathematical model is a system of partial differential equations of the parabolic type with moving boundaries. Difficulties are encountered in the analytical solution of these problems due to the nonlinearity of the governing equations. Exact solutions are only possible in similarity form for some limited cases. Approximate methods of solution for nonsimilar cases have been developed by a number of authors. For example, one can mention the heat balance integral method of Goodman and Shea (1960), and the variational method of Biot (1970).

Perturbation methods based on the assumption of a small Stefan number, which is the ratio of sensible heat to latent heat, have also been used to deal with finite domain solidification problems. A regular perturbation analysis of the single-phase problem with the liquid phase initially at the freezing temperature for convective and radiative cooling has been carried out by Yan and Huang (1979). Significant progress was reported by Weinbaum and Jiji (1977) for the situation in which the liquid is initially superheated, i.e has a temperature above the freezing point. They used a matched asymptotic method which considers a finite domain of planar or cylindrical one-dimensional geometry with an isothermal solid boundary and an adiabatic or isothermal liquid boundary. However, the effect of shrinkage of the material during solidification was not considered. Shrinkage is due to a difference in density between the solid and the liquid. Voids are formed due to shrinkage upon solidification. The present work includes the effect of shrinkage and void formation. It also covers convective cooling at the solid boundary. This is more general than an isothermal condition, which it includes as a special case. Perturbation methods are used for the analysis, and the solutions obtained are verified numerically. For simplicity the geometry is taken to be one-dimensional as shown in Figure 1. The molten material at temperature T_i is initially between $x = 0$ and $x = l$. Convective cooling at temperature T_0 is then applied at $x = 0$ which represents the surface of the mold. In the precooling stage, there is thermal contact between the liquid and the mold with a heat transfer coefficient $\tilde{h}$. Eventually the temperature of the liquid comes down to the freezing point and solidification begins. As the material solidifies, it shrinks and a void is formed between the solidifying material and the mold. This is the region between $x = 0$ and $x = \gamma s(t)$, where $\gamma = (1 - \rho_l/\rho_s)$ is the parameter quantifying the effect of shrinkage. Heat transfer across this void is by convection with constant heat transfer coefficient h (Reddy and Beckermann, 1993). The outer boundary of the liquid at $x = l$ is taken to be adiabatic.

TEMPERATURE DISTRIBUTION BEFORE SOLIDIFICATION

In an isothermal cooling problem (Weinbaum and Jiji, 1977) the material would begin to solidify as soon as cooling is applied. In the present problem, however, there is a period of precooling before the solidification can actually start. The material is all in liquid form for time $t < t^*$, where t^* is the time necessary to bring the cold boundary to the freezing temperature. Before looking at solidification, we would like to determine the temperature distribution in the liquid at $t = t^*$.

In the precooling stage heat transfer in the liquid is by single-phase conduction. The governing equation and boundary conditions for the temperature distribution, $T_l(x,t)$, are

$$\begin{aligned}
\alpha_l \frac{\partial^2 T_l}{\partial x^2} &= \frac{\partial T_l}{\partial t}, \quad 0 \le x \le l \\
\frac{\partial T_l}{\partial x}(l,t) &= 0 \\
k_l \frac{\partial T_l}{\partial x}(0,t) &= \tilde{h}\left[T_l(0,t) - T_0\right] \\
T_l(x,0) &= T_i
\end{aligned}$$

These can be nondimensionalized to

$$\begin{aligned}
\frac{\partial^2 \tilde{\phi}}{\partial \eta^2} &= \frac{\partial \tilde{\phi}}{\partial \tau}, \quad 0 \le \eta \le 1 \\
\frac{\partial \tilde{\phi}}{\partial \eta}(1,\tau) &= 0 \\
\frac{\partial \tilde{\phi}}{\partial \eta}(0,\tau) &= \frac{\tilde{Bi}}{\lambda}\tilde{\phi}(0,\tau) \\
\tilde{\phi}(\eta,0) &= 1
\end{aligned}$$

The nondimensional liquid temperature, distance and time are given by

$$\begin{aligned}
\tilde{\phi} &= \frac{T_l - T_0}{T_i - T_0} \\
\eta &= \frac{x}{l} \\
\tau &= \frac{\alpha_l t}{l^2}
\end{aligned}$$

respectively. The governing parameter is the nondimensional heat transfer coefficient, the Biot number, defined by $\tilde{Bi} = \tilde{h}l/k_s$ where $\tilde{h}$ is the heat transfer coefficient due to thermal contact between the liquid and the mold. Also $\lambda = k_l/k_s$. It is easy to find a series solution to this single-phase conductive problem (Carslaw and Jaeger, 1959). The resulting temperature distribution is

$$\tilde{\phi}(\eta,\tau) = \sum_{n=0}^{\infty} A_n \exp(-k_n^2\tau)\cos\left[k_n(1-\eta)\right]$$

where k_n is the nth positive eigenvalue determined from the transcendental equation

$$\tan k_n = \frac{\tilde{Bi}}{\lambda k_n}$$

and

$$A_n = \frac{2\sin k_n}{k_n\left[1 + \tilde{Bi}/(\tilde{Bi}^2 + \lambda^2 k_n^2)\right]}.$$

Using this solution, the time τ^* when the cold end drops to the freezing point can be found. Defining

$$\tilde{\phi}(0,\tau^*) = \tilde{\phi}^* = \frac{T_f - T_0}{T_i - T_0},$$

the temperature distribution in the liquid at the instant solidification begins is

$$\tilde{\phi}(\eta,\tau^*) = \sum_{n=0}^{\infty} A_n \exp(-k_n^2\tau^*)\cos\left[k_n(1-\eta)\right]$$

This temperature distribution becomes flatter as the Biot number decreases, as shown in Figure 2. In Figure 8, it shows that the time for solidification to begin τ^*, goes up sharply as the precooling Biot number $\tilde{Bi}$ is reduced.

GOVERNING EQUATIONS DURING SOLIDIFICATION

Once solidification begins we have to deal with a two-phase problem. However, heat transfer in either phase is by conduction alone. Due to shrinkage there is a void formed which we have assumed to be near the cold end. With void formation there is bulk motion of the solid phase; this adds a convective term to the heat conduction equation in the solid. It is assumed, however, that there is no convective motion in the liquid (Wilson and Solomon, 1986). The governing equations are thus

$$\alpha_s \frac{\partial^2 T_s}{\partial x^2} = \frac{\partial T_s}{\partial t} + \gamma \frac{ds}{dt}\frac{\partial T_s}{\partial x}, \quad t > t^*, \quad \gamma s \le x < s \tag{1}$$

$$\alpha_l \frac{\partial^2 T_l}{\partial x^2} = \frac{\partial T_l}{\partial t}, \quad t > t^*, \quad s \le x \le l \tag{2}$$

for each one of the two phases separated by the interface at $x = s(t)$. The boundary and initial conditions are

$$\begin{aligned}
T_s(s,t) &= T_f \qquad (3)\\
T_l(s,t) &= T_f \\
\frac{\partial T_l}{\partial x}(l,t) &= 0
\end{aligned}$$

$$
\begin{aligned}
k_s\frac{\partial T_s}{\partial x}(\gamma s,t) &= h\left[T_s(\gamma s,t)-T_0\right]\\
\rho_l L\frac{ds}{dt} &= k_s\frac{\partial T_s}{\partial x}(s,t)-k_l\frac{\partial T_l}{\partial x}(s,t)\\
s(t^*) &= 0\\
T_l(x,t^*) &= \tilde{T}(x)
\end{aligned}
\tag{4}
$$

We introduce the liquid and solid nondimensional temperature variables

$$
\begin{aligned}
\phi &= \frac{T_l-T_f}{T_i-T_f}\\
\theta &= \frac{1}{\lambda}\frac{T_s-T_f}{T_i-T_f}
\end{aligned}
$$

A Landau transformation is used to convert the moving boundary problem into one of fixed domain. We note that this nondimensionalization can only be used if $T_i > T_f$. The new spatial variables in solid and liquid are

$$
\begin{aligned}
\xi &= \frac{x}{s}\\
\eta &= \frac{x-s}{l-s}
\end{aligned}
$$

The nondimensional position of the solid-liquid interface is $\sigma = s/l$. Also let $\mu = \alpha_l/\alpha_s$. The governing equations in these variables are

$$
\begin{aligned}
\frac{\partial^2\theta}{\partial\xi^2} &= \mu\left[\sigma^2\frac{\partial\theta}{\partial\tau}-(\xi-\gamma)\sigma\frac{d\sigma}{d\tau}\frac{\partial\theta}{\partial\xi}\right],\ \gamma\le\xi\le 1\\
\frac{\partial^2\phi}{\partial\eta^2} &= (1-\sigma)^2\frac{\partial\phi}{\partial\tau}-(1-\eta)(1-\sigma)\frac{d\sigma}{d\tau}\frac{\partial\phi}{\partial\eta},\ 0\le\eta\le 1
\end{aligned}
$$

with boundary and initial conditions

$$
\begin{aligned}
\theta(1,\tau) &= 0\\
\phi(0,\tau) &= 0\\
\frac{\partial\phi}{\partial\eta}(1,\tau) &= 0\\
\sigma(1-\sigma)\frac{d\sigma}{d\tau} &= \epsilon\left[(1-\sigma)\frac{\partial\theta}{\partial\xi}(1,\tau)-\sigma\frac{\partial\phi}{\partial\eta}(0,\tau)\right] && (5)\\
\frac{\partial\theta}{\partial\xi}(\gamma,\tau) &= \sigma Bi\left[\theta(\gamma,\tau)-\theta^*\right] && (6)\\
\sigma(\tau^*) &= 0\\
\phi(\eta,\tau^*) &= (\tilde{\phi}(\eta,\tau^*)-\tilde{\phi}^*)/(1-\tilde{\phi}^*)
\end{aligned}
$$

The nondimensional parameters controlling the solidification process are

$$
\begin{aligned}
\epsilon &= c_l\frac{T_i-T_f}{L}\\
Bi &= \frac{hl}{k_s}\\
\theta^* &= \frac{1}{\lambda}\frac{T_0-T_f}{T_i-T_f}
\end{aligned}
$$

where ϵ is the Stefan number, Bi is the Biot number, and θ^* is the cooling temperature. The system has all its physical properties represented by the seven nondimensional parameters ϵ, μ, λ, γ, $\tilde{Bi}$, Bi, and θ^*. The parameter Bi is proportional to h, which is the convective heat transfer coefficient after the separation of the solidified material from the mold. $\tilde{Bi}$, on the other hand is its value before solidification begins, i.e. before the void is formed. Thus, Bi can be expected to be much smaller than $\tilde{Bi}$. For numerical simplicity only, the results plotted here assume the same value for both. When $Bi \to \infty$ and $\gamma \to 0$, the boundary condition (6) reduces to the isothermal condition analyzed by Weinbaum and Jiji (1977). Here, however, we will investigate the problem for finite Bi. We will assume that μ, λ, and $(1-\gamma)$ are all fixed by material properties and are of $O(1)$. In addition we will take $\theta^* \sim O(1)$.

Since the parameter ϵ only appears in the interface condition (5), it is natural to use it as a small parameter to develop a perturbation solution. Physically it means that we are restricting ourselves to a small ratio of the sensible heat due to superheat to the latent heat.

SOLUTIONS FOR $Bi \sim O(\epsilon^{-1/2})$

Let us first consider a large convective heat transfer coefficient corresponding to $Bi \sim O(\epsilon^{-1/2})$. For this we seek perturbation solutions of the form

$$
\begin{aligned}
\theta(\xi,\tau) &= \sum_{n=0}^{\infty}\epsilon^{n/2}\theta_n(\xi,\tau) && (7)\\
\phi(\eta,\tau) &= \sum_{n=0}^{\infty}\epsilon^{n/2}\phi_n(\eta,\tau)\\
\sigma(\tau) &= \sum_{n=0}^{\infty}\epsilon^{n/2}\sigma_n(\tau) && (8)
\end{aligned}
$$

Substituting these expansions in the governing equations and boundary conditions, we can obtain the following:

$$
\begin{aligned}
\sigma_0 &= 0\\
\sigma_1 &= -\frac{1}{Bi^*(1-\gamma)}+\sqrt{\frac{1}{Bi^{*2}(1-\gamma)^2}-\frac{2\theta^*(\tau-\tau^*)}{(1-\gamma)}}\\
\sigma_2 &= \frac{-1}{\sqrt{1-C^*(\tau-\tau^*)}}\sum_{n=0}^{\infty}C_n\\
&\left\{\frac{1-\sqrt{1-C^*(\tau-\tau^*)}\exp\left[-(n+\frac{1}{2})^2\pi^2(\tau-\tau^*)\right]}{(n+\frac{1}{2})\pi}\right.\\
&+\frac{\sqrt{-C^*}\exp\left[\frac{(n+\frac{1}{2})^2\pi^2}{-C^*}\right]}{(n+\frac{1}{2})^2\pi^{\frac{3}{2}}}\\
&\left(\operatorname{erf}\left[(n+\frac{1}{2})\pi\sqrt{(\tau-\tau^*)-\frac{1}{C^*}}\right]\right.\\
&\left.\left.-\operatorname{erf}\left[(n+\frac{1}{2})\pi\sqrt{-\frac{1}{C^*}}\right]\right)\right\}\\
\theta_0 &= \frac{\sigma_1 Bi^*\theta^*}{\sigma_1 Bi^*(1-\gamma)+1}(\xi-1)
\end{aligned}
$$

$$\theta_1 = \frac{\sigma_2 Bi^* [\theta_0(\gamma,\tau) - \theta^*]}{\sigma_1 Bi^*(1-\gamma)+1}(\xi - 1)$$

$$\phi_0 = \sum_{n=0}^{\infty} C_n \sin\left[(n+\frac{1}{2})\pi\eta\right] \exp\left[-(n+\frac{1}{2})^2\pi^2(\tau-\tau^*)\right]$$

where

$$Bi^* = Bi\sqrt{\epsilon}$$
$$C^* = 2(1-\gamma)Bi^{*2}\theta^*$$
$$C_n = \frac{1}{1-\tilde{\phi}^*}\left\{\frac{-2\tilde{\phi}^*}{(n+\frac{1}{2})\pi} + \sum_{m=0}^{\infty}\frac{2A_m \exp(-k_n^2\tau^*)(m+\frac{1}{2})\pi\cos k_m}{(n+\frac{1}{2})^2\pi^2 - k_m^2}\right\}.$$

The perturbation solution of $\sigma(\tau)$ has been obtained up to $O(\epsilon)$. The series converges fast as seen from the comparison between the terms σ_1 and σ_2 in Figure 3. The second order solution is mainly important near the beginning of solidification.

Figure 4 shows the displacement of the solidification front for different Biot numbers, Bi. The front moves faster for higher Bi. In Figure 5 and 6 the shrinkage factor, γ, is varied.

At time $\tau = \tau_c$, solidification is completed and $\sigma = 1$. From Figure 8, it can be seen that the time for solidification to begin, τ^*, is much smaller than τ_c. Due to large latent heat, diffusion of heat in the material is much faster than its solidification.

SOLUTION FOR $Bi \sim O(1)$

This corresponds to a moderate heat transfer coefficient.

Inner solution

If we follow the previous form of the perturbation expansions (7)-(8), we find that $\sigma_{2n+1} = 0$. Actually, in both the perturbation expansion of nondimensionalized temperature and solid-liquid interface position function, the odd n terms drop out. A regular perturbation solution is then

$$\sigma_0 = 0$$
$$\sigma_2 = -Bi\theta^*\tau + \sum_{n=0}^{\infty}\frac{C_n}{(n+\frac{1}{2})\pi}[\exp(-(n+\frac{1}{2})^2\pi^2\tau) - 1]$$
$$\sigma_4 = \frac{1}{2}\sigma_2^2 + Bi\theta^*[1 + Bi(1-\gamma)]\int_0^\tau \sigma_2 d\tau - \int_0^\tau \frac{\partial\phi_1(0,\tau)}{\partial\eta}d\tau$$

where ϕ_1 is the first-order nondimensional temperature distribution in the liquid which can be (for example, numerically) determined from

$$\frac{\partial^2\phi_1}{\partial\eta^2} = \frac{\partial\phi_1}{\partial\tau} - 2\sigma_2\frac{\partial\phi_0}{\partial\tau} - (1-\eta)\frac{d\sigma_2}{d\tau}\frac{\partial\phi_0}{\partial\eta}$$
$$\frac{\partial\phi_1}{\partial\eta}(1,\tau) = 0$$
$$\phi_1(0,\tau) = 0$$
$$\phi_1(\eta,0) = 0$$

A further inspection of this regular perturbation solution shows that when τ is large all the exponential terms are negligibly small. The interface position tends to

$$\sigma \to -\epsilon Bi\theta^*\tau - \frac{1}{2}Bi(1-\gamma)(\epsilon Bi\theta^*\tau)^2 + O(\epsilon^3)$$

This solution is not valid near $\sigma = 1$, since the higher order terms are comparable to the lower order ones if $\tau \sim 1/\epsilon Bi\theta^*$. So only the early stage of solidification is described well by this solution, but not the later stage. This is thus an inner solution. The inner solution indicates that solidification begins with a very small interface velocity.

Outer solution

To find the outer solution we change the time scale to $\hat{\tau} = \epsilon\tau$. Then we obtain

$$\hat{\phi}_0 = 0$$
$$\hat{\sigma}_0 = \frac{-1}{Bi(1-\gamma)} + \sqrt{\frac{1}{Bi^2(1-\gamma)^2} - \frac{2\theta^*(\hat{\tau}-\hat{\tau}_0)}{(1-\gamma)}}$$

as the leading terms, where $\hat{\tau}_0$ is a constant of integration. A general form of the next order interface position is

$$\sigma_1 = \frac{C}{1 + (1-\gamma)Bi\sigma_0}$$

From the matching requirement, we find that the constant $C = 0$.

Matching

We would like the inner and outer solutions to be matched for a properly chosen $\hat{\tau}_0$. To do this we construct a composite solution near an intermediate time $\hat{\tau}_m$ and select $\hat{\tau}_0$ such that the inner and outer solutions share the common leading order value of $\sigma(\tau)$ and its first derivative at $\hat{\tau} = \hat{\tau}_m$. The functional form of the inner and outer solution guarantees the existence of this matching intermediate time $\hat{\tau}_m$.

After matching, the perturbation solution is found to be

$$\sigma = \begin{cases} -\epsilon\{\frac{Bi\theta^*\hat{\tau}}{\epsilon(1-\gamma)} + \sum_{n=0}^{\infty}\frac{C_n}{(n+\frac{1}{2})\pi}\left[\exp\{-(n+\frac{1}{2})^2\pi^2\frac{\hat{\tau}}{\epsilon}\} - 1\right]\} \\ \qquad + O(\epsilon^2), \hat{\tau} \le \hat{\tau}_m \\ -\frac{1}{Bi(1-\gamma)} + \sqrt{\frac{1}{Bi^2(1-\gamma)^2} - \frac{2\theta^*(\hat{\tau}-\hat{\tau}_0)}{(1-\gamma)}} + O(\epsilon), \hat{\tau} > \hat{\tau}_m \end{cases}$$

Figure 7(a) shows the matching of the inner and outer solutions, and Figure 7(b) an enlargement near the matching region. From Figure 8, it turns out that $\hat{\tau}_0$ and $\hat{\tau}_m$ are very small compared to the total solidification time, τ_c, so that the outer solution is the one that is valid for most of the time. Notice also that the order of accuracy of both solutions is actually the same, both one order lower than the leading term.

At $\tau = \tau_m$ the temperature distribution in the liquid is almost uniform since τ_m is long enough for nonuniformities to decay. Hence, the outer solution is similar to what would be obtained in a single-phase problem.

Other Bi

The $Bi \sim O(\epsilon^{-1/2})$ solution is also valid for any Biot number larger than $O(\epsilon^{-1/2})$. As a special case it is valid for $Bi \to \infty$ which is the case of isothermal cooling. In fact it can be checked that in this limit the solution calculated here tends to that given by Weinbaum and Jiji (1977).

We can also consider the range of Bi between $O(1)$ and $O(\epsilon^{-1/2})$. The interface position computed from either approximation is similar, as shown in Figure 9. The starting velocity is identical for both solutions.

For $Bi < O(1)$, the matched solution for $Bi \sim O(1)$ should also be formally valid. For the same reason the outer solution holds well for $Bi < O(1)$, except the extent to which the nonuniformity of liquid temperature almost dies out at $\tau = \tau^*$.

NUMERICAL VALIDATION

The problem was also solved numerically to check the validity of the perturbation solutions described here. We use an enthalpy method in which the solid and liquid regions are treated as a continuum except for an enthalpy jump at the interface. The method is versatile, convenient, adaptable and easily programmable for phase change problems.

To implement the method, we introduce

$$\zeta = \begin{cases} \frac{x-\gamma s}{(1-\gamma)l}, & \gamma s(t) \le x \le s(t) \\ \frac{x}{l}, & s(t) < x \le l, \end{cases}$$

$$\Theta = \begin{cases} \frac{T_l - T_f}{T_i - T_f} \\ (1-\gamma)\frac{1}{\lambda}\frac{T_s - T_f}{T_i - T_f} \end{cases}$$

$$H = \begin{cases} \mu(1-\gamma)^2\Theta, & \Theta \le 0 \\ \Theta + 1/\epsilon, & \Theta > 0 \end{cases}$$

The original system of equations (1)–(2) and boundary conditions (3)–(4) are reduced to

$$\begin{aligned} \frac{\partial^2 \Theta}{\partial \zeta^2} &= \frac{\partial H}{\partial \tau}, \; 0 \le \zeta \le 1 \\ \frac{\partial \Theta}{\partial \zeta}(0,\tau) &= 0 \\ \frac{\partial \Theta}{\partial \zeta}(0,\tau) &= (1-\gamma)Bi\Theta(0,\tau) - Bi\theta^* \\ \Theta(\zeta,\tau^*) &= \tilde{\phi}(\zeta,\tau^*) \end{aligned}$$

with

$$\Theta = \begin{cases} \frac{H}{\mu(1-\gamma)^2}, & 0 < H \le 1/\epsilon \\ H - 1/\epsilon, & H > 1/\epsilon \end{cases}$$

A second order implicit scheme with successive overrelaxation or an explicit time marching scheme can be chosen to solve the system (Alexiades and Solomon, 1993; Ozisik, 1980). Figure 10 shows that there is good agreement between the analytical and numerical solutions for $\epsilon = 0.04$.

CONCLUSIONS

Regular and multiple-scale perturbation solutions for small Stefan numbers have been obtained for the one-dimensional problem of liquid solidification by convective cooling. The shrinkage due to solidification is taken into account.

The material is initially all liquid. Once cooling is applied, there is a precooling stage, $\tau < \tau^*$, after which solidification begins. The liquid temperature at this instant is not uniform. This nonuniformity is significant if $Bi \sim O(1)$ or larger. For $Bi \sim O(\epsilon^{-1/2})$ or larger, a regular perturbation solution can be obtained for solidification that is valid for all time. For $Bi \sim O(1)$, we find an inner solution valid up to an intermediate matching time τ_m, and an outer solution after that. The analytical solutions have been numerically verified.

ACKNOWLEDGMENT

We are grateful to A. E. Goetze Inc. for support of this research.

REFERENCES

Alexiades, V., and Solomon, A.D., 1993, *Mathematical Modeling of Melting and Freezing Process*, Hemisphere Publ. Corp., Washington,D.C.

Biot, M.A., 1970, *Variational Principles in Heat Transfer*, Clarendon Press, Oxford.

Carslaw, H.S., and Jaeger, J.C., 1959, *Conduction of Heat in Solids*, 2nd ed., Oxford University Press, London.

Goodman, T.R., and Shea, J.J., 1960, "The melting of finite slabs," *Journal of Applied Mechanics*, Vol. 27, pp. 16–24.

Ozisik, M.N., 1980, *Heat Conduction*, John Wiley and Sons, New York.

Reddy, A.V. and Beckermann, C., 1993, "Measurements of metal-mold interfacial coefficients during solidification of Sn and Sn-Pb alloys," *Experimental Heat Transfer*, Vol. 6, pp. 111-129.

Weinbaum, S., and Jiji, L.M.,1977, "Singular perturbation theory for melting or freezing in finite domains initially not at fusion temperature," *ASME Journal of Applied Mechanics*, Vol. 44, pp. 25–30.

Wilson, D.G., and Solomon, A.D, 1986, "A Stefan-type problem with void formation and its explicit solution," *IMA Journal of Applied Mathematics*, Vol. 37, pp. 67–76.

Yan, M.M., and Huang, P.N.S., 1979, "Perturbation solutions to phase change problem subjected to convection and radiation," *ASME Journal of Heat Transfer*, Vol. 101, pp. 96–100.

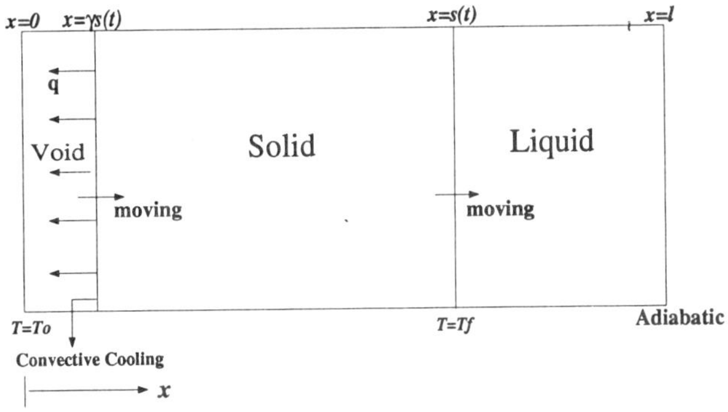

FIGURE 1: SCHEMATIC OF THE PHYSICAL PROBLEM

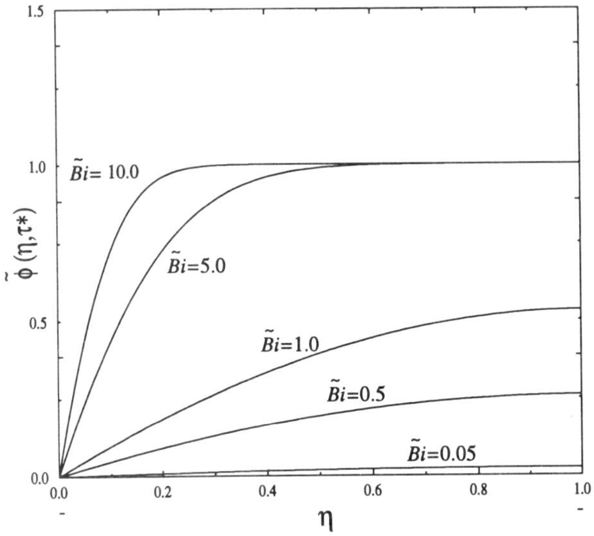

FIGURE 2: INITIAL TEMPERATURE DISTRIBUTION IN LIQUID FOR $\lambda = 1$

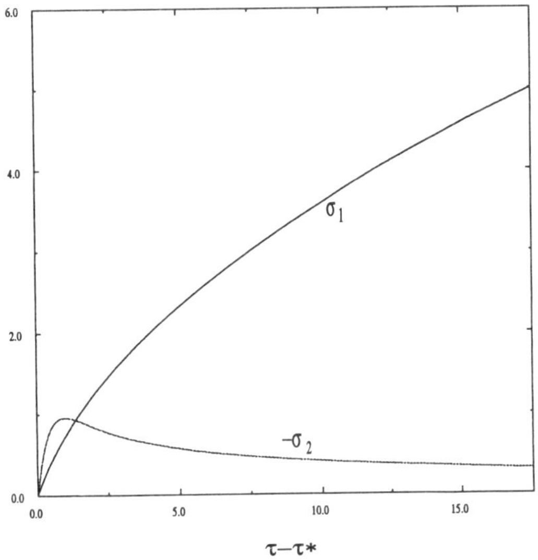

FIGURE 3: COMPARISON OF THE FIRST AND SECOND ORDER SOLUTIONS

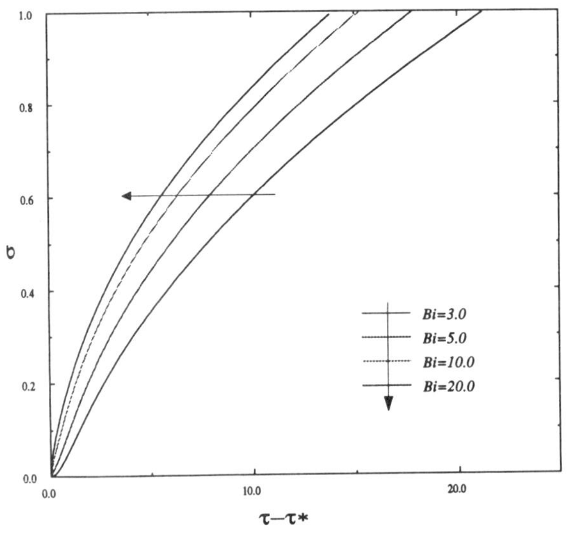

FIGURE4: SOLID-LIQUID INTERFACE DEVELOPMENT FOR $\varepsilon = 0.04$

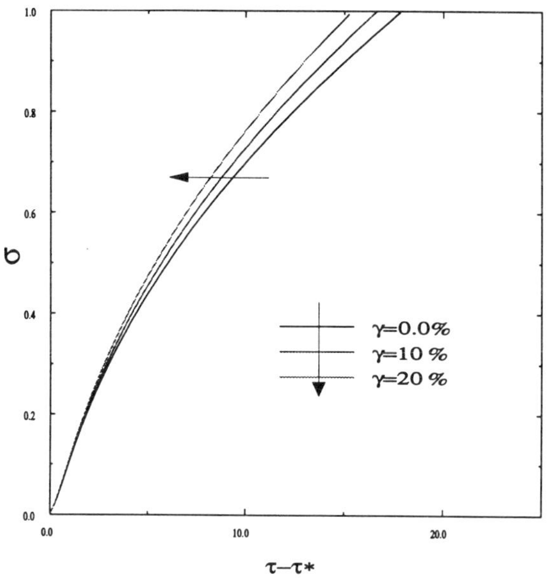

FIGURE 5: SOLID-LIQUID INTERFACE DEVELOPMENT FOR Bi =5.0, ε =0.04

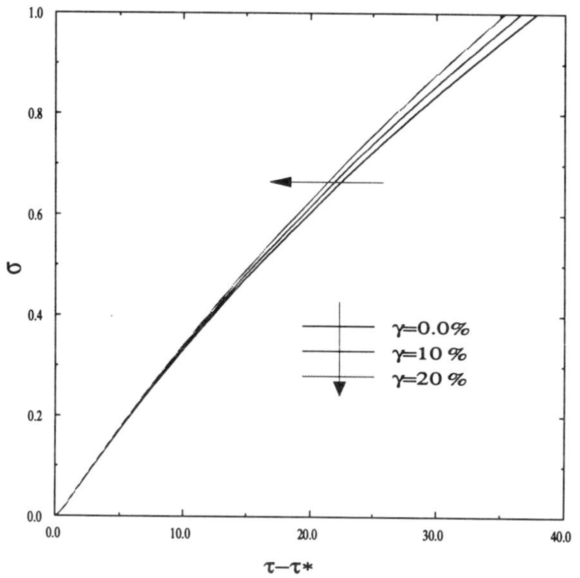

FIGURE 6: SOLID-LIQUID INTERFACE DEVELOPMENT FOR Bi = 1.0, ε =0.04

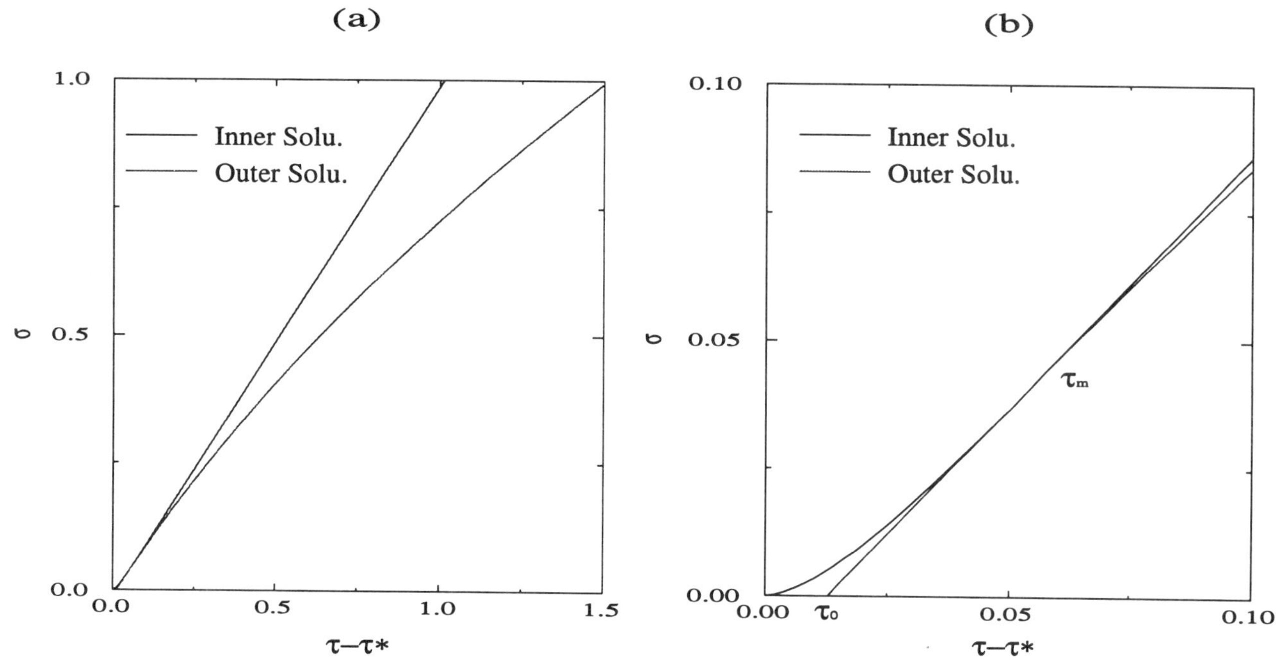

FIGURE 7: MATCHING OF THE INNER AND OUTER SOLUTION
(a) INNER AND OUTER SOLUTION UP TO σ = 1
(b) ENLARGEMENT OF THE MATCHING REGION

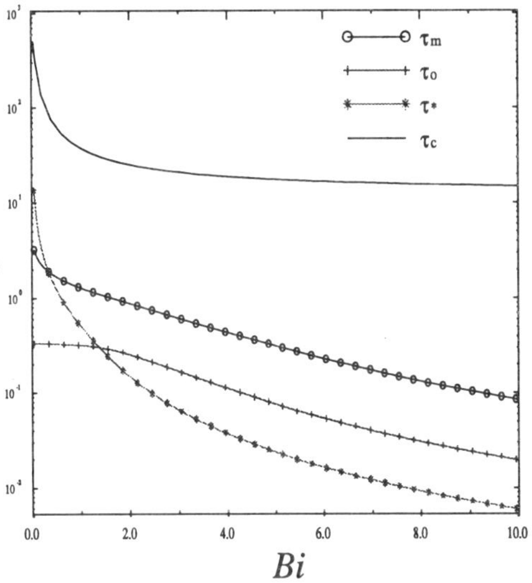

FIGURE 8: VARIATIONS OF CHARACRISTIC TIME FOR $\varepsilon = 0.04$

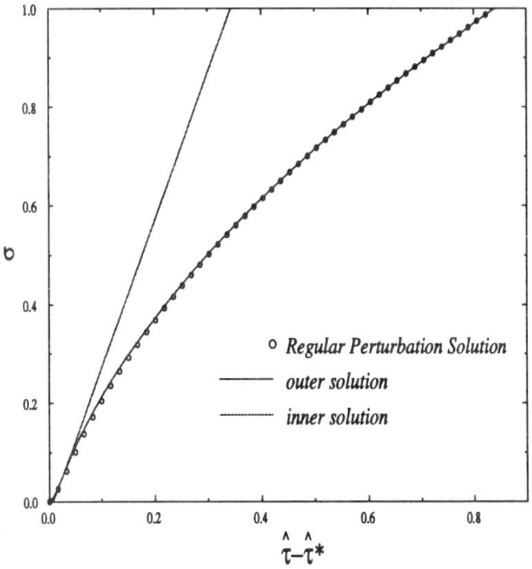

FIGURE 9: COMPARISON OF THE REGULAR AND MATCHED ASYMPTOTIC SOLUTIONS FOR AN INTERMEDIATE BIOT NUMBER

$\varepsilon = 0.04$, $Bi = (\varepsilon^{-1/2}+1)/2 = 3.0$

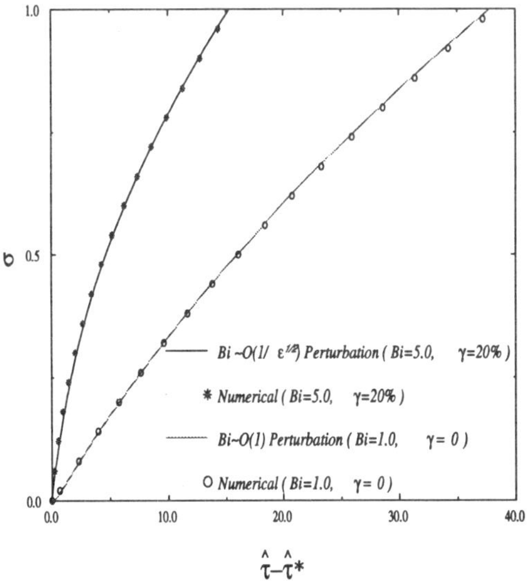

FIGURE 10: COMPARISON OF THE NUMERICAL AND PERTURBATION SOLUTIONS FOR $\varepsilon = 0.04$

HTD-Vol. 284/AMD-Vol. 182, Transport Phenomena in Solidification
ASME 1994

CONVECTIVE HEAT TRANSFER FOR COLD TUBE BUNDLES WITH ICE FORMATIONS IN A STREAM OF WATER AT STEADY STATE

Paul A. Intemann and Michael Kazmierczak
Department of Mechanical, Industrial
and Nuclear Engineering
University of Cincinnati
Cincinnati, Ohio

ABSTRACT

Experiments were conducted on cold tube banks subjected to a crossflow of water. The tubes were internally cooled below the freezing temperature and became enveloped in ice. The resulting ice shapes, which formed on the outside surfaces of the tubes, were allowed to stabilize and their impact on the total steady-state rate of energy exchange between the tubes and the flowing water was investigated.

Both in-line and staggered tube bank geometries were considered with tests conducted in the low to moderate Reynolds Number range (Re_d = 100 - 2000) and for cooling temperature ratio variations of $0.5<\Theta< 8$. The ice formations were directly observed and photographed, and the total heat transfer rate for the tube bank was inferred from a simple energy balance on the system.

The ice shapes which formed around the tubes were characterized as falling into one of three distinct categories: ice formations with no linkage occurring between any adjacent tubes; ice formations with partial linkage of some adjacent tubes; and, for the staggered tube bank, a complete linkage of a majority of the tubes.

The experiments showed that the ice formations dramatically affected the convective heat transfer rate of the tube banks (when compared to non-icing tube banks at the same Re_d) and that the change in heat transfer rate is dependent on the tube bank geometry. In the no-link category, the ice formations were found to either increase or decrease the tube bank heat transfer rate depending on the amount of ice build-up accumulated; the staggered configuration showing a greater overall rise with Θ than the in-line geometry. Ice linkage between adjacent tubes was found to be detrimental to the heat transfer rate of the staggered bank, however, the same phenomena on the in-line tube bank did not seriously impede its heat transfer rate. Correlations expressing the heat transfer behavior of both in-line and staggered tube banks with ice formations at steady state have been developed.

NOMENCLATURE

A	tube bank total exterior surface area, cm^2
AR	aspect ratio of tube bank, h/l
c1	correction factor for short tube bank heat transfer calculation
d	tube outside diameter, cm
h	vertical distance between adjacent tubes, cm
k	thermal conductivity, mW/cm-K
K	heat transfer parameter, Equation (5)
l	horiz. distance between adjacent columns of tube, cm
Nu	average experimental Nusselt number, Equation (4)
Pr	Prandtl Number, υ/α
Q	heat transfer rate, W
Re	Reynolds Number, Equation (2)
T	temperature, K
V	velocity, cm/s
W	work, W

Greek Symbols

α	thermal diffusivity, cm^2/s
Θ	cooling temperature ratio, Equation (3)
μ	dynamic viscosity, g/cm-s
υ	kinematic viscosity, cm^2/s
ρ	fluid density, g/cm^3

Subscripts

bank	tube bank

c	parameter corrected for short tube bank data
d	tube exterior diameter
f	fluid (water)
i	ice/water interface
max	maximum
pump	centrifugal water pump
spool	heated spool piece
system	water tunnel
w	tube wall
∞	freestream condition

<u>Superscript</u>

—	denotes quantity is average of all tubes

INTRODUCTION

The phenomenon of forced convective freezing of ice in a tube bank geometry is one which has only recently received the attention of the scientific research community; primarily due to the increased interest in commercially-viable phase change thermal energy storage systems. While studies of fluid flow and heat transfer by tube banks without phase change, as well as research into melting and freezing heat transfer in general, have been reported by the research community, investigations into the simultaneous occurrence of both phenomena has only recently been explored by a small group of investigators.

The heavy reliance on tube bundle heat exchangers in many industrial applications was partially responsible for the upsurge in research activities of tube bank fluid flow and heat transfer characteristics which occurred during the 1950's and continued unabated into the 1970's. Due to the well-documented flow complexities associated with flow through tube bundles, such as flow separation and non-uniform tube heat transfer film coefficients, most of the studies to date and the resulting design data generated from these studies has come from experimental investigations. The most thorough and complete study of the experimental heat transfer and fluid flow characteristics exhibited by tube banks in crossflow is found in Zukauskas and Ulinskas (1988).

In contrast, solid-liquid phase change heat transfer, also known as melting and freezing heat transfer, is a research area which historically has enjoyed a rather rich yet generally unnoticed tradition in the open literature; but which, due to the energy crisis during the early seventies, has literally exploded during the past two decades. The majority of these studies were concerned with conduction-dominated phase change heat transfer and, unfortunately, dealt with convective solidification problems in a much more limited sense by considering only very simple flow fields and geometries; conditions exactly opposite of those which exist in a tube bank geometry flow field. As many researchers investigating these simple flow fields have discovered, under certain situations, the interaction between the solid/liquid interface and the surrounding flow field may become sufficiently strong to the point where only a coupled solution to the problem would yield reasonable results. The problem investigated in this paper is one such case where the mutual dependence between the interface and the flow field must be taken into account.

As far as we have been able to surmise, only a very limited number of published studies exist that investigate the phenomenon of forced convective freezing of ice on anything resembling a tube bank geometry. While many studies focusing on single or dual cylinder arrangements in a crossflow have been reported, Okada et al. (1987) was the very first to explore the ice formation of staggered cooled cylinders in a water crossflow. This was followed by Hirata and Matsui (1990) who investigated the ice formation phenomena around a single line of isothermally cooled cylinders. Next, Torikoshi and Nakazawa (1990,1992) investigated the formation of ice around horizontally mounted tubes in both in-line and staggered arrangements; but all of their freezing experiments were conducted with the tubes immersed in a stagnant water bath without any externally imposed crossflow occurring past the tubes. Most recently, Hirata and Matsui (1992) released a study reporting the freezing heat transfer with water flow around isothermally cooled cylinders in both staggered and aligned arrangements. Even though the cylinder arrangements used by Hirata and Matsui (1992) were in effect a single line of tubes, flanked on either side by semi-cylindrical tubes attached to the test facility tunnel bounding walls, and therefore not exactly a full-fledged tube bank design, the study represents the latest and therefore perhaps the best attempt to date to look at the forced convective freezing of an experimental configuration which is similar in design to a "real world" tube bank heat exchanger.

The steady state experiments presented in this study significantly expand the existing data base and, for the first time, document the heat transfer rate of both a staggered and in-line multi-row, multi-column tube bank in a crossflow of water with ice formation. The trends observed are expressed in empirical correlations similar in form to those developed by Zukauskas and Ulinskas (1988), but include the dimensionless cooling temperature ratio Θ as a new additional parameter.

EXPERIMENTAL APPARATUS

<u>Test Facility</u>

All experiments were performed in the University of Cincinnati Experimental Freezing/Melting Water Tunnel shown schematically in Figure 1. An actual photo layout of the test facility is shown in Figures 2 -4. The experimental setup as outlined in Figure 1 consisted of four major sub-systems: the water tunnel and its flow control, the test section, the cooled tube bank, and the data acquisition and process control equipment.

<u>Water Tunnel and Flow Control</u>. The main body was constructed primarily of 1.91 cm thick clear Plexiglas and, in areas where fluid observation was deemed nonessential, was assembled using schedule 80 PVC piping and fittings. The major subassemblies of the tunnel consisted of:

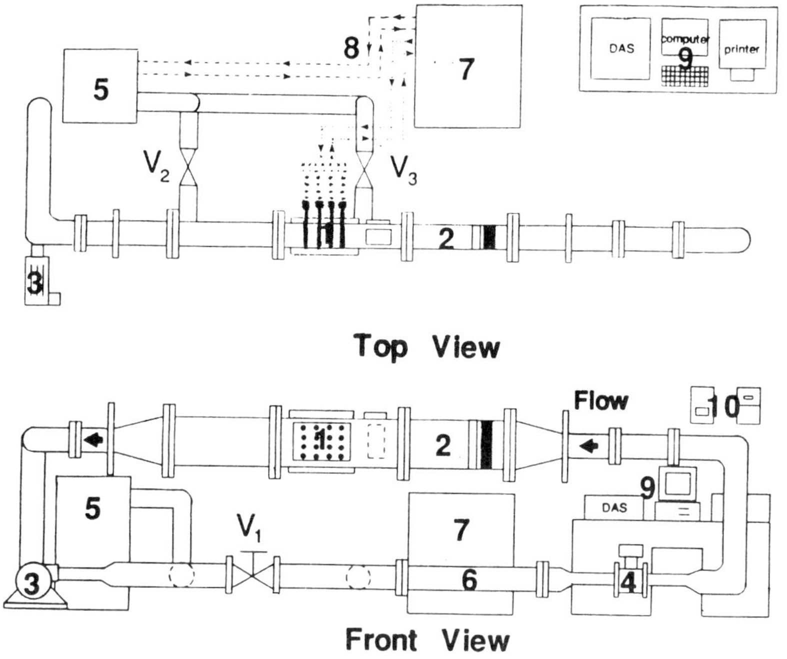

KEY:
1. Test Section with Tube Bank
2. Flow Conditioning Elements
3. Pump
4. Magnetic Flow Meter
5. Plate Heat Exchanger
6. Heated Spool Piece
7. Low Temperature Chiller
8. Glycol Piping
9. Data Acquisition System
10. Flow Control Devices

VALVE SCHEDULE

valve	cooldown mode	normal operation
V1	closed	open
V2	open	closed
V3	open	closed

FIGURE 1. SKETCH OF FREEZING AND MELTING WATER TUNNEL

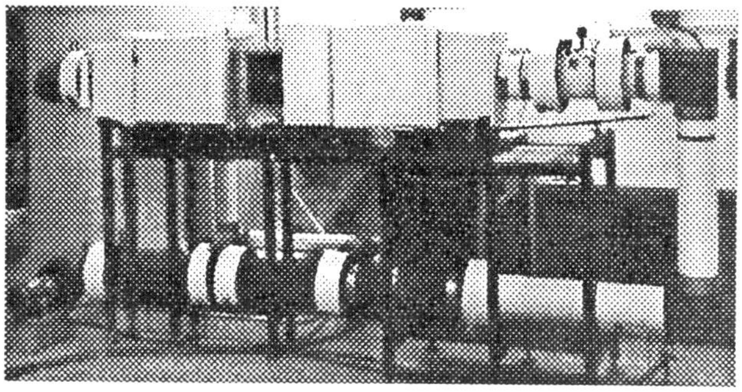

FIGURE 2. FREEZING/MELTING WATER TUNNEL

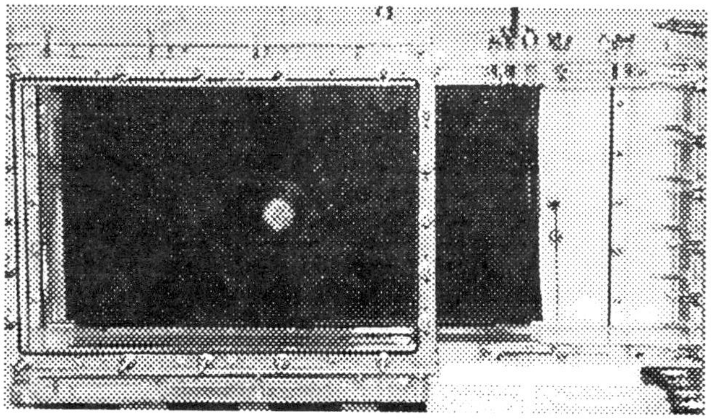

FIGURE 3. TEST SECTION

- A 3 hp variable speed centrifugal water pump with a design speed of 3600 RPM connected to a digital electronic control device. The electronic control unit was capable of setting the pump speeds to any RPM value required by the operator within 6 RPM; for the experiments reported in this study the flow rates ranged from 0.9 to 14.8 m^3/hr (4 to 65 GPM).
- A Foxboro magnetic flowmeter device was used to measure the tunnel's water flow rates with an accuracy of +/- 1.0% of the indicated flow rate.
- A flow conditioning section located upstream of the test section was used to ensure a uniform flow distribution at the test section inlet. It consisted of a diffuser vane, two baffle plates, polyfoam material, and a honeycomb flow straightener. This configuration was found to yield acceptable vertical and horizontal velocity profiles, as confirmed by hydrogen bubble flow visualization, at the tube bank inlet.
- A plate heat exchanger, a high capacity low temperature chiller and a heated spool piece were collectively utilized to accurately control the tunnel water temperature. The chiller and plate heat exchanger were used during the initial tunnel cool-down period when the water was brought from an ambient room temperature down to a near freezing temperature in a matter of hours. The heat exchanger was then valved out of the system (see Figure 1) and the chiller was then piped to supply the tube bank with a 50/50 glycol-water mixture to begin the ice-making process. The energy extraction of the tube bank was usually greater than the combined system energy gain through the tunnel walls and pump work gain, so a heated spool piece was added to the configuration to maintain the temperature of the water entering the test section at a constant value. Active control of the heated spool piece was automated by means of a digital PID temperature controller which measured the tube bank inlet water temperature, compared it to the required setpoint temperature, and automatically varied the power to

FIGURE 4. PLEXIGLAS TUNNEL SECTIONS

the spool piece section to maintain the aforementioned setpoint temperature within +/-0.1 degrees C.

Tunnel Test Section. The actual freezing of water was initiated and maintained by the cold tube banks which were inserted inside the test section. The dimensions of the test section where the solidification occurred measured 25.4 cm high by 12.7 cm deep by 38.1 cm long. Figure 3 shows the test section and, clearly visible, the two (front and rear) large removable test windows which were used to hold the tubes in place. Two different sets of windows, one with a staggered hole arrangement and one with an in-line arrangement, were machined to study the effects of tube placement on the ice formation process. The exact tube bank dimensions used in the present study are shown in Figures 5 and 6. The test section walls were manufactured using double-layered Plexiglas plates in order to reduce both the heat gain into the test section through the windows and to prevent unwanted condensation on the exterior surfaces.

Tube Bank and Tubes. Both of the tube banks which were tested consisted of 16 identical tubes. They were all cooled internally, in parallel, to below the fusion temperature of water with a 50/50 glycol and water mixture supplied by the low-temperature chiller. Coolant entry into and exit out of the tubes was located on the same side of the tunnel to permit unimpeded viewing of the test section and ice formations during the experiments. A schematic lay-out of the test tube architecture is given in Figure 7. Once the water-glycol mixture entered the coolant reservoir, it proceeded down the thin-walled inner center tube, exited that tube through a series of small end holes and returned back to the reservoir via the annulus formed by the inner tube and the copper pipe on whose exterior the ice formations occurred. All the tubes were manufactured using a commercially available thick-walled copper pipe. In order to obtain the tube wall temperatures and verify the isothermal condition of the copper pipe, three type T thermocouples, evenly spaced along the length, were imbedded in the surface of each tube.

Tube Bank Heat Transfer Rate. The heat transfer rate Q_{bank} through the ice-covered tube bank was calculated using a relatively simple form of energy balance on the flowing water. It included the work added to the system by the water pump W_{pump}, which was calculated from known pump pressure rise and efficiency information, and the energy added to the water via the heated spool piece Q_{spool}. The final term needed in the energy balance equation was the heat gain of the system due to the environmental imbalances between the water temperature and the test facility room temperature. This Q_{system} was determined prior to collecting any freezing data by elevating the above the ambient room temperature and, knowing W_{pump} and Q_{spool} with Q_{bank} equal to zero, simply calculating the Q_{system} value once the system had attained steady state. This procedure was repeated for a range of ΔT's between the water and the room, and resulted in a linear relation for Q_{system} with temperature difference. With this information, the steady state tube bank heat transfer rate was then calculated as follows:

$$Q_{bank} = Q_{system} + Q_{spool} + W_{pump} \quad (1)$$

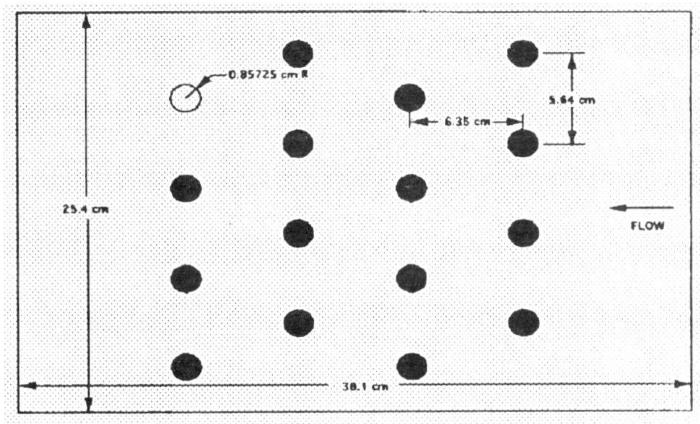

FIGURE 5. STAGGERED TUBE BANK ARRANGEMENT

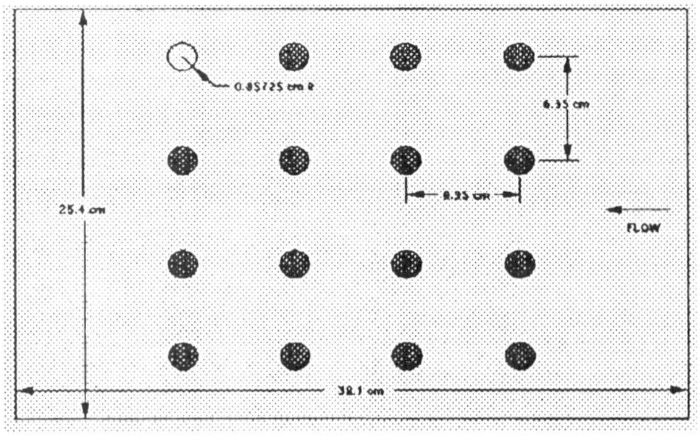

FIGURE 6. IN-LINE TUBE BANK ARRANGEMENT

Data Acquisition and Process Control. All measurements and data collection was done using an HP 75000 data acquisition system in conjunction with an HP Vectra 386/20 computer running LabTech Notebook software. A closed single loop feedback control algorithm was implemented using the data acquisition unit that incrementally increased the centrifugal pump speed to maintain constant volumetric flow, thereby correcting for changes in flow resistance brought about by test section constrictions due to large ice build-up on the tube banks. In addition, the system was set up to continuously monitor the heater PID controller output signal and, from this information, determine the energy added to the system by the heated spool piece. All temperatures (tube wall, water and glycol circuits), flow rate, spool piece wattage, and pump speed were automatically scanned and recorded by the data acquisition system and saved on the hard disk of the PC.

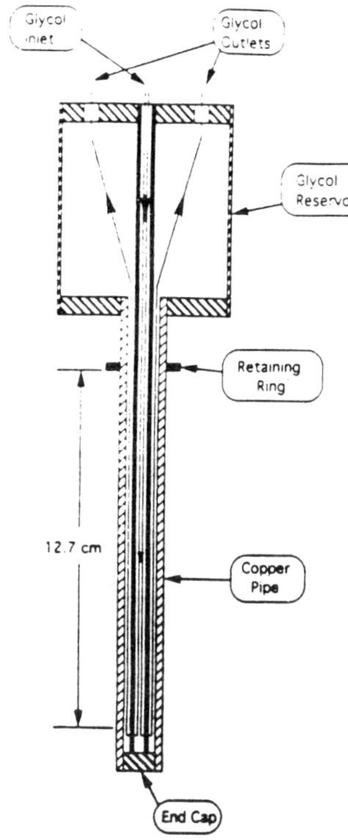

FIGURE 7. TUBE CUT-AWAY VIEW

Experimental Procedure and Data Reduction

All steady state experiments followed essentially the same basic procedure. Initially, the plate heat exchanger was valved into the system and, once the low-temperature chiller had reached an adequately low glycol/water temperature, the tunnel water temperature was lowered until it was approximately 2 to 3 degrees C. This typically took anywhere from 1 to 2 hours. Once this was accomplished the plate heat exchanger was valved out and the chiller glycol/water temperature was reset to a new value. This new chiller set temperature was determined based upon the desired cooling temperature ratio Θ of the current test. Once this new value was achieved, the glycol/water mixture was then circulated through the tube bank to cool the tubes and to begin the freezing process. Initially the ice grew rapidly, but slowed significantly with time. Eventually, when $Q_{conduction} = Q_{convection}$ at the ice-water interface, the growth stopped and steady state conditions prevailed. The length of time it took for the system to achieve a steady state condition varied somewhat depending on imposed test conditions, but in general 12 to 18 hours were usually sufficient to allow the system to stabilize. Once steady state was achieved the data was logged by the data acquisition system. This data was then reduced using a spreadsheet program which calculated the Reynolds Number Re_f based on the freestream conditions and maximum fluid velocity through the tube bank, the value Θ which is the ratio of the ice subcooling to the crossflow water superheating, and the average Nusselt number $\overline{Nu_f}$ of each experimental test condition:

$$Re_f = \frac{\rho V_{max} d}{\mu}, \tag{2}$$

$$\Theta = \frac{(T_i - T_w)}{(T_\infty - T_i)}, \tag{3}$$

$$\overline{Nu_f} = \frac{Q_{bank} \times d}{kA(T_\infty - T_i)}. \tag{4}$$

In addition, the program also calculated the $\overline{K_f}$ factor, or the modified Nusselt number with the Prandtl number dependence eliminated, as defined below:

$$\overline{K_f} = \frac{\overline{Nu_f}}{Pr_f^{0.36}\left(Pr_f / Pr_i\right)^{0.25}}, \tag{5}$$

where the exponents are the accepted empirically derived constants from the work of Zukauskas and Ulinskas (1988).

Finally, all fluid property values such as density, viscosity, thermal conductivity, as well as the Prandtl numbers were calculated by the program using table curve look-up routines evaluated at the test conditions free stream water temperature.

Uncertainty Analysis

The procedure presented by Moffat (1988) applicable to single-sample experimental data collection/reduction was implemented to obtain a measure of the uncertainty in the reported results for Re_f and $\overline{K_f}$. The typical uncertainty associated with the Reynolds number and in $\overline{K_f}$, spanning all 63 experimental data points collected, was determined to be approximately 1.3% and 5.7%, respectively. The maximum uncertainty in $\overline{K_f}$ (Exp. 38) was found to 8.70%. Note that these results include both bias and random errors of the measured variables. The possible sources of error in the reported Reynolds numbers included the water flow velocity uncertainty, the tube diameter measurement accuracy, and the inherent "fossilized" error in the reference water viscosity. The uncertainty in $\overline{K_f}$ arises from the possible errors in the numerous variables used in calculating its final value, starting from the required measurements needed for the evaluation of the various terms in the energy balance. Heated spool piece supply voltage fluctuations, thermocouple accuracy uncertainties, environmental heat gain calibration curve fit accuracy, and "fossilized" errors in fluid properties are examples of some of the potentially larger sources of errors that were considered in the analysis.

Tube Bank Heat Transfer Validation Runs

Before performing any freezing tube bank experiments, it was necessary to first verify the accuracy of the method used to measure the tube bank heat transfer rate as outlined above. A series of non-icing experiments were therefore conducted in which our measured rate of heat transfer was compared to the classical results obtained by Zukauskas and Ulinskas (1988). Since our data was obtained using a 4-column tube bank and the reported correlations apply to 20+ column tube banks, the $\overline{Nu_f}$ and $\overline{K_f}$ values obtained were appropriately corrected using the Zukauskas and Ulinskas (1988) factors for short tube banks as shown below:

thus $$Nu_{fc} = c1 \times \overline{Nu_f} \quad (6)$$

and $$K_{fc} = c1 \times \overline{K_f}, \quad (7)$$

where c1 for 4-column tube banks are determined to be:

c1=1.00 for $Re_f < 1000$ and
c1=0.91 for $Re_f > 1000$ for in-line tube banks,
c1=0.94 for $Re_f < 1000$ and
c1=0.90 for $Re_f > 1000$ for staggered tube banks.

Comparison of our test data with the correlations given by Zukauskas and Ulinskas (1988) (shown in the top left-hand corners of Figures 8 and 9) shows very good agreement for both geometries of interest. It is interesting to note that, since our test data spans the Reynolds number range of 1000, a value at which the correlation changes, we find that our data for the staggered arrangement (Fig. 8) displays the expected change in slope, but the data for the in-line arrangement rather appears to be "sandwiched somewhere between" the two respective correlations listed in Figure 9. Regardless of this subtle difference between the two figures and our data, and due to the close agreement between the validation run results and these well accepted correlations (over the entire Reynolds Numbers range investigated during the freezing experiments), it is concluded that the system energy balance method described earlier is deemed adequate for finding Q_{bank}.

RESULTS AND DISCUSSION

Staggered Tube Bank

A total of 40 steady state experiments were performed using the staggered tube bank in which the inlet Reynolds number and the dimensionless cooling temperature ratio Θ were varied from 170 to 1750 and 0.5 to 8, respectively. Results of these runs, where K_{fc} (fifth column of Table 1) was calculated according to Eq. (5) using the measured Nu_{fc}, are reported in Table 1. While the differences in heat transfer between our experimental results obtained with ice formations and those given by Zukauskas and Ulinskas (1988) for a clean tube bank without ice can be rather significant (sixth column of Table 1), an interesting trend develops when the results are plotted as shown in Figure 10. It appears that the tube bank heat transfer

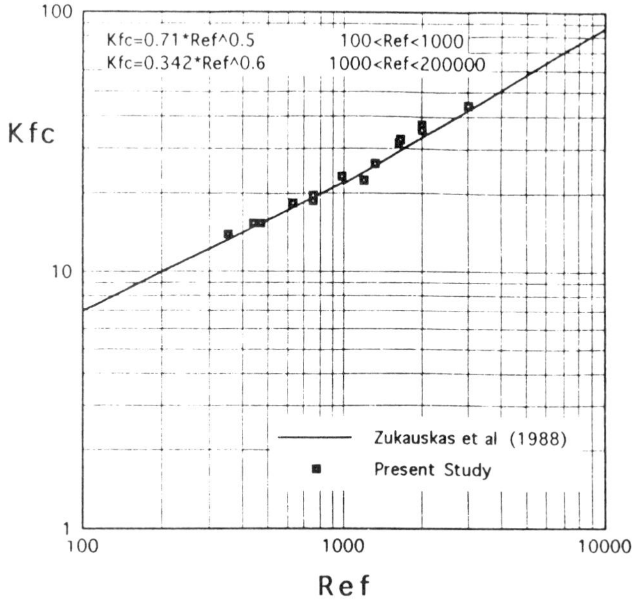

FIGURE 8. STAGGERED NON-FREEZING TUBE BANK HEAT TRANSFER VALIDATION

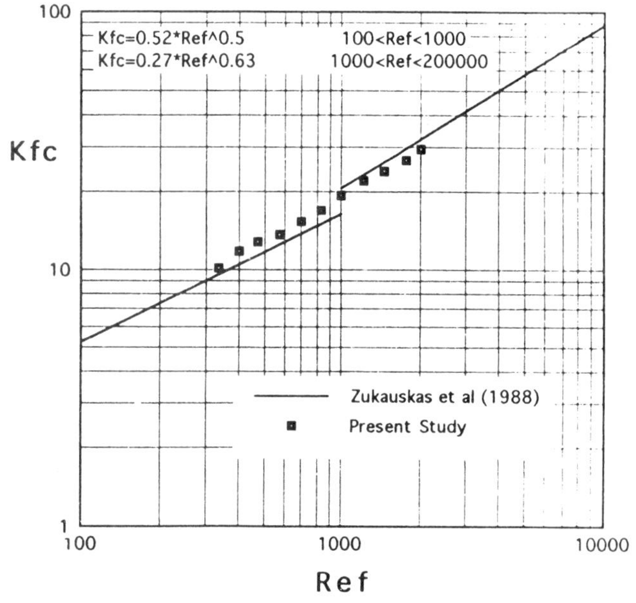

FIGURE 9. IN-LINE NON-FREEZING TUBE BANK HEAT TRANSFER VALIDATION

with ice build-up is less than the non-icing tube bank heat transfer when the dimensionless cooling temperature ratio is less than 1 and, for larger Re_f experiments, in some cases $\Theta = 2$, but becomes significantly larger than a non-icing tube bank when the temperature ratio is 4 and above. It is interesting to note that experiments 17 and 23 (Table 1) resulted in partial ice bridging between adjacent tubes and that one run, experiment 37, resulted in a steady state configuration where 13 of the 16 tubes were completely connected. Figure 11a shows the ice shape for run 21 that represents typical steady-state ice shapes (with no linkage) for the majority of runs, while Figure 11b shows the case of almost complete linkage of run 37. Experiment 37 has been highlighted on

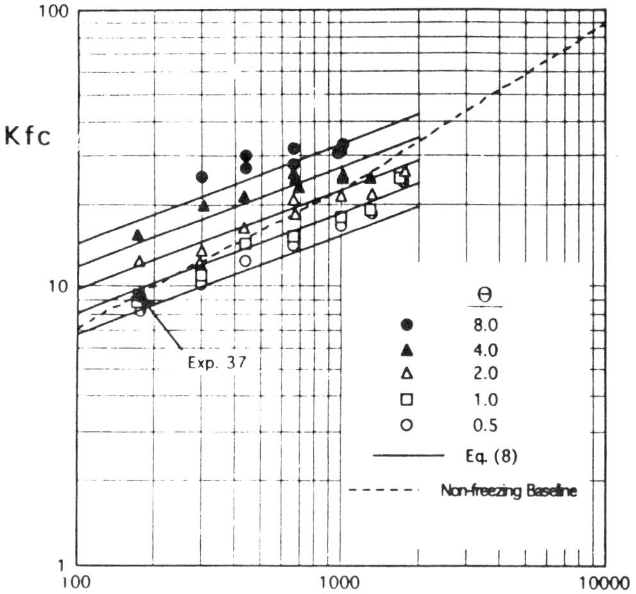

FIGURE 10. STAGGERED FREEZING TUBE BANK HEAT TRANSFER RESULTS

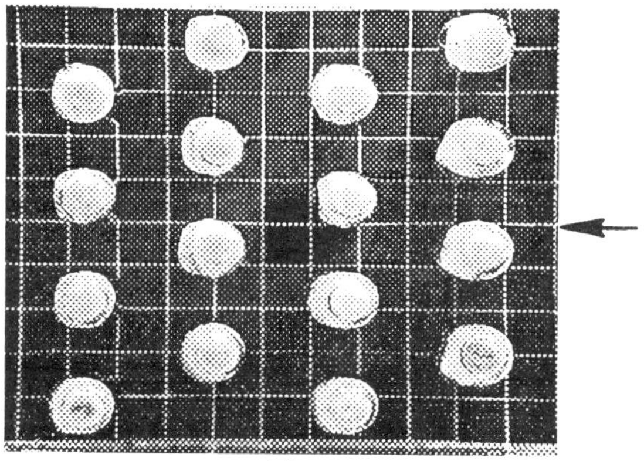

(a)

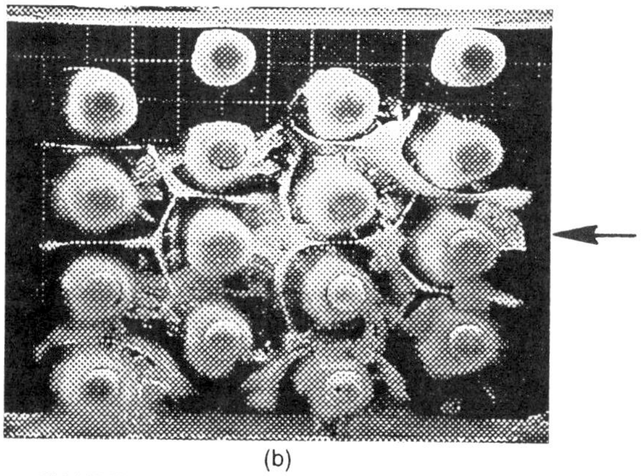

(b)

FIGURE 11. STAGGERED TUBE BANK ICE SHAPES: (a) RUN 21, (b) RUN 37

TABLE 1. SUMMARY OF STAGGERED FREEZING TUBE BANK RESULTS

Run	Re_f	Θ	$\overline{Nu_f}$ (Eq. 4)	K_{fc} (Experiments)	% Error[1] vs. Zukauskas Correlation	% Error[2] vs. (Eq. 8) Correlation
1	671	3.83	55.96	24.79	34.78	5.92
2	670	2.10	41.56	18.41	0.17	-7.10
3	661	1.12	34.64	15.20	-16.74	-8.32
4	664	0.55	31.94	14.08	-23.03	9.28
5	663	4.14	58.85	26.02	42.31	9.28
6	664	7.99	73.73	31.89	74.34	11.60
7	964	8.11	70.90	30.66	39.10	-6.60
8	1004	7.57	66.82	30.96	39.87	-5.27
9	1010	3.96	54.71	25.70	15.69	-6.16
10	995	1.99	47.96	21.39	-4.52	-4.95
11	1000	1.05	40.11	17.90	-20.28	-5.20
12	1005	0.53	34.96	16.70	--24.60	6.77
13	430	2.00	37.53	16.43	11.56	-1.35
14	438	1.04	32.61	14.40	-6.08	2.65
15	439	0.53	28.26	12.48	-16.07	7.59
16	438	8.48	69.35	30.00	101.97	20.00
17	437	8.30	62.89	27.21	83.32	9.53
18	293	1.88	27.74	12.21	0.36	-14.49
19	306	4.21	44.95	19.86	59.81	9.65
20	302	1.10	25.04	11.08	-10.16	-10.78
21	301	0.48	22.80	10.18	-17.28	3.27
22	298	8.26	58.54	25.29	106.42	17.07
23	1298	3.68	52.60	24.95	-3.38	-15.00
24	1322	2.06	45.31	21.65	-17.09	-14.08
25	1298	1.04	39.79	19.13	-25.93	-7.07
26	1325	0.51	38.45	18.59	-28.93	8.34
27	1745	1.65	54.14	26.43	-14.31	1.05
28	664	8.35	65.19	28.17	53.97	-2.63
29	691	4.14	52.32	23.11	23.85	-4.39
30	1009	4.31	52.85	24.77	11.58	-11.57
31	1014	7.99	71.50	33.14	48.88	-0.45
32	1674	0.99	50.57	24.79	-17.58	10.66
33	1733	0.51	49.30	24.30	-20.89	29.08
34	172	2.09	27.83	12.42	33.26	2.47
35	171	4.06	35.43	15.55	67.34	6.93
36	173	1.09	20.87	9.34	-0.11	-7.88
37	176	5.55	20.70	9.26	-1.64	Not included
38	176	0.50	18.29	8.21	-12.73	-0.05
39	170	1.05	20.10	9.00	-2.70	-9.27
40	299	1.95	31.39	13.82	12.56	-4.69

[1] [(K_{fc}(EXPERIMENTAL) - K_{fc}(ZUKAUSKAS & ULINSKAS)) / K_{fc}(Z & U)] * 100
[2] [(K_{fc}(EXPERIMENTAL) - K_{fc}(EQ. 8)) / K_{fc}(EQ. 8)] * 100

Figure 10 and clearly shows that significant ice bridging between adjacent tubes, generally occurring at lower Re_f and higher Θ values, is detrimental to the overall heat transfer rate exhibited by the tube bank.

While at first it may seem surprising to the casual observer that the heat transfer on an ice-on-tube bank design should exhibit the behavior shown in Figure 10, the explanation for the <u>increase</u> of K_{fc} <u>above</u> the non-freezing baseline data may be relatively simple. If the tube bank were tested at Θ = 0 one would expect the resulting data points in Figure 10 to fall somewhere very close to the dashed non-freezing baseline. As Θ is increased and more ice forms on the exterior surface of the tube, the ice surface area exposed to convection becomes much larger. Also, the increase in flow velocity (and turbulence) within the tube bank due to the thicker ice layers at higher values of Θ is another influencing factor. These two combined effects, we feel, are responsible for increasing the overall tube bank heat transfer rate of the bank, beyond that of a non-icing tube bank of the same geometry, at elevated cooling temperature ratios. It is worth reporting that a similar trend was previously reported by Cheng et al. (1981) who earlier studied steady state convection from a single tube with ice formation in a crossflow of water. While a quantitative comparison between the results generated in this study and the previously published experimental works is not possible, due to the inherent differences in test configurations, it is nonetheless interesting to note that the work with a single tube revealed the same overall trend, when varying Reynolds number and Θ, in the reported heat transfer rate; i.e. the heat transfer was enhanced and its magnitude increased with Θ. Now on the other hand, the reasons responsible for the reduction of K_{fc} below the non-freezing baseline results (dashed line of Figure 10) are not yet clear. Data analysis to determine the local convective heat transfer coefficient at the ice-water interface of each tube is currently underway, to help explain the unexpectedly low values of K_{fc} found to occur at Θ values less than 1 and, for larger Re_f experiments, in some cases Θ=2, and will be reported at a later time.

The experimental data points shown in Figure 10 were statistically analyzed to determine if a correlating equation describing the experimental steady-state data existed. Judging from the data trends observed, an equation similar to that of Zukauskas and Ulinskas (1988) was expected and tried, but with the obvious inclusion of the Θ parameter. The best equation to date, with the least error, that has been generated to fit the measured data of this study is the correlation shown below:

$$K_{fc} = 1.545 \times Re_f^{\,0.361} \times \Theta^{0.277}, \qquad (8)$$

This equation is plotted as the solid lines in Figure 10 for five different Θ values and shows the correct general behavior

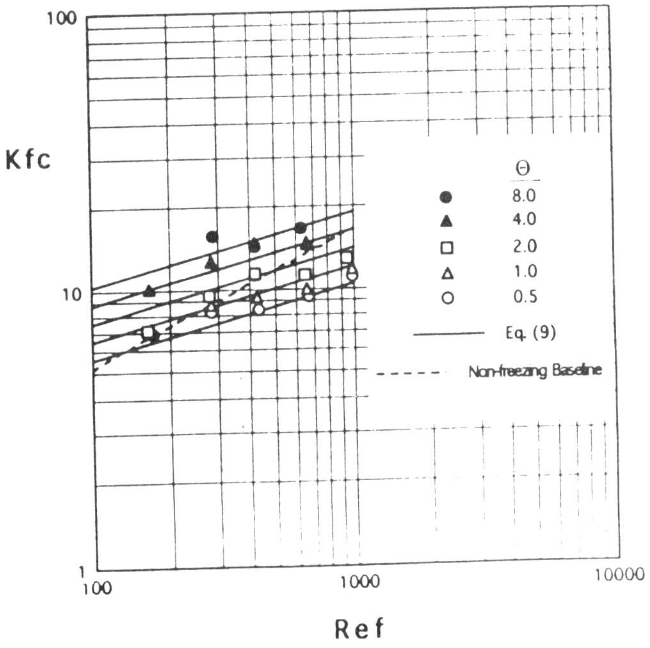

FIGURE 12. IN-LINE FREEZING TUBE BANK HEAT TRANSFER RESULTS

with fair to good agreement with the experimental data. The point-by-point deviation from this new correlation is tabulated in the last column of Table 1 and the multiple coefficient of determination R^2 is 0.94.

In-line Tube Bank

Following the conclusion of the data runs utilizing the staggered tube bank arrangement, the in-line tube bank was installed in the water tunnel and a total of 23 steady state experiments were conducted. While the range of cooling temperature ratios was the same as for the staggered tube bank experiments, the Reynolds number range was reduced to only cover Re_f = 170 through 1000 due to the lack of appreciable ice coating on the tubes at Reynolds numbers beyond 1050. Table

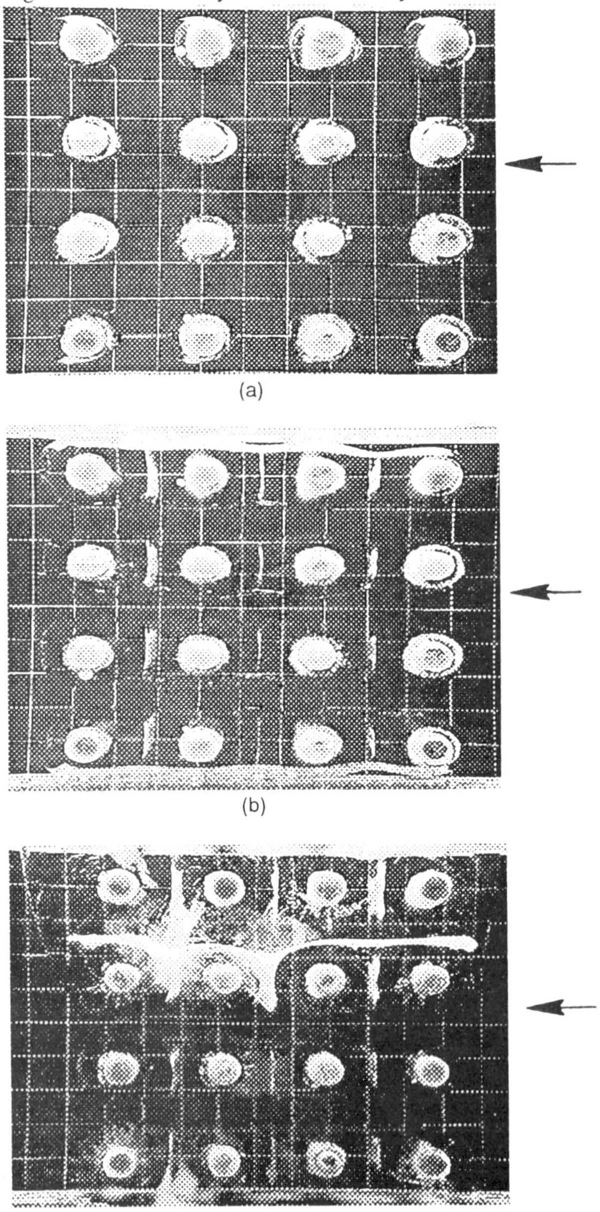

FIGURE 13. IN-LINE TUBE BANK ICE SHAPES: (a) RUN 8, (b) RUN 7, (c) RUN 9

2 is a summary of the results obtained for the in-line tube bank using the appropriate Pr dependence in defining K_{fc} for in-line tube bank. The data again shows a significant difference in heat transfer when compared to the case without ice (Table 2, sixth column), although the deviation is smaller in magnitude than the results previously obtained for the staggered tube bank arrangement. The data is plotted in Figure 12 and exhibits the same basic behavior as found with the staggered bank array, i.e., K_{fc} increases with Θ but is below the non-freezing baseline for small Θ and above it for higher Θ. During the experiments it was noted that the adjacent tubes in the in-line tube bank configuration were much more likely to connect via an ice bridge than adjacent tubes in the staggered tube bank arrangement at comparable Re_f and Θ values. For example, in the in-line arrangement, 10 of the 23 runs had partial or total linking of one or more rows, as compared to only three experiments with linkage in the staggered arrangement. Figure 13 shows three representative examples of in-line tube bank ice shapes: without linkage (Figure 13a, run 8), separate linked rows (Figure 13b, run 7), and multiple linked rows connected (Figure 13c, run 9).

TABLE 2. SUMMARY OF IN-LINE FREEZING TUBE BANK RESULTS

Run	Re_f	Θ	$\overline{Nu_f}$ (Eq. 4)	K_{fc} (Experiments)	% Error[1] vs. Zukauskas Correlation	% Error[2] vs. (Eq. 9) Correlation
1	414	2.01	27.41	11.39	7.55	2.76
2	424	0.98	22.05	9.28	-13.31	-2.86
3	429	0.47	19.82	8.39	-22.05	2.60
4	414	4.01	35.32	14.70	38.85	14.33
5	418	7.89	34.91	14.34	34.94	-3.72
6	288	8.42	38.23	15.68	77.73	14.73
7	165	4.03	24.29	10.08	50.74	·0.35
8	658	3.93	35.19	14.64	9.72	0.98
9	632	6.07	40.49	16.69	27.66	6.00
10	172	0.50	16.29	6.91	1.30	6.65
11	169	0.97	16.95	7.17	6.20	-3.59
12	163	2.08	16.98	7.16	7.93	-17.47
13	284	0.50	19.76	8.28	-5.60	11.44
14	285	1.00	21.18	8.85	0.87	2.67
15	282	1.96	22.95	9.55	9.45	-3.80
16	286	3.94	30.27	12.57	43.05	-3.91
17	665	1.00	23.37	9.93	-25.93	-8.33
18	671	0.50	21.98	9.39	-30.30	0.44
19	650	2.01	26.63	11.22	-15.39	-10.32
20	943	1.97	29.77	12.86	-19.49	-6.61
21	977	0.98	26.80	11.73	-27.85	-2.01
22	989	0.51	25.13	11.05	-32.40	5.98
23	660	4.00	35.08	14.58	9.19	015

[1] [(K_{fc}(EXPERIMENTAL) - K_{fc}(ZUKAUSKAS & ULINSKAS)) / K_{fc}(Z & U)] * 100
[2] [(K_{fc}(EXPERIMENTAL) - K_{fc}(EQ. 9)) / K_{fc}(EQ. 9)] * 100

One explanation which could account for the greater affinity of the in-line tube bank to link may be found in the "shadowing" effect present in the in-line tube bank arrangement but not found in the staggered arrangement. This effect increases when the ice formation diameters on the first column of tubes in the bank grow to the point where the downstream tubes are effectively blocked more and more from direct flow impingement by the water due to the increased upstream wake effects. As the ice diameters on the first column of tubes become larger, the downstream tubes in essence then sit in a region of even lower fluid velocities, a condition which, in turn, promotes even greater ice growth until adjacent tubes within the same row readily connect as shown in Figure 13b. The variation of K_{fc} with Re_f and Θ for the in-line geometry is very similar to that exhibited by the staggered tube bank arrangement and can be explained in a similar fashion as before, but with the following slight modification. While the "shadowing" effect of the tubes may contribute to reduce the K_{fc} values, the increased flow velocity down the narrowed fluid "channels" formed by the linked tube bank rows at higher levels of Θ, and its concurrent rise in convective heat transfer along those surfaces, is believed to be sufficient to elevate the K_{fc} values above those of the non-freezing baseline without ice formations.

A statistical analysis of the in-line experimental data was also performed. All data points, including those which exhibited ice bridging between adjacent tubes, were included in the analysis. The correlation which fits the in-line tube data is as follows:

$$K_{fc} = 1.8784 \times Re_f^{\,0.270} \times \Theta^{0.215}. \qquad (9)$$

This equation is shown plotted in Figure 12 for a range of five Θ values and shows a fair to good agreement, similar to the staggered case, with the experimental data (R^2 = 0.92). Comparing the Θ parameter exponent of the in-line tube bank with ice formation correlation, 0.215 (Eq. 9), with the staggered tube bank with ice formation correlation Θ exponent, 0.277 (Eq. 8), clearly shows that the in-line tube bank heat transfer is less sensitive to Θ variation as compared to the staggered configuration.

CONCLUSIONS

A total of 40 and 23 steady state forced convection ice-on-tube experiments were conducted using both 16-tube staggered and in-line tube bank arrangements, respectively. The two arrangements were found to be similar in overall behavior yet different in magnitude of their ability to function as effective heat exchangers. While icing of both tube bank arrangements involving small Θ was found to be detrimental to the overall tube bank heat transfer rate, experiments having larger ice build-up on the tubes (higher Θ) were found to increase the heat transfer capability of both arrangements to beyond that of a similar geometry non-icing tube bank at the same test Reynolds Number. Ice bridging, which was found to seriously affect the heat transfer rate through the staggered tube bank arrangement, occurred more often but had less impact on the in-line tube bank and was presumably due to the tube "shadowing" effect. Finally, correlations for both in-line and staggered tube bank arrangements were developed for future use in ice-on-tube phase change design studies.

REFERENCES

Cheng, K.C., Inaba, H., and Gilpin, R.R., 1981, "An Experimental Investigation of Ice Formation Around an

Isothermally Cooled Cylinder in Crossflow," Journal of Heat Transfer, Vol. 103, pp 733-737.

Hirata, T. and Matsui, H., 1990, "Ice Formation and Heat Transfer With Water Flow Around Isothermally Cooled Cylinders Arranged in a Line," ASME Journal of Heat Transfer, Vol. 112, pp 707-713.

Hirata, T. and Matsui, H., 1992, "Freezing and Thawing Heat Transfer with Water Flow around Isothermally Cooled Cylinders in Staggered and Aligned Arrangements," ASME Journal of Heat Transfer, Vol. 114, pp 681-687.

Moffat, R.J., 1988, "Describing the Uncertainties in Experimental Results," Experimental Thermal and Fluid Science, Vol.1, pp 3-17.

Okada, M., Goto, K., and Nakamura, S., 1987, *Proc. 65th National Conference of JSME* (in Japanese), No. 870-4, pp 304-305.

Torikoshi, K., Nakazawa, Y., and Yamashita, H., 1990, "An Experimental Study of Formation and Melting of Ice About Horizontal Tubes," ASME HTD-Vol. 143, pp 57-63.

Torikoshi, K. and Nakazawa, Y., 1992, "An Experimental Study of Formation and Melting of Ice around Horizontal Tubes: Influence of Tube Array on Ice Formation and Melting Characteristics," ASME HTD-Vol. 205, pp 19-25.

Zukauskas, A., and Ulinskas, R., *Heat Transfer in Tube Banks in Crossflow*, Hemisphere Publishing Corporation, New York, 1988.

HTD-Vol. 284/AMD-Vol. 182, Transport Phenomena in Solidification
ASME 1994

CONTINUOUS PRODUCTION CHARACTERISTICS OF LIQUID ICE BY USE OF FLUIDIZED BED

S. Fukusako, M. Yamada, A. Horibe, and K. Hatakeyama
Department of Mechanical Engineering
Hokkaido University
Sapporo, Japan

H. Kawabe
Hokkaido College
Senshu University
Bibai, Japan

ABSTRACT

This paper presents an experimental study dealing with the continuous production characteristics of liquid ice by use of a fluidized bed. Ethylene–glycol aqueous solution was cooled by a vertical circular cylinder immersed in a primary air–liquid two phase fluidized bed. Experiments were carried out for a variety of conditions of initial concentration of solution, cooled–wall temperature, and airflow rate for fluidization in order to determine the production performances of the liquid ice. It was observed that a frozen layer which formed along the vertical circular cylinder might be separated from the cooled surface owing to the fluidization motion to be the liquid ice. An operation range for continuous production of liquid ice was identified.

NOMENCLATURE

C_0 = initial concentration of solution, wt%
d = diameter of cooled cylinder, mm
D = inner diameter of test section, mm
H = height of test section, mm
I.P.F. = ice packing factor (= mass ratio of ice to ethylene–glycol aqueous solution), %
Q_a = airflow rate, m^3/s
Q_s = volume of solution, m^3
t = elapsed time from beginning of run, min.
T_a = airflow temperature, °C
T_b = bulk temperature of fluidized bed, °C
T_w = surface temperature of cooled cylinder, °C
V_a = superficial air velocity, m/s

INTRODUCTION

Solidification phenomena are encountered extensively in nature and many technologically important processes. Casting of metals, growth of pure crystals from melts and solutions, and latent heat–of–fusion thermal energy storage are a few of the important applications which have motivated research in this area. Solidification processes might be grouped into two major categories: one is solidification of pure substances, and the other is solidification of multi–component substances. The solidification of a pure substance is in general characterized by a clear solid/liquid interface. The solidification of a multi–component substance, on the other hand, is characterized by a mixed–phase region, usually termed "the mushy zone," consisting of a combination of liquid solute and solid crystals (Viskanta, 1988).

Utilization of thermal energy storage system air conditioning has recently been considered for the purposes of saving energy and reducing peak electrical demand (Miyasaka, 1987; Sagara, 1987; Nihei, 1987; Yanagihara, 1987). For conventional ice–storage systems using a pure ice as the phase change material (PCM), it has been demonstrated (Rieger and Beer, 1984, 1986; Hirata et al., 1993; Torikoshi et al., 1989, 1991) that melting heat transfer performance decreases with the time because the heating tube and ice tend to be separated by a liquid phase.

The frozen layer of an aqueous solution, such as ethylene–glycol solution, varies in its characteristics owing to both the freezing and flow–field conditions (Yamada et al., 1991, 1993). Furthermore, it is known that there are some conditions under which the frozen layer exhibits a fluidity like sherbet. Extensive attention has, hence, been paid to the frozen layer of a solution having the fluidity characteristic, so called "liquid ice", as a new PCM instead of the pure ice. Research on effective processes to produce liquid ice has been carried out (Endo and Hoshino, 1987; Horibe et al., 1992).

For industrial equipment, "liquid ice" is in general produced by freezing the aqueous solution under some flow conditions (Endo and Hoshino, 1987). The authors have studied the effect of convection produced by forced flow on the freezing characteristics of an aqueous binary solution along both a vertical plate (Fukusako et al.,1990) and a horizontal cylinder (Yamada et al., 1992), and they reported that the flow field causes a marked influence on the freezing characteristics. Horibe et al. (1992) proposed an efficient continuous production method of liquid ice using the process of marine icing caused owing to seawater droplets in the northern winter sea.

As for the freezing of aqueous binary solutions without main flow, a number of experimental and numerical studies have been performed. Extensive reviews are available (Viskanta, 1990; Incropera and Viskanta, 1992). Bennon and Incropera (1987a) developed a continuum model for momentum heat and concentration transport during solidification in a binary alloy. This model was utilized to solve numerically the problems of solidification of a binary alloy in a rectangular mold (Bennon and Incropera, 1987b, 1988), as well as in a horizontal annulus (Neilson et al., 1990). The effect of surface tension on the buoyancy-induced convection during solidification of a binary alloy with free surface in a rectangular vessel was investigated (Incropera et al., 1989; Engel and Incropera, 1989). Numerical and experimental results on the freezing of an aqueous solution (ammonium chloride) in a rectangular vessel were also reported (Christensen and Incropera, 1989; Christensen et al., 1989).

Kerr et al. (1990a, 1990b) developed two theoretical models for solidification of a binary alloy cooled from above: one is based on equilibrium thermodynamics; the other is based on non-equilibrium thermodynamics. They (Kerr et al., 1990c) also studied the late time compositionally zoned solid formed when the alloy is cooled from above. The problem of solid growth from a thin wire in a binary alloy was solved numerically by Poulikakos (1988) and Poulikakos and Cao (1989). Cao and Poulikakos (1992) also investigated experimentally transient solidification characteristics of a binary mixture of water and ammonium chloride in an inclined rectangular cavity. A similar study involving freezing around a horizontal cooled cylinder was performed using a two-wavelength holographic interferometry technique (Spatz and Poulikakos, 1992), which might be breaking new ground.

All of the aforementioned studies treating freezing of aqueous binary solution have been carried out under conditions of no main flow or with monotonical main flow. This paper reports results of an investigation on freezing characteristics of an aqueous binary solution along a vertical cooled cylinder immersed in an air-liquid two-phase fluidized bed. The effects of the initial concentration of the solution, cooled-wall temperature, and airflow rate on the freezing behavior are presented.

EXPERIMENTAL APPARATUS AND PROCEDURES

Experimental Apparatus

A schematic diagram of the experimental apparatus is shown in Fig.1. The essential components of the apparatus are the test section, a cooling brine circulating loop, an air-supply loop, and the associated instrumentation.

Figure 2 shows details of the test section, which consists basically of a test vessel, a cooled tube, a distributor, and a calming section. The test vessel is a transparent acrylic pipe of 150 mm inner diameter and 300 mm height. A cooled tube was installed vertically at the center of the test vessel.

The cooled tube is constructed of coaxial tubing and the cooling brine was sprayed from the small holes of the inner tube to the outer tube in order to keep the cooling temperature uniform. The temperature of the cooled tube was kept uniform by controlling both the flow rate and power input to the heater in the temperature controlling section. To measure the surface temperature of the cooled tube, 6 chromel–alumel thermocouples (0.1 mm O.D.), which were respectively inserted through the tube wall from the inner side, were attached to the surface of the tube. The uncertainty of the temperature was estimated to be approximately 0.8 %.

To measure the temperature within the vessel, three chromel-alumel thermocouples (0.3 mm O.D.), which are respectively 30, 150, and 270 mm from the distributor, were set. The distributor consists of a piece of 200 mesh brass wire screen sandwiched

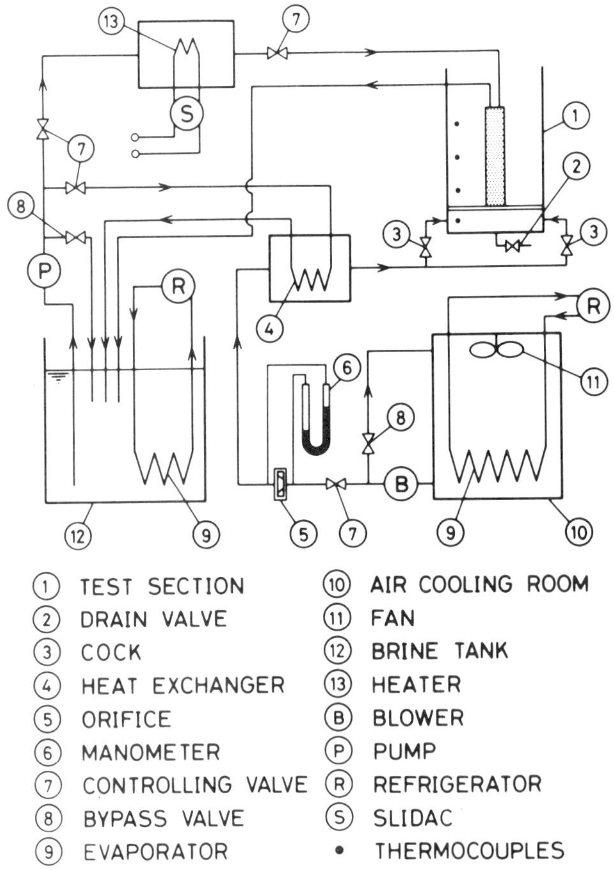

Fig. 1 Schematic diagram of experimental apparatus

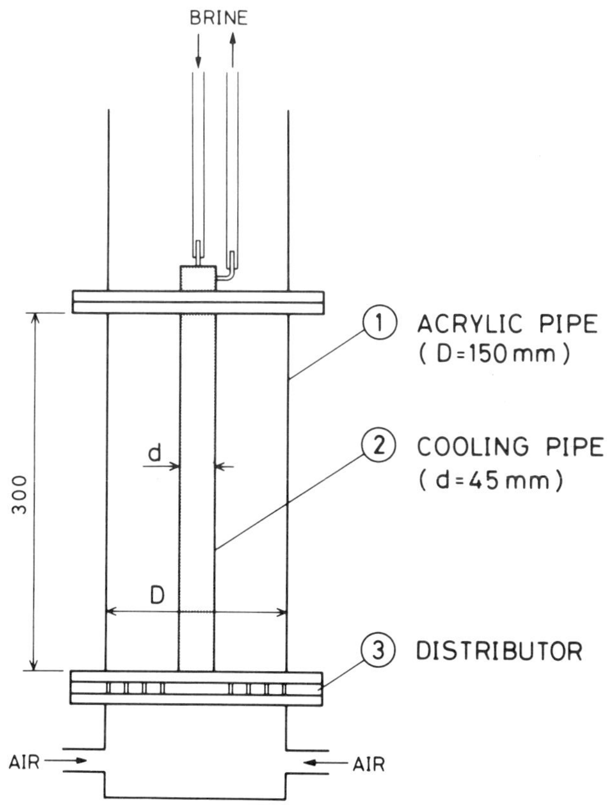

Fig. 2 Details of test section

between two perforated lucite plates with staggered 1.5 mm diameter holes spaced circumferentially 10 mm apart center to center. To ensure uniform airflow, a calming section of honeycomb design was set at the bottom of the test vessel.

Air was utilized to make a fluidized bed. Dry air was prepared in a temperature-regulated (about −20°C) chamber whose flow rate was measured by use of an orifice. Using an electric heater, the temperature of the supplied air was controlled so as to be equal to that of the bulk temperature of the fluidized bed.

Experimental Procedures

Ethylene-glycol solutions of 10, 15, and 30 wt percent concentration were adopted as the test fluids. Production characteristics of the liquid ice were determined under a variety of concentrations, cooled tube temperatures, and airflow rates. The start of the experiment was defined as the time at which the cooling brine started to circulate through the cooled tube.

Photographs of the freezing phenomena were taken at appropriate intervals (this work was immediately performed under the condition of no air supply for fluidization). The temperatures of the cooled tube as well as those in the testing vessel were continuously recorded. To avoid heat input from the environment, the test section was carefully covered with insulation (styrofoam of 100 mm in thickness) except during observation. To counter the effect of air supply on the heat balance, the temperature of the air supply was controlled so as to be equal to the bulk temperature of the fluidized bed by use of an electric heater installed in the mixing box.

Assessment of I.P.F.(Ice Packing Factor)

In the present study, I.P.F.(ice packing factor) was defined as

$$\text{I.P.F.} = W_i / W_s \qquad (1)$$

where W_i is mass of ice and W_s is mass of ethylene-glycol aqueous solution. The I.P.F. was assessed based on the bulk temperature T_b in the fluidized bed under the assumption that the bulk temperature corresponds to the equilibrium freezing temperature of the aqueous binary solution.

RESULTS AND DISCUSSION

The three independent parameters of the current study are the concentration of the aqueous solution, the cooled-wall temperature, and the airflow rate. The effect of these parameters on the production characteristics of the liquid ice will be presented and discussed.

General Observations

Figure 3 shows the formation of a frozen layer along the vertical cooled tube for 20 wt percent solution, −17°C wall temperature, and 20 min elapsed time under the condition of no airflow. The frozen layer appears to consist of fine, needle-shaped crystals, namely a dendritic layer (Viskanta, 1988; Fukusako and Yamada, 1989) which is quite similar to that observed by Yamada et al., (1992, 1993).

Figure 4 shows the fluidization behavior of the air-water two-phase fluidized bed just after the initiation of the experiment. It is seen that a variety of bubbles are markedly active in the vessel, which may cause efficient stirring. This stirring action may be closely related to the processes which separate the frozen layer from the cooled surface. Figure 5 shows the formation of the liquid ice (a mixture of fine ice particles and aqueous binary solution) after 20 min. The photograph was taken immediately when the air flow was stopped. An inspection of the figure reveals that the vessel is full of fine ice particles as well as the aqueous binary solution, namely the liquid ice.

Effect of Initial Concentration of Aqueous Binary Solution

Figures 6 and 7 show the characteristics of I.P.F. against the elapsed time for C_0 =10 and 20 wt percent solution, respectively. In Fig. 6, these are three groupings of data which correspond to T_w =−6, −8, and −10°C. The general trend through the data is that the I.P.F. value attains around 5 wt% when about 10 min passed, and then decreases monotonically to become zero. It is evident from the figure that the decrease in I.P.F. is accentuated as the cooled-wall temperature decreases. This behavior is demonstrated visually in Fig.8. For these parameters, fine ice particles formed in the vessel (see Fig. 8(a)) tend to disappear as the time elapses (see Fig.8(c)).

On the other hand, Fig. 7 for C_0=20 wt percent solution

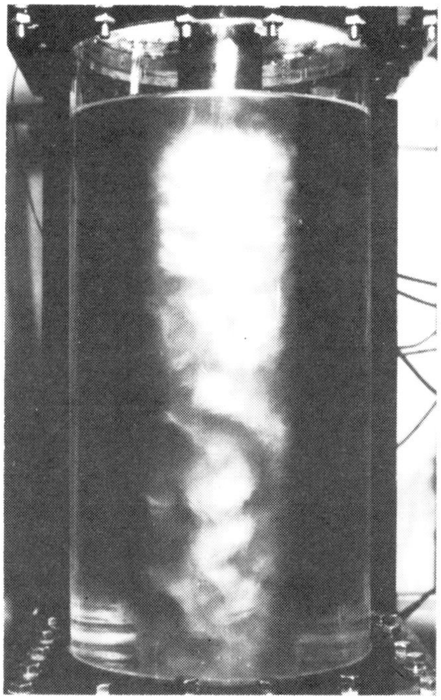

Fig. 3 Frozen layer of aqueous binary solution

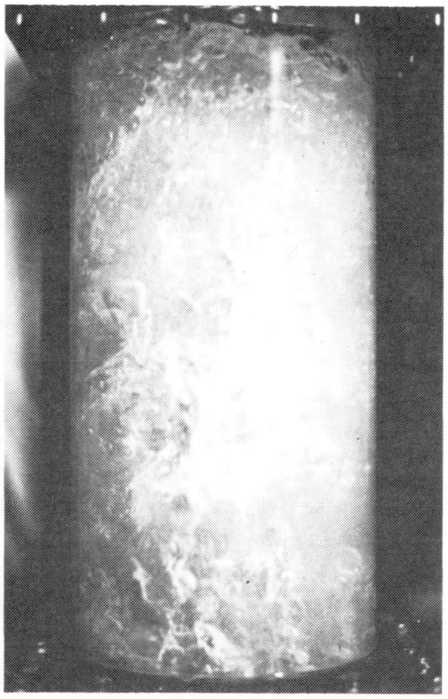

Fig. 4 Fluidizing motion

Fig. 5 Liquid ice (air flow is stopped)

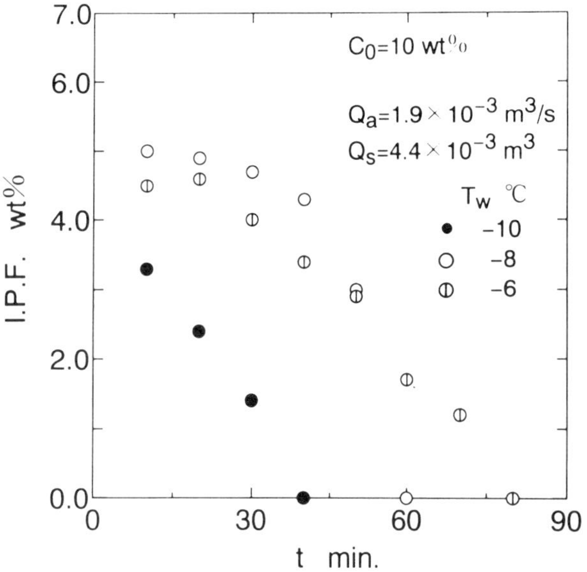

Fig. 6 Ice production performance

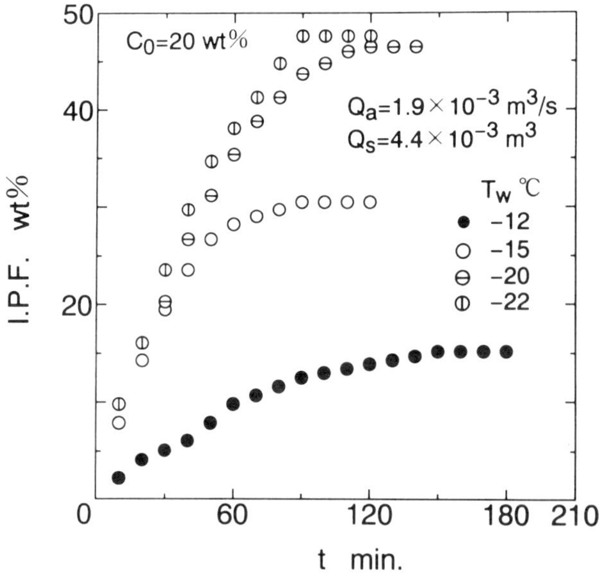

Fig. 7 Ice production performance

elucidates that the I.P.F. value increases monotonically with the time, and then attains a constant value, which is in common all through the data. This fact indicates that the fine ice particles formed in the aqueous binary solution never disappear unlike the behavior observed for C_0=10 wt percent solution (see Fig. 6), thus suggesting that the continuous production of the liquid ice may be available in this operating condition.

Consideration will now be given to the feasibility of

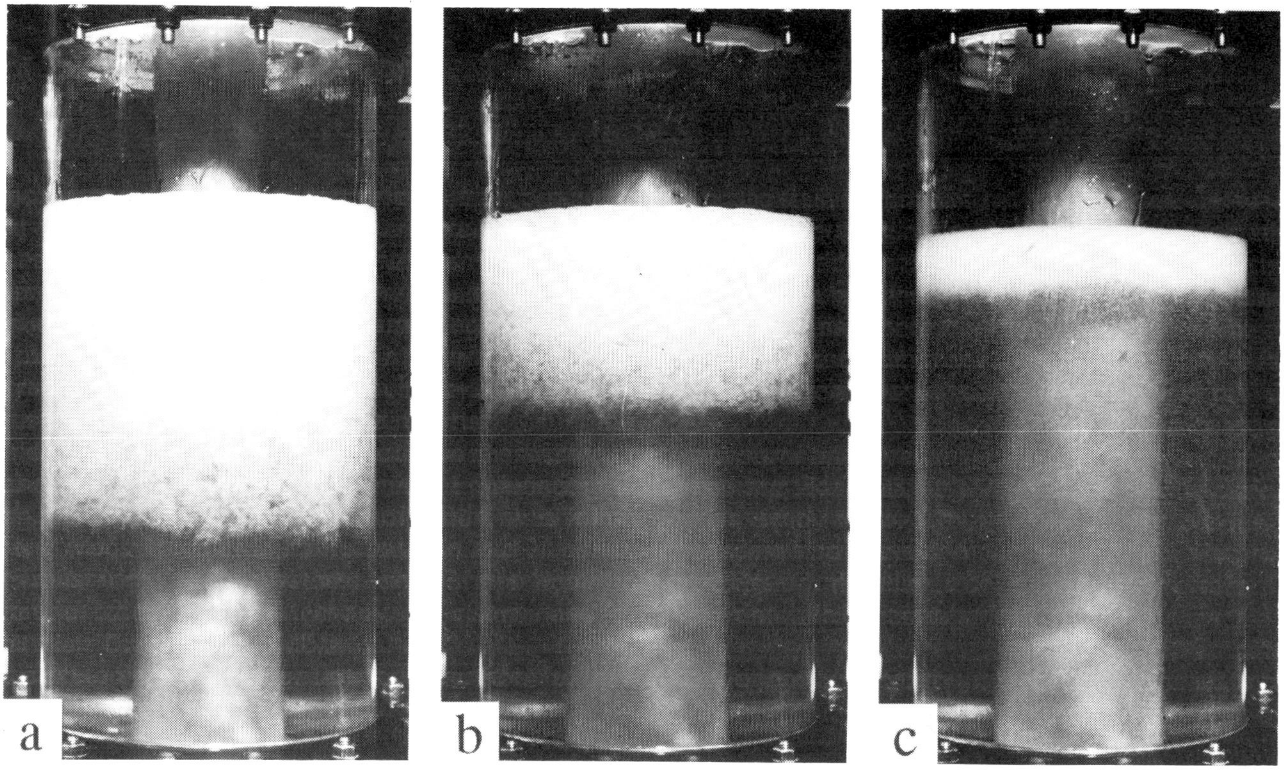

Fig. 8 Frozen-up of ice particles (air flow is stopped), C_0=10 wt%, T_w=-10°C, Q_a=1.9x10^{-3} m^3/s, a; t=10 min., b; t=20 min., c; t=30 min.

separating frozen-layer from the cooled wall. Three factors, mutually related, may be considered: (1) the physical property of the frozen layer; (2) the stickiness between the frozen layer and the fine ice particles floating in the vessel; (3) the growth velocity of the frozen layer. An increase in concentration of aqueous binary solution may cause the frozen layer to be relatively mild, because more dense brine tends to be trapped within the frozen layer, which results in an easy separation of the frozen layer from the cooled tube. In addition, the stickiness between the frozen layer and the floating ice particles is expected to decrease as the concentration of aqueous binary solution increases, which may disturb the refreezing of the fine ice particles on the frozen layer surfaces. Based on the facts stated above, the continuous production of the liquid ice (an increase in I.P.F. with the time) may be available for C_0=20 wt percent solution.

Another interesting behavior observed in Fig. 7 is that the I.P.F. value reaches a constant value at larger time. Figure 9 plots the relationship between the bulk temperature of the vessel and the time. The general trend through all the data is that the bulk temperature decreases monotonically as the time elapses, and then reaches a constant value. The growth of the frozen layer causes an increase in concentration of aqueous binary solution in the vessel, which corresponds to a decrease in freezing temperature of the liquid. This suggests that no additional growth of the frozen layer (a constant value of I.P.F.) may be attained owing to the heat balance at interface between the frozen layer and the liquid ice, as shown in Fig.7.

Effect of the Cooled-Wall Temperature

In Figs. 6 and 7, there are three and four groupings of data which respectively correspond to the cooled-wall temperatures.

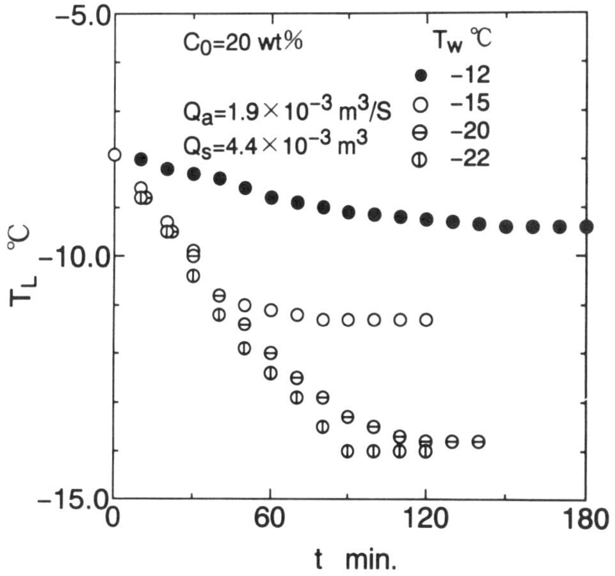

Fig. 9 Bulk temperature behavior

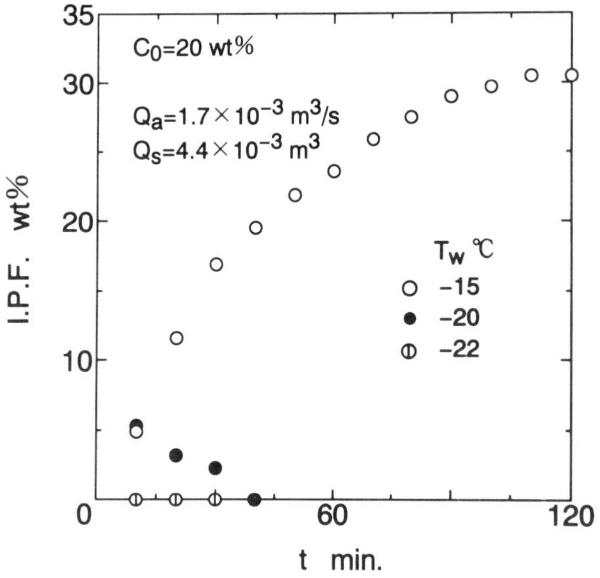

Fig. 10 Ice production performance

As shown in Fig. 6, a decrease in the I.P.F. with time appears to be accentuated as the cooled-wall temperature decreases. For T_w=-10°C the I.P.F. value reaches zero at t≒40 min, which suggests that the fine ice particles in the liquid disappeared completely owing to melting of the fine ice particles in the aqueous binary solution as well as the refreezing on the frozen layer. It was also observed that for cooled-wall temperatures less than −11°C the liquid ice could not be observed all through the experimental run. A decrease in the cooled-wall temperature may causes an increase in growth velocity of the frozen layer as well as increasing stickiness between the frozen-layer surface and the fine ice particles in the aqueous binary solution, which is in support of the phenomena indicated in Fig. 6.

For C_0=20 wt percent solution (Fig. 7), it is evident that the I.P.F. value increases monotonically as the time elapses to reach a constant value for the cooled-wall temperatures ranging from −12 to −22 °C. The constant value of I.P.F. tends to be accentuated with decreasing cooled-wall temperature. In addition to the fact that the difference in the constant value between T_w=−20 and −22 °C is quite small, the frozen layer was found not to be separated from the cooled-wall for the cooled-wall temperatures less than −23°C. This may be interpreted in terms of the increased stickiness between the cooled wall and the frozen layer owing to the decreasing cooled-wall temperature.

Effect of Airflow Rate

Attention will now be turned to the effect of airflow rate on the production of liquid ice. The I.P.F. characteristics for Q_a=1.7x10^{-3} m^3/s are shown in Fig. 10 against the elapsed time from the start of the experiment. As compared with Fig. 7, it is

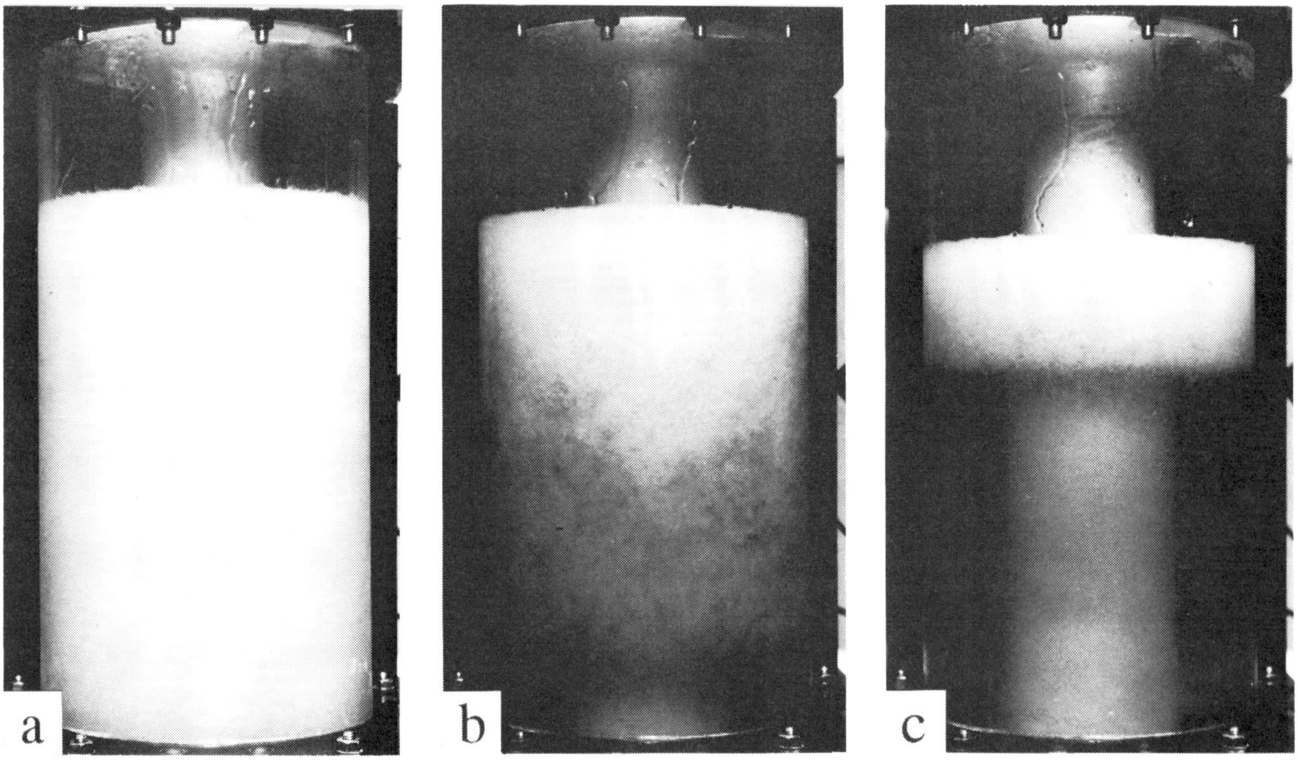

Fig. 11 Frozen-up of ice particles (air flow is stopped), C_0=20 wt%, T_w=-20°C, Q_a=1.7x10^{-3} m^3/s, a; t=10 min., b; t=20 min., c; t=30 min.

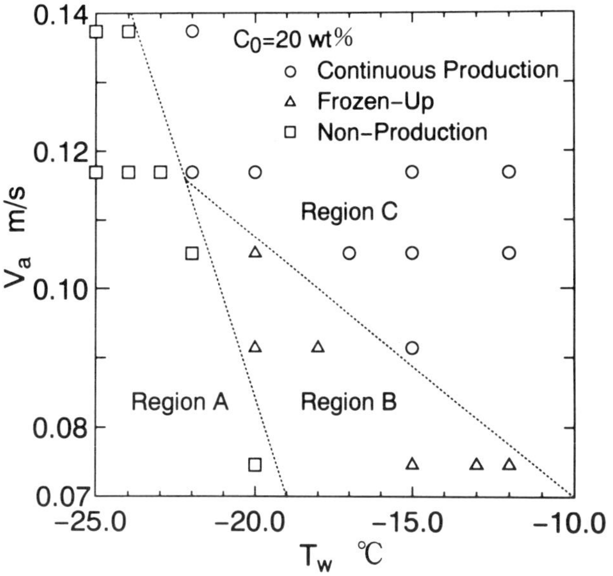

Fig. 12 Condition of ice production

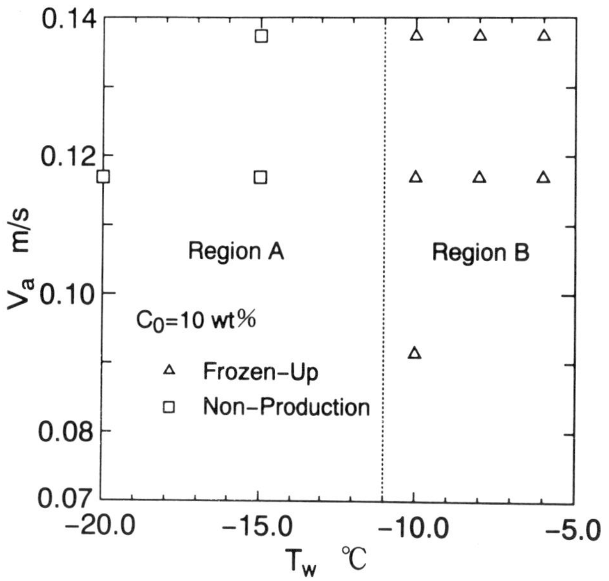

Fig. 13 Condition of ice production

evident from Fig. 10 that for the cooled-wall temperature of -20°C the I.P.F. value tends to decrease monotonically after taking a maximum value of about 5%, whose behavior is visually shown in Fig. 11. This may be explained by considering that a decreasing airflow rate causes decreasing separation of the frozen layer from the cooled wall owing to the weakened fluidization.

On the other hand, observations were performed for the airflow rates up to 2.7×10^{-3} m^3/s. The findings were that there might be a certain region in which the continuous production of the liquid ice is respectively available for the cooled-wall temperatures.

Condition for Continuous Production of Liquid Ice

A number of experiments for a variety of initial concentrations of aqueous binary solution, cooled-wall temperatures, airflow rates were carried out to study the freezing characteristics. Attention will now be turned to identification of the conditions for continuous production of liquid ice. It was found that there are three typical regions in the freezing behavior: region A, where only the frozen layer forms on the cooled tube; region B, where the fine ice particles, which once have been formed within the liquid, disappear to adhere to the frozen layer; region C, where the continuous production of the fine ice particles in the aqueous binary solution (the liquid ice) is available.

By arranging the experimental results for C_0=20 wt percent solution, and setting the superficial air velocity V_a as the ordinate and the cooled-wall temperature T_w as the abscissa, Fig. 12 is obtained. It is evident from the figure that the operating conditions for continuous production of liquid ice are favorably available as a function of the superficial velocity and the cooled-wall temperature. On the other hand, the data for C_0=10 wt percent solution are plotted in Fig. 13, in which there is no region C of the continuous production of the fine ice particles in the aqueous binary solution as the liquid ice.

CONCLUDING REMARKS

The continuous production characteristics of liquid ice by use of a fluidized bed were investigated experimentally. Ethylene-glycol aqueous solution was adopted as a test fluid. The effects of the initial concentration of the solution, cooled-wall temperature, and airflow rate on the freezing behavior under fluidization were considered. For the initial concentration of 20 wt percent solution, it was found that there might be three typical regions of the freezing behavior: region A, where only the frozen layer formes on the cooled tube; region B, where the fine ice particles, which once have been formed within the liquid, disappear to adhere to the frozen layer; region C, where the continuous production of the fine ice particles in the aqueous solution (liquid ice) is available.

REFERENCES

Bennon, W. D. and Incropera, F.P., 1987a, "A Continuum Model for Momentum, Heat and Species Transport in Binary Solid-Liquid Phase Change Systems - I: Model Formulation, " Int. J. Heat Mass Transfer, Vol.30(10), pp.2161-2170.

Bennon, W. D. and Incropera, F.P., 1987b, "A Continuum Model for Momentum, Heat and Species Transport in Binary Solid-Liquid Phase Change Systems - II: Applications to Solidification in a Rectangular Cavity, " Int. J. Heat Mass Transfer, Vol.30(10), pp.2171-2187.

Bennon, W. D. and Incropera, F.P., 1988, "Numerical Analysis of Binary Solid-Liquid Phase Change Using a Continuum Model, " Numer. Heat Transfer, Vol.13(3), pp.277-

296.

Cao, W.Z. and Poulikakos, D., 1992, "Transient Solidification of Binary Mixture in an Inclined Rectangular Cavity," AIAA Journal of Thermophysics and Heat Transfer, Vol.6(2), pp. 326–332.

Christensen, M. S., Bennon, W. D., and Incropera, F. P., 1989, "Solidification of an Aqueous Ammonium Chloride Solution in a Rectangular Cavity – II. Comparison of Predicted and Measured Results, " Int. J. Heat Mass Transfer, Vol. 32(1), pp. 69–79.

Christensen, M. S. and Incropera, F. P., 1989, "Solidification of an Aqueous Ammonium Chloride Solution in a Rectangular Cavity – I. Experimental Study," Int. J. Heat Mass Transfer, Vol. 32(1), pp. 47–68.

Endo, M. and Hoshino, M., 1987, "Crystallized Liquid Ice Thermal Storage System," Refrigeration, Vol. 62, pp.481–486.

Engel, A. H. and Incropera, F. P., 1989, "Solidification of Binary Mixture in a Square Cavity With a Free Surface," Wärme- und Stoffübertragung, Vol.24(15), pp.279–288.

Fukusako, S. and Yamada, M., 1989, "Freezing Characteristics of Ethylene Glycol Solution," Wärme- und Stoffübertragung, Vol.24, pp.303–309.

Fukusako, S., Yamada, M., and Morizane, H., 1990, "Freezing Characteristics of Ethylene-Glycol Solution on the Vertical Cooled Plate," Trans. of the JAR, Vol.7, pp.57–65.

Hirata, T., Makino, Y, and Kaneko, Y., 1993, "Analysis of Natural Convection Melting Inside Isothermally Heated Horizontal Rectangular Capsule," Wärme- und Stoffübertragung, Vol.28, pp.1–9.

Horibe, A., Fukusako, S., Yamada, M., Tago, M., and Inoue, W., 1992, " Production Characteristics of Liquid Ice as a New PCM by Aqueous Solution Spraying Method," Proc. 1st Int. Conf. Transp. Pheno. Process., pp.1517–1526.

Incropera, F.P., Engel, A. H., and Bennon, W. D., 1989, "Numerical Analysis of Binary, Solid-Liquid Phase Change With Buoyancy and Surface Tension Driven Convection," Numer. Heat Transfer, Vol 16(1), pp.407–427.

Incropera, F. P. and Viskanta, R., 1992, "Effects of Convection on the Solidification of Binary Mixtures," in Heat and Mass Transfer in Material Processing, ed. I. Tanasawa and N. Lior, pp.295–312.

Kerr, R. C., Woods, A. W., Worster, M. G., and Huppert, H. E., 1990a, "Solidification of an Alloy Cooled From Above. Part 1. Equilibrium Growth," J. Fluid Mech., Vol.216, pp.323–342.

Kerr, R. C., Woods, A. W., Worster, M. G., and Huppert, H. E., 1990b, "Solidification of an Alloy Cooled From Above. Part 2. Non-equilibrium Interfacial Kinetics," J. Fluid Mech., Vol.217, pp.331–348.

Kerr, R. C., Woods, A. W., Worster, M. G., and Huppert, H. E., 1990c, "Solidification of an Alloy Cooled From Above. Part 3. Compositional stratification With the Solid," J. Fluid Mech., Vol.218, pp.337–354.

Miyasaka, A., 1987, "Current Trends of Ice Storage System in U.S.A.," Refrigeration, Vol.62, pp.382–392.

Neilson, D. G., Incropera, F. P., and Bennon, W. D., 1990, "Numerical Simulation of Solidification in a Horizontal Cylinder Annulus Charged With an Aqueous Salt Solution," Int. J. Heat Mass Transfer, Vol 33. pp.367–380.

Nihei, T., 1987, "Closed Circuit Ice Storage System for Exhibition Museum of Tokyo Electric Power Company," Refrigeration, Vol.62, pp.459–471.

Poulikakos, D., 1988,"On the Growth of a Solid From a Line Heat Sink in a Binary Alloy," Numer. Heat Transfer, Vol.14(1), pp.113–126.

Poulikakos, D. and Cao, W. Z., 1989, "Solidification of a Binary Alloy From a Cold Wire or Pipe: Modeling of the Mixed Phase Region," Numer. Heat Transfer, Vol.15(A), pp.197–219.

Rieger, H. and Beer, H., 1984, "The Influence of Density Anomaly of Water on the Melting Process of Ice Inside a Horizontal Cylinder, ASME Paper, 84-HT-10.

Rieger, H. and Beer, H., 1986, "The Melting Process of Ice Inside a Horizontal Cylinder: Effects of Density Anomaly," Trans. ASME J. Heat Transfer, Vol.108, pp.166–173.

Sagara, N., 1987, "Performance of Glycol Ice Storage System with Ice-on-Coil Type Heat Exchanger," Refrigeration, Vol.62, pp.393–401.

Spatz, T. L. and Poulikakos, D., 1992, "A Two-Wavelength Holographic Interferometry Study on the Solidification of a Binary Alloy Around a Horizontal Pip," ASME J. of Heat Transfer, Vol.114, pp.998–1010.

Torikoshi, K., Nakazawa, Y., Kawabata, K., Yamamoto, H., and Fushimi, K., 1989, "An Experimental Study of Melting of Ice About Horizontal Cylinders," Proc. 2nd. Int. Symp. Cold Reg. Heat Transfer, pp.45–50.

Torikoshi, K., Yamashita, H. and Nakazawa, Y., 1991, "An Experimental Study of Melting of Ice About Horizontal Cylinders," Proc. ASME/JSME Therm. Engng., Vol.1, pp.269–274.

Viskanta, R., 1988, "Heat Transfer During Melting and Solidification of Metals," ASME J. Heat Transfer, Vol.110, pp.1205–1219.

Viskanta, R., 1990, "Mathematical Modeling of Transport Processes During Solidification of Binary Systems," JSME Int. Series II, Vol.33, pp.409–423.

Yanagihara, Y., 1987, "An Economic Study of Ice Storage Type HVAC Systems," Refrigeration, Vol.62, pp.487–497.

Yamada, M., Fukusako, S., and Tago, M., 1991, "Freezing Characteristics of Aqueous Solution on a Horizontal Downward Facing Cooled Plate," Proc. ASME/JSME Therm. Engng. Joint Conf., pp.285–290.

Yamada, M., Fukusako, S., Tago, M., and Horibe, A., 1993, "Freezing Characteristics Along a Horizontal Cooled Tube Immersed in Aqueous Binary Solution With Main Flow," ASME J. of Engineering Materials and Technology, Vol.115, pp.54–62.

HTD-Vol. 284/AMD-Vol. 182, Transport Phenomena in Solidification
ASME 1994

THERMAL ANALYSIS OF THE SOLID-MELT INTERFACE IN SCAN WELDING

Charalabos C. Doumanidis

Department of Mechanical Engineering
Tufts University
Medford, Massachusetts

ABSTRACT

In fusion welding, the geometric dimensions and heat transfer conditions at the weld pool interface (or mushy zone) define the weld nugget cross section and material structure in the weld bead. In the novel scan welding process, involving a rapidly reciprocating torch to generate a continuous heat distribution on the part surface, these fundamental joint characteristics are modeled by both an analytical, finite-state model and a numerical thermal simulation. Both models describe the composite heat source power distribution, the double-stream circulation regime in the weld pool, the fusion/solidification conditions at the melt interface and the conductive transfer in the solid with heat loss at the part surface. The predictions of the models are verified by experimental tests of both classical and scan welding under various conditions. The new scanned process is shown to generate a uniform temperature field and to deposit the full weld bead simultaneously, under controlled solidification conditions, resulting in a favorable metallurgical structure and mechanical properties of the joint. These models are currently used for the design and evaluation of a thermal control system for scan welding, employing infrared temperature feedback and torch parameter adaptation.

INTRODUCTION

Among non-disassembling methods for joining of metal parts in modern manufacturing technology, fusion welding has undoubtedly dominated in industrial applications because of the superior loading capacity of welded over riveted or bonded joints, for example. This advantageous mechanical strength of the weld, which approaches that of the original part material, stems from the thermal development of a continuous, uninterrupted material structure over the full weld joint (McClintock and Argon 1966). The weld bead is deposited by autogenous fusion and solidification of the base metal, as in Gas Tungsten Arc Welding (GTAW), possibly combined with external material addition from a consumable electrode as in Gas Metal Arc Welding (GMAW), so as to bridge the gap between the parts. As a localized heat source moves progressively along the weld centerline and the resulting molten puddle sweeps the joint boundary, the foremost surface of the liquid-solid interface (fusion front) intercepts and melts the material of the welded parts. This is subsequently united and resolidified when swept by the rearmost interface part (solidification front). Since the geometric and heat transfer characteristics of the weld pool-solid interface, also known as boundary or mushy zone, determine the load-carrying section of the joint and the mechanical properties of the bead material, they are of paramount importance for the weld quality.

In the welding bibliography, these weld interface features, such as its width and penetration size, have been investigated extensively in relation to the torch power and motion variables for most traditional welding techniques. The objective of this analytical, numerical and experimental modeling in the literature is to provide a basis for off-line regulation of the weld bead outputs by proper selection of the heat source inputs, or even for their real-time control by feedback of in-process measurements. In all cases, however, the concentrated, sequentially moving welding torch generates a localized, highly-peaked temperature field, which affects adversely the material structure in the heat affected zone or the mechanical properties due to residual stress concentrations related to the cooling rates. For example, in welding of precipitation-hardened aluminum alloys, a satisfactory weld bead geometry may be accompanied by detrimental overaging of the θ-phase or a cracking tendency (Hayden et al. 1965, Linnert et al. 1968). Thus, to obtain simultaneous control of the weld interface dimensions together with the metal microstructure and mechanical stress fields, a new scan welding technique is introduced to provide the required flexible heat input distribution on the joint surface (Figure 1). In scan welding, the heat source is rapidly reciprocated along the entire length of the weld centerline, as well as parallel sidelines on dynamically modulated trajectories, and the torch power is adjusted in real time so as to provide any desired thermal distribution. This modulation of the intensity and

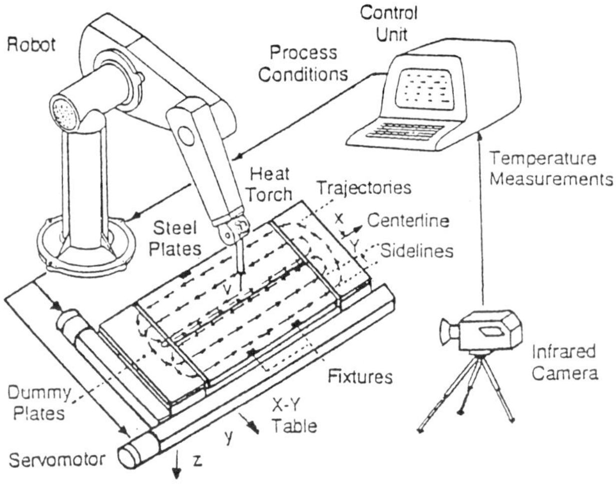

FIGURE 1: EXPERIMENTAL ARRANGEMENT FOR SCAN WELDING WITH TEMPERATURE FEEDBACK.

motion of the torch by the robot or the welded parts by the servodriven X-Y table, is performed by in-process feedback control of the temperature field, measured on the weld surface by an infrared pyrometer camera. Thus, the specified temperature distribution develops the desired thermal stress, material and weld bead characteristics during the operation. For example, in welding of age-hardening aluminum alloys the peak temperature on the weld centerline can be specified at the lowest possible setting that will ensure the desired penetration while minimizing the width of the overaged heat affected zone.

Consequently, unlike the localized, serial nature of fusion and solidification phenomena at the melt-solid interface in conventional welding methods, scan welding involves by design a distributed, parallel thermal actuation and heat transfer on the full weld joint simultaneously. Since there is no modeling precedent for this novel scanned configuration in the welding literature, new flexible thermal descriptions must be established for computational simulation of both classical and scan welding, and for the design of closed-loop control strategies for thermal welding features. These composite models will describe multiple, coupled heat transfer regimes in several weld regions, as well as their interaction effects at the interface surfaces. Such a comparative analysis by modeling of these thermal phenomena in traditional and scanned welds will be the main objective in the sequel of this article.

HYBRID WELDING MODELING

As already indicated, the great variety of thermal and material phenomena composing the fusion welding process requires a modeling flexibility with process nonlinearities and temporal- spatial boundary effects, afforded only by numerical models (Hibbitt and Marcal 1973, Friedman 1975, Goldak 1989, Karlsson and Lindgren 1990). However, the computational efficiency limitations of such detailed simulations of the temperature and material structure fields restrict their use for off-line process analysis only. For the design of an in-process thermal controller, the simplicity and computational speed of a dynamic, finite-state analytical description of welding is needed as a real-time reference model of the control algorithm (Rosenthal 1941, Wells 1952, Barry et al. 1963, Myers et al. 1967, Malmuth et al. 1974, Nunes 1983, Tsai 1988). Thus, two complementary models, an analytical and a numerical one, will be developed in parallel below and validated experimentally. These hybrid models will consist of integrated descriptions of thermal effects in each individual weld area with a different heat and mass transport regime.

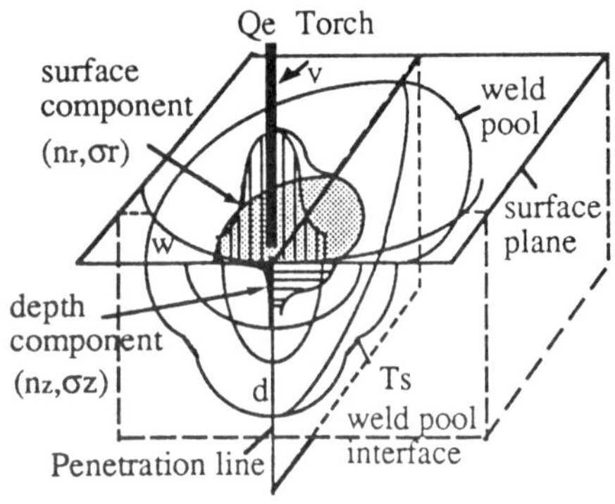

FIGURE 2: COMPOSITE HEAT DISTRIBUTION FROM TWO GAUSSIAN SURFACE AND DEPTH COMPONENTS.

Heat Source

The action of the welding torch on the part surface for a wide variety of heat sources such as arc, plasma, Laser beam etc. is usually modeled by a moving 2-D Gaussian distribution of heat, momentum and possibly mass, when a consumable electrode is used, as in GMAW (Doumanidis 1993). This distribution can be modified as necessary for eccentric locations of the torch or a filler rod for material addition. However, in a homogeneous and isotropic medium of unconstrained geometry, this radially normal heat transfer on the weld surface alone always yields isotherms of ellipsoidal cross section, which do not resemble the actual dished-in contours of the weld bead interface, i.e. the solidus-liquidus zone, with its lateral extensions and penetration finger (Figure 2). Thus, to account for the thermal power release in the depth direction of the molten pool, through deceleration of energy carriers (metal globules, ions, electrons etc), electromagnetic stirring, Joule heating etc, a second 1-D penetration component, i.e. a line-Gaussian in-depth heat distribution, was combined with the original surface component. This torch configuration results in a composite heat source with the power densities:

$$q(x,y) = \frac{n_r Q_e}{2\pi\sigma_r^2} \exp\left(-\frac{x^2+y^2}{2\sigma_r^2}\right) \quad q(z) = \frac{n_z Q_e}{\sqrt{2\pi}\,\sigma_z} \exp\left(-\frac{z^2}{2\sigma_z^2}\right) \qquad (1)$$

where (n_r,σ_r) and (n_z,σ_z) are the partial efficiencies and distribution radii of the two components, and Q_e the total torch power. These source parameters can be adjusted by off-line experimental calibration or real-time identification methods along the torch path; for example, $n_z=0$ for the arc on a solid region of the weld surface. Thus the resulting composite temperature field can generate a variety of realistic cross section profiles for the weld pool/solid interface.

Molten Puddle

In the weld pool underneath the torch, the experimental evidence suggests that the melt circulation in general comprises two individual flow streams in each symmetric half of the puddle in Figure 3 (Doumanidis 1992), with opposite

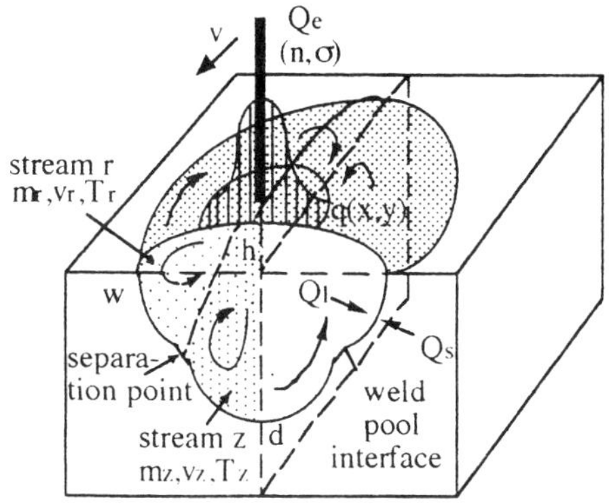

FIGURE 3: DOUBLE-STREAM CIRCULATION PATTERN IN THE WELD POOL.

longitudinal vorticity components, i.e. sense of circulation: The surface stream (r), driven by surface tension and inert gas shear, and moving radially outwards and down at the solid interface, and the penetration stream (z), driven by torch momentum and buoyancy effects in the depth direction, and diverging upwards at the pool bottom. Both streams originate at the fusion front of the puddle interface, or the distribution surface of the externally added material, and eventually terminate at the solidification front at the back of the pool. This general double-stream configuration covers occasional single-cell circulation patterns, in which one of the streams dominates and absorbs the other.

Thus, for an analytical, lumped formulation of the melt flow in the weld, each stream can be described by its total mass m_i, average velocity v_i and equivalent temperature T_i, i=r,z. These scalar stream states are related by local, one-dimensional mass, momentum and energy balances, determining their rates of change. The expressions of the respective laws provide for material fusion-solidification and latent heat effects (subscript $_m$), external transfer from the torch ($_e$), heat transfer by convection in the liquid ($_l$), conduction to the solid ($_s$) and losses to the environment ($_a$), as well as exchange effects between the two streams ($_{rz}$) because of their interaction:

* mass balance (continuity): $\dot{m}_i = \dot{m}_{mi} + \dot{m}_{ei} + \dot{m}_{rz}$

* momentum bal. (Navier-Stokes): $\dot{J}_i = \Sigma F_{ki} + F_{ei} + \dot{J}_{rz}$ (2)

* energy balance (1st law): $\dot{E}_i = -Q_{si} - Q_{ai} - Q_{mi} + Q_{ei} + \dot{E}_{rz}$

where the second subscript ($_i$) of the terms denotes the stream direction. The interaction terms $\dot{m}_{rz}$, $\dot{J}_{rz}$, $\dot{E}_{rz}$ consist of a static exchange component because of the longitudinal motion of the pool following the torch, and a dynamic one due to the relative displacement of the boundary between the streams in Figure 3, determined by the local momentum difference at the separation point. In the equations for momentum J, the partial equivalent forces ΣF_k acting on each stream include the natural convection (Buoyancy) forces, inert gas jet shear, surface tension (Marangoni), electromagnetic stirring (Lorenz) and viscous friction forces to the solid interface. Analytical expressions for these terms are derived in the references (Doumanidis 1992).

The numerical simulation of the melt flow in the weld pool requires simultaneous integration of the distributed-parameter forms of the above balances of fluid mechanics. This is complicated by the variable geometry of the solid-liquid interface, the unknown boundary conditions in the melt, and the distribution of the secondary phenomena listed above, such as Joule heating, which are problematic to incorporate in the flow expressions. For an incompressible and inviscid flow of the melt, the conservation laws can be combined into the relation:

$$\frac{DT}{Dt} \equiv \frac{\partial T}{\partial t} + v_x\frac{\partial T}{\partial x} + v_y\frac{\partial T}{\partial y} + v_z\frac{\partial T}{\partial z} = \frac{k_l}{\rho_l c_l}\nabla^2 T - \cancelto{\emptyset}{\frac{p}{\rho_l c_l}\nabla\underline{v}} + \cancelto{\emptyset}{\Phi} \quad (3)$$

where the Eulerian derivative of temperature DT/Dt contains both the Lagrangian temporal term $\partial T/\partial t$ and the three convective transport terms $v_i \partial T/\partial x_i$, dependent on the velocity components v_x, v_y, v_z. k_l is the thermal conductivity of the liquid metal, ρ_l its density, c_l the specific heat capacity, p the pressure and Φ the dissipated work of viscous friction per volume and time. To circumvent the ambiguity and complexity of the flow problem in the welding literature, proportionality is assumed between the temporal and material derivative of temperature and an equivalent conduction factor γ is defined (Giedt et al. 1984, Doumanidis 1993):

$$\frac{\partial T}{\partial t} = \gamma\frac{DT}{Dt} \Rightarrow \frac{\partial T}{\partial t} = \alpha'\nabla^2 T \quad \text{where} \quad \alpha' = \gamma.\alpha_l = \gamma\frac{k_l}{\rho_l c_l} \quad (4)$$

is the equivalent thermal diffusivity of the melt. This expression is conveniently of the same form as the Fourier conduction equation in the solid region, and is integrated similarly as explained below.

Solid-Liquid Interface (Mushy Zone)

The conservativeness of the elliptic thermal and flow fields in the pool suggests that the geometric features of the weld interface surface are primarily dependent on the local temperature and melt velocity distribution, while remote thermal and flow conditions have only an indirect effect through the local ones. Thus for the lumped analytical model, the dynamic variations of the maximum width w and depth d of the mushy zone will be determined by the local flow conditions in the surface stream r and penetration stream z of the pool respectively: (5)

* width w: local energy balance in r: $\rho H\dot{w} = Q_{mr} = Q_{lr} - Q_{sr}$

* depth d: local energy balance in z: $\rho H\dot{d} = Q_{mz} = Q_{lz} - Q_{sz}$

where H is the latent heat of fusion/solidification, and Q_{li}, Q_{si} the heat fluxes on the liquid and solid side of the mushy zone for the two streams. As the maximum pool cross section sweeps the weld bead during the motion of the torch, these features define the geometry of the weld nugget. Moreover, in welding techniques such as GMAW, the maximum height of the weld bead h in Figure 3 can be determined by a local mass balance of the molten reinforcement, accounting for external material addition and solidification at the rear surface of the mushy zone.

In the numerical simulation, the local interface balances above can serve for real-time estimation and adjustment of the equivalent conduction conditions in the melt. To reflect the different circulation regimes in the two pool streams, two distinct directional conduction factors γ can be identified in the radial and depth direction:

$$\gamma_r = \alpha.Q_{lr}/\alpha_l.Q_{sr} \quad \gamma_z = \alpha.Q_{lz}/\alpha_l.Q_{sz} \quad \Rightarrow$$

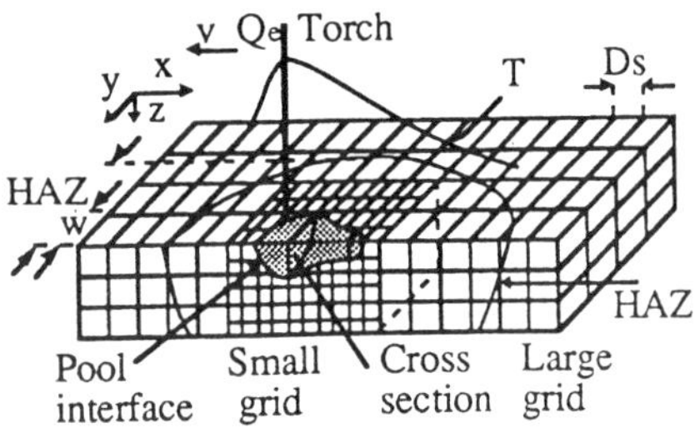

FIGURE 4: GEOMETRICAL CONFIGURATION OF THE NUMERICAL SIMULATION MODEL.

$$\frac{\partial T}{\partial t} = \alpha_l \left[\gamma_r \frac{\partial^2 T}{\partial x^2} + \gamma_r \frac{\partial^2 T}{\partial y^2} + \gamma_z \frac{\partial^2 T}{\partial z^2} \right] \qquad (6)$$

where α and α_l are the thermal diffusivities of the solid and melt. If k and k_l is the thermal conductivity of the solid and liquid material, l_i the characteristic cross-sectional sizes of the two streams, h_i their respective heat transfer coefficients to the solid boundary and T_s the solidus temperture, the heat fluxes Q_{si} and Q_{li} can be determined as (Doumanidis 1992):

$$Q_{li} = (h_i + k_l/l_i)(T_i - T_s), \quad h_i = 0.68 k_l \sqrt{v_i/a_l l_i} \quad i=r,z,$$
$$Q_{sr} = k \cdot \partial T/\partial y(w) \quad Q_{sz} = k \cdot \partial T/\partial z(d) \qquad (6a)$$

Solid Region

A mathematical description of the conduction temperature distribution in the welded parts is necessary to provide consistent and locally accurate Dirichlet boundary conditions to the flow and thermal field of the pool at the interface zone. Following again the lumped model approach, linear conductive heat flow is assumed in ideal orthogonal plates of finite thickness D, with temperature- invariant material properties, no latent phase transformations and no surface heat losses. Under these assumptions (Rosenthal 1941, Tsai 1988), an analytical expression for the composite dynamic temperature field can be derived by superposition of the thermal distributions generated by the surface and penetration components of the heat source: (7)

$$T(x,y,z;t) = T(x,y,z;0) + \sum_{k=-\infty}^{\infty} \left[\int_0^t \frac{n_r Q_e}{\pi \rho c} \cdot \frac{(4\pi\alpha\tau)^{-1/2}}{2\alpha\tau + \sigma_r^2} . \exp\left(-\frac{(x+v\tau)^2 + y^2}{4\alpha\tau + 2\sigma_r^2} - \frac{(z+2kD)^2}{4\alpha\tau} \right) dt + \int_0^t \frac{n_z Q_e}{4\rho c} \cdot \frac{1}{(\pi\alpha\tau)^{3/2}} . \exp\left(-\frac{(x+v\tau)^2 + y^2}{4\alpha\tau} - \frac{(z+2kD)^2}{4\alpha\tau + 2\sigma_z^2} \right) dt \right]$$

where v is the torch velocity, $\alpha = k/\rho c$ the thermal diffusivity of the solid material, k its conductivity, ρ the density and c the specific heat capacity. This expression, employing heat source images, is evaluated only at distinct material points of interest, such as the ones adjoining to the maximum cross section of the mushy zone in Figure 3. On this pool interface surface, the boundary condition of temperature compatibility with the thermal field in the melt at the solidus isotherm T_s is enforced by in-process identification and adaptation of the partial torch efficiencies n_r, n_z as explained in the sequel.

In the numerical simulation, the transient conduction (Fourier) equation is integrated in discrete time steps Dt and space elements Ds, using an explicit finite-difference formulation:

$$\frac{\partial T}{\partial t} = \alpha \nabla^2 T \Rightarrow \quad T(x,y,z;t+Dt) = T(x,y,z;t) + Fo \left[\sum_{j=1}^{6} T_j(x \pm Ds, y \pm Ds, z \pm Ds; t) - 6\, T(x,y,z;t) + \frac{2Ds}{k} Q_a \right] \qquad (8)$$

where T is the temperature at node (x,y,z) and time t, and T_j the temperatures of its surrounding 6 nodes in the three dimensions. $Fo = \alpha \cdot Dt/Ds^2$ is the dimensionless Fourier number, and the heat loss flow rate Q_a is present in this expression only for nodes on the external part surface. The simulation program employs two separate 3-D grids of nodes for different spatial resolution Ds of the thermal field in the weld bead and the heat affected zone (Figure 4). In traditional welding, the grids are relocatable and follow the torch motion, while the time increment Dt is selected so as to ensure integration stability, i.e. $Fo \leq 1/6$ (Crank-Nicholson). In scan welding, the grids are stationary and encompass the entire weld joint length, to cover the full reciprocation of the torch, which must complete its travel on one grid element within an integer

similar numerical formulation is used for the thermal field in the weld pool, with the melt parameters in place of those for the solid part, and with the directional equivalent diffusivities $\alpha'_r = \alpha_l \cdot \gamma$ and $\alpha'_z = \alpha_l \cdot \gamma_z$ in the radial and depth direction respectively. The same formulation is also used for the mushy zone between the solidus T_s and liquidus T_l for alloys, or the subcooling and superheating isotherms in pure metals. Since conduction prevails both in the geometrically connected solid part and in the connected liquid part of the solid-melt interface, the expressions above apply with an equivalent diffusivity value: (9)

$$\alpha_i = \frac{k_i}{\rho_i c_i} \quad \text{where} \quad \rho_i = \frac{1}{2}(\rho + \rho_l), \quad c_i = \frac{H}{T_l - T_s}, \quad k_i = \frac{2k a_i Ds}{2k + a_i Ds}$$

where a_i is the convection coefficient at the solid-pool interface. The computational simulation provides also the convenience of temperature-dependent material properties (Doumanidis 1993).

External Surface

The numerical model affords direct incorporation of local conductive, convective and radiative boundary heat transfer to the environment from the weld surfaces, as well as the effect of the heat source. The external heat flux Q_a in Eq. 8 can be expressed as:

$$Q_a = \frac{Q_e}{Ds^2} - \frac{k\alpha_e}{2\alpha Ds}(T - T_a) - a(T - T_a) - \varepsilon\sigma(T^4 - T_a^4) \qquad (10)$$

where a is the convection coefficient on the weld surface, ε its total emissivity, σ the Stefan-Boltzmann constant and T_a the ambient medium temperature. When the welded parts are in contact with solid objects such as fixtures etc, the equivalent conductive diffusivity $\alpha_e = \alpha . \sigma/\sigma_Y$ depends on the applied normal stress σ between the parts to overcome the surface roughness, and on the yield strength σ_Y of the softest between the materials in contact.

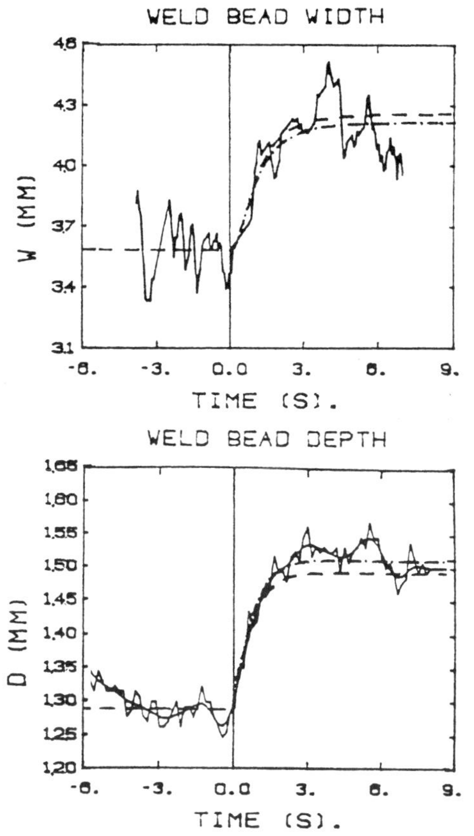

FIGURE 5: RESPONSES OF THE WELD INTERFACE GEOMETRICAL FEATURES IN CLASSICAL GMAW.
___: EXPERIMENT, -·-·-: SIMULATION, - - -: ANAL. MODEL

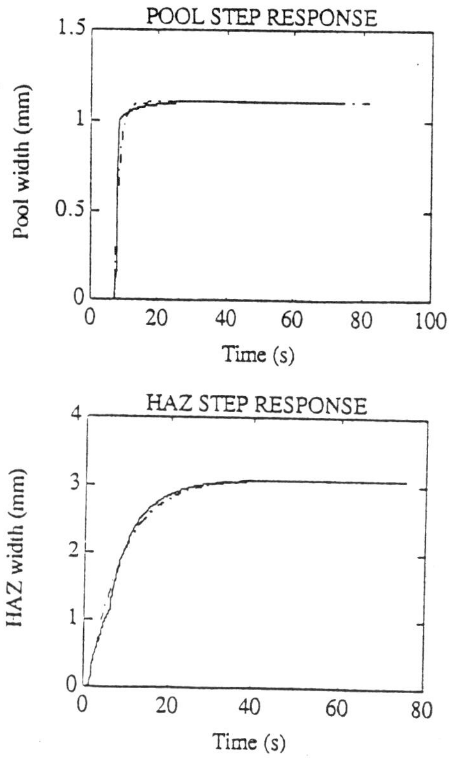

FIGURE 6: RESPONSES OF THE WELD BEAD AND HEAT AFFECTED ZONE WIDTH IN SCANNED GTAW.
___: NUMERICAL SIMULATION, -·-·- : ANAL. MODEL

The analytical lumped model and the numerical simulation were both implemented in Fortran code. The unknown torch distribution parameters, i.e. the deviation radii σ_r and σ_z of its surface and penetration components are calibrated off-line by matching the predicted width w and penetration d of the pool interface to experimental measurements of the weld nugget dimensions, obtained at the nominal process conditions. Both models yield complete dynamic information on the weld thermal field, such as maps and section contours of the 3-D thermal and phase field, 2-D temperature hill and isotherm surfaces, as well as the time responses of important lumped thermal characteristics, such as the cross-sectional dimensions of the weld bead and the heat affected zone.

EXPERIMENTAL MODEL VALIDATION

Besides verification of the thermal model predictions, the laboratory tests provide a comparative study of the new scan welding method and traditional processes for various welding techniques (GTAW, GMAW), materials (mild and stainless steel) and torch power and motion conditions. The steady longitudinal travel speed of conventional welding and the transverse deflection of the parts in scan welding was provided by a high-speed X-Y positioning table. The fast longitudinal reciprocation of the torch in scan welding was driven by a slider and a rotating cam, with the scanning cycle schedule encoded on its circumferential geometry. The temperature distribution on the top weld surface was monitored by a stationary infrared pyrometer camera, with a mechanical galvanometer scanner an a liquid nitrogen cooled HgCdTe detector, sensitive in a wavelength range of 8-12 μm. The thermal emissivity of the polished part surface is determined by off-line comparative thermometry experiments with thermocouples. The thermal images from the IR camera are recorded during the process in standard composite video format, and analyzed off-line using a computer with a frame grabber and image processing software.

The traditional GMAW experiments were carried out on butt mild steel plates, 12.7 mm thick, with ER70S-6 consumable wire of 0.89 mm diameter and with 0.4 l/s inert gas supply (Ar-2%O_2). At the nominal conditions the voltage is 30 V, the torch velocity 6 mm/s and the wire feed rate 254 mm/s, providing a heat input of 417 W/mm per unit length of the joint. Starting at this operating point, the torch current is suddenly increased to yield a final power of 555 W/mm. The resulting experimental responses of the optically monitored width w and the off-line measured depth d by longitudinal sectioning of the weld bead are shown in Figure 5, together with the respective predictions of the numerical simulation and the analytical model. It can be seen that both model responses follow closely the dynamic test measurements, except for the noise of the experimental data due to the oscillatory solidification at the rear front of the pool interface, causing the familiar ripples of the weld bead surface (Linnert et al. 1968). Also, the slight deviation of the steady-state model

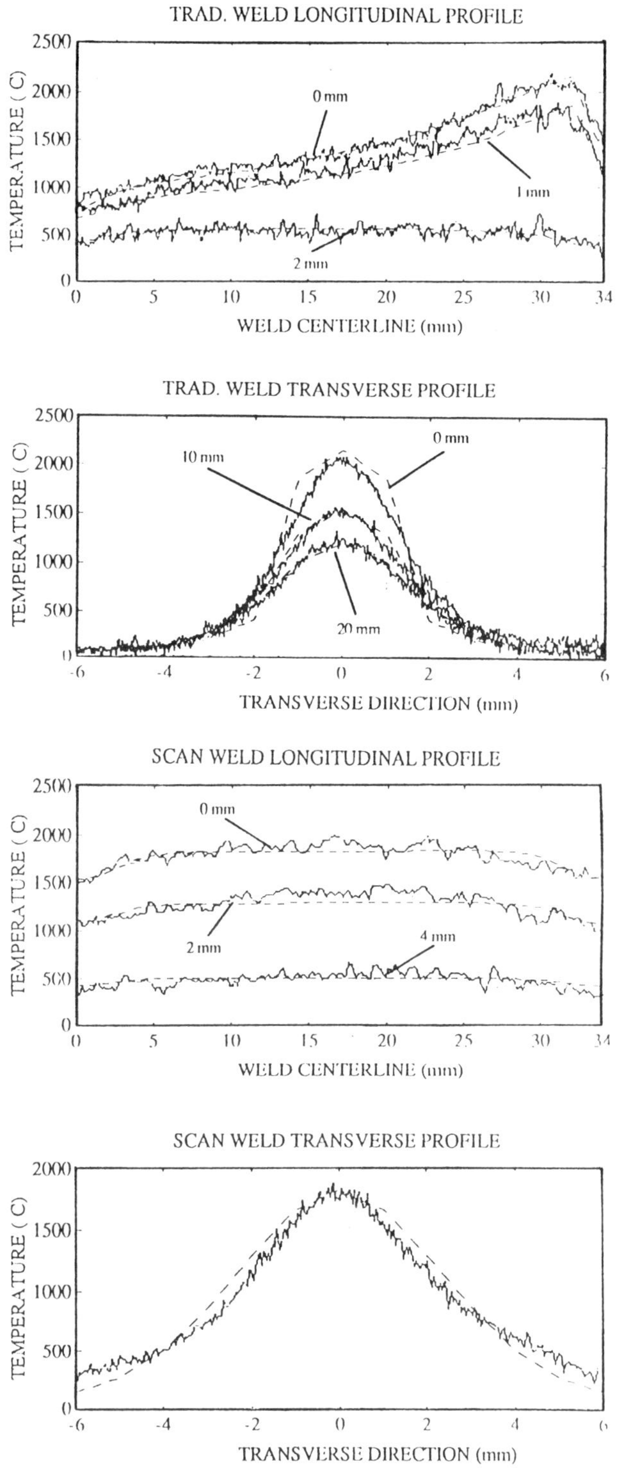

FIGURE 7: COMPARISON OF TEMPERATURE PROFILES FOR TRADITIONAL AND SCAN WELDING AT VARIOUS INDICATED DISTANCES FROM THE TORCH POSITION.
A. LONGITUDINAL PROFILES ___ : EXPERIMENT
B. TRANSVERSE PROFILES - - - : SIMULATION.

predictions indicates an apparent alteration of the calibrated source parameters (partial efficiencies n_r, n_z) after the step change of the welding conditions, and calls for their in-process identification by an adaptive thermal control system.

The classical and scan GTAW tests were performed by bead-on-plate welding of thin (3 mm) stainless steel plates (304), on 30 mm long test coupons. The inert gas flow was 0.4 l/s, the arc length 3 mm, the voltage 15 V and the current range 60-110 A. The torch was reciprocated along the weld centerline and parallel sidelines at an offset of 1 mm, at a frequency of 2 Hz, yielding an average constant velocity of 120 mm/s, while in traditional welding the speed was 3 mm/s. For these conditions, the torch efficiency parameter values n_r=0.58, n_z=0.09 and the equivalent conduction factors γ_r=3.49, γ_z=2.92 where identified by the lumped model. Figure 6 illustrates the model responses of the pool interface width (w) and the heat affected zone (HAZ) width from start to steady-state scan welding conditions. The longer initial delay of the bead width is attributed to the higher solidus isotherm (T_s=1400°C) encompassing the weld interface, which thus takes longer for the torch to develop in the welded plates. On the other hand, the HAZ width develops sooner but grows more slowly, because its lower sensitization isotherm (T_h=554°C) is located farther from the source, and thus it takes thermal conduction more time to reach that distance. Notice also the change in the growth rate of the HAZ at the time of formation of the pool, since the heat transfer is accelerated by the melt convection.

Figure 7 compares the temperature profiles of conventional and scan welding along longitudinal and cross sections of the top surface temperature hills, as measured by the IR camera and simulated by the numerical model. As expected, the difference between the gradients of the temperature hills show that in scan welding the temperature distribution is more uniform and less peaked than in the classical technique. Scan welding produces an almost invariant thermal profile in the centerline direction, with smooth transverse temperature slopes across the bead, in contrast to the steep longitudinal acclivity and high cooling rate of traditional welding. Because of these effects, as well as the lower peak temperature developed on the weld centerline, the thermal distortion of the joint is less for the scan than for classical welds, despite the larger heat affected zone of lower isotherms. The predictions of the calibrated simulation generally match the measured temperature profiles. The noise of these experimental measurements is because of emissivity variations on the weld surface, and their deviations from the results of the numerical model near the solid-melt interface and the plate edges is because of uncertainties in the assumed material and heat transfer parameters respectively.

Thus, unlike traditional welding methods where a steep, non-uniform temperature hill produces the weld bead in progressive longitudinal steps as the torch moves, the fast scan welding reciprocation of the source traverses the full weld centerline, and deposits the entire weld bead simultaneously, in gradual cross-sectional increments. This is illustrated in Figure 8, showing the simulated steady-state weld pool boundary interface (i.e. the solidus isotherm) for both welding techniques. The almost uniform cross section of the elongated scan weld pool, as opposed to the ellipsoidal shape of the conventional melt puddle, attests to the longitudinal invariance of the thermal field in scan welding.

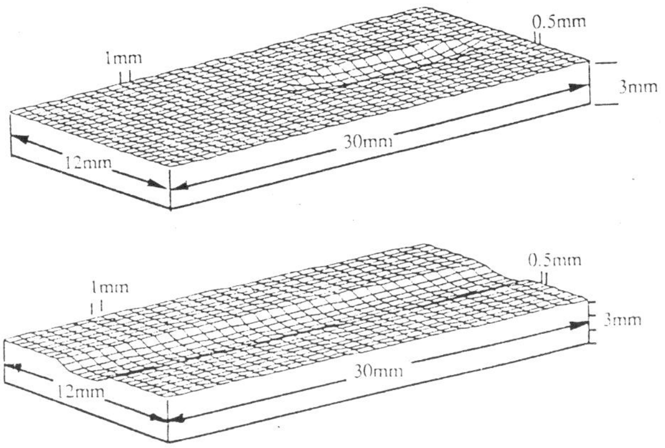

FIGURE 8: COMPARISON OF SIMULATED INTERFACE GEOMETRY FOR TRADITIONAL AND SCAN WELDING.

This difference in the liquid-solid interface geometry, as well as the dissimilar thermal boundary conditions from the heat source in the two methods, result in different melt circulation patterns in the weld pool. In conventional, serial welding processes, the steady-state geometrical configuration of the weld pool following the torch motion (Figure 8), yields at the equilibrium conditions a fully developed, constant 3-D flow field with intense convective heat transfer and rapid melting and freezing of the metal at the leading and trailing interface fronts respectively. This vigorous circulation of the melt results in steep temperature gradients in the pool and fast solidification in the mushy zone, causing certain weld defects such as dendritic columnar structure, microsegregation, uneven grain size, porosity, entrapped inclusions and thermal microcracks. On the other hand, in parallel scan welding the distributed heat input produces much smoother thermal slopes on the pool surface, and thus considerably weaker surface tension and torch momentum-induced flow streams, yielding a conduction-dominated heat flow. The elongated puddle with the dynamically changing cross sectional geometry results in a transient 2-D circulation scheme, agitated periodically at each torch pass and causing fusion and solidification in progressive steps at the lateral weld interface. The controlled melt freezing and the slow development of the scan weld bead limits drastically the solidification defects above, and generates a favorable material structure.

Figure 9 compares the microscopically observed weld nugget sections of a classical and a scan weld bead, produced under the previous process conditions, after polishing and etching in a HCl/HNO_3 solution. The higher width/depth ratio of the scan weld is attributed to the wider heat input distribution because of scanning of the sidelines by the torch. Note the extensive interweaving between the grains at the interface, and the continuity of the metal structure between the bead and the unmolten region, which results from the gradual solidification of the melt. The well-interlaced mushy zone of the scan weld reduces the tendency for incomplete fusion and interfacial cracks on the sharp, continuous boundary of conventional welds (Hayden et al 1965). In addition, the scan weld bead surface does not display the usual ripples observed above in traditional GMAW, and the start/finish torch defects (arc strikes, craters, transients etc), since the torch can be initiated and terminated anywhere along the weld centerline or its extension.

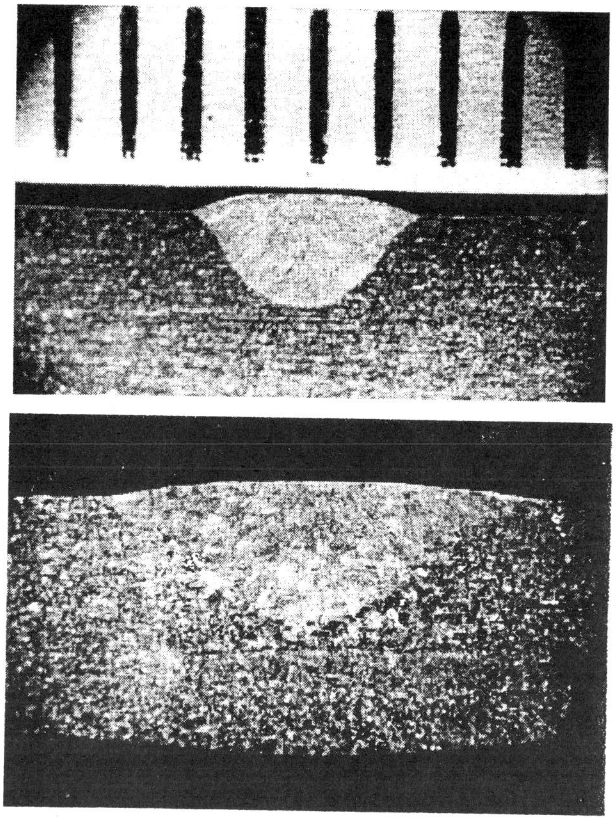

FIGURE 9: COMPARISON OF WELD BEAD CROSS SECTIONS FOR TRADITIONAL AND SCAN GTAW (9 X).

These favorable geometrical and material characteristics of the scan weld joint limit the stress concentration and potential failure initiation sites, thus improving the mechanical properties of the weld. A consistent increase of the tensile strength of scan welds by about 5% over comparable traditional joints was assessed in the laboratory by off-line standard tension testing (ASTM 370-92, Doumanidis 1994). This improvement is currently optimized by parametric studies of the scan welding process, both by experiments and by the thermal simulation models developed above.

CONCLUSION AND THERMAL CONTROL

In summary, it was shown that in classical fusion welding with a localized, sequentially moving source, the concentrated heat input of the torch yields a double-stream circulation pattern in the molten pool, and a highly-peaked composite conduction field in the solid region. This standard flow and thermal distribution result in limited controllability over the serial deposition of the weld bead along its axis, the metallurgical transformations of the material and the residual stress field generated by the steep thermal gradients. Thus, a novel scan welding process, implemented by rapid sweeping of the weld joint by a reciprocating torch with real-time modulated power and motion, was developed to enable simultaneous, independent control of all thermal quality characteristics of the joint. An analytical, lumped-state dynamic model of scan welding was derived by mass,

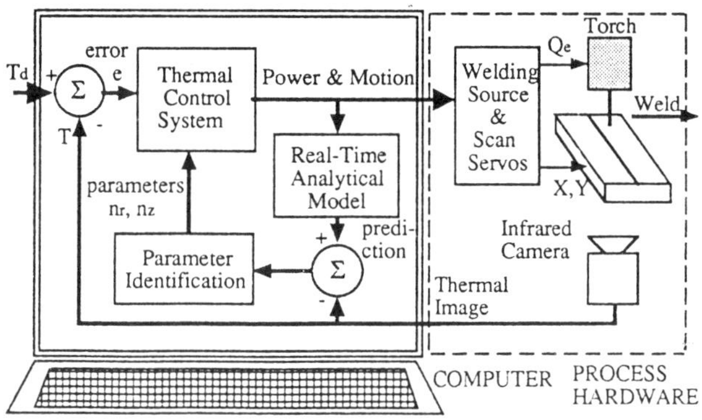

FIGURE 10: DISTRIBUTED-PARAMETER, ADAPTIVE THERMAL CONTROL SYSTEM FOR SCAN WELDING.

momentum and energy balances, and a numerical simulation of the temperature field was developed and calibrated experimentally for process analysis. The regulated heat distribution generated on the weld surface by scan welding fuses and deposits the entire length of the bead in parallel, cross-sectional increments, and develops a longitudinally uniform temperature field, with smooth transverse gradients. The resulting breakdown of the surface tension and torch momentum-induced flow in the pool, in combination to its prolonged, periodic thermal exposure, lead to a slow, controlled solidification of the weld bead material, and a pronounced interweaving of grains on its boundary interface to the unmolten region. These effects, as well as the regulated material microstructure and low thermal stress due to the smooth temperature hill slopes in the heat affected zone, are responsible for the increased experimental mechanical strength of scan welds.

Finally, the thermo-fluid models of scan welding enable the design of a closed-loop thermal control system of the torch actuation, employing feedback of real-time surface temperature measurements by the IR camera, to regulate the weld interface geometry and material structure in-process. This is illustrated in Figure 10, in which the measured 2-D temperature hill T(t) on the top surface is compared to a desired dynamic thermal distribution $T_d(t)$, yielding the specified weld bead and heat transfer zone features. This desired temperature field may be derived by off-line thermal process optimization using the simulation model, or it can be experimentally obtained and recorded during a reference test in the laboratory, in order to be reproduced during actual scan welding. In real-time operation, the temperature deviation distribution $e(t)=T_d(t)-T(t)$ determines the heat source intensity as well as its trajectory, which follows the locus of maxima of the error surface e(t), to guide the torch where its heat input is needed most. The control algorithm employs the real-time analytical process formulation developed above as a reference model for the in-process identification of the torch parameters, i.e. the partial torch efficiencies n_r, n_z, needed for the modulation of the torch power $Q_e(t)$ and determination of its motion. The performance of this thermal controller is currently under investigation, using the numerical simulation as a first computational testbed rather than the actual scan welding setup. The laboratory implementation and application of this adaptive, distributed-parameter thermal regulation strategy will be the subject of a future article.

ACKNOWLEDGMENT

This research was supported by NSF Grant DDM-9209141.

REFERENCES

Barry J.M., Paley Z, and Adams C.M, 1967"Heat Conduction from Moving Arcs in Welding", *Welding J.* 42, pp. 97s-104s.

Doumanidis C.C, 1992, "GMA Weld Bead Geometry: A Lumped Dynamic Model", *3rd ASM Intl. Conference on Trends in Welding Research*, Gatlinburg TN, pp. 63-68.

Doumanidis C.C, 1993, "Eulerian Multiple Source Simulation of Serial Fusion Manufacturing Processes", *IASTED Intl. Conf. on Applied Model. and Simulation*, Vancouver, p. 71-74

Doumanidis C.C, 1994, "Scan Welding: A Parallel Distributed Processing Technique", *1994 NSF Design and Manuf. Grantees Conference*, MIT, Cambridge, MA, pp. 541.

Friedman E, 1975, "Thermomechanical Analysis of the Welding Process Using the Finite Element Method", *J. Pressure Vessel Technology* 97(3), pp. 206-213.

Giedt W.H, Wei X.C, and Wei C.R, 1984, "Effect of Surface Convection on Stationary GTA Weld Zone Temperatures, *Welding J*, Dec. 1984, pp. 376s-383s.

Goldak J, 1989, "Modeling Thermal Stresses and Distortions in Welds", *Trends in Welding Research*, ASM International, Gatlinburg TN, pp. 71-81.

Hayden H.W, Moffatt W.G, and Wulff J, 1965, "The Structure and Properties of Materials", Vol. III, Mechanical Behavior, Wiley, New York, NY.

Hibbitt H.D, and Marcal P.V, 1973, "A Numerical Thermomechanical Model for the Welding and Subsequent Loading of a Fabricated Structure", *Comp. & Structures* 3(5), pp. 1145-74.

Karlsson L, and Lindgren L.E, 1990, "Combined Heat and Stress-Strain Calculations", *Modeling of Casting, Welding and Advanced Solidification Processes V*, TMS, pp.187-202.

Linnert G.E. et al, 1968, "Arc Welding", Metals Engineering Inst, ASM, Metals Park, OH.

Malmuth N.D, Hall W.F, Davis B.I, and Rosen C.D, 1974, "Transient Thermal Phenomena and Weld Geometry in GTA Welding", *Welding J.* 53, pp. 388s-400s.

McClintock F.A, and Argon A.S, 1966, "Mechanical Behavior of Materials", Addison-Wesley, Reading MA.

Myers P.S, Uyehara O.A, and Borman G.L, 1967, "Fundamentals of Heat Flow in Welding", *Weld. Res. Council Bulletin* 123.

Nunes A.C, 1983, "An Extended Rosenthal Model", *Welding J*, June, pp. 165s-170s.

Rosenthal D, 1941, "Mathematical Theory of Heat Distribution During Welding and Cutting", *Welding J.* 20(5), pp. 220s-234s.

Tsai C.L, 1988, "Modelling of Thermal Behaviours of Metals During Welding", *Trends in Welding Research in the US*, ASM, Metals Park OH, pp. 77-89.

Wells A.A, 1952, "Heat Flow in Welding", *Welding J.* 31(5), pp. 263s-267s.

HTD-Vol. 284/AMD-Vol. 182, Transport Phenomena in Solidification
ASME 1994

ON THE MORPHOLOGY OF ICE CRYSTALS GROWN FROM AMMONIUM CHLORIDE SOLUTIONS

M. V. A. Bianchi and R. Viskanta
Heat Transfer Laboratory
School of Mechanical Engineering
Purdue University
West Lafayette, Indiana

ABSTRACT

During solidification of a binary solution a two-phase region or "mushy zone" develops, and the study of the transport of momentum, heat, and species requires the understanding of its morphology. Solidification of ammonium chloride solutions has been extensively studied because of its similarities with metal alloy solidification. In particular, the analogy with metal alloys is based primarily on the dendritic growth of the salt crystals during the process of solidification of hypereutectic solutions. The growth of ice crystals from low to moderate concentration salt solutions is also of interest in many purification and separation applications, environmental sciences and the freezing of foods and biological tissues. In some studies the solidification of hypoeutectic solutions of ammonium chloride has been treated both experimentally and theoretically in order to understand the associated phenomena and to test computational models; however, the morphology of the crystals was not investigated. The present experimental study is concerned with the morphology of ice crystals grown from an ammonium chloride solution. A novel experimental setup is used to investigate the effects of initial composition and solidification rate on the ice crystal morphology. The experimental results obtained are presented and discussed.

NOMENCLATURE

Bi Biot number, Eq. (1)
d distance between reservoirs
h heat transfer coefficient
k thermal conductivity
L latent heat of solidification
T temperature
V solidification rate
x distance from the hot reservoir

Greek Symbols
α thermal diffusivity, $k/\rho c_p$
δ thickness
λ primary dendritic arm spacing
ρ density

Subscripts
c cold temperature base
$glass$ glass cover
h hot temperature base
m metallic slide
sol solution sample
∞ environment

INTRODUCTION

Solidification of non-eutectic binary or multicomponent mixtures, in contrast to pure substances and eutectic mixtures, can be characterized by the presence of a two-phase (mushy) region over an extended temperature range and a difference in solubility between liquid and solid phases. In order to model the transport of momentum, heat and species inside the mushy zone, it is necessary to know its geometric characteristics, described by the morphology of its crystals.

Solidification of ammonium chloride solutions has been extensively studied because of its similarities with metal alloys solidification (Jackson et al., 1966). In particular, the analogy with metal alloys is based primarily on the dendritic growth of the salt crystals during the process of solidification of hypereutectic solutions. In some studies the solidification of hypoeutectic solutions of ammonium chloride has been treated both experimentally and theoretically in order to understand the associated phenomena and to test computational models; however, the morphology of the crystals has not been investigated (Cao and Poulikakos, 1989, 1990, 1992; Spatz and Poulikakos, 1992; Braga and Viskanta, 1991; Yoo and Viskanta, 1992).

The motivations for the present work include the following: 1) the solidification of binary alloys is relevant to metallurgical problems, 2) the growth of ice crystals from low to moderate concentration salt solutions is of interest in many purification and separation applications, environmental sciences, and 3) the freezing of foods and biological tissues is of interest to preservation of materials.

Recently, considerable research attention has been focused on the understanding of the solidification process at both macroscopic and microscopic scales. Some analytical and experimental work was done in order to understand the heat and mass transfer processes during solidification of water-salt solutions in water on a microscopic scale (Rubinsky and Ikeda, 1985; Kourosh et al., 1990; Kourosh et al., 1990; Shigematsu and Komatsu, 1991; Rubinsky et al., 1993), but no study could be identified on the growth of ice crystals from ammonium chloride solutions.

The present experimental study is concerned with the morphology of ice crystals grown from an ammonium chloride solution. The experimental setup (Rubinsky and Ikeda, 1985; Rubinsky et al., 1993) was used to investigate the effects of initial composition and solidification rate on the ice crystal morphology. The experimental results obtained are presented and discussed.

EXPERIMENTAL METHOD

An experimental apparatus was designed based on the cryomicroscope developed to study the freezing of biological materials (Rubinsky and Ikeda, 1985; Rubinsky et al., 1993). The design is based on the so-called directional solidification principle, using the Bridgman technique (Flemings, 1974; Kurz and Fisher, 1989). The advantage of this specific design is that both the temperature gradient and the solidification rate can be accurately controlled. A detailed description of the directional solidification system used can be found elsewhere (Rubinsky and Ikeda, 1985; Rubinsky et al., 1993).

The experimental apparatus is shown in Fig. 1. Two controlled temperature reservoirs, which are heat exchangers made of copper and maintained at constant temperatures, T_h and T_c, and are separated by a gap d. The temperature of the hot reservoir, T_h, is higher than the liquidus temperature of the solution, and the temperature of the cold reservoir, T_c, is lower than the solidus temperature. A stage made of aluminum is placed over the reservoirs and is moved at a constant velocity V by a encoder mike (model 20200) which is controlled by a controller (model 18011), both manufactured by ORIEL. Over the stage, the sample (water-NH_4Cl solution) and a glass cover are located. Solidification of the sample occurs due to the controlled velocity V from the hot reservoir in the direction of the cold reservoir. A reflection microscope (Olympus, Model BHT) is used to observe the solid-liquid interface of the sample.

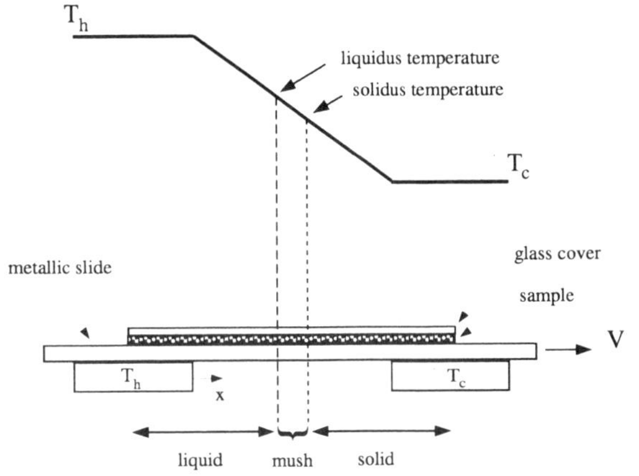

Figure 1: Schematic of the experimental design

In order to properly control the temperature gradient, several conditions must be satisfied:

- The contact resistance between the reservoirs and the microslide is small.
- The temperature throughout the thickness of the microslide is uniform. To satisfy this condition, convective heat transfer from the environment should be much smaller than conduction through the metal slide or
$$Bi = \frac{h\delta_m}{k_m} \ll 1 \tag{1}$$
- Heat conduction through the slide is much higher than heat conduction through the sample,
$$\frac{k_{sol}\delta_{sol}}{k_m\delta_m} \ll 1 \tag{2}$$
- Heat conduction through the slide is much higher than heat conduction through the glass cover,
$$\frac{k_{glass}\delta_{glass}}{k_m\delta_m} \ll 1 \tag{3}$$
- Heat conduction through the slide is much higher than heat convection to the environment,
$$2\frac{hd}{k_m}\frac{d}{\delta_m}\frac{(T_\infty - T_c)}{(T_h - T_c)} \ll 1 \tag{4}$$
- Heat conduction through the slide is much higher than heat advection due to the movement of the slide,
$$\frac{Vd}{\alpha_m} \ll 1 \tag{5}$$

- Heat conduction through the slide is much higher than the latent heat released through solidification.

$$\frac{\rho_{sol} V L \delta_{sol} d}{k_m \delta_m (T_h - T_c)} \ll 1 \qquad (6)$$

If all of the above conditions are satisfied, the heat conduction through the metallic slide is the most important process that imposes the thermal gradient on the sample solution. One can show that

$$T(x) = T_h - \left(\frac{x}{d}\right)(T_h - T_c) \qquad (7)$$

This temperature distribution is linear and controlled solely by the temperature of the reservoirs (T_c and T_h) and the distance between the reservoirs, d, that was not changed and is equal to 5 mm. Thermocouples were embedded in the metallic slide in order to measure the temperature gradient.

The system used in this work has an advantage over the previous design (Rubinsky and Ikeda, 1985; Rubinsky et al., 1993), because the microslide is made of aluminum that has a thermal conductivity much higher than glass (two orders of magnitude). This feature is possible because the microscope uses reflected light from the sample, rather than transmission through the sample.

EXPERIMENTAL RESULTS AND DISCUSSION

The temperature gradient was fixed and set at 1.5 K/mm. Four different initial concentrations of NH_4Cl were studied: 1%, 10%, 15%, and 19.7% (eutectic composition). These concentrations were arbitrarily chosen in order to cover the entire hypoeutectic region of the phase diagram for NH_4Cl-H_2O solutions (Flemings, 1974). The solidification rates V were 1, 10 and 100 μm/s.

The nucleation process is extremely important to the process of solidification. Nucleation would occur with some undercooling typically less than 10 K. Chaotic as it is, it allows different directions of growth to appear in the beginning of the experiment. Some of these directions will disappear, but more than one will survive until the end of the experiment. This observation is important to understand the nonuniform morphology of the mushy zone. Mathematical models of the mushy zone should account for the different directions of dendrites and their interaction when simulating the transport phenomena occurring within the zone.

Figure 2 shows the solidification front of ice from a 1% solution, when the solidification rate is 1 μm/s. The interface is planar, because at this small velocity the process is stable. Due to the necessary undercooling, the nucleation is not controlled and prior to the formation of the planar front the interface is cellular. This explains the details that can be seen in the left side (solid) of Fig. 2. After a stagnant front has been achieved, the stage starts moving (a jump start) at the desired velocity of 1 μm/s, and the stable planar front was reached. When the solidification rate is increased to 10 μm/s, the interface becomes unstable, as it

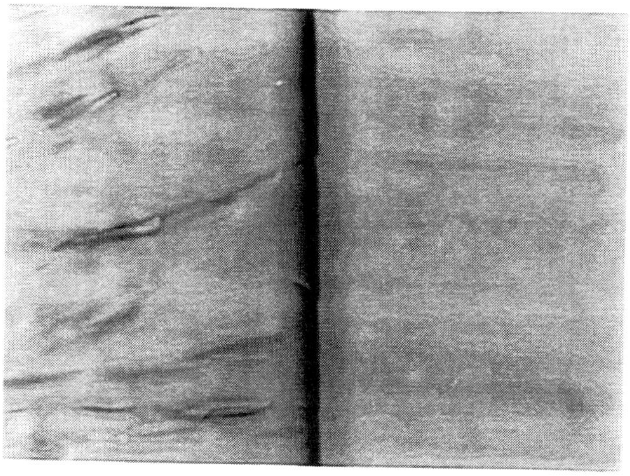

Figure 2: Solidification front for 1% solution and 1 μm/s (magnification $\approx$ 65X).

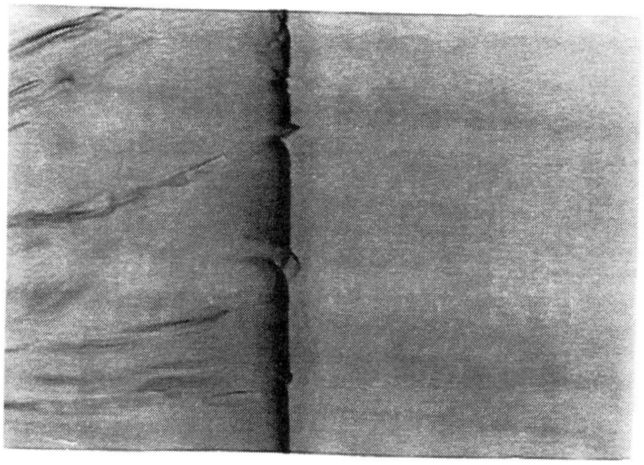

Figure 3: Unstable front for a 1% solution when the velocity was abruptly raised from 1 to 10 μm/s (magnification $\approx$ 65X).

can be seen from Fig. 3. During the transient the phenomena of cessation of growth of some cells and the division of other cells were observed (Kurz and Fischer, 1989), and at steady state the crystal growth becomes cellular/dendritic. The secondary arms are, however, very small as seen in Fig. 4. The crystals are very asymmetric in this stage of growth, and it is possible that the glass cover has some influence on this asymmetry. Cellular dendrites (Fig. 4) have received little research attention in the past and additional observations are necessary to understand this morphology. It is important to note that convection does not play a role, because the thickness of the sample is too small ($\delta \approx 100 \mu$m) and there is no forced flow imposed over the front. The ice crystals grown from the same concentration salt solution for a solidification rate of 100 μm/s are shown in Fig. 5. It can be observed that the number of dendrites increases and the arm spacing becomes smaller. The crystals show an inclination with respect to the temperature gradient (the axis of the cells are not align with the heat flux). The morphology of the crystals is similar to the ice crystals grown from a NaCl-water solution (Rubinsky et al., 1993).

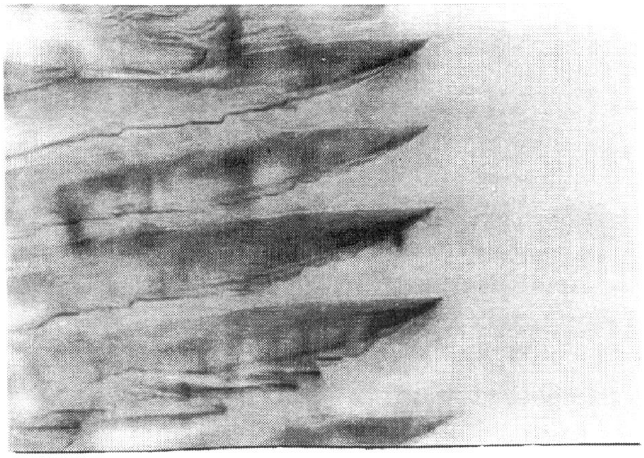

Figure 4: Steady-state crystals (1% solution) for 10 μm/s (magnification $\approx$ 65X).

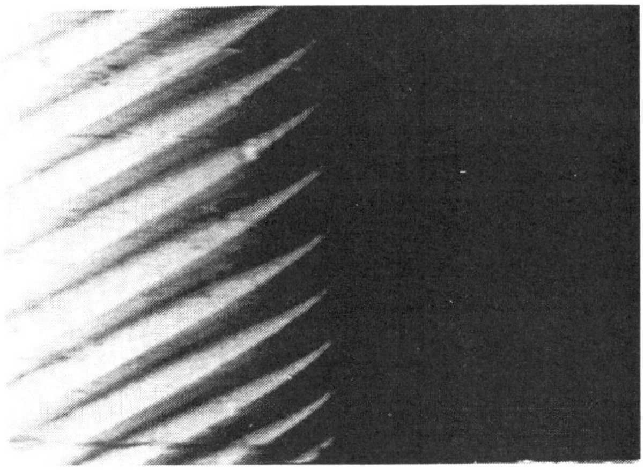

Figure 5: Solidification front for a 1% solution and 100 μm/s (magnification $\approx$ 65X).

For an initial concentration of 10%, Fig. 6 shows the crystal growth for a solidification rate equal to 1 μm/s. As seen in the figure, the front is non-planar, because the velocity is too high to attain a stable interface. The crystals look cellular-like and there is overlapping between adjacent crystals. Contrary to expectations (see Kurz and Fischer, 1989), the cells have their axes in different direction than that of the heat flow. A possible explanation for this inclination could be the fact that the steady state was not achieved, although the photograph shown in Fig. 6 was under observation for over 20 minutes and presented no change. The nucleation process itself may be responsible for the behavior. As the growth shown in Fig. 6 didn't start from a planar interface (because even for velocities as small as 0.5 μm/s the interface was not stable), the directions established by the nucleation process were still present. An abrupt increase in the solidification rate to 10 μm/s disturbs the growth and creates different cells (Fig. 7), and at steady-state the front is fully dendritic (Fig. 8). The secondary arms are relatively large, and as expected the primary arm spacing is smaller. The dendrites observed in Fig. 8 have an asymmetry that could be explained by the influence of the different layers of dendrites below the observed layer. The effect of the presence of more than one layer of dendrites in the thickness of the sample may disturb the concentration field in such a way that the growth becomes asymmetric. Additionally, the observed dendrites are actually three-dimensional.

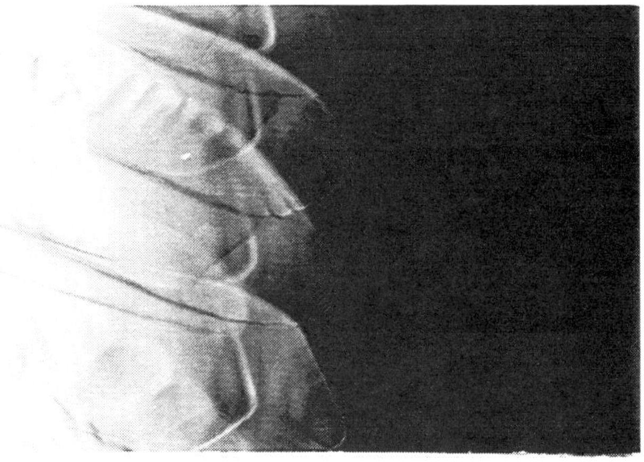

Figure 6: Unstable front grown at 1 μm/s in a 10% solution (magnification $\approx$ 65X).

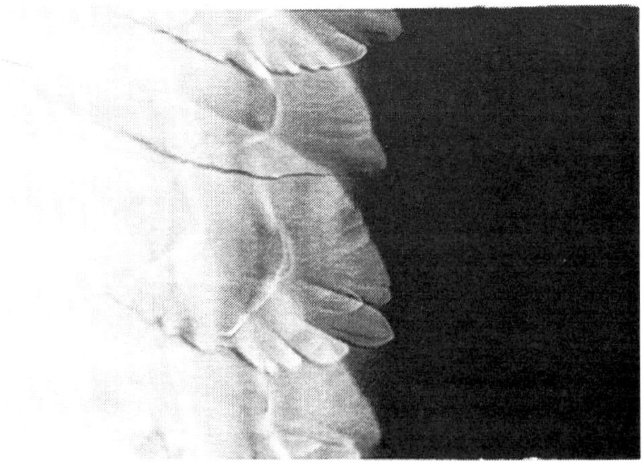

Figure 7: Transient behavior of the front when the velocity was raised from 1 to 10 μm/s (magnification $\approx$ 65X).

It is interesting to note that there is more than one direction of growth for the same imposed temperature gradi-

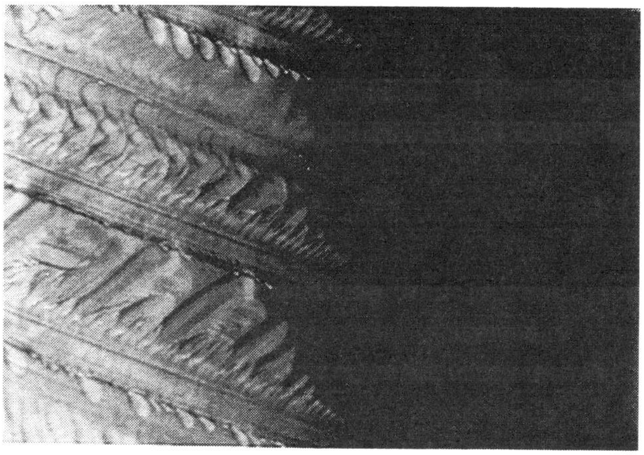

Figure 8: Steady-state crystals (10% solution) for 10 μm/s (magnification $\approx$ 65X).

ent. Figure 9 shows another region of the front for the same conditions as for Fig. 8. The morphology of these needle-like dendrites is completely different than those in Fig. 8, although they are growing under the same conditions. The different directions, as already mentioned, appear during the nucleation processes, specifically in the case when there is no planar front established. The mushy zone ends, and the eutectic forms in the interdendritic space. This is clearly evident from Fig. 10, which shows the compactness of the mush close to the eutectic. It is not possible to distinguish the dendrites in this region. The eutectic arm spacings could not be seen even for the highest magnification, but the interaction of the eutectic with the ice crystals can be studied using the present experimental set-up. Figure 11 shows the front for a solidification rate of 100 μm/s. The primary arm spacing is smaller, but the secondary arms are still large.

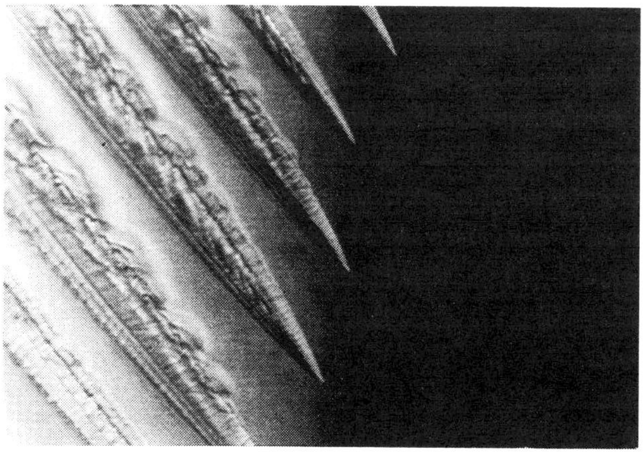

Figure 9: Steady-state crystals (10% solution) for 10 μm/s in a region of the sample different than that of Fig. 8 (magnification $\approx$ 65X).

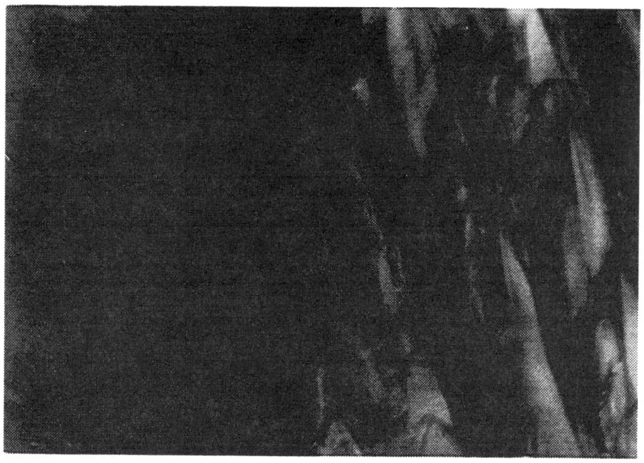

Figure 10: Eutectic growth over the mushy zone (10% solution) for 10 μm/s (magnification $\approx$ 65X).

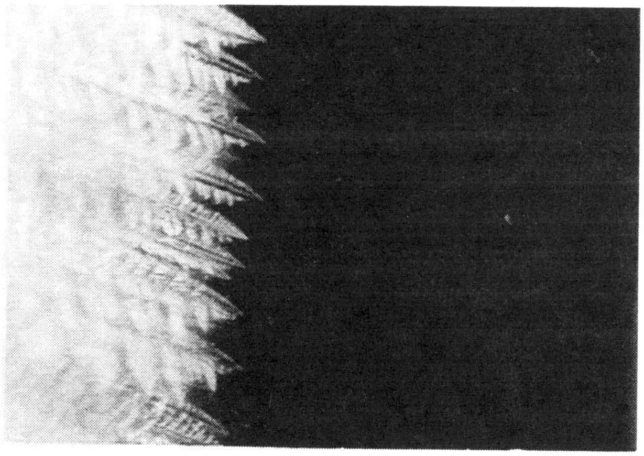

Figure 11: Solidification front (10% solution) for 100 μm/s (magnification $\approx$ 65X).

Figure 12 illustrates the solidification front for a 15% solution with a solidification rate of 10 μm/s. The morphology is dendritic with large secondary arms. For a solidification rate of 100 μm/s, there is little change in the morphology of the front, but the secondary arms become much smaller (Fig. 13). Figure 14 shows a detail of the secondary arms for this same velocity. The secondary arms are seen to grow in the direction of the heat flow.

As expected, the growth of the eutectic is planar (19.7% NH_4Cl) for any solidification rate. Details of eutectic growth can possibly be investigated with the present experimental set-up, provided the magnification is higher.

One of the most important parameters in alloy solidification is the dendritic primary arm spacing and the experimental device described in the present work can be used to measure it. Some primary arm spacing data are given in Table 1. The results were obtained for different conditions with respect to the history of the process and are approxi-

Figure 12: Steady-state crystals (15% solution) for 10 μm/s (magnification $\approx$ 65X).

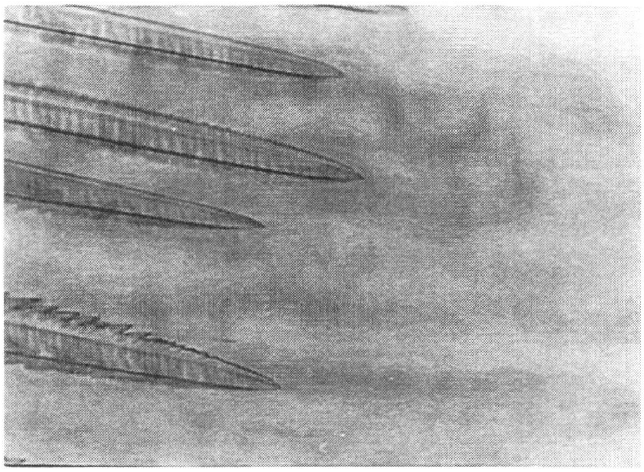

Figure 13: Solidification front (15% solution) for 100 μm/s (magnification $\approx$ 65X).

mate. The range of possible arm spacings appears to depend on the time history of the growth. For instance, if the solidification rate is increased by 1μm/s from stationary until it reaches 10μm/s, the arm spacing is different than if the velocity is suddenly increased to 10μm/s. The experimental results confirm the fact that there is a wide allowable range of dendritic arm spacings for given growth conditions (Weidong *et al.*, 1993).

CONCLUDING REMARKS

A new experimental technique for studying solidification processes on a microscopic scale was used to examine the morphology of ice crystals grown from an ammonium chloride-water solution for hypoeutectic concentrations. The observations reported in this work should be considered preliminary. From the observations made in this study, it can be concluded that ice crystals have a different morphology than ammonium chloride crystals, because the

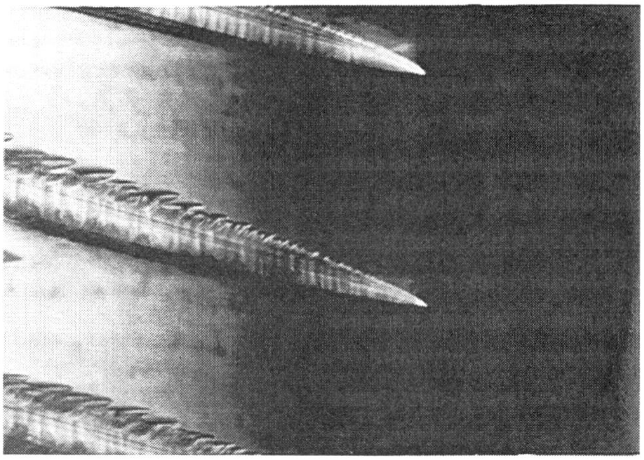

Figure 14: A detail of the crystals (15% solution) for 100 μm/s (magnification $\approx$ 130X).

$V[\mu m/s]$	$\lambda[\mu m]$
1	400 – 500
10	200 – 300
100	50 – 80

Table 1: Primary arm spacings for 10% solution

crystals grown from hypereutectic solutions of ammonium chloride have a sharper structure, with secondary arms perpendicular to the primary arms of the crystals. This raises the possibility to use hypoeutectic solutions as an analogue of binary metallic alloys which have a morphology similar to the one observed in the present work.

With the use of the experimental apparatus described herein, quantitative measurements of arm spacings will be performed, complementing the present work in describing the morphology of the solidification of ice crystals from hypoeutectic concentrations of ammonium chloride solutions. From the arm spacing data, it will be possible to model the permeability of the mushy zone more realistically and, consequently, predict more accurately the fluid and heat flow during the process of solidification.

ACKNOWLEDGMENTS

One of the authors (M. V. A. Bianchi) gratefully acknowledges support by the Conselho Nacional de Desenvolvimento Científico e Tecnológico (CNPq - Brazil).

REFERENCES

Braga, S. L. and Viskanta, R., 1990, "Solidification of a Binary Solution on a Cold Isothermal Surface," *Interna-*

tional Journal of Heat and Mass Transfer, Vol. 33, No. 4, pp. 745–754.

Cao, W.-Z. and Poulikakos, D., 1990, "Solidification of an alloy in a cavity cooled through its top surface," *International Journal of Heat and Mass Transfer*, Vol. 33, No. 3, pp. 427–434.

Cao, W.-Z. and Poulikakos, D., 1989, "Freezing of a Binary Alloy Saturating a Packed Bed of Spheres," *AIAA Journal of Thermophysics Heat Transfer*, Vol. 5, No. 1, pp. 46–53.

Cao, W.-Z. and Poulikakos, D., 1992, "Transient Solidification of a Binary Mixture in an Inclined Rectangular Cavity," *AIAA Journal of Thermophysics Heat Transfer*, Vol. 6, No. 2, pp. 326–332.

Flemings, M. C., 1974, *Solidification Processes*, McGraw-Hill, New York.

Jackson, K. A., Hunt, J. D. , Uhlmann, D. R. and Seward, T. P., 1966, "On the Origin of Equiaxed Zones in Castings," *Transactions of the Metallurgical Society of AIME*, Vol. 236, pp. 149–158.

Kourosh, S., Crawford, M. E. and Diller, K. R., 1990, "Microscopic Study of Coupled Heat and Mass Transport during Unidirectional Solidification of Binary Solutions – I. Thermal Analysis," *International Journal of Heat and Mass Transfer*, Vol. 33, No. 1, pp. 29–38.

Kourosh, S., Diller, K. R. and Crawford, M. E., 1990, "Microscopic Study of Coupled Heat and Mass Transport during Unidirectional Solidification of Binary Solutions – II. Mass Transfer Analysis," *International Journal of Heat and Mass Transfer*, Vol. 33, No. 1, pp. 39–53.

Kurz, W. and Fisher, D. J., 1989, *Fundamentals of Solidification*, Trans. Tech. Publ., Aedermannsdorf, Switzerland.

Rubinsky, B. and Ikeda, M., 1985, "A Cryomicroscope using Directional Solidification for the Controlled Freezing of Biological Material," *Cryobiology*, Vol. 22, pp. 55-68.

Rubinsky, B., Lee, C. and Chaw, M., 1993, "Experimental Observations and Theoretical Studies on Solidification Processes in Saline Solutions," *Experimental Thermal and Fluid Science*, Vol. 6, pp. 157–167.

Shigematsu, K. and Komatsu, H., 1991, "Growth of Ionic Crystals from Concentrated Aqueous Solutions – Hypothesis of Cation Dehydration and Insertion to Growing Interfaces," *Japanese Journal of Applied Physics*, Vol. 30, No. 8, pp. 1779–1786.

Spatz, T. L. and Poulikakos, D., 1992, "A Two-Wavelength Holographic Interferometry Study on the Solidification of a Binary Alloy Around a Horizontal Pipe," *Journal of Heat Transfer*, Vol. 114, No. 4, pp. 998–1010.

Weidong, H., Xingguo, G. and Yaohe, Z., 1993, "Primary spacing selection of constrained dendritic growth," *Journal of Crystal Growth*, Vol. 134, pp. 105–115.

Yoo, H. and Viskanta, R., 1992, "Effect of Anisotropic Permeability on the Transport Process during Solidification of a Binary Mixture," *International Journal of Heat and Mass Transfer*, Vol. 35, No. 10, pp. 2335–2346.

HTD-Vol. 284/AMD-Vol. 182, Transport Phenomena in Solidification
ASME 1994

EFFECTS OF MIXED CONVECTION ON DENDRITE FRAGMENTATION DURING ALLOY SOLIDIFICATION

C. J. Paradies, R. N. Smith*, and M. E. Glicksman

Department of Materials Engineering
and
*Department of Mechanical Engineering,
Aeronautical Engineering, and Mechanics
Rensselaer Polytechnic Institute
Troy, New York

ABSTRACT

Experiments have been conducted to observe fragmentation events in a model alloy (succinonitrile and acetone) solidifying in the presence of forced convection in the superheated melt. Measurements of fragmentation rates have been made, and an attempt was made to relate the results to the controllable parameters of the system. A microscope—video system recorded the mushy zone-melt interface, and the fragmentation process and fragmentation rates could be determined from a frame-by-frame analysis of the video images. Experiments were conducted for varying cooling rates, overall temperature differences, melt flow rates, and for two different concentrations of acetone (1.3 wt% and 6.1 wt%).

Significant dendritic fragmentation occurred for all runs. In addition, the influence of buoyancy forces is clearly evident from particle motion near the mushy zone-melt interface. Fragmentation rates appear to correlate well with the magnitude of particle velocities near the interface, with increasing fragmentation being associated with higher particle velocity *magnitude* (either in the same or the opposite direction to the mean flow) for the 1.3 wt% acetone mixture. However, the correlation is quite different for the higher concentration. The relationship between these results and the possible mechanisms for fragmentation are discussed. Although it appears that either constitutional remelting or capillary pinching are likely of importance, hydrodynamic shear forces or some other mechanism, as yet undiscovered, cannot be completely discounted, although circumstantial evidence suggests that mechanical shearing is inconsistent with observations both made here and already in the published literature. The results provide a step in the development of solidification models that incorporate fragmentation processes in the mushy zone as an important mechanism of grain refinement and a potential source of macrosegregation in ingots and large castings.

INTRODUCTION

It has long been recognized that refining the microstructure of an alloy casting improves its low temperature strength, toughness, heat treatment characteristics, and hot tearing tendency. Solidification microstructures are, in reality, frozen remnants of a two-phase region, commonly called the "mushy zone", which has a transitory existence during the progressive freezing of any alloy. It is within the mushy zone that chemical microsegregation and the resultant phase relationships are established for the fully frozen or as-cast material. Although the initial dendrite microstructure may be altered substantially by heat treatment and mechanical working subsequent to solidification, the initial dendritic patterns within a material are, as a practical matter, never fully eliminated. Furthermore, competitive processing methods increasingly rely upon near-net shape casting, rheocasting, and as-cast materials which increase the need for microstructural control during the solidification process.

It is usually desirable to control the number and dispersion of crystallites, or grain density, since the resultant cast microstructure is metallurgically most useful when a fine, uniform, random distribution of equiaxed grains occurs. Typical commercial practice in non-ferrous foundries involves adding, just prior to casting, "grain refiners", which are proprietary mixtures of catalytically active materials that stimulate the nucleation process within an alloy melt by reducing its free energy barrier to crystallite formation. However, this practice does not always work well, particularly for certain aerostructural alloys containing strong carbide formers like zirconium. An alternative procedure is to induce grain refinement mechanically, rather than chemically, by stirring the molten metal with sufficient vigor, so that a portion of the fine, columnar, dendritic crystals may break free from the leading edge of the mushy zone and be carried away by the surrounding melt stream. These "seeds" or grain fragments become the sites for new grains, which in turn might provide new "seeds" if the fluid mechanical, thermal, and chemical conditions are favorable.

The comminution, detachment, dispersion, and regrowth of grain fragments constitutes a significant but complex grain refinement process that is totally independent of nascent nucleation events and the action of grain refiners. In fact, grain refiners and nucleation events operate as *molecular-scale* phenomena, whereas grain fragmentation can be controlled at the *macroscopic* level by appropriate melt flow augmentation and temperature control. A number of aluminum producing companies have recognized for several years the commercial advantages for melt shearing as a grain refining practice, and are currently employing some form of on-line mechanical fragmentation control (Fang, 1989; Vives, 1990; Desnain, et al., 1988).

However, little is currently known about the detailed crystallite fragmentation mechanism, since solidification processes in metals preclude direct observation of actual crystal fragmentation events. Moreover, the motion, speed, and hydrodynamic characteristics of the melt flow adjacent to the columnar dendritic zone within a casting cannot be observed in the normally opaque, chemically aggressive environment of molten metals at typical casting temperatures.

Jackson *et al.* (1966) examined fragmentation of mushy zones and concluded that localized remelting was the mechanism of detachment. Their investigation attempted to explain the equiaxed region in a casting by the observation of a solidifying NH_4Cl-H_2O solution. They studied a series of rudimentary castings including some in which a motor-driven propeller was used to stir the melt. Their study concluded that fragmentation results from solute rejection during dendritic growth, producing conditions under which a side branch may begin to remelt at its base and subsequently will "pinch off". This occurs because the local equilibrium temperature at the tip of a side branch becomes larger than that at the base, so that growth at the tip is favored over growth at the base. The heat and solute generated by the growing side branch can raise the local temperature and concentration experienced by the base of the side branch, causing "constitutional" remelting of the stem. If the fluid flow is sufficiently vigorous, then the free side branch will be carried by the flow until it grows sufficiently large to settle to the bottom of the mold. Jackson *et al.* concluded that the localized remelting was a function of undercooling and solute concentration, whereas it was the stirring along that allowed the fragments to be carried into the equiaxed zone more easily.

Christenson *et al.* (1989a, 1989b) conducted another study of NH_4Cl-H_2O which shows similar fragmentation resulting from remelting. Their experimental arrangement consisted of a long rectangular cavity heated on one side. This geometry was found to produce significant buoyancy driven convection in the melt. Remelting occurred at the top of the cavity. Often, dendrite arms detached from this region and were carried by free convection into the melt, subsequently settling in the bottom of the container. The NH_4Cl-H_2O system crystallizes by precipitation of the cubic solid phase, rejecting the less dense water. Lower density, higher temperature solution flows to the top of the container and causes local remelting of the growing mushy zone by both increasing the temperature and the H_2O concentration. This is analogous to the conditions which exist in a forced convection alloy melt system where warm melt impinges on the mushy zone. The concentration of the bulk melt increases due to macrosegregation. Both depleted solute content and elevated temperature of the melt can lead to remelting in the mushy zone.

Additional evidence of dendrite detachment was observed in the recent work conducted by Rubinstein (1989). In experiments on dendritic growth of pure camphene, a remarkable number of such detachments were observed when nucleation occurred at small undercoolings. Because this was a pure material growing from the melt without significant bulk fluid convection, neither mechanical shearing nor constitutional remelting (Jackson, et al., 1966) are suspected as mechanisms responsible for fragmentation of the dendrites. Rather, it appears that changes in the local solid-liquid equilibrium temperatures resulting from variation of interface curvatures can lead to local remelting at the dendrite base. Some of the issues related to this type of Ostwald ripening phenomena were discussed by Huang and Glicksman (1981), and an extensive review of the subject for alloy systems has been presented by Voorhees (1990).

Smith *et al.* (1991) studied the effects of stirring on fragmentation and coarsening of primary silicon particles in an Al-19%Si alloy system. They found that the number of crystallites formed increased with higher stirring rates, but that this also tended to encourage coalescence of particles. Although they discussed the effect of shear rate on particle sizes and number density, no mechanism for particle formation was observed. In another study of model alloy solidification, Kerr *et al.* (1989) solidified aqueous solutions of sodium sulfate (Na_2SO_4) in a rectangular chamber which was cooled from above. They noticed after a period of time crystals growing on the bottom of their chamber; however, they were unable to determine whether these had nucleated in place or had detached from the original mushy layer subsequent to their growth at the top of their chamber.

Fang and Bruno (1991) found that mechanical stirring of an aluminum melt reduced the thickness of the chill zone and reduced the equiaxed grain size of a 6 inch diameter ingot. Although the results were initially thought to be due to high shear forces or turbulence in the melt, control of the melt superheat (not the stirring speed) was found to be the most important variable for obtaining the desired degree of grain refinement. The transition from columnar to equiaxed growth was also accelerated by stirring the melt; however, there was a maximum stirring speed beyond which further reduction in the columnar zone thickness did not occur. Bryson, et al. (1991) introduced a system of baffling for ingot casting which would direct the melt flow during pouring into the mushy zone. The reduction in grain size, as well as the uniformity across the ingot, are attributed to action of the melt flow which initiates fragmentation and keeps fragments produced by the flow from settling to the bottom of the mold sump.

Vives (1990) and Desnain, et al., (1988) indicated that a maximum flow velocity of the melt is reached above which the grain size in the solidified casting either does not change or even increases, suggesting that grain refinement is not controlled by the breaking of dendrites by shear forces alone. Durand (1992) found that stirring of the melt produced a sharp recalescence and stimulated nucleation of an equiaxed zone, and concluded that the mechanism might be the detachment of dendritic fragments during recalescence.

It is clear from the previous discussion that the mechanisms by which the melt interacts with the growing mushy zone during solidification to produce either fragments or nucleation sites for grain refinement, or for transition from columnar to equiaxed growth, are not understood. This has stimulated the current study, the goal of which was to observe fragmentation events in a model alloy solidifying in a controlled manner while interacting with forced convection in the superheated melt. The rate of fragmentation, that is, the rate at which particles appear in the melt from the mushy zone, has been measured, and an attempt has been made to relate it to the controllable parameters of the system—namely, the melt flow rate, the level of superheat in the melt, and cooling rate (i.e., the rate of growth of the mushy zone). Before describing the experimental system which was constructed to accomplish this, it is useful to outline briefly the three mechanisms which have been proposed for the production of crystallite fragments, based on the experimental observations presented above. However, it was not a goal of the present study to determine specifically which mechanism might be dominant, except as might become apparent from observation of the phenomena.

MECHANISMS FOR FRAGMENTATION

Remelting of dendrite side branches because of compositional variations in the melt was first suggested by Jackson *et al.* (1966). As the side branches begin growing in the region of high solute concentration around a growing dendrite (i.e., into a region where the equilibrium melting temperature is lowered), they extend into the bulk melt, where the local solute concentration diminishes, and the equilibrium melting temperature for the tip becomes higher than that of the stem. Therefore, growth at the dendrite tip is favored over growth of the stem, and conditions by which the melting temperature at the stem becomes less than the local melt temperature may easily be envisioned. This process would clearly be influenced and abetted by additional redistribution of solute by convection.

Attributing the formation of fragments to mechanical shearing by the melt cannot be dismissed; however, there is substantial circumstantial evidence suggesting that this mechanism is *not* of great importance. For example, Jackson *et al.* (1966) noticed a time delay between the onset of stirring and the generation of free crystallites. If fragmentation were being produced solely by the shear forces of the flowing melt on the mushy zone, the fragmentation should have begun promptly. A similar observation was made in a preliminary experimental study by the authors (Paradies *et al.*, 1993). Furthermore, the present experiments involved bulk melt velocities of less than 12 cm/second, which corresponds to a Reynolds number based on the hydraulic diameter of the flow passage of only a few hundred. The melt flow velocity in the vicinity of the mushy zone was substantially less than this, as well, partially due to the buoyancy forces in the region nearest the mushy zone. In addition, some of the data show that there is a *decrease* in the fragmentation rate with increasing melt velocity. Nonetheless, the comparative influence of mechanical shearing as opposed to remelting certainly warrants further discussion.

The contribution of Ostwald ripening to crystallite fragmentation occurs on a different time scale than that of constitutional remelting. In addition, the temperature differences associated with variations in interfacial curvature are substantially less than those from solute redistribution in the melt. However, this mechanism may increase the rate of remelting of the side branch stem, particularly as the stem narrows prior to "pinch off", and the local curvature of the stem becomes much larger than the curvature of the tip.

The goal of the present experiment was to examine the effect of forced convection on the rate of fragmentation within the mushy zone. Whether one or another process is dominant is, at this stage of our understanding, of secondary importance to the fact that processes exist permitting detachments of dendrite arms over time. Also of importance are the solidification parameters that control the "pinch off" processes, including alloy composition, the magnitude of the forced convection, the level of melt superheat, and the cooling rate. In the course of the study, it became apparent that buoyancy forces are of great significance in determining the nature of the melt flow field, even to the extent of causing a reversed flow in the region nearest the mushy zone under certain conditions.

PRELIMINARY RESULTS

The present study was motivated directly by the results of a preliminary experiment (Paradies, et al., 1993) which was designed to investigate the feasibility of observing the effects of forced flow over the mushy zone of an alloy melt using a transparent model system. In that study, a succinonitrile-acetone mixture was induced to flow in a horizontal, annular passage, the inner wall of which was cooled by a chilled, ethylene glycol and water mixture circulating through the inner tube. This was a recalescence experiment for which the mushy zone nucleated on the chill tube after its temperature was reduced to a level sufficiently below the liquidus and then grew very quickly to an equilibrium position in the channel. A constant level of superheat in the melt prevented further growth of the mushy zone. Significant fragmentation was observed during the recalescence period. The results indicated that increasing the velocity of the forced flow in the tube increases the rate of fragmentation during recalescence; however, the largest cumulative total of fragments was produced by an intermediate flow rate. Furthermore, there was a delay in the onset of fragmentation until after the beginning of the recalescence period, so that a mechanism based on dendrite shearing for the creation of fragments cannot adequately explain the fragmentation process.

Two difficulties with the preliminary experimental design were that the growth period of the mushy zone was very short, so that fragmentation during solidification could not be observed, and that substantial asymmetry of the mushy zone was present, probably caused by buoyancy effects in the horizontal growth chamber. An improved experimental configuration and procedure was undertaken to correct these deficiencies.

EXPERIMENTAL APPARATUS

The forced convection flow loop and solidification chamber used in this study is shown schematically in Figure 1. The loop consisted of a 1.7 liter melt reservoir connected to a vertically-oriented annular growth chamber, connected to a magnetically coupled pump that circulated the melt through the annulus. The pump could produce a maximum flow rate of succinonitrile-acetone mixture of about 6 liters per minute, which corresponded to a maximum average velocity in the annular region of about 14 cm/sec and a Reynolds number, based on hydraulic diameter of 340. The entire loop was contained in a temperature-controlled chamber ("hot box") to maintain the temperature of the melt. A separate reservoir containing acetone was connected to the main reservoir, but sealed from it during operation and positioned outside the "hot box" because of the volatility of acetone. The growth chamber consisted of a 28 mm square cross section Pyrex tube 60 cm length with a Pyrex chill tube of circular cross section extending through the center of the square tube for the full length, except for a 8.4 cm test section made of stainless steel, upon which the mushy zone developed. The test section began 332 mm from the inlet of the growth chamber and included a 44 mm long stainless steel bellows to allow for expansion and

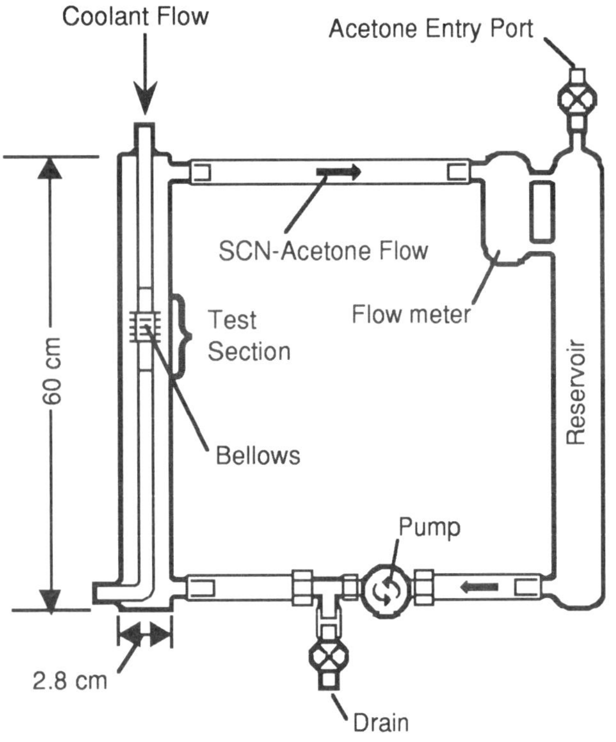

FIGURE 1 FLOW LOOP SCHEMATIC

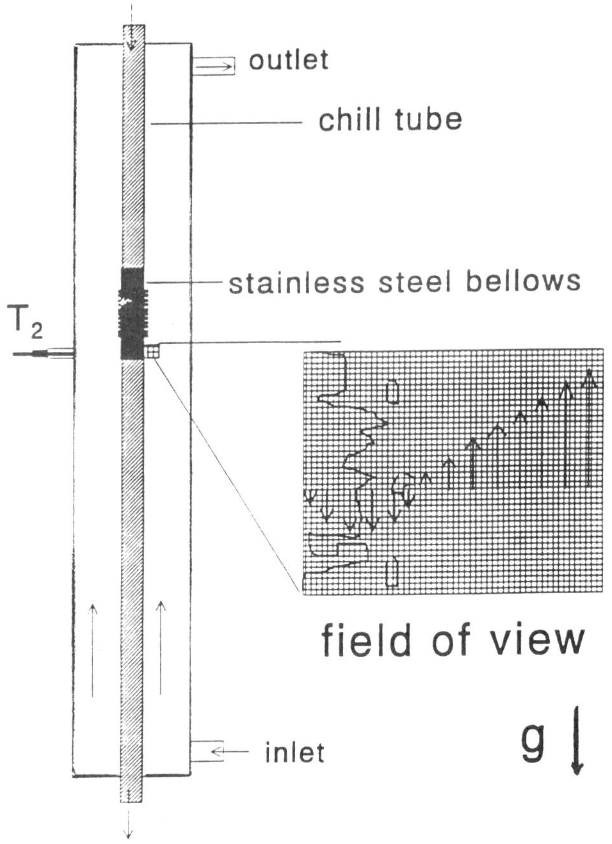

FIGURE 2 SCHEMATIC OF THE VERTICAL GROWTH CHAMBER SHOWING THE MICROSCOPE — VIDEO CAMERA FIELD OF VIEW

contraction of the assembly as the temperatures of the chill tube and the melt were varied. On each end of the bellows was a smooth extension of stainless steel tubing of 20 mm length. The field of view within the growth chamber is located on the smooth portion of the stainless steel tube as indicated in Figure 2. The growth of the mushy zone could be observed within this field of view along the smooth portion of the stainless steel test section beginning 337 mm from the inlet to the growth chamber.

An ethylene glycol and water mixture was circulated through the inner tube to a refrigerated bath to provide cooling for initiating and maintaining solidification on the outside wall of the inner tube (outer diameter = 1 cm). The bath temperature could be controlled to within ± 0.1 K using a computer-controlled interface to the bath, and the *rate of decrease* of the coolant temperature could also be controlled.

Temperatures within the system were measured by stainless steel jacketed type K thermocouples placed at the growth chamber inlet; inside the growth chamber outer wall at the bottom of the field of view; inside the chill tube at the bottom of the field of view; and at a point near the field of view within the hot box. The thermocouple inside the chill tube was positioned in contact with the chill tube wall to provide an indication of the wall temperature at the point where the mushy zone was growing and the fragmentation events were being observed.

The temperature of the melt could be controlled by a computer algorithm which monitored the temperature within the hot box and provided outputs to a combination of electric resistance heaters within the hot box, heating tapes which wrapped around the pump to provide auxiliary heating, and a fan which could introduce room temperature air into the hot box. Additional fans maintained uniform temperature within the hot box.

The resulting control allowed the temperature of the melt and of the coolant in the chill tube to be decreased at a controlled rate of up to 0.6 ± 0.03 K/min during an experimental run, so that solidification could be initiated and maintained at an approximately steady rate.

Magnified images of the growing mushy zone were recorded on videotape using a Javelin Ultrachip CCD camera attached to a Sony U-Matic videocassette recorder. A Wild M420 Apozoom microscope combined with the CCD camera magnified the images a total of 58.5 X on the video monitor. The dimensions of the field of view were approximately 4 mm × 5 mm. The depth of field was approximately 2 mm. An arbitrary length along the mushy zone of 1.71 mm (100 mm on the monitor screen), the depth of focus, and the width of the screen define an approximate "control volume" within the field of view for counting fragments. The photographs provided in the paper were obtained using a Polaroid free frame connected to the recording device and have a total magnification of 21.8 X. The mushy zone was backlit by a collimated white light source.

The model alloy chosen for these experiments was succinonitrile [$NC(CH_2)_2CN$] (SCN) with dilute concentrations of acetone [CH_3COCH_3]. SCN is a transparent material with a melting point of 58 C, convenient for use in the laboratory; its thermophysical and chemical properties are well established. SCN solidifies as a body-center cubic, non-faceted, dendritic crystal similar in many respects to cubic metal systems. The density of the liquid and solid phases differ, as do metals, by about 3%, and the thermal conductivity of the solid and liquid differe only by 0.5 %. The Prandtl number is 22.4 at the melting point. The phase diagram for SCN-acetone reveals a liquidus slope of –2.8 K/wt% and an equilibrium distribution coefficient of 0.1. Because SCN has a very high solubility for air (N_2), the entire flow loop was maintained under a vacuum.

EXPERIMENTAL PROCEDURE

All solidification experiments were begun with a very thin layer of solid maintained on the chill tube to prevent undercooling of the melt from occurring, which in turn would cause an uneven growth of the mushy zone to occur in the early stages of a run. Each run was initiated by setting the pump speed (flow rate) and the temperatures of the chill tube and the hot box enclosure (approximately the melt temperature). The rate of cooling was selected for both the chill tube and the enclosure to maintain a constant temperature difference between the melt and the chill tube throughout the run, and the video recording system was started. The volume rate of flow was periodically monitored using an in-line flow meter to ensure that the flow rate remained constant during a run. As the mushy zone advanced across the growth chamber, the field of view was adjusted using the computer operated position controller. Each run extended until the outer edge of the mushy zone had grown to a distance approximately one-half way across the flow annulus, at which time the SCN-acetone mixture was remelted and the parameters of the system were reconfigured for the next solidification run.

The parameters which could be controlled included the acetone concentration (0.0 to 6.1 wt%), the average melt velocity, based on constant volume flow rate, (1.8 to 11.9 cm/s), the chill melt temperature difference (8 K to 18 K), and the cooling rate (0.1 K/minute to 0.6 K/minute). The maximum concentration of acetone (6.1 wt%) was dictated by the reduction in the liquidus (41 C) and the solidus, which made solidification difficult. Most runs were conducted at a concentration of 1.3 wt% acetone, with only one complete run at 6.1 wt% and a limited number of runs at 0.0 and 0.3 wt % acetone, for which no fragmentation was observed. However, the mushy zones for the 1.3 and 6.1 wt% concentrations generated many fragments, and discussion in the succeeding section will focus on these cases.

At any one time, a large number of fragments visible in the field of view originated from areas above or below the field of view and were carried by the flowing melt through the field of view. It proved to be difficult to distinguish between a fragment that separated from the mushy zone within the field of view, from the much greater number of "background" fragments traveling *through* the field of view from other areas. The quantitative procedure by which this was accomplished will be described in the next section.

RESULTS

A dendritic mushy zone was observed for the higher solute concentrations (1.3 and 6.1 wt% acetone). As the initial melt and chill tube were cooled, dendrites grew from the preexisting solid layer. Figure 3 shows photographs, taken from the video images, of the development of the mushy zone for a typical run (1.3 wt% acetone, cooling rate = 0.07 K/min, temperature difference = 10 K, average melt velocity = 11.9 cm/s). The initial growth of the mushy zone is shown in Figure 3(a). As the mushy zone thickness (the distance between the chill tube and the mushy zone-melt interface) increased (Figures 3(b) and 3(c)), the amount of fragmentation was also observed to increase.

For a number of runs with 1.3 wt% acetone concentration, an interesting mixed convection phenomena with reversed flow was observed. A typical "flow morphology" was as follows: At very early times, the mushy zone was thin, the average velocity in the annular region was the lowest, and the temperature difference between the mushy zone-melt interface and the outer channel wall was the largest. These conditions are all consistent with the greatest influence of buoyancy forces on the flow. In fact, particles generated from fragmentation of the mushy zone dendritic structure were observed to travel downward in the region nearest to the mushy zone, while the flow away from the mushy zone was *upward*. At later times, the flow area was reduced, because of the mushy zone growth, serving both to increase the velocity of the net forced flow and to reduce the macroscopic length scale for buoyancy forces. Also, the temperature difference between the mushy zone-melt interface (approximately the liquidus) and the outer wall of the flow channel was reduced due to the downward "ramping" of the temperature of the hot box. Particles nearest the mushy zone-melt interface were nearly motionless, even though the velocity away from the mushy zone increased because the annular opening for the flow had been reduced while the flow rate remained nearly constant. At still later times, it appeared that the forced convection flow field dominated over buoyancy forces, and the particles near the mushy zone moved upward rapidly at a velocity which was 20-30% of the nominal melt velocity. While this reversed flow phenomenon did not occur for all runs involving the 1.3 wt% acetone concentration, the tendency toward a higher velocity of the melt in the region nearest the mushy zone was consistently observed. At the single experimental run performed at a higher, 6.1 wt% acetone concentration, no reversed flow occurred; however the tendency for the fragments nearest the mushy zone to move more rapidly as time progressed into the run was similar. Unfortunately, the total volume of SCN-acetone mixture was less than the total volume of the flow loop, so that the stainless steel tube was not covered with solution unless the pump was in operation. Therefore, pure natural convection conditions could not be obtained for the present experiments.

An interesting morphological phenomenon which was observed was the formation of "weldments," in which a fragment would impinge on the outer edge of the mushy zone and stick or "weld" to it. The mushy zone would then continue to grow from and around a "weldment," which tended to occur more frequently for the higher fragmentation rates. Because the weldment would seldom break free subsequently from the mushy zone, it might be surmised that the shear forces are insufficient to produce breakage of the mushy zone dendrites. Under some conditions a layer of weldments seemed to suppress further columnar growth of the mushy zone, beginning a new "equiaxed" layer of dendritic growth. This may be an alternative to the settling of fragments from the bulk melt for producing what appears to be an equiaxed zone in a casting. When a sufficient number of free fragments reattach to the mushy zone to arrest further columnar-dendritic growth, the new layer of fragments begins to grow.

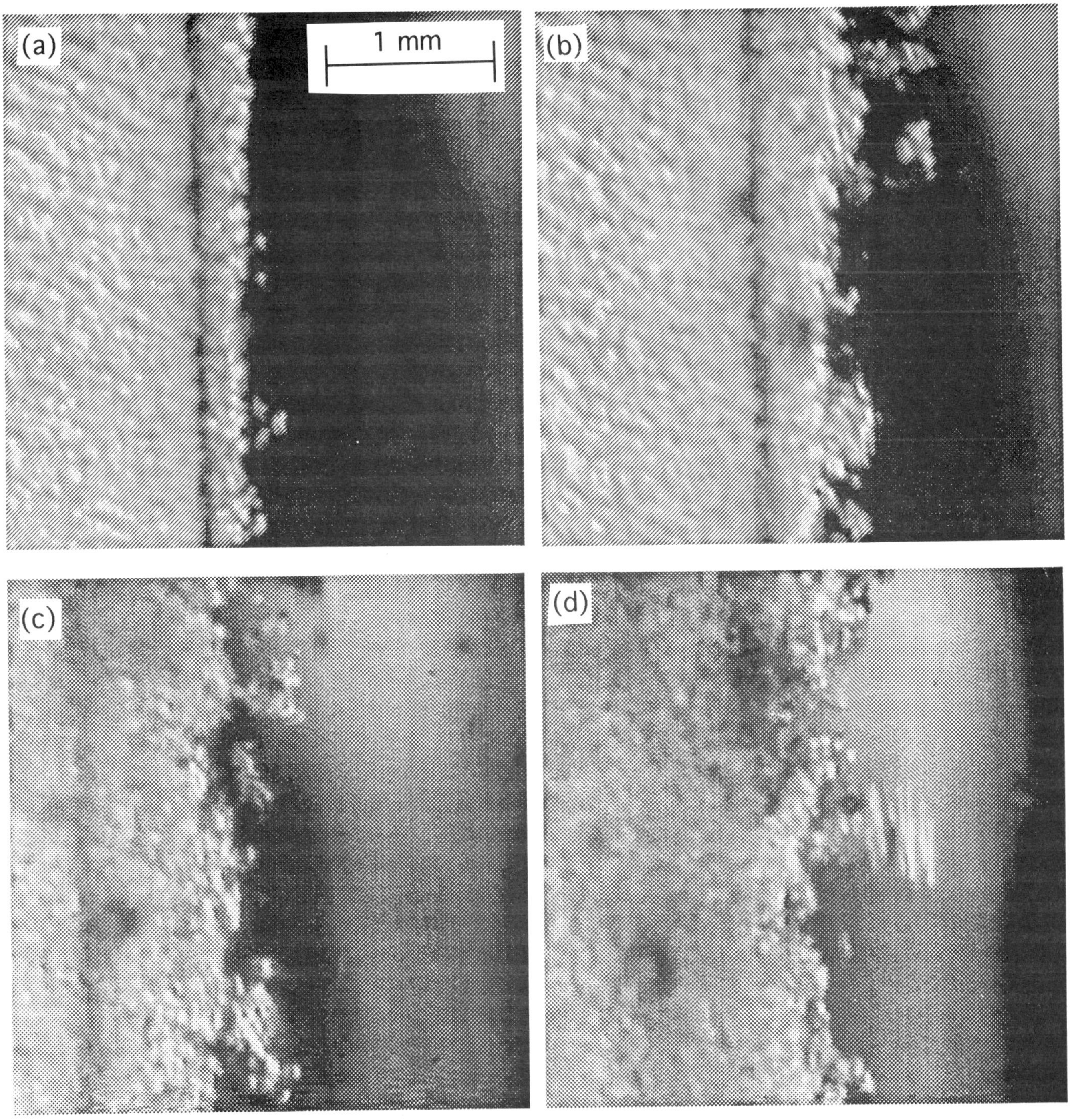

FIGURE 3 PHOTOGRAPHS SHOWING THE DEVELOPING MUSHY ZONE FOR EXPERIMENTAL RUN #1.14 AT (A) 43.9 MINUTES, (B) 48.1 MINUTES, (C) 51.4 MINUTES, AND (D) 64 MNUTES

QUANTITATIVE ANALYSIS OF VIDEOTAPE IMAGES

A principal goal of these experiments was to quantify the rate of fragmentation from a growing mushy zone and to attempt to correlate the results with the overall operating parameters of the system, namely the flow rate of the melt, the cooling rate, and the overall temperature difference. The "raw data" for this process consist of the videotape records of the mushy zone growth. The method employed was to observe the mushy zone-melt interaction on a frame-by-frame basis and to count the number of fragments which were generated. A detailed description is

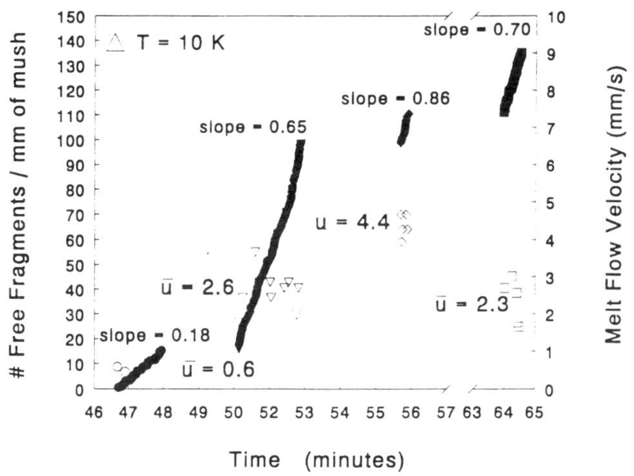

FIGURE 4 EXAMPLE OF CUMULATIVE FRAGMENTATION DATA FOR ONE RUN. DATA FOR $\bar{u}$ REPRESENT THE MEASURED VELOCITIES OF INDIVIDUAL PARTICLES

contained in Paradies (1993), and only a brief summary will be described here.

A grid was placed over the video monitor and the number of particles generated by the portion of the mushy zone within the field of view and within the grid boundaries was determined by counting, on a frame-by-frame basis, the number of fragments which crossed the borders of the control volume, which in this case is comprised by a length of 1.7 mm along the axis of the growth chamber (100 mm on the screen), a depth equal to the depth of focus (approximately 2 mm), and the width of the visible portion of the mushy zone (between 0.1 to 0.6 mm). The difference between the number of particles exiting the control volume and the number which entered during a sampling period of a few frames (the time it would take for a particle to traverse the entire field of view) was taken to be the number of fragments detaching from the mushy zone during that period. Portions of the mushy zone that may have detached but remained obscured by the mushy zone could not be counted. It is possible that fragmentation occurred within the mushy zone that also could not be observed, because the fragments never freed themselves from the mushy zone. However, those particles would not be of interest in forming new nucleation sites. The counting method relied on a single observer, since criteria to determine whether a particle was "in focus"—and hence "countable"—were subjective. However, the counts were reproducible in all but two cases within 5%, the two exceptions involving very little fragmentation where one or two additional fragmentation events were discovered upon a second count.

The results were collected in terms of the cumulative number of fragments per mm vs. time, representing the number of crystallites detaching from the mushy zone in the control volume divided by 1.7 mm, the length of the control volume along the axial direction of the mushy zone. Although these data do not represent the total number of fragments being generated, they should be proportional to the number of free fragments generated by any arbitrary surface area of mushy zone over time. Figure 4 shows a typical collection of this cumulative fragmentation data for the same run depicted photographically in Figure 3. The solid symbols represent the cumulative number of fragments generated. The breaks in the data merely indicate that the counting process was stopped for a few minutes (e.g., between 48 and 50 minutes), then restarted. Since it was desired to determine the relative fragmentation *rates*, based on the slopes of these particle generation data, the lack of an absolute number of particles is not important.

In the case of this particular example, the values of the slopes are indicated in the plot. The slope, or the fragmentation rate, increased with time for the first three data sets, but decreased slightly at a later time during the run. The fragmentation *rates* were determined for the same time periods as for the cumulative fragmentation, as indicated in Figure 4. Therefore, for the time duration associated with a single fragmentation rate, the temperature difference between the chill wall, the cooling rate, and the flow rate were relatively steady.

Attempts to correlate the fragmentation rate data as simple functions of the three controllable parameters of the system were unsuccessful. This might have been expected given the rather drastic changes of fluid mechanical behavior which were observed even during a single experimental run. However, during the course of the experiments and the subsequent analysis of the video images, it was observed that the fragmentation rate seemed to be closely associated with the velocity of the fluid nearest the mushy zone. When the flow was downward, as indicated by the downward movement of the particles, a finite fragmentation rate was still observed. As time went on during a run, and this reversed flow began to diminish, the detachment of particles also diminished, approaching zero as the fluid motion nearest the mushy zone ceased. Then as the mushy zone grew and the flow in this region turned upward, in the same direction as the main flow stream, fragmentation events began to increase again.

The only means available from the present data to determine a value for this velocity was the motion of the particles themselves, and typical values for these velocities, indicated by the symbol $\bar{u}$, are depicted in Figure 4. To reduce the errors inherent in comparing the velocity of entrained particles to the velocity of the stream, only small fragments (less than 0.2 mm) that are in focus, that make physical contact with the mushy zone by striking a dendrite somewhere in the field of view, and that stay within a boundary defined by 0.2 mm beyond the longest dendrite and 0.4 mm into the mushy zone were used to measure the flow velocity. The individual velocities of the fragments measured during the period used to determine a single fragmentation rate were then averaged to yield a single value for $\bar{u}$ which could be associated with that fragmentation rate.

Figure 5 summarizes the fragmentation rate data for the SCN-1.3 wt% acetone alloy runs as a function of the average velocity, $\bar{u}$, of the free fragments adjacent to the mushy zone for experimental runs conducted under 3 cooling rates and for three different overall temperature differences, overall comprising 24 solidification runs. The data indicate that, as the magnitude of $\bar{u}$ increases, the fragmentation rate increases, regardless of the cooling rate or the overall temperature difference. It should be mentioned here that the magnitude of $\bar{u}$ is much smaller than the average velocity of the melt flow in the annulus; however, these small flow velocities around the dendrites in the mushy zone appear to control the fragmentation rate. The horizontal error bars which appear on the data points in Figure 5 correspond to the

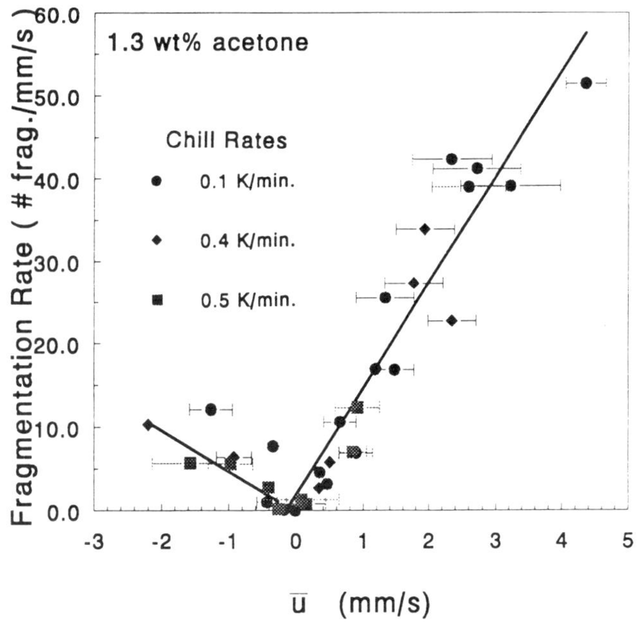

FIGURE 5 CORRELATION OF FRAGMENTATION RATES WITH THE AVERAGE VELOCITY OF PARTICLES NEAR THE MUSHY ZONE - MELT INTERFACE (SCN-1.3 WT% ACETONE)

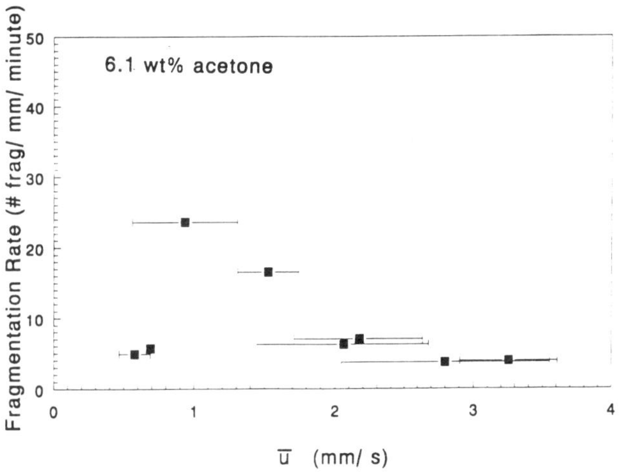

FIGURE 6 CORRELATION OF FRAGMENTATION RATES WITH THE AVERAGE VELOCITY OF PARTICLES NEAR THE MUSHY ZONE - MELT INTERFACE (SCN-6.1 WT% ACETONE)

standard deviation associated with determining the average value of $\bar{u}$ from a number of particle observations.

It is apparent that the fragmentation rates for downward flow (negative values of $\bar{u}$) are less than for upward flow, for equal magnitudes of $\bar{u}$. Furthermore, the fragmentation rate appears to go to zero as the velocity of the free crystallites adjacent to the mushy zone approaches a value of – 0.21 mm/s. A crude estimate based on the data of Zakhem, et al. (1993) yields a settling velocity of about 0.2 mm/s for particles of the size and density of those typical of these experiments, suggesting that at this measured value of $\bar{u}$, the actual fluid velocity would be zero.

It is possible that the rejection of low density acetone by the growing dendrites within the mushy zone might offset some of the buoyancy forces caused by the temperature difference between the chill tube and the melt. This might reduce the penetration of the mushy zone for downward flows (negative values of $\bar{u}$) while increasing the penetration for upward flows (positive values of $\bar{u}$) for equal magnitudes of $\bar{u}$. Alternatively, observations of the mushy zone morphology (not discussed in detail in the present paper), showed that the downward flowing melt increased the angle of inclination of the primary dendrites more than for the upward flowing melt. This may alter the shape and number of the channels for fluid flowing through the mushy zone and could also account for the difference in observed fragmentation rates. Finally, it is likely that the downward flowing melt is cooler than the surrounding melt, because the buoyancy forces causing the melt flow arise from the higher density of the lower temperature melt. The cool melt may not accelerate the local remelting as quickly as the generally warmer upward flowing melt. If the primary mechanism for dendritic detachment is either capillary pinching or constitutional remelting, this explanation provides a simple, direct and significant reason for a difference in the rates of fragmentation observed between similar magnitudes of downward and upward flowing melt velocities.

Figure 6 displays the fragmentation rate data as a function of $\bar{u}$ for SCN-6.1 wt% acetone. No downward flow was observed for this run, as discussed earlier. The increase in the concentration of acetone causes a maximum in the fragmentation rate at a value of $\bar{u}$ of about 1 mm/sec. It is possible that the lower concentration alloy might also display such a maximum, but limitations of the apparatus precluded achieving high enough values of $\bar{u}$ to test this hypothesis. Because of the limited number of concentrations that were tested in the present study, generalizations to rationalize the differences between the trend in Figure 5 from that shown in Figure 6 would be speculative. However, one possible justification follows:

Consider the growing mushy zone layer. An increase in either the temperature gradient or the growth rate reduces the interdendritic spacing and secondary arm spacing, decreasing the permeability. In contrast, adding acetone *increases* the primary dendrite spacing, while *reducing* the secondary arm spacing. For an increasing acetone concentration, the increasing interdendritic spacing tends to favor increasing melt flow velocity within the mushy zone. Therefore, the magnitude of $\bar{u}$ may increase. However, the secondary dendrite arm spacing is reduced and may decrease the permeability of the mushy zone unless channels are opened by coarsening, remelting, or fragmentation of the side branch arms. As the level of solute increases, the channels that form in the direction of the bulk fluid flow are impeded by the refined side branch arms, whereas the permeability in the direction of the primary dendrite stems increases. This could cause any flow that penetrates the mushy zone to be forced through a few widely spaced channels, reducing the opportunity for localized remelting to occur. In this case the value of $\bar{u}$ could continue to increase while the area of the mushy zone affected by the flowing melt would decrease. Clearly, more work needs to be done to clarify the role of solute additions on the fragmentation process.

CONCLUSIONS

The discovery that the velocity adjacent to the mushy zone appears to correlate with the rate of detachment of free crystallites for various cooling rates, temperature differences, and forced flow velocities for a single alloy composition may permit solidification models to be developed that incorporate the fragmentation rate of the mushy zone as an important mechanism of grain refinement and a potential source of macrosegregation. However, the relationship among the macroscopic controlling parameters of the system and the value of $\bar{u}$ needs to be determined. Furthermore, this superficial velocity measurement, which was the only one possible with the present configuration, must be related to the mixed convection flow within the mushy zone itself, where the fragmentation process actually occurs. At this point, a specific mechanism for the fragmentation cannot be delineated. Although it appears that either constitutional remelting or capillary pinching are likely mechanisms of importance, hydrodynamic shear forces or some as yet other undiscovered mechanism cannot be discounted, although evidence suggests that mechanical shearing seems inconsistent with a number of observations both reported here and in the published literature.

Future work includes expansion of the data base with the present apparatus to include a wider range of concentrations and flow velocities, including pure natural convection in the melt. In addition, experiments with other transparent model alloys will be conducted. Finally, a modeling effort is also underway to predict the growth of the mushy zone under these mixed convection conditions to determine how the flow velocity in the melt very near to the edge of the mushy zone is related to the flow within the porous mushy zone itself, further shedding light on the interaction between the melt and the evolution of the mushy zone.

ACKNOWLEDGMENT

Support from the National Science Foundation, under Grant No. DMR-9214852 is gratefully acknowledged. Early phases of this work were supported through grants from the ALCOA Technical Center, Alcoa PA, and from the New York State Science and Technology Foundation.

REFERENCES

Bryson, N.B., J.G. McCubbin, C.M. Read, P.G. Enright and S.C. Flood (1991), International Patent Application Published under the Patent Cooperation Treaty, PCT/CA91/00216, International Publication Number WO 91/19578.

Christenson, M.S. and F.P. Incropera (1989), "Solidification of an Aqueous Ammonium Chloride Solution in a Rectangular Cavity - I. Experimental Study," *International J. of Heat and Mass Transfer*, **30**, 47-68.

Christenson, M.S., W.B. Bennon, and F.P. Incropera (1989), "Solidification of an Aqueous Ammonium Chloride Solution in a Rectangular Cavity - II. Comparison of Predicted and Measured Results," *International J. of Heat and Mass Transfer*, **30**, 69-79.

Desnain P., *et al.* (1988), "Effects of the Electromagmetic Stirring on the Grain Size of Industrial Aluminum Alloys: Experiments and Theoretical Predictions," *Light Metals 1988*, TMS, Warrendale, Pa, 487-493.

Durand, F. (1992), *Dynamic Interactions of Convection and Solidification*, S.H. Davis, et al. (editors), NATO ASI Series.

Fang Q.T. (1989), ALCOA Technical Center, ALCOA Center, PA, Private Communication.

Fang, Q.T. and M.J. Bruno (1991), *Light Metals 1991*, E.L. Rooy (editor), TMS, Warrendale, PA, p. 856.

Huang, S.C. and M.E. Glicksman (1981), "Fundamentals of Dendritic Solidification--II Development of Sidebranch Structure," *Acata Metallurgical*, **29**, 717-734.

Jackson, K.A., J.D. Hunt, D.R. Uhlmann, and T.P. Seward (1966), "On the Origin of the Equiaxed Zone in Castings," *Trans. Metallurgical Soc. of AIME*, **236**, 149-158 .

Kerr, R.C., Woods, A.W., Worster, M.G., and Huppert, H.E. (1989), "Disequilibrium and macrosegregation during solidification of a binary melt," *Nature*, **340**, 357-362.

Paradies, C.J., G.T. Kim, M.E. Glicksman, and R.N. Smith (1993), "The Effect of Flow Interactions with Dendritic Mushy Zones: A Model Experiment," *Modeling of Casting, Welding and Advanced Solidification Processes—VI*, T.S. Piwonka, et al. (editors), TMS, Warrendale PA, 309-316.

Rubinstein E.R. (1989), "Dendritic Growth Kinetics and Structure," Ph.D. Thesis, Rensselaer Polytechnic Institute, Troy, NY.

Smith, D.M., J.A. Eady, L.M. Hogan, and D.W. Irwin (1991), "Crystallization of a Faceted Primary Phase in a Stirred Slurry," *Metallurgical Transactions A*, **22A**, 575-584.

Vives C. (1990), "Hydrodynamic, Thermal, and Crystallographic Effects of an Electromagnetically Driven Rotating Flow in Solidying Aluminum Alloy Melts," *International J. of Heat and Mass Transfer*, **33**, 2585-2598.

Voorhees, P.W. (1990), "Coarsening in Binary Solid-Liquid Mixtures," *Metallurgical Trans. A*, **21A**, 27-37.

Zakhem, R., Pl.D. Weidman, and H.D. deGroh III (1993), "On the Drag of Model Dendrite Fragments at Low Reynolds Number," *Proceedings of the First International Conference on Transport Phenomena in Processing*, S.I. Guceri (editor), Technomic Publ. Co., Lancaster PA, 219-228.

HTD-Vol. 284/AMD-Vol. 182, Transport Phenomena in Solidification
ASME 1994

VISUALIZATION OF HOAR FROST WITH CONFOCAL MICROSCOPY

John G. Georgiadis , Paul Greywall, and Albert Tenbusch

Department of Mechanical & Industrial Engineering
University of Illinois at Urbana-Champaign
Urbana, Illinois

ABSTRACT

Hoar frost is frozen dew which is deposited on a cold surface exposed to humid air. Frost growth has a profound effect on the performance of an evaporator at freezer temperatures and engineers commonly oversize refrigeration systems to overcome the degradation of heat exchange owing to the presence of the frost layer. In an attempt to understand the behavior of frost, morphological information (at the near-micron range) is needed. We report here a high-resolution, video rate (30 frames per second) visualization of frost forming on a horizontal steel surface exposed to stagnant room air. Sub-micron resolution of the crystalline structure of frost is achieved by employing Scanning Confocal Microscopy. This technique obviates the difficulties with conventional microscopy and allows 3-D and time-resolved quantitative visualization of the frost morphology. Such studies bolster our understanding of several fundamental frost phenomena (during its early growth stage), such as the growth of ice crystals and their interaction with subcooled droplets.

INTRODUCTION

When a humid air stream is brought in contact with a cooled surface at a temperature below the dew and freezing points, frosting will occur on the surface. The earliest scientific study of hoar frost (or frozen dew) was performed in 1886-87 by Aitken (1923). He made careful observations of frost deposition under near-ground atmospheric conditions, and explained (by considering the vapor pressure differential between ice and water at the same temperature) why the supersaturation level of the air-vapor mixture appears to be higher with respect to an ice surface than to a liquid water surface. Early experimental evidence [mentioned by Aitken (1923) that the vapor pressure of ice is less than that of water has been bolstered by careful measurements by Kraus and Greer (1984).

A thorough understanding of the fundamentals of frost formation is crucial to the refrigeration industry. In air-to-air heat pumps and refrigeration equipment, most studies have focused mainly on the economics of alternative defrost schedules. It has also been estimated that performance and reliability considerations cause designers to oversize refrigeration equipment by 50% to ensure capacity under frosting conditions, and that frost is responsible for a 25% degradation in average system performance [Besant *et al.* (1990)]. Frost growth can be divided into two stages: an early, relatively short crystal growth period, and a mature frost layer growth period. Designing frost-free surfaces requires the complete structural characterization of frost during the early period. Defrosting or suppressing the growth of frost requires similar information during the later period. In both cases, fast high-resolution techniques for in-situ characterization of the frost layer are needed.

The microscopic characterization of frost has been somewhat neglected in the pursuit of materials that are more technologically important. Frost consists of a lattice of fragile ice crystals in the form of a light-scattering heterogeneous porous medium. It is therefore very difficult to estimate its density (or porosity) distribution or to measure interstitial temperature distributions directly. As a consequence, theoretical studies have outdistanced precise experimental investigations.

There is a plethora of *macroscopic* empirical and analytical studies of frost growth, see for example O'Neal and Tree (1985) and references therein, as well as Kondepudi and O'Neal (1989, 1990), and Tao *et al.* (1993). The majority of experimental methods for frost characterization are destructive [Mao *et al.* (1991), Östin and Anderson (1991)] or simply give frost thickness [Besant *et al.* (1990), Monaghan *et al.* (1991), Mao *et al.* (1992)]. Mature frost growth rates are consistently found to increase with humidity and surface-to-air temperature difference. Using numerical simulation, Tao *et al.* (1993) showed how the complex behavior of the local heat and mass transfer coefficients affects mature frost growth on a clean cold surface. Good agreement with experimental data was reported, provided that the *proper* transport properties are used. The relationship between frost thermal conductivity and density is strongly affected by the details of the microstructure of frost, in a fashion analogous to what happens in trying to deduce "effective" thermophysical properties of fluid-saturated porous media from their microstructure, cf. Georgiadis (1991). Semi-empirical relationships using the density (or porosity) as a parameter are not enough.

Attempts to describe the internal structure of frost have produced only qualitative descriptions [Hayashi *et al.* (1977), Tokura *et al.* (1983)]. A particularly interesting phenomenon during the early stage of frost formation is the growth of ice at sites where subcooled-liquid nucleation occurs. The only non-invasive frost density distribution measurements for mature frost known to us are by Bong *et al.* (1991), but the reported uncertainties are at least 20%.

We report here the novel use of Scanning Confocal Microscopy (SCM) for high-resolution (submicron) visualization of frost. This technique has seen explosive growth in the field of biological imaging during the last ten years, and has come full cycle back to the applied sciences. The presentation here first focuses on the imaging principles and then on the physics of frost formation.

SCANNING CONFOCAL MICROSCOPY (SCM): PRINCIPLES AND EXPERIMENTAL SETUP

The conventional (wide-field) light microscope receives light from planes above and below the plane of focus. This results in loss of depth discrimination. In contrast, the working principle of confocal microscopy is that only one plane perpendicular to the line of view is in focus at a time. Effectively, by using a very narrow depth of field and by limiting the field of view, the instrument can produce very sharp images. Confocal microscopes have a strong *optical sectioning* property: one can reconstruct a three-dimensional surface by moving the in-focus plane (z-sectioning) and recording the intensity of the collected light. State-of-the-art SCM systems use scanning laser beams (point illumination sources) and point detectors.

SCM improves spatial resolution and depth discrimination by rejecting a portion of the light with a detector pinhole. In the experimental setup depicted in Figure 1, the condenser lens is eliminated, and the microscope uses the objective lens twice: first to illuminate a small spot and then to collect light from the same (confocal) spot. The resolution is improved by a factor of two at the expense of the field of view. The field of view is recovered by scanning the confocal spot on the object in a raster pattern on the xy-plane normal to the z-axis.

The improvement of resolution in SCM compared to conventional microscopy is more apparent because the image contrast is also increased. Adding signal from out-of-focus planes (which is not detected in SCM) degrades contrast because these planes appear "blurred". Recall that detected contrast is proportional to the difference in signal intensity between two image areas divided by the average image brightness. Contrast is stronger in SCM operating in reflection mode where unscattered radiation is not detected. The reader is referred to the articles by Sheppard (1987) and Cheng and Summers (1989) for more details on SCM fundamentals.

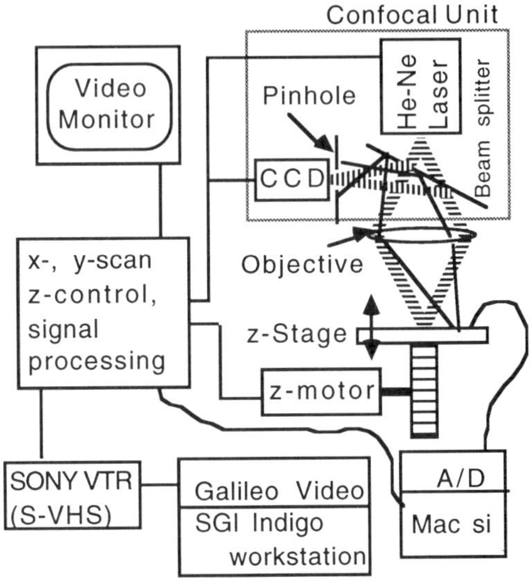

Figure 1 Scanning confocal microscope, data acquisition and processing system.

Figure 1 depicts our experimental setup along with image processing and analysis hardware. The SCM system is built around a conventional Nikon microscope operating in reflection mode. In order to achieve large working distances, a set of objective lenses (10X, 20X, 40X, and 100X) of low numerical aperture are used. The 100X objective produces 4800X magnification (on a 14" monitor) and a 45 µm field of view. The system consists of a confocal optical system, a laser illuminating source (1.5 mW He-Ne 632.8 nm, polarized), a video-rate beam scanner, a linear CCD sensor, a z-axis controller, a signal processing unit, and a video monitor. Through the use of a scanning mirror for y-, and an acousto-optical deflector for x-scanning, a polarized beam is raster-scanned at video rates over the field of view. It takes as little as 1/30th of a second to obtain the image of the in-focus slice.

The samples (1cmX1cm stainless steel plates cooled from below) are positioned under the microscope objective. A large number of images are acquired with variable control of the z-stage. Video rate scanning allows the visualization of moving interfaces. During imaging, the signal processing unit outputs the video signal to a frame-accurate video recorder at a "fast" rate (30 frames per second). Image processing is performed off-line. The video recorder outputs analog video at a "slow" rate to a graphics workstation via a digitizing board. After the useful segments of the original video stream have been sampled and digitized, 3D image reconstruction can be performed using available image analysis software. Basically, the data are organized into 3D "snapshots" of the interface, with each snapshot corresponding to a stack of z-slices obtained with "fast" imaging (and hence "frozen" in time). Measurements and calculations are made using available image analysis software. Finally, a sequence of meaningful frames or 3-D "snapshots" can be animated and recorded back to the video deck for purposes of demonstration.

QUALITATIVE OBSERVATIONS

As an example, in Figure 2 we present a reconstructed image of the frost layer formed on a stainless steel plate cooled at -5°C from below and exposed suddenly to 22°C stagnant ambient air from above. We are viewing the 3-D rendered object from below, i.e., looking up from the solid surface. This is a portion of the original 3-D structure which was acquired with 700 µm field of view. Fourteen z-sections (10 µm apart) were acquired and digitized to create the composite. On the basis of our observations of the evolution of this frost layer in time, we can report the following "frosting scenarios":

Phase IA: Within seconds from the surface exposure to air, dropwise condensation occurs. The droplets coalesce to form larger droplets, while ice crystals appear on their periphery, gradually filling the space between the drops and forming closed rings. We have performed repeated visualizations for -10°C and -15°C surface temperatures with similar results. The size of the droplets (before their growth is arrested by the frost rings mentioned above) decreases as we decrease the surface temperature.

Phase II: After 20-30 minutes, the growth of mature frost occurs. This is primarily characterized by "coarsening" (larger crystals).

Phase IB: If one wipes the surface clean from frost, an alternative scenario occurs. Frost restarts from submicron nucleation sites left in the grooves of the metal surface, without visible condensation. No frost rings are noticed and the structure of frost is characteristically columnar and disordered, in agreement with earlier conventional studies, cf. Hayashi *et al.* (1977).

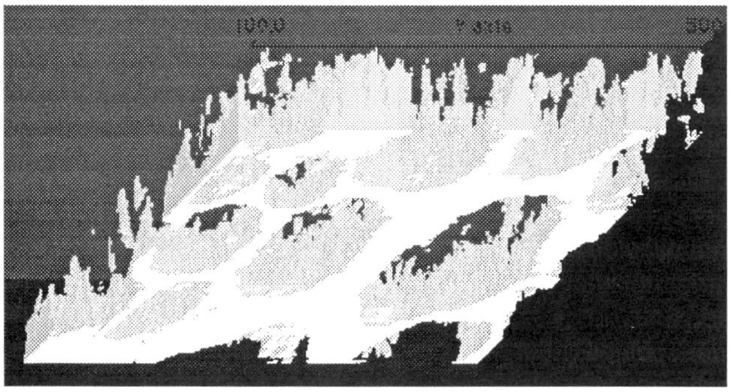

Figure 2. Volumetrically rendered image of a block of frost growing on -5°C temperature surface. The 3D layer is created by reconstructing 14 horizontal slices (10 µm apart) obtained with SCM. The horizontal dimension is 400 µm and the height (along the z-axis) is 140 µm. The perspective view is from below, that is, as if the viewer was looking up from the cold surface.

It is obvious that surface quality is an important parameter in early stages of frost formation, as is the case for most surface-driven transport processes. It is easier to comment on Phase IB: by wiping the surface, we coat it with small ice crystals which act as nucleation sites. In contrast, Phase IA pertains to a dry cold metal surface which is not in equilibrium with the room-temperature air. Despite the fact that the surface temperature is below both the dew point and the freezing point of water, large-scale dropwise condensation precedes ablimation (or frosting).

The droplets coalesce and freeze abruptly during Phase IA. In Figure 3, we present a high-resolution view (acquired with a 100X objective) of the freezing process in the vicinity of a large droplet (dark patch in the lower part of the frames). The appearance of crystalline ice structures on the periphery of the droplet signals the inception of frost which grows at the interface between the droplet and the metal surface. At the same time, a micron-size hemispherical water droplet [shown in (a-b)] diminishes in size and disappears [in (c)]. The same "evaporation" of small supercooled droplets (which have a depressed freezing point owing to capillary effects) near freezing interfaces is been observed in a plethora of other locations in our frost experiments.

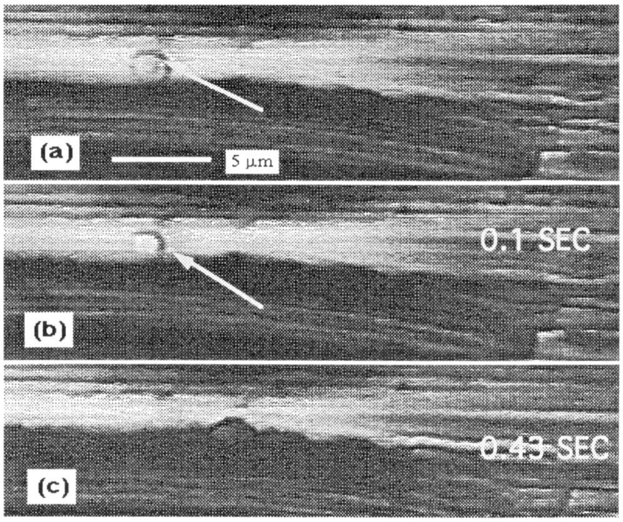

Figure 3. Frames acquired from (30 frames/second) SCM imaging of the metal surface (fixed z-stage) near freezing. A segment of the frame is shown. Frame (b) was acquired 0.1 seconds after (a), and frame (c) was acquired 0.33 seconds after (b).

QUANTITATIVE VISUALIZATION

In order to produce quantitative 3D reconstruction with SCM, we have to rely on extensive image processing and image analysis. By using a commercially-available software package (ANALYZE, Mayo Foundation), we can extract an estimate of the density of frost from the raw data of Figure 2. This estimate is obtained by averaging frost sections over constant z-planes. Figure 4 gives the variation of the frost density as a function of z.

Technical details of the image processing involved in such estimates are given by Greywall (1994). It is important to mention that significant image correction may be needed to remove artifacts which SCM images contain. Like any optical microscopy images, SCM data might contain reflection and refraction artifacts. Frost being normally a reflecting optical medium, structures at higher z (closer to the microscope objective) could potentially "shadow" underlying structures. Understandably, this shadowing is less of a problem during early growth stages. During that stage, the dominant artifacts are caused by the refraction of the light pencil emanating from the objective and impinging on lens-like frozen droplets like these depicted in Figure 3.

Time-resolved imaging and measurement is also possible because our SCM system can acquire up to 30 slices per second. As an example, we recorded and digitized the image at a fixed z-location during refrosting at -8^{0}C over the same steel surface during phase IB. Achieving sub-micron resolution with SCM and employing digital image analysis allows discrimination of nucleation sites and measurement of crystal size, as shown in Figure 5. From these measurements, the growth rate of microscopic frost crystals can be estimated. Figure 6 gives the profile areas of two such crystals (both located in the frame depicted in Figure 5) as a function of time. The growth rate of a characteristic length (such as the diameter of the profile area) has a square root of time behavior, which is typical of such phenomena, cf. Tokura *et al.* (1983).

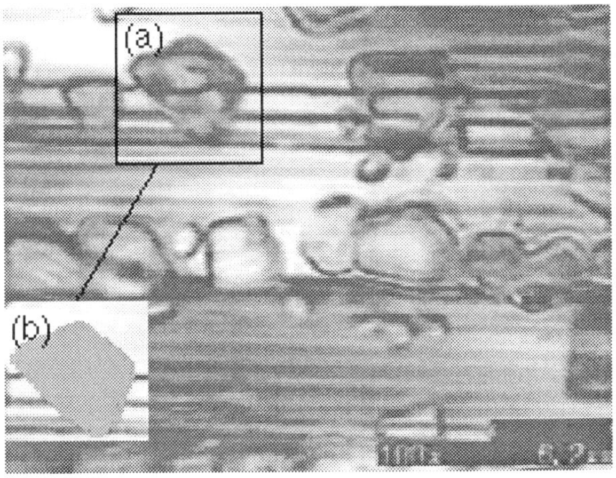

Figure 5. Image analysis of a segment from a digitized frame acquired in 1/30 second with SCM fitted with 100X objective focusing on a fixed xy-plane. The resolution in the marked segment is 100X95 pixels and its physical dimensions are 6.9 μmX6.5 μm. (a) Ice crystal growing from nuclei left in the metal micro-abrasions (grooves shown as horizontal striations) captured at 7.66 seconds after refrosting inception. (b) Same as (a) but with grayscale-equalized pixels inside crystal profile. The area of the profile can be measured with digital image analysis software.

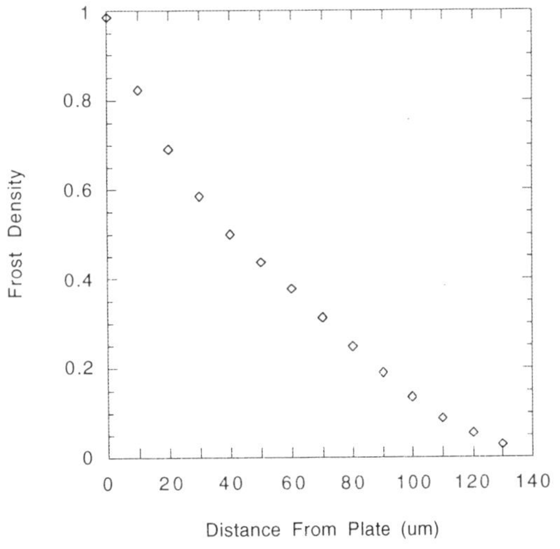

Figure 4. Measurement of the average frost density as a function of z-position (above the cold plate) for the frost layer depicted in Figure 2. After the refraction artifacts are corrected, the density at each position is estimated by computing the average grayscale value over the corresponding slice. Frost density values are normalized, with unity denoting solid ice.

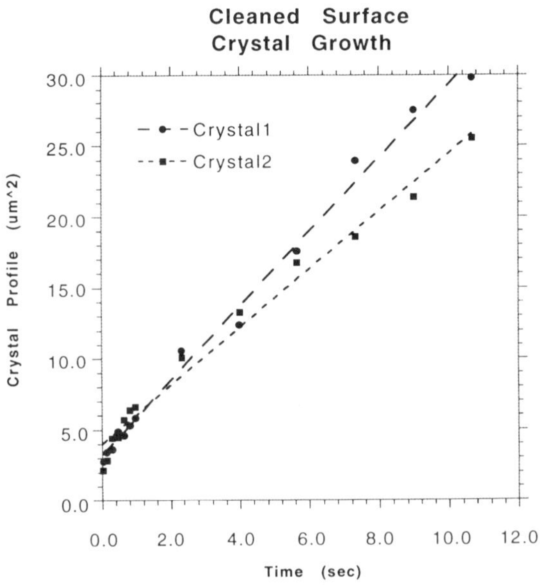

Figure 6. Plot of the crystal profile area (gray domain delineated in Figure 5(b)) as a function of time for two crystals in the field of view shown in Figure 5. Crystal2 is marked by the solid frame. The areas tend to grow linearly with time. This implies that the characteristic length of the crystals grow with the square root of time.

CONCLUSIONS

When a humid air stream is brought in contact with a cooled surface at a temperature below the dew and freezing points, ablimation (vapor to ice transition) will occur on the surface. In order to assess the efficiency of any anti-frost methodology, one needs first to probe and understand the early stages of frost growth. We have been able to visualize quantitatively the frost evolution in-situ with unprecedented resolution using Scanning Confocal Microscopy (SCM). The samples (surfaces in small cavities under thermal control) are positioned under the SCM objective. A large number of images are acquired during repeated z-sectioning by moving the z-stage incrementally. In addition to the observation of droplet-frost interaction, SCM provides high-resolution three-dimensional visualization of frost structure very near the cold surface, which allows the measurement of frost density and the measurement of crystal growth rates.

Researchers in the field of heat transfer are particularly interested in developments in noninvasive imaging schemes that allow the reconstruction of three-dimensional interfaces, cf. Mayinger (1993). We believe that SCM should be added to the arsenal of quantitative visualization methods, cf. Georgiadis (1994), because of its great potential in visualizing the evolution of gas-liquid, gas-solid, or liquid-solid interfaces. Problems that are natural candidates for SCM are slowly moving complex interfaces that allow direct optical access but demand high resolution.

ACKNOWLEDGMENTS

This work was partially supported by NSF grant CTS-9396252. Additional support was provided by Nikon and DuPont. Special thanks to the staff of the Optical Visualization Facility (directed by Bridget Carragher) at the Beckman Institute of the University of Illinois, and to Professor W. Dunn for bringing the manuscript on hoar frost by Aitken to our attention.

REFERENCES

Aitken J. (1923), "Note on Hoar-Frost" in *Collected Scientific Papers of John Aitken,* C. Knott (ed.), Cambridge University Press, 120-122.

Besant R.W., Rezkallah K.S. , Mao Y., and Falk J. (1990), "Measurement of Frost Thickness Using a Laser Beam and Light Meter," *ASHRAE Transactions* **96**(1), 3361-64.

Bong T.Y., Wijeysundera N.E., Saw E.L., and Lau K.O. (1991), "Comparison of Beta-Ray and Gamma-Ray Transmission Methods for Measurement of Frost Density Distribution," *Exp. Thermal Fluid Science* **4**, 567-576.

Cheng P.C. and Summers R.G. (1989), Image Contrast in Confocal Microscopy, in *The Handbook of Biological Confocal Microscopy,* J Pawley (ed), University of Wisconsin, Madison, 163-179.

Georgiadis J.G. (1991), "Future Research Needs in Heat & Mass Transport in Porous Media", in *Convective Heat and Mass Transfer in Porous Media* (ed. S. Kakaç, B. Kilkis, F.A. Kulacki and F. Arinç), NATO Advanced Study Institute Series, vol. E **196**, pp. 1073-1088. Kluwer Academic Publishers, The Netherlands .

Georgiadis J.G. (1994), "Multiphase Flow Quantitative Visualization", *Applied Mechanics Review,* **47**(6), part 2, S315-S319.

Greywall P. (1994),*"Confocal Microscopy and Magnetic Resonance Imaging of Freezing Interfaces,"* M.S. Thesis, University of Illinois at Urbana-Champaign.

Hayashi Y., Aoki A., Adachi S., and Hori K. (1977), "Study of frost properties correlating with frost formation types," *J. Heat Transfer* **99**, 239-245.

Kondepudi S. N., and O'Neal D. L. (1989), "Effect of Frost Growth on the Performance of Louvered Finned Heat Exchangers," *Int. J. Refrigeration* **12**, 151-158.

Kondepudi S. N., and O'Neal D. L. (1990), "The Effects of Different Fin Configurations on the Performance of Finned-Tube Heat Exchangers Under Frosting Conditions," *ASHRAE Transactions* **96**(2), 439-444.

Kraus G.F. and Greer S.C. (1984), "Vapor Pressures of Supercooled H_2O and D_2O," *J. Phys. Chem.* **88**, 4781-85.

Mao Y., Besant R.W., and Rezkallah K.S. (1991), "A method of Measuring Frost Density Using Flush-Mounted Removable Disks," *ASHRAE Transactions* **97**(1), 26-30.

Mao Y., Besant R.W., and Rezkallah K.S. (1992), "Measurement and Correlations of Frost Properties with Airflow over a Flat Plate," *ASHRAE Transactions* **98**(2), 65-78.

Mayinger F. (1993), Image-Forming Optical Techniques in Heat Transfer: Revival by Computer-Aided Data Processing, *J Heat Transfer* **115**, 824-834.

Monaghan P.F., Redfern M., Oosthuizen P.H., Grealish F.W., and Finn D.P. (1991), "An Automatic Noncontact Measurement Technique for Investigation of the Effect of Frosting on Wind Convector Heat Transfer Performance," *Exp. Thermal Fluid Science* **4**, 399-405.

O'Neal D. and Tree D. (1985), "A Review of Frost Formation in Simple Geometries," *ASHRAE Transactions* **91**(2), 267-281.

Östin R. and Anderson S.(1991), "Frost Growth Parameters in a Forced Air Stream, "Int. *J. Heat Mass Transfer* **34**(4/5), 1009-17.

Sheppard C.J.R. (1987), Image Contrast in Confocal Microscopy, in *Advances in Optical and Electron Microscopy* **10**, Academic Press, London, 1-98.

Tao Y.-X., Besant R.W., and Rezkallah K.S. (1993), "A Mathematical Model for Predicting the Densification and Growth of Frost on a Flat Plate, "Int. *J. Heat Mass Transfer* **36**(2), 353-363.

Tokura I., Saito H. , and Kishinami K. (1983), "Study on Properties and Growth Rate of Frost Layers on Cold Surfaces," *J. Heat Transfer* **105**, 895-901.

HTD-Vol. 284/AMD-Vol. 182, Transport Phenomena in Solidification
ASME 1994

SIMULATION OF INTERFACIAL INSTABILITIES DURING SOLIDIFICATION: CONDUCTION AND CAPILLARITY EFFECTS

H. S. Udaykumar and W. Shyy
Department of Aerospace Engineering,
Mechanics and Engineering Science
University of Florida
Gainesville, Florida

Abstract

The solidification of pure materials has been simulated using a combined Eulerian–Lagrangian numerical method. The interface tracking procedure employs marker particles and is the Lagrangian component of the calculation. The field equations are solved in a fixed Eulerian framework, so that the interface passes through the grid layout. Information from the explicitly tracked interface is used to apply boundary conditions at the exact interface location in each computational cell, in contrast with other Eulerian schemes. Consistent with the the established theory, in the absence of surface tension, the present simulations result in different types of behavior such as tip–splitting and cusp formation. Due to the lack of physical length scales, the solutions are qualitatively affected by grid resolution with no unique solution available. In contrast, with substantial surface tension values the initial perturbation grows to form long fingers. The finger shapes reflect the stabilizing effects of capillarity. Unique solutions can be reached with nonzero surface tension.

1. Introduction

Numerous physical systems, in natural as well as man made environments, contain interfaces demarcating regions of distinct physico–chemical properties [1,2]. The interfaces in these systems may be idealized as discontinuities across which compositions, phases, material properties and flow features change rapidly. Under certain conditions, usually characterized by one or more control parameters, these interfaces experience instabilities in viscous fingering [3–5], solidification[1,2,6,7], and other phenomena [8–11]. Typically, a cascade of interfacial instabilities leads to the formation of patterns and morphological structures reflecting the interaction of the microscopic and macroscopic properties of the system. For example, the formation of deep cells in the growth of impure (i.e. multi–component) materials, has considerable significance in regard to the resulting compositional inhomogeneities (*segregation*), which may affect the performance and properties of doped semiconductors and the structural integrity of alloy materials [6,7].

Conventionally, the onset and linear growth of disturbances in the above mentioned phenomena have been investigated using linear stability theory. Weakly nonlinear analyses in extension of the onset behavior have also been performed [12]. However, far from onset, the interfaces undergo successive instabilities of various types and in some systems the final observed pattern may deviate significantly from that predicted by linear stability analyses. In other cases, the instability may be triggered by large amplitude disturbances and such subcritical phenomena are obviously not accessible to linear stability considerations. The mechanisms by which the nonlinear phenomena induce reorganizations and coherent patterns in unstable systems are not therefore clarified by analyses restricted to small perturbations. Thus, sufficient motivation exists for developing general investigative capabilities in order to study the above mentioned phenomena in their highly non–linear stages. This regime is most accessible to laboratory and computational experiments. The effort presented herein is devoted to developing a tool for computational study of the instability of interfaces far into the nonlinear growth stages.

We choose, as our model system, the growth of crystals of pure materials from the melt. The mechanisms of instability and various aspects of pattern selection and transport phenomena have been thoroughly investigated over the years and the literature abounds in references [12–16]. Thus, we detail only such features of the morphological evolution as are necessary to provide a motivation for the numerical procedure developed here.

Consider the typical crystal growth situation depicted in Fig. 1(a). Let the wall on the liquid side be maintained at a temperature T_l such that $T_l < T_m$, the melting temperature of the material, i.e., the melt is *undercooled*. The interface between solid and liquid corresponds approximately to the isotherm $T(x,t)= T_m$. Thus, the protrusion of the bump into the liquid leads to a clustering of the isotherms in the vicinity of the tip, implying a higher temperature gradient there. The bump is thereby induced to lose latent heat more rapidly in comparison with the other regions of the interface, which causes the disturbance to run away to form a finger. For growth of an unstable front in the pure material system, the available exact solutions were obtained by Ivantsov [12,14–16] in the form of paraboloids of revolution. These solutions have the property that , for given values of undercooling, they represent a continuous family of solutions, and specify only the combination $R_t V_t$, where R_t is the tip radius and V_t is the tip velocity of the paraboloid. However, it is observed that the tip radius and velocity assume unique values as functions of undercooling in real growth systems [14]. Thus, a selection mechanism is missing from the Ivantsov model, which fails to take account of an important physical ingredient, namely surface tension (γ). Surface tension appears as the controlling factor, to select a discrete set of solutions from the continuum of solutions [1]. The stabilization of the interface is accomplished by surface tension by modifying the interfacial temperature, which no longer corresponds to the T_m isotherm. In particular, in two dimensions the Gibbs–Thomson condition for the interfacial temperature reads:

$$T_i = T_m(1 - (\gamma(\phi) + \frac{\partial^2 \gamma(\phi)}{\partial \phi^2}) \varkappa / L) \qquad (1)$$

where $\gamma(\phi)$ is the surface tension, ϕ is the angle between the normal and the x–axis , L is the latent heat of fusion and $\varkappa$ is the interfacial curvature [7]. The dependence on orientation, i.e. the surface tension anisotropy, is a reflection of the underlying solid lattice structure. From Eq. (1), it is evident that surface tension depresses the temperature at the tip, reducing the effective undercooling there, and providing a stabilizing effect. In essence, surface tension, reflecting the existence of a critical nucleation radius, provides a short wavelength cutoff for the instabilities. The selected dendrite tip is highly sensitive to noise and behaves like an amplifier [17]. Thus, the final shape of the crystal is not usually represented by a smooth paraboloid, but a highly branched structure, with successive instabilities ensuing on side–branches at different scales [14].

Recently, much interest has also been generated in regard to the effects of convection, natural and forced, on the macroscopic and microscopic interfacial characteristics [16, 18, 19], motivated by low–gravity crystal growth experiments [20], and the possibility of controlling micro–structure using forced convection [21]. Convection further complicates the issues by bringing in length and time scales disparate from the interfacial instability phenomena, and breaking symmetry. While phenomena at the macroscopic scale have been well investigated [16], at the morphological scales studies thus far have only been of an idealized nature. These effects will be studied in the future, by extending the numerical methods presented in this work.

In our previous effort [22] we developed an interface tracking procedure that can handle highly deformed interfaces and surmounts the conventionally accepted difficulty in handling topological changes. In the context of Lagrangian methods, Glimm et al [23] have applied similar approaches to perform merger/breakup operations for the viscous fingering problem. In the approach presented here, we seek to exploit the knowledge of exact interfacial location in formulating conservative and consistent differencing schemes via the control volume formulation. This is the advantage that the surface–tracking method [22–29] affords in contrast to volume–tracking schemes [30–35]. Performing the calculations on a stationary Cartesian grid yields conveniently to a control volume formulation [36,37] and iterative line solvers. Thus far, Cartesian grid methods have either been restricted to volume–tracking procedures or have failed to exploit the explicit specification of the interface position. In other cases, such as in [38], particle tracking has been employed. However, in each case the exact boundary conditions have not been rigorously applied in the finite difference formulation. The concern in these works was not directed as in our case, on conservation across the interface. Cartesian grid solutions for arbitrarily shaped bodies which pass through the grid, have been advanced recently for inviscid flow over stationary obstacles [39]. While more detailed assessment is needed, the use of fixed grids with cell partition technique to accommodate the irregular internal boundary appears promising.

The interface grows in perimeter in the course of the instability. Interfaces may merge or fragment. The solution procedure is therefore required to follow the evolution of an interface under these circumstances. The behavior of the interface is very sensitive to the intricate details of the boundary conditions applied at the interface. In particular, as we demonstrate later, surface tension is a highly delicate mechanism but has a significant effect on the finally attained shape. Since the surface tension multiplies the curvature of the interface, the numerical scheme is required to compute the interface shape and the first and second derivatives of the interfacial curve accurately in order to faithfully represent the physics. The interface velocity is given, in the case of solidification, by the expression [16]:

$$\varrho L V_n = (k_s \nabla T_s - k_l \nabla T_l) \cdot \vec{N} \qquad (2)$$

Here, ϱ, L, V_n and k are respectively density, latent heat, normal velocity of the interface and thermal conductivity, $\vec{N}$ is the normal to the interface and the subscripts l,s represent liquid and solid phases. This is in fact the statement of conservation of energy for a control volume positioned at the interface. Thus, unless a field equation solver is developed to enforce this condition strictly at the interface, the interfacial velocity will be inaccurately obtained.

Keeping in view the requirements imposed on the numerical method by the physics detailed above, we design a solution methodology to track highly distorted fronts. Two primary tasks are involved in simulating the crystal growth phenomenon, namely, interface tracking and solution of the field equations. There is no ambiguity regarding the location of the interface, and the evaluation of heat fluxes through each face of the irregular polygonal control volume is performed by conventional methods [36,37]. Some details of the algorithm are presented below.

2. Formulation & Solution Algorithm

The following equations are solved on the domain displayed in Fig 1 (b).
Heat conduction in each phase,

$$\frac{\partial T_i}{\partial t} = \alpha_i \nabla^2 T_i \quad , \quad i = l, s \qquad (3)$$

and conservation across the interface, yielding an expression for the interfacial velocity, Eq. (2), with the boundary conditions,

$T(X, Y_l, t) = T_l$ at the top (liquid side) and $T(X, 0, t) = T_s$ at the bottom (solid side), with temperature continuity, $T_l (X_i, Y_i, t) = T_s (X_i, Y_i, t)$ at the interface. (4)

At the sides of the domain adiabatic conditions are imposed, i.e.,

$$\frac{\partial T}{\partial N}(0, Y, t) = \frac{\partial T}{\partial N}(\Xi, Y, t) = 0 \qquad (5)$$

where Ξ is the extent of the domain, along x–direction in the Fig 2.
At the interface, the Gibbs–Thomson condition [16] is applied, in the form,

$$T = T_m (1 - (\gamma \varkappa / L)) \qquad (6)$$

where surface tension is considered to be isotropic for simplicity.

It is important, in simulating the morphological instability phenomena, to take account of the length and time scales of the physical mechanisms. Linear stability analysis of a planar interface indicates that the critical wavelength for morphological stability is given by [13],

$$\lambda_c = O(\sqrt{(d_o l_T)}) \qquad (7)$$

Here, $d_o = \gamma/L$ is the capillary length scale of the order of Angstroms, l_T is the thermal diffusion length scale, typically of O(mm). Thus, λ_c = O(microns). The instability events that we are interested in all occur at the scale of λ_c. Thus, as described in [25], the chosen scales are λ_c for the length scale, and $\Delta\lambda_c/l_T$ for the temperatures scale, where Δ, the applied undercooling = $T_L - T_m$, T_L being the temperature at the liquid boundary. The velocity scale is chosen to be $\mathcal{V} = O(St\, \alpha_L/l_T)$, where α_L is the thermal diffusivity and the time scale of motion of the interface is $\tau = \lambda_c / \mathcal{V} = \lambda_c l_T / \alpha_L St$.

Non–dimensionalizing the equations above with the scales decided upon, and defining a field $\theta_i = T_i^* - T_m^*$, where T^* represents the non–dimensional temperature, we obtain the following equations for θ_i,

$$\frac{\lambda_c}{l_T} St \frac{\partial \theta_i}{\partial t^*} = \nabla^{*2} \theta_i \quad , \quad i = l, s \qquad (8)$$

where $\lambda_c/l_T << 1$ and the starred quantities are dimensionless. For the small Stefan numbers, i.e. undercoolings , usually employed in crystal growth experiments, $\varepsilon_1 = \lambda_c St/l_T << 1$. In our calculations we set $\varepsilon_1 = 5\times10^{-4}$. The interface motion equation, for the non–dimensional velocity v_n now reads,

$$v_n = \left(-\frac{\partial \theta}{\partial n_L^*} + \frac{k_S}{k_L}\frac{\partial \theta}{\partial n_S^*}\right) \qquad (9)$$

with the boundary conditions, $\theta(x, y_S, t) = \theta_S$ and $\theta(x, y_L, t) = \theta_L$ at the solid and liquid boundaries, (x,y) are now non–dimensional coordinates , v_n is the dimensionless velocity and $\vec{n}^*$ is non–dimensional normal vector.

The Gibbs–Thomson condition assumes the form, $\theta_i = -\varepsilon_2 \theta_m \gamma^* \varkappa^* = -\gamma_{eff} \varkappa^*$, where $\varepsilon_2 = d_o/\lambda_c$ and we designate $\gamma_{eff} = \varepsilon_2 T_m \gamma^*$ to be the effective surface tension. The adiabatic boundary conditions are,

$$\frac{\partial \theta}{\partial n^*} = 0 \quad at \quad x = 0, \quad x = \chi \qquad (10)$$

where $\chi = \Xi / \lambda_c$ is the non–dimensional domain length in the x–direction. It is noted that γ_{eff} now contains T_m and ε_2 and is dependant on both material properties and operating conditions.

Since Eq. 8 has the small parameter ε_1 in front of the time derivative, the temperature field is nearly quasi–stationary. Thus, the solution to the Laplace equation is imposed as the initial temperature field in each phase. The interface is perturbed in the form, f(x,y,0)= *ymean*+0.1(1–2cos($2\pi x/\chi$)). A *ymean* value of 10.5 was specified in the simulations presented here. The evolution of this initial perturbation was then followed in time.

Consider the situation depicted in Fig. 2, which shows an interface lying arbitrarily on a grid representing part of the computational domain. The interfacial curve, as explained in [22], is tracked with the aid of marker particles indicated by crosses in the figure. Two primary tasks are to be performed in advancing the interface and thermal field in time. Firstly, the interface position has to be determined along with such features as the interfacial normals and curvature. Thus, the boundary conditions at the interface are known. The interface velocity is obtained from the computed normal gradients of temperature in each phase and is calculated from Eq. (9). The interface position is then updated. The information regarding the interface location and temperature are then fed to the field equation solver and the new thermal field obtained. All these procedures are performed in a fully–coupled manner over each iteration and time step.

Given the interface position, the thermal field calculations involve the following procedures:

(a) Classify the control volumes and associate with them the indices of the control volume markers, if any, lying on the faces of the volumes.

(b) Identify the phase in which a control point belonging to a computational cell lies.

(c) Assemble the control volumes and compute the fluxes to ensure conservation.

(d) Compute the temperature field.

The information gathered from the interface tracking routine aids in performing the above procedures. Since the interface cuts through the grid as shown in Fig. 3 the cells in the vicinity of the interface are fragmented. Thus the control volumes adjoining the interface have to be treated in special fashion in the discretization of the governing equations. This is accomplished in the control volume formulation by redefining the control volumes and defining partner cells as described in Fig. 3. Thus, due to the reassignment of control volume fragments and the fluxes through them, the control volumes in the interfacial region are no longer rectangular. Instead, 4 – or 5–sided polygons can arise. The integration of the governing equations for such control volumes can be performed by evaluating the normal fluxes through each face of the control volume. For all except the interfacial face of the cell, the calculation of normal fluxes is straightforward. However, for the interfacial side, the evaluation of the normal temperature gradient requires special procedures. This gradient is also a crucial quantity in obtaining the interfacial velocity. To do so, one obtains the gradient by projecting a normal into each phase from the interfacial segment and estimating the value at the end of the normal from a biquadratic definition of the temperature field at that point. The biquadratic function definition is obtained by considering the values of six surrounding points in the same phase. Once all the fluxes are obtained it is a simple matter to obtain a discretized equations. Central differencing of spatial gradients is performed. Backward Euler time stepping is used and the resulting equations are solved via a line SOR procedure.

3. Results and Discussion

The computational domain is configured as shown in Fig. 4. The domain is partitioned into three regions. Coarse grids are employed in the regions I and III, away from the interface, while fine grids are employed in the region II close to the interface. However, as the interface rapidly grows out of region II there is a need for introducing a fine grid that precedes the interface in order to be able to calculate the gradients ahead of it with desired accuracy. To achieve this, grid lines are added such that a sufficiently extended region ahead of the interface is replenished with fine grids, throughout the evolution of the interface. The values of field variables in this region are obtained by linear interpolation. The grid addition takes place at a frequency depending on the extent of the domain traversed by the interface.

In the computations to follow, we employ *nmax* grid points along the x–direction, where *nmax* was 21, 41 or 81. Since χ=4, and $y_l = 40$ in all subsequent calculations, we have $\Delta x = 4/nmax$. Depending on the value of Δx, we employ grid points in the region II, such that $\Delta y_{II} = \Delta x$. As mentioned before, as the interface grows and propagates grids are added ahead of and deleted behind the interface. Thus the extent of region II increases as the computation proceeds. The domain of computation is shown in Fig. 1(b). The liquid end was maintained at $\theta_l = -40$, with the solid side at θ=1. The side boundaries are adiabatic, i.e. $\frac{\partial \theta}{\partial x} = 0$. The Stefan number for the system is 1 as obtained from the scaling procedure. Thus, the solidification process is being viewed not at the diffusion time scale, but at the time scale corresponding to interface motion. The system of equations solved, namely the heat conduction equation, which is nearly quasistationary.

3.1 Zero surface tension

The evolution of an isothermal interface was tracked on grids with *nmax*=21,41 and 81. The results are presented in Figs. 7. Clearly, for the isothermal interface the results are governed to a large degree by the grid spacing. The behavior of interfaces with zero surface tension has been under scrutiny, with calculations indicating cusp–formation or tip–splitting [41]. Since, *in the absence of surface tension, no stabilization mechanism exists at any length scale,* i.e., there is no smoothing effect, *disturbances of all wavelengths are amplified.* Thus, finite–time singularities can form on the interface. Our calculations show that on the *nmax*=21 grid, displayed in Fig. 5(a), *the perturbation grows for the period of calculation and loses symmetry.* The source of asymmetry comes from the uni–directional procedure used to define the interface shape and temperature gradients. For *nmax*=41, Fig. 5(b), the interface first loses its symmetry, similar to the 21 grid case, and as time elapses, the perturbation wavelengths permitted by the grid lead to a *tip–splitting instability.* A trough is formed upon tip–splitting, and rapid accumulation of latent heat ensues there leading quickly to the formation of a cusp in that region. Thus, the sharp corner created there cannot be smoothed out in the absence of surface tension. For an even finer grid, *nmax*=81, as shown in Fig. 5(c) the interface becomes unstable to grid–scale oscillations. These *short wavelength oscillations grow faster than the disturbances that are captured on the coarser grid and a cusp rapidly forms at the boundary where the imposed periodicity condition becomes incompatible with the asymmetric breakdown of the interface.* The results on this fine grid correspond to our previous results obtained by employing boundary–fitted adaptive grids [25]. There, in the absence of surface tension, the cusp formed at the boundary, and short wavelength oscillations developed on the interface. The simulation in this case, could however be carried farther than previously, because the grid is not required to conform to the interface. The behavior of the interface under different grid resolutions has been investigated. *It is interesting that with the different grid resolutions, different modes of instability, including asymmetry, singularities and tip–splitting can appear.* Figure 5 indicates that there is no preferred morphological shape for the zero surface tension case. Furthermore, because there is no prevailing physical length scale contained by the instability development itself, the numerical resolution, in effect controls the smallest length scales of the instability. As the grid is refined, finer instability scales appear, implying that no grid independent solution can be obtained with zero surface tension. It is noticed in each case that asymmetry develops in the interface profiles. It was found in most of our calculations where the interface was highly unstable (i.e. for zero and low surface tensions) that asymmetric breakdown persisted. In addition, the breakdown always occurred on the same side of the domain, namely on the left. Such asymmetric breakdowns have been remarked upon in connection with experiments on the Saffman–Taylor instability [5] and in the Boundary Integral simulations of [27]. In the latter, when symmetry was not imposed, the interface became unstable asymmetrically. When sufficient surface tension is present, it will be shown that the asymmetry is eliminated. Thus, for the highly sensitive low surface tension cases, any small noise generated in the course of the computation leads to a breakdown of the smooth perturbation. Here the first appearance of asymmetry comes from the bias of the line iterative procedure in the course of computation. The other procedures, namely assembly of control volumes, definition of partner cells and interface definition were performed in the reverse order and the asymmetry was found to persist.

3.2 Low surface tension

The sensitivity of the solution procedure can be demonstrated by adding a surface tension $\gamma_{eff} = 10^{-3}$ where, as defined previously, $\gamma_{eff} = \varepsilon_2 \theta_m \gamma^*$. Since the curvature is O(1), the Gibbs–Thomson condition [16] will lead to interface temperatures variations of $O(10^{-3})$. This modification of the temperature at the interface is extremely small when compared to the non–dimensionalized undercooling value $T_l = -40$ is imposed at the liquid boundary. When this small value of surface tension is added for the *nmax*=81 calculation, it eliminates the singularities at the interface. However, the perturbations along the interface continue to grow. Following the interface evolution further, a series of instabilities develop in the vicinity of the tip and result in the asymmetric convoluted structure shown in Fig. 6(a). The interface is highly distorted in this case, demonstrating the ability of the numerical technique developed here to handle such strongly multiple–valued shapes. It is also noted that while one side of the interface appears to break into a cascade of protuberances in the vicinity of the tip, the other side remains quite stable. The further development of the side branches is found to be arrested due to the accumulation of heat in the sides of the growing finger. The imposition of the adiabatic side–wall condition prevents the removal of heat from this region. Figures 6(b) and (c) show the isothermal contours in the vicinity of the interface in the early and later stages of the development shown in Fig. 6(a). As is clearly seen, the temperature field calculation responds to the highly distorted nature of the interface, even for such a low value of the interface temperature. Furthermore, the clustering of the isotherms to the left of the tip clearly drives the instability in that region, leading to a mutually enhancing dynamic process between the interface and thermal field. In comparison the isotherms on the right side are seen to be less crowded. With regard to the question of asymmetry, as already pointed out, this feature results from the fact that our cell cutting procedure is conducted along a given direction, which can create initial noises along that direction. These initial noises, once formed, influence the paths of subsequent development morphologically. However, this aspect does not affect the solution accuracy when surface tension plays a more substantial role, as will be discussed later.

For low surface tension cases computational studies that impose symmetry result in interface patterns different from those without such constraint, due to the fact that the morphology of the interface is highly path dependent. Any change in the boundary conditions or computational details will create different numerical noises, which in turn, yields different final interface shapes. To illustrate the impact of enforcing symmetry on the interface for low surface tension, we compute the development of only half the perturbation by imposing symmetry condition for the other half. For the *nmax*=81 case, with low surface tension $\gamma_{eff} = 10^{-3}$ the resulting symmetric structure is shown in Fig. 7(a). There is again a series of instabilities in the vicinity of the tip reminiscent of the structures observed in the Saffman–Taylor experiments with tip bubbles [42]. On a finer grid, *nmax*=161, a similar phenomenon results as shown in Fig. 7(b), except that in this case the tip breaks down at shorter wavelengths, and the instability development is much more rapid than in the case of the coarser grid calculations. Thus, imposition of symmetry does not influence the stability of this low surface tension interface. The shape of the computed interface is however, very different from the case where symmetry is not explicitly imposed i.e., Fig. 6(a). Nevertheless, the changing wavelengths in both Figs. 6 and 7, indicate that grid resolution is the main cut–off length scale with zero or low surface tension. It should be clarified however that as long as surface tension is non–zero, there exists a physical length scale to control the morphological length scale of the interface. The results discussed so far, however, are for very low surface tensions, which creates a length scale too small to be resolved by the grid spacing employed here. To ascertain the numerical accuracy of the present algorithm, a higher effective surface tension is considered next.

3.3 Stable fingers for higher surface tensions

The extreme sensitivity of the low surface tension cases to grid spacing, which yield widely different behaviors upon refinement prompts us to confirm grid independence for the more stable higher surface tension cases. As already explained, this exercise can be conducted only for non–negligible effective surface tension cases. It should be again emphasized that the so–called low and high surface tensions are defined with respect to our grid resolution. Furthermore, it is the effective surface tension under consideration here, which involves both material properties and operating conditions, and hence can vary substantially. Figure 8(a) compares the interface shape and velocity of an interface with $\gamma_{eff} = 10^{-2}$, *nmax*=41 (full lines) and *nmax*=81 (open circles) . While in the initial stages of development the profiles as well as interface velocities are in agreement, as the perturbation develops to large amplitudes the coarser grid calculation under–estimates the instability magnitude. In fact the final stage of the fine grid calculation shows a vastly different value of velocity. Figure 8(b) compares the same interfacial development for *nmax*=81 (full line) and *nmax*=161 (open circles). As can be seen, the two calculations maintain close consistency, even in the large amplitude stage. The velocities in the final stage are in close agreement. Thus, for high enough surface tension, grid effects are suppressed and the stable finger growth converges under grid refinement. In subsequent calculations we employ *nmax*=81.

Next, we present results of long time simulation of two different γ_{eff} to further contrast the effect of surface tension. Figure 9 shows the development of a finger for $\gamma_{eff} = 10^{-2}$, along with the derivatives along the interface. The first observation to make regarding these results is the well maintained symmetry of the front. Figure 10 shows the development of the finger for $\gamma_{eff}=10^{-1}$. The interfaces are shown at the same instants of time. The effects of surface tension are brought forth by comparing these two sets of results. The qualitative features are in agreement with the computations of [27] who used the boundary element method . In particular, the rapid accumulation of heat on the sides of the finger leads to a rapid slowdown of the interface in that region. The front propagates upward farther in the higher surface tension case before the instability gathers momentum. The amplitudes of the $\gamma_{eff} = 10^{-2}$ finger (aspect ratio $\approx$ 4) is greater than the $\gamma_{eff} = 0.1$ finger (aspect ratio $\approx$ 2.5) demonstrating the higher degree of instability for lower surface tension. The higher surface tension (10^{-1}) causes the finger to spread laterally, leading to a multiple–valued interface with respect to x. The sides of the lower surface tension (10^{-2}) finger are almost flat and vertical, indicating minimal lateral spreading. The circular arc fits for representing the interfacial segments holds up very well even for such a flat vertical surface. The finger in the higher surface tension case has a more rounded tip and there is a wide region near the tip where the curvature is nearly constant. In contrast, the $\gamma_{eff} = 10^{-2}$ finger is sharper at the tip. At the stage of the development shown, as seen from the plots of interfacial derivatives against x, the interfaces in both cases appear to have attained stable, shape–preserving growth. However, as observed by Saffman and Taylor [3], over a substantial length and time, the growth velocity of the finger is not constant and the tip is still accelerating, due to the finite domain size in our calculation. As the finger reaches an asymptotically invariant shape, the tip velocity will approach a constant value.

Figure 10(b) shows the isotherms in the vicinity of the interface for the $\gamma_{eff} = 0.1$ case. The finger in this case extends from about Y=12 to 21. Clearly the clustering of the isotherms at the tip drives the instability. The Gibbs–Thomson effect causes the isotherm corresponding to $\theta = -2.2 \times 10^{-2}$ to curve inward in the tip region where the curvature is positive. The symmetry of the isotherms confirms our previous statement regarding the ability of the surface tension to suppress asymmetry. Fig. 10(c) shows isotherms across the interface. The effect of the Gibbs–Thomson condition is seen to propagate far down the solid finger as evident from the curvature of the -2.19×10^{-2} isotherm at Y=18, which is well into the solid finger. The curvatures of the isotherms however change sign further down, as for the $\theta=3.53 \times 10^{-3}$ isotherm. The isotherm plot for $\gamma_{eff} = 0.01$, Fig. 9(b), shows no sign of the Gibbs–Thomson condition for the available contour resolution. The first negative isotherm is in the correct position since the tip of the finger is located approximately at Y=27, in agreement with the isotherm plot.

4. Conclusions

We have presented simulations for the solidification problem at the morphological scale, based on a combined Eulerian–Lagrangian method. The method can explicitly specify the location and shape of the interface and to apply the boundary conditions at the exact location of the interface; it does not need to have grid either translated with the interface or periodically smoothed and redistributed.The results illustrate the effects of surface tension. In the absence of surface tension, singularities quickly develop on the front for sufficient grid resolution. The grid resolution governs the wavelength of noise permitted on the interface and thus affects interfacial development. In particular, at very low surface tensions the disturbances allowed by the grid strongly influence the fate of the interface. Thus care needs to be exercised in interpreting results in this range of surface tension parameter. For sufficient interfacial tension, the results have been demonstrated to converge under grid refinement. The initial perturbation develops in time into long fingers, as in the Saffman–Taylor problem. The qualitative features are in agreement with other simulations of the fingering phenomenon. The finger shapes reached a steady–state , while the tip accelerated due to the fixed domain size and boundary conditions.

5. Acknowledgements

The work presented here has been partially supported by the NASA, AFOSR URI program, and BDM Federal.

6. References

1. D. A. Kessler, J. Koplik and H. Levine, Pattern selection in fingered growth phenomena, *Advances in Physics*, Vol. 37, No. 3, pp. 255–339 (1988).
2. U. Nakaya , *Snow Crystals*, Harvard University Press, Cambridge, MA (1954).
3. P. G. Saffman and G. I. Taylor , The penetration of a fluid into a porous medium or Hele–Shaw cell containing a more viscous fluid, *Proc. Royal Soc. Lond.*, A 245, pp. 312– 329 (1958).
4. D. Bensimon, Stability of viscous fingering, *Phys.*

Rev. A, Vol. 33, pp. 1302–1308 (1986).
5. P. Tabeling, G. Zocchi and A. Libchaber, An experimental study of the Saffman–Taylor instability, *J. Fluid Mech.,* Vol. 177, pp. 67–82 (1987).
6. M. C. Flemings, *Solidification Processing,* McGraw–Hill, New York (1974).
7. D. P. Woodruff , *The Solid–Liquid Interface*, Cambridge Press, Cambridge, UK (1973).
8. J.–M. Flesselles, A. J. Simon and A. J. Libchaber, Dynamics of one–dimensional interfaces: an experimentalist's view, *Adv. Phys.*, Vol. 40, No. 1 , pp. 1–51 (1991).
9. P. Huerre, Spatio–temporal instabilities in closed and open shear flows, in *Instabilities and Nonequilibrium Structures*, Eds. E. Tirapegui and D. Villaroel, pp. 141–177, Dodrecht, Reidel, Germany (1987).
10. D. H. Sharp, An overview of Rayleigh–Taylor instability, *Physica 12D,* pp. 3–18 (1984).
11. P. G. Drazin and H. W. Reid, *Hydrodynamic Stability,* Cambridge University Press, Cambridge, UK (1981).
12. J. S. Langer , Instabilities and pattern formation in crystal growth, *Rev. Mod. Phys.,* Vol. 52, No.1, pp. 1–56 (1980).
13. J. S. Langer and Muller–Krumbhaar, Theory of dendritic growth, Parts I, II, and III, *Acta Metall.*, Vol. 28, pp. 1681–1708 (1978).
14. M. E. Glicksmann and S.–C. Huang , Fundamentals of dendritic solidification, I and II, *Acta Metall.,* Vol. 29, pp. 701–734 (1981).
15. P. Pelce , *Dynamics of Curved Fronts*, Academic Press Inc., New York (1988).
16. W. Shyy, *Computational Modelling for Fluid Flow and Interfacial Transport*, Elsevier, Amsterdam, The Netherlands (1994).
17. R. Pieters and J. S. Langer, Noise–driven sidebranching in dendritic crystal growth, *Phys. Rev. Lett.,* Vol. 56, pp. 1948–1952 (1986).
18. M. Rappaz, Modelling of microstructure formation in solidification processes, *Inter. Mat. Rev.*, Vol. 34, No. 3, pp. 93–123 (1989).
19. R. A. Brown , Theory of transport processes in single crystal growth from the melt, *A. I. Ch. E. J.*, Vol. 34, pp. 881–911 (1988) .
20. S. Ostrach, Fluid Mechanics in Crystal Growth, *J. Fluids Engg.*, Vol. 105, pp. 5–20 (1983).
21. Ph. Bouissou, B. Perrin and P. Tabeling, Influence of an external periodic flow on dendritic crystal growth, in *Nonlinear Evolution of Spatio–temporal Structures in Dissipative Dynamical Systems,* Eds. F. H. Busse and L. Kramer, Plenum Press, New York (1990).
22. H. S. Udaykumar and W. Shyy, Development of a grid–supported marker particle scheme for interface tracking, *11th AIAA Comp. Fluid. Dyn. Conf., Paper No. AIAA–93–3384,* Orlando, Florida (1993).
23. J. Glimm, J. Grove, B. Lindquist, O. A. McBryan and G. Tryggvason, The bifurcation of tracked scalar waves, *SIAM J. Sci. Stat. Comput.,* Vol. 9, No. 1, pp. 61–79 (1988).
24. J. M. Floryan and H. Rasmussen, Numerical methods for viscous flows with moving boundaries, *Appl. Mech. Rev.,* Vol. 42, No. 12, pp. 323–341 (1989).
25. W. Shyy, H. S. Udaykumar and S.–J. Liang , An interface tracking method applied to morphological evolution during phase change, *Int. J. Heat Mass Transf.*, Vol. 36, No. 7, pp. 1833–1834 (1993).
26. J. M. Sullivan and H. Hao, Comparison of simulated dendritic tip characteristics to those experimentally observed in unconfined environments, HTD–Vol. 234, ASME 1993, pp. 14–19 (1993).
27. A. J. DeGregoria and L. W. Schwartz, Finger breakup in Hele–Shaw cells, *Phys. Fluids,* Vol. 28, No. 8, pp. 2313–2314 (1985).
28. S. O. Unverdi and G. Tryggvason, A front–tracking method for viscous, incompressible multi–fluid flows, *J. Comp. Phys.,* Vol. 100, pp. 25–37 (1992).
29. L. N. Brush and R. F. Sekerka, A numerical study of a two–dimensional crystal growth forms in the presence of anisotropic growth kinetics, *J. Crystal Growth,* Vol. 96, pp. 419–441 (1989).
30. C. W. Hirt and B. D. Nichols, Volume of Fluid (VOF) method for the dynamics of free boundaries, *J. Comp. Phys,* Vol. 39, pp. 201–225 (1981).
31. N. Ashgriz and J. Y. Poo, FLAIR : Flux Line–Segment Model for Advection and Interface Reconstruction, *J. Comp. Phys.,* Vol. 93, pp. 449–468 (1991).
32. D. B. Kothe and R. C. Mjolsness, RIPPLE : A new method for incompressible flows with free surfaces, *AIAA J.,* Vol. 30, No. 11, pp. 2694–2700 (1992).
33. J. A. Sethian and J. Strain, Crystal growth and dendritic solidification, *J. Comp. Phys.,* Vol. 98, No. 2, pp. 231–253 (1992).
34. R. Kobayashi, Modeling and Numerical Simulations of Dendritic Crystal Growth, *Physica D,* Vol. 63, pp. 410–423 (1993).
35. A. A. Wheeler, B. T. Murray and R. J. Schaefer, Computations of Dendrites using a Phase Field Model, *Physica D.,* Vol. 66, pp. 243–262 (1993).
36. S. V. Patankar, *Numerical Heat Transfer and Fluid Flow,* Hemisphere Publishing Corp., Washington D.C. (1980).
37. J. C. T. Wang and G. F. Widhopf, A high–resolution TVD finite volume scheme for the Euler equations in conservation form, *J. Comp. Phys.*, Vol. 84, pp. 145–173 (1989).
38. H. Miyata, Finite difference simulation of breaking waves, *J. Comp. Phys.,* Vol. 65, pp. 179–214 (1986).
39. J. J. Quirk, An alternative to unstructured grids for computing gas dynamic flows around arbitrarily complex two–dimensional bodies, *ICASE Report No. 92–7,* NASA Langley Research Center, Hampton, VA (1992).
40. J. Crank , *Free and Moving Boundary Problems,* Oxford University Press, Oxford, UK (1984).
41. D. Bensimon and P. Pelce, Tip–splitting solutions to the Stefan problem, *Phys. Rev.,* A 33, pp. 4477–4478 (1986).
42. Y. Couder, N. Gerard and M. Rabaud, Narrow fingers in the Saffman–Taylor instability, *Phys. Rev. A,* Vol. 34, No. 6, pp. 5175–5178 (1986).

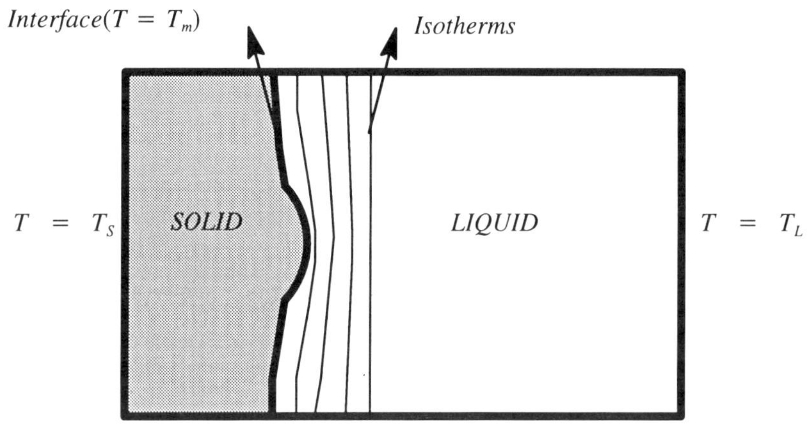

(a) Typical crystal growth situation involving an undercooled melt showing clustering of isotherms in front of the bump

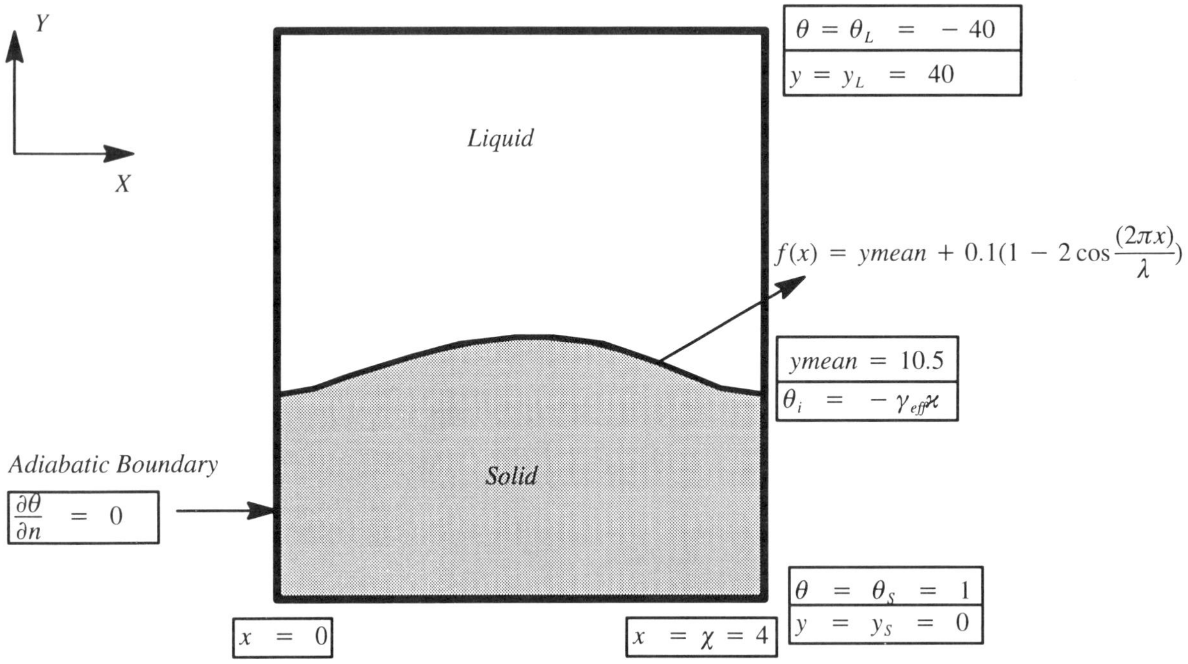

(b) Illustration of computational domain and boundary conditions in non–dimensional form

Fig. 1 Illustration of the (a) physical and (b) computational configurations for the instability simulations

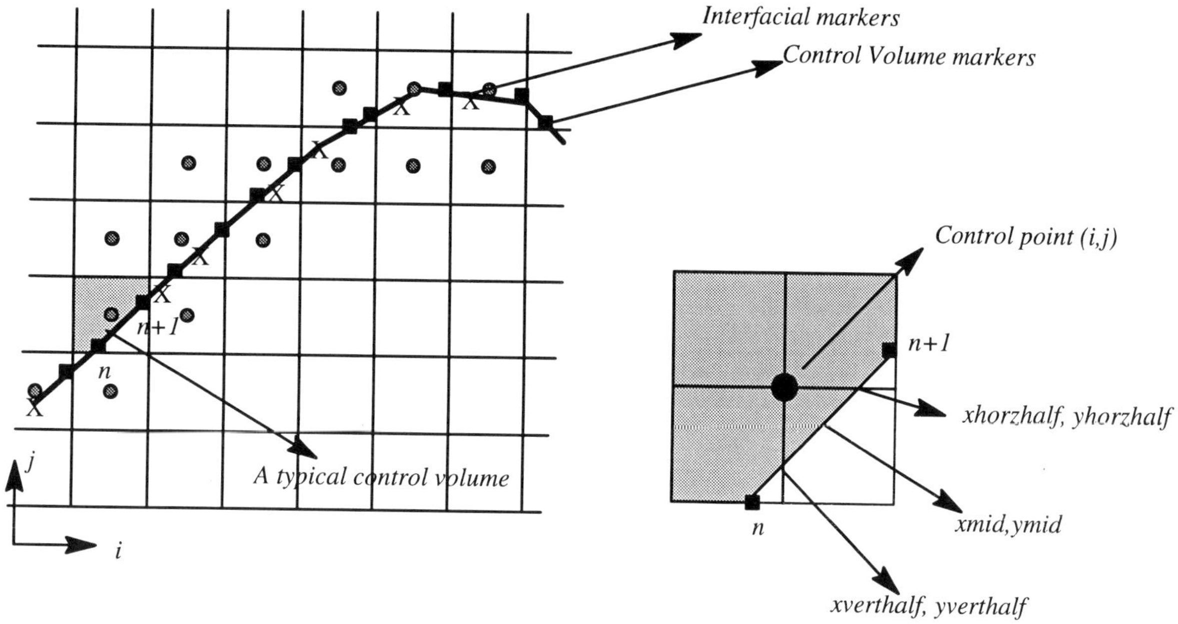

Fig. 2 Arrangement of interfacial and control volume markers and definition of a typical control volume. n and n+1 are indices of the control volume markers

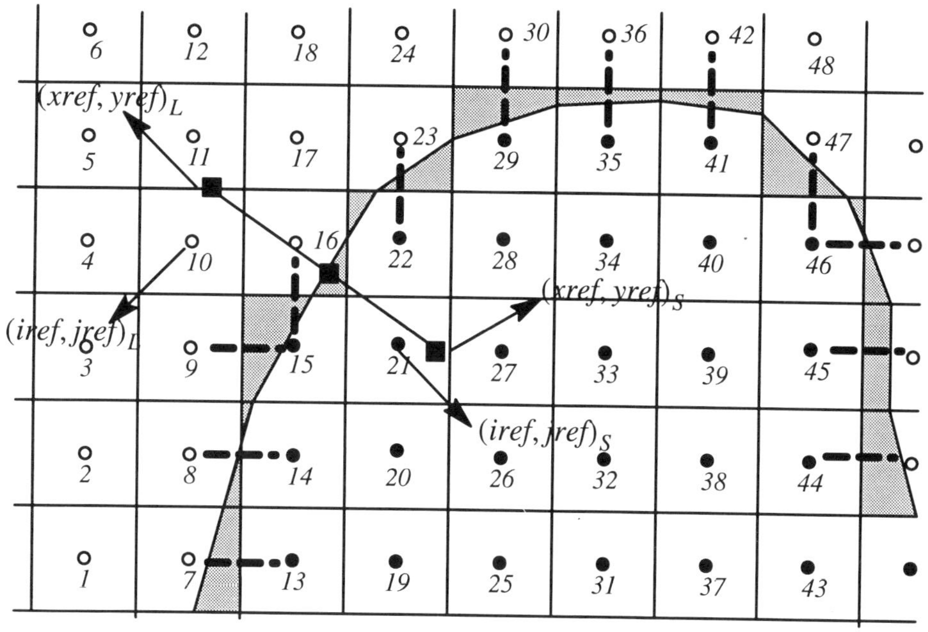

Fig. 3 Illustration of cut cells, partner cells and method for determining the normal gradient at the interface (see cell 16). Normal is projected from point (xmid,ymid) in cell 16 along the normal at that point. The probe of length dp ends at the points (xref,yref) in each phase. (iref,jref) is the index of the cell in which (xref,yref) lies. Solid phase control points are denoted by filled circles, liquid by open circles. Partner cells are indicated by the linkages between cells.

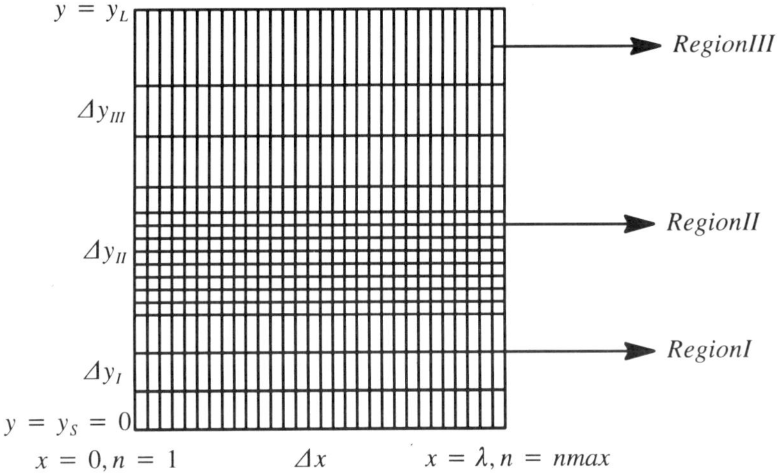

Fig. 4 Grid arrangement for the computational domain. Region II extends along with the interface.

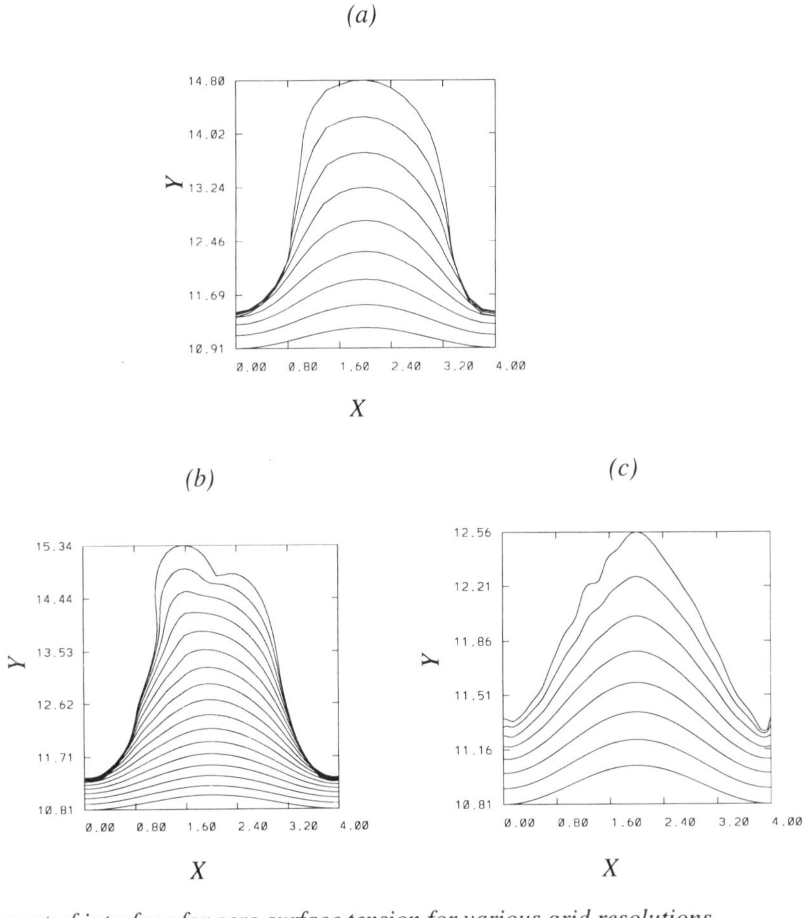

Fig. 5 Development of interface for zero surface tension for various grid resolutions.
(a) Interface shapes at different time instants for nmax=21 grid, upto time=1.8, in steps of dt=0.2. Symmetry is broken in this case. (b) Interface shapes for nmax=41 grid, upto time=1.8, in stepa of dt =0.1. In this case symmetry is first broken and tip–splitting follows. (c) Interface shapes for nmax=81 grid, upto time=0.8 in steps of dt=0.1. Computations were stopped early in this case due to cusp formation at the boundary. Note that shorter wavelengths are allowed on this finer grid, which become unstable more rapidly.

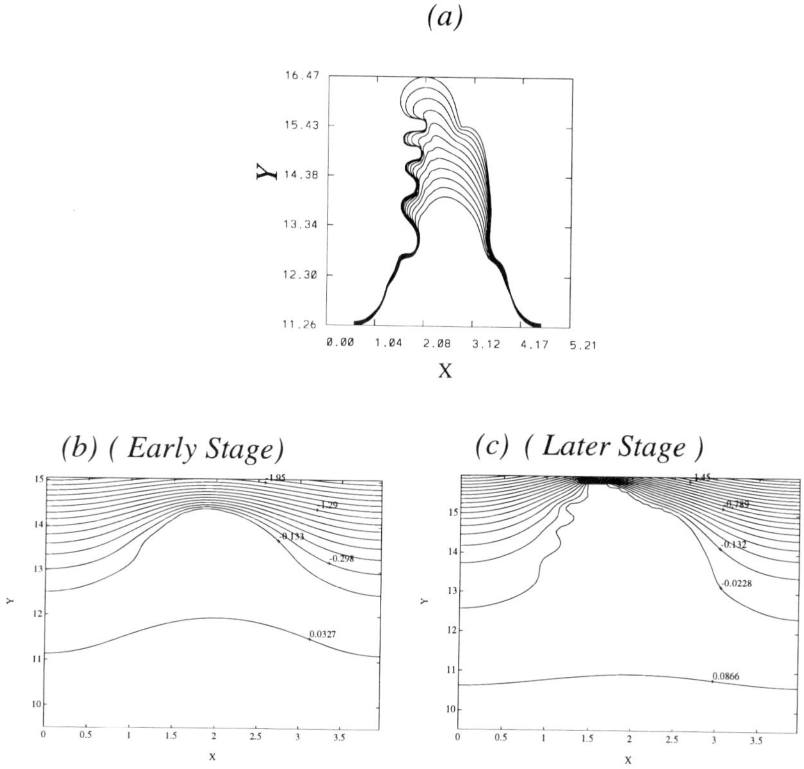

Fig. 6 Development of interface for low surface tensions (10^{-3}) on nmax=81 grid. From time t=0.8 to t=2.0. (a) Interface shapes at different time instants showing successive instabilities. (b) Isotherm plot at early stage showing asymmetry. (c) Isotherms at later stage showing response of thermal field to distorted interface even for the very low value of surface tension.

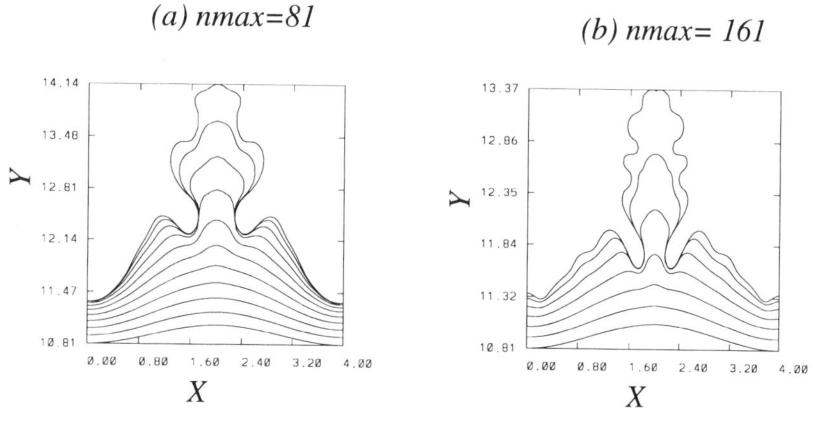

Fig. 7 Effect of imposition of symmetry on development of interface for low surface tension ($\gamma_{eff} = 10^{-3}$). (a) On nmax=81 grid (b) nmax=161 grid. Interface shapes are shown after reflection across the centerline.

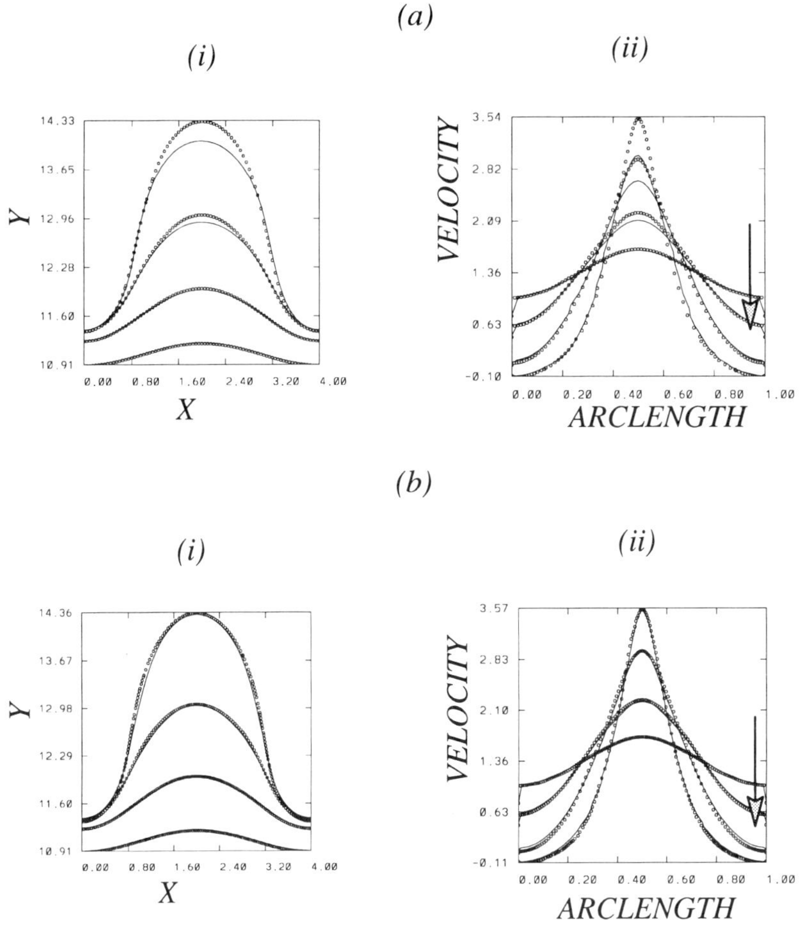

Fig. 8 Comparison of solutions for surface tension γ_{eff} =0.01. (a) nmax=41 (full lines) and nmax=81 (full circles). (b) nmax=81 (full lines) and nmax=161 (full circles) grids. (i) Interface shapes at different time instants (ii) Interface velocities at time instants corresponding to (i).

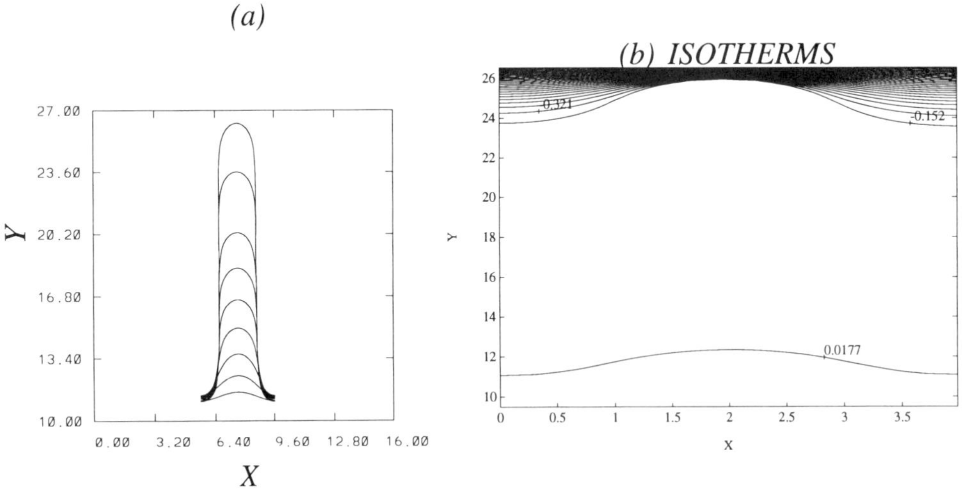

Fig. 9 Development of solutions for surface tension γ_{eff} =0.01. Upto t=4.0. (a) Interface shapes at equal intervals of time. The finger has been drawn to scale. (b) Isotherm contours including entire interface.

(a)

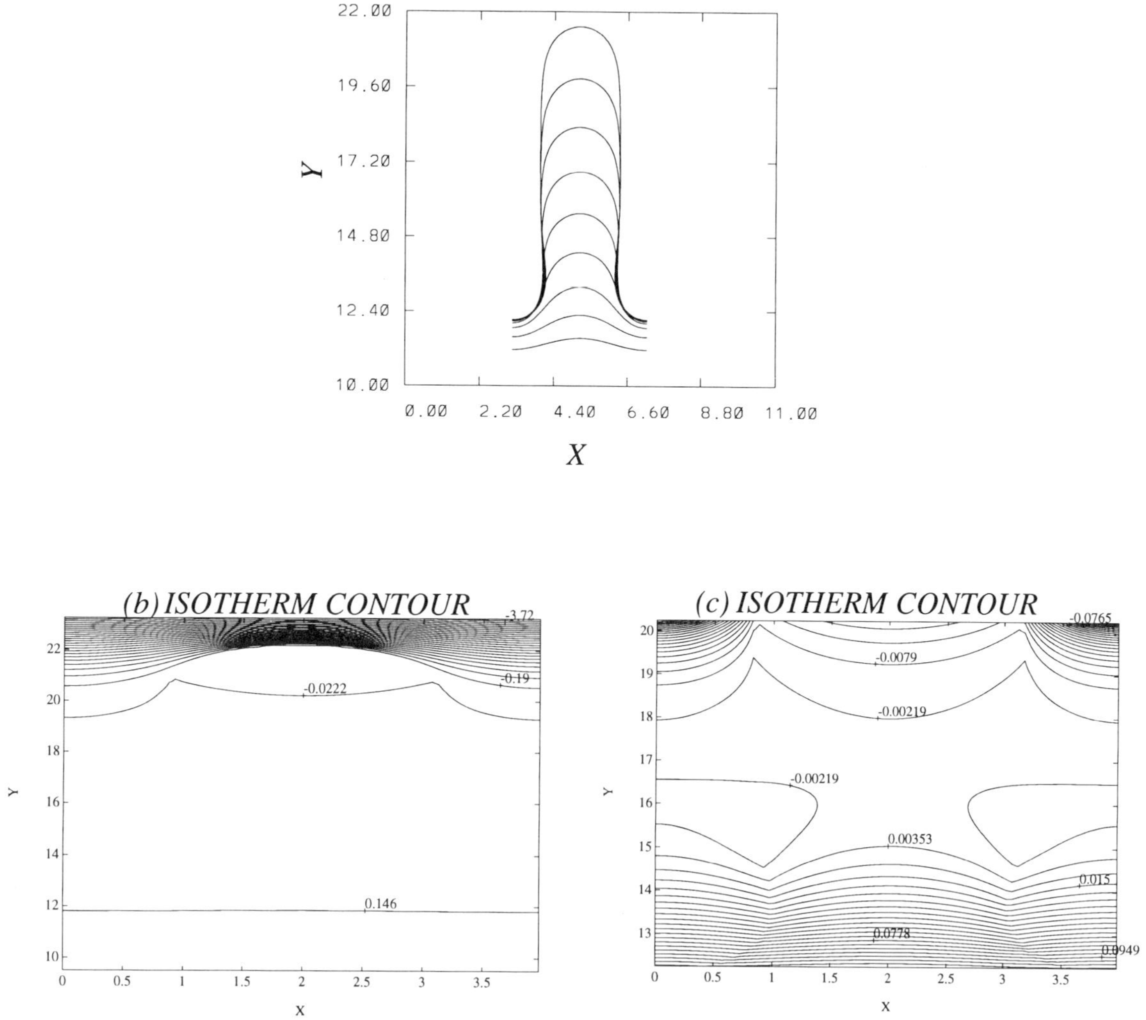

Fig. 10 Development of solutions for surface tension γ_{eff} =0.01. Upto t=4.0. (a) Interface shapes at equal intervals of time. The finger has been drawn to scale. (b) Isotherm contours including entire interface.

HTD-Vol. 284/AMD-Vol. 182, Transport Phenomena in Solidification
ASME 1994

MICROSCOPICAL STUDY ON HEAT TRANSFER AND MUSHY ZONE EVOLUTION IN CASTING OF METAL MATRIX COMPOSITES

Jinghong Fan
Department of Engineering Science and Mechanics
University of Tennessee
Knoxville, Tennessee

R. Gibson and D. Hageman
Department of Aerospace Engineering and Engineering Mechanics
University of Cincinnati
Cincinnati, Ohio

ABSTRACT

The main concern of this work is to develop a methodology of numerical simulation for investigating the microscopical thermal fields around fibers in solidification of melted metal matrix. Two kinds of microscopical representative unit cells are proposed to investigate heat transfer and mushy zone evolution around fibers in a fiber-preform-based casting of metal matrix composites. Instead of sharp transition from the hot liquid of pure metal to the solid region, a multiphase area of liquid and solid (i. e., mushy zone) has been simulated by finite element method. A thermal analysis is performed to determine the transient temperature history during the solidification process and track the movement of the mushy zone. The analysis for the unit cell with one fiber is an axisymmetric problem and represents composites with low fiber volume fraction. The results of the simulation show that the mushy zone evolution depends on both the initial temperature of preform and boundary cooling parameters. The analysis for unit cell with eight fibers is an plane problem and represents composites with high fiber volume fraction. The simulation results show that the temperature distribution and mushy zone evolution are quite different in the triangular interstice from that in the square interstice for a compact fiber arrangement.

1.0 INTRODUCTION

During the past decade, preform-based cast processing has emerged as one of the most economical methods of synthesis of metal matrix composites (MMC's). In this process, a preform consisting of fibers or ceramic particles, whiskers, etc. is put into a chamber or mold. Since such preforms are porous when the melted matrix fills the chamber, the matrix will infiltrate into this preform and form MMC's (Misra, Fishman, 1991, Mortensen, 1990). Net shape casting requires no further machining process and has great potential to solve the problem of poor workability for high-performance composite materials. Therefore, the preform-based cast processing has great potential as the primary means of manufacturing end-products economically for composite structure in aerospace structures, automobiles, etc.

This immerse potential motivated several researchers in the material community (Fabietti, Sekhar, et al. 1991, Sekar, et al. 1991, Motensen et al. 1989, Trivedi, et al. 1990, and many others) to conduct analytical and experimental investigations for the understanding of the underlying micromechanisms of the preform-based cast processing. It has been found that the morphology of the solidification microstructure is controlled by local processing variables. In presence of fibers these variables include temperature gradient, solidification velocity, the size of liquid channel, chemical composition, and surface energy of the solid/fiber interface (Fabietti, et al. 1991). Examples of the effects of temperature gradient and the size of liquid channel on microstructure and behavior can be found as follows.

(a) The heat flow direction controls whether the dendrite microstructure is columnar or equiaxial. When the heat flow is opposite to the solid growth direction, "the resulting dendritic microstructure is most often columnar or directional" and "when the heat flows from the solidifying crystal to the melt, the resulting dendritic microstructure is most often equiaxial".

(b) The change of solidification microstructure from circular to dendritic is affected by the fiber packing when channels were smaller than the primary dendrite spacing.

(c) The majority of defects in a casting are established during the solidification stage where both liquid and solid coexist (i. e., the mushy zone). The defects contained in casting consist of different scale of features, for example, microporosity, microsegregation, macroporosity, magrosegragation and gas porosity. These defects are closely related to distributions of temperature, pressure, and solid/liquid transformation in the mushy zone.

(d) The morphology of the solidification microstructure controls the microstructure of solid such as grain parameters and, in turn, controls the thermomechanical behaviors, such as the fracture toughness, hot-tearing temperature, etc. (Lin, Sekhar, 1993[a], 1993[b]).

These examples are significant because it means that by controlling the temperature gradient and the change rate of cooling, etc., the defects, dendrite spacing, grain size and, in turn, mechanical properties may be controlled. However, current work in this field is mainly limited to qualitative descriptions of the relationship between the local processing parameters and the solidification microstructures. Consequently, no comprehensive investigation for the interrelationship between local processing parameters, microstructures, and mechanical behaviors seems to exist at the present time.

The main concern of this work is to develop a methodology of numerical simulation for investigating the microscopical fields around fibers of metal matrix composites. It is hoped that based on the proposed methodology, the above complicated intertriangular relationship of processing parameters-microstructure-mechanical behavior can be effectively investigated. More specifically, a thermal analysis is performed to determine the transient temperature history during the solidification process and track the movement of mushy zone. Two micromechanical representative unit cells of MMC's with one single fiber and eight fibers, respectively, will be used to carry on analysis for the temperature field of melting aluminium matrix around the fiber. The analysis for the unit cell with one fiber is an axisymmetric problem and represent the MMC's with low fiber volume fraction. The unit cell with eight fibers is used to investigate the temperature distributions within trianglar and square interstices between compact fibers. This problem is a plane problem and represent the MMC's with high fiber volume fraction.

2.0 GOVERNING EQUATIONS OF HEAT TRANSFER IN LIQUID, SOLID AND MUSHY PHASES

The focus of the thermal analysis is to (1) determine the transient temperature history during the solidification process of a liquid metal and (2) track the movement of mushy zone. (3) distinguish the temperature distributions in square interstice from that in triangular interstice. The specific problem under consideration is one in which liquid aluminum is initially at a uniform temperature which is equal to the melting temperature T_m. The initial fiber temperature is assumed as the preheat temperature of the preform. Instead of sharp transition from the hot liquid of pure metal to the solid region, a multiphase approach is used for the transition area. Now during solidification the aluminum can exist in three phases, solid phase, liquid phase, and transition phase (mushy zone). The mushy zone correspond to elements that are not completely solid or liquid, but exist in a state between the two. It is through the mushy zone that the energy jump, latent heat of fusion, between the liquid and solid phases are accounted for, thus controlling the movement of the freezing interface.

The enthalpy H of these three phases can be described mathematically by their temperatures T, latent heat L, the liquid fraction f_l, the solid heat capacity C_{ps}, and liquid heat capacity C_{pl} as follows (Basu, Sekhar, 1989).

Solid phase:

In this region, the substrate temperature is below the solidus line, i.e., $T<T_E$. The relation between temperature and enthalpy can be expressed through the heat capacity coefficient C_{ps} of solid as

$$H = C_{ps}T \tag{1a}$$

Liquid phase:

In this region, the substrate temperature is above the liquids line, i. e., $T > T_l$. The enthapy-temperature relationship can be expressed through the heat capacity coefficient C_{pl} of liquid as

$$H = C_{pl}T \tag{1b}$$

Mushy zone:

In this region, liquid and solid phase coexist. The expression of enthalpy is

$$H = C_{ps}T+f_l*L \tag{1c}$$

where f_l is the fraction of liquid in the mush zone which can be expressed through te temperature T_s of solidus line as follows

$$f_l = (T_s-T)/(T_s-T_l) \tag{1d}$$

The energy equations in cylindrical coordinate and Cartesian coordinate systems are, respectively, as follows

$$\varrho\frac{\partial H}{\partial t} = \frac{1}{r}\frac{\partial}{\partial r}(kr\frac{\partial T}{\partial r}) + \frac{\partial}{\partial z}(k\frac{\partial T}{\partial z}) \tag{2a}$$

$$\varrho\frac{\partial H}{\partial t} = \frac{\partial}{\partial x}(k\frac{\partial T}{\partial x}) + \frac{\partial}{\partial z}(K\frac{\partial T}{\partial z}) \tag{2b}$$

Since in the mushy zone the liquid fraction f_l is a function of temperature, by using eqn.(1d) the derivative of enthalpy with respect to time t can be expressed as:

$$\frac{\partial H}{\partial t} = C_p^{mushy}\frac{\partial T}{\partial t} \tag{3a}$$

with

$$C_p^{mushy} = (C_{ps} - \frac{L}{T_E-T_L}) \tag{3b}$$

Substituting eqs. (1a, 1b, 3a) into the left hand of eq. (2a,2b), the governing equations for heat transfer can be obtained. Taking cylindrical coordinate system as an example, the governing equations for the three phases have the following unified form

$$\varrho C_p\frac{\partial T}{\partial t} = \frac{1}{r}\frac{\partial}{\partial r}(Kr\frac{\partial T}{\partial r}) + \frac{\partial}{\partial z}(k\frac{\partial T}{\partial z}) \tag{4}$$

where C_p should take C_{ps}, C_{pl}, and C_p^{mushy} for solid, liquid and mushy zone, respectively.

3.0 FINITE ELEMENT FORMULATION

Performing a Galerkin weak type of formulation on the energy equation (2) yields:

$$C_{ij}*\frac{dT_j}{dt} + K_{ij}*T_j = F_i \; . \tag{5}$$

where C_{ij} is the components of the heat capacity matrix C, K_{ij} is the components of the thermal stiffness matrix K, F_i is the components of the thermal load vector F, T_i is the components of the nodal temperature vector T.

Since no heat convection was considered at the boundary of the unit cells, the K matrix does not include the effects of convection boundary conditions. For three node triangular elements which is used in the present analysis, Matrix K and Matrix C can be expressed as:

$$K = \sum_e \begin{vmatrix} C_1(A_1^2+B_1^2)-C_2*A_1 & C_1(A_1*A_2+B_1*B_2)-C_2*A_2 & C_1(A_1*A_3+B_1*B_3)-C_2*A_3 \\ C_1(A_1*A_2+B_1*B_2)-A_1*C_2 & C_1(A_2^2+B_2^2-C_2*A_2)-C_2*A_2 & C_1(A_2*A_3+B_2*B_3)-A_3*C_2) \\ C_1(A_1*A_3+B_1*B_3)-A_1*C_2 & C_1(A_2*A_2+B_2*B_3)-A_2*C_2 & C_1(A_3^2+B_3^2)-A_3*C_2 \end{vmatrix}$$

$$C = \sum_e \begin{vmatrix} 2*C_3 & C_3 & C_3 \\ C_3 & 2*C_3 & C_3 \\ C_3 & C_3 & 2*C_3 \end{vmatrix} \qquad (6a,b)$$

wheree Σ covers all finite elements in the unit cell and subscript "e" denotes the related quantities belong to generic element e, (A_1, A_2, A_3) relate to element geometry, (C_1, C_2) are functions of heat conductivity coefficient K_e, C_3 is proportional to element value of specific heat. Their explicit expressions are listed as follows:

$$\begin{aligned} A_1 &= Z_{node2} - Z_{node3} \quad & B_1 &= X_{node3} - X_{node2} \\ A_2 &= Z_{node3} - Z_{node1} \quad & B_2 &= X_{node1} - X_{node3} \\ A_3 &= Z_{node1} - Z_{node2} \quad & B_3 &= X_{node2} - X_{node1} \\ C_1 &= K_e*r_{bar}/(4*AREA_e) \\ C_2 &= K_e/6 \\ C_3 &= Cp_e*\varrho_e*AREA_e*r_{bar}/12 \end{aligned} \qquad (7)$$

For the problem at hand the only specified heat flux boundary conditions have values of zero and since there is no convection of heat sources the thermal load vector F is zero.

If the nodal temperature vector at time t_n is T^n (Remark: $t_n=t_{n-1}+\Delta t$ with Δt being a time increment step), the integration scheme employed for the governing equation (4) is as follows:

$$(\underset{\sim}{C}/\Delta t+\gamma\underset{\sim}{K})\underset{\sim}{T}^n = \underset{\sim}{F}_{n-1} + (\underset{\sim}{C}/\Delta t - (1-\gamma)\underset{\sim}{K})\underset{\sim}{T}^{n-1} \qquad (8)$$

where γ is introduced for increase the stability of the numerical analysis. In the present analysis, $\gamma = 0.85$ is found to give good results.

The outer surface boundary condition at $r= r_{max}$ of the unit cells is modeled using the following relationship

$$T_0(t) = T_a + (T_m - T_a)\exp(-Qt) \qquad (9)$$

where T_m - melting temperature of metal matrix (^{0}K), T_a - final steady state temperature (^{0}K),

Q - cooling rate parameter (sec^{-1}), t - time (sec).

4.0 THERMAL ANALYSIS FOR TWO KINDS OF REPRESENTATIVE UNIT CELLS

Based on the above mentioned governing equations and the finite element formulation, temperature distribution and mushy zone evolution in two kinds of representative unit cells of metal matrix composites have been investigated in this work. The parameters and material constants used in the present analysis are (Basu, Sekhar, 1989):

For Aluminum matrix:

T_s=821 ^{0}K $\quad$ T_l=921 ^{0}K $\quad$ T_m=933 ^{0}K

C_{pl}=882 J/kg^{0}K $\quad$ C_{ps}=924 J/kg^{0}K $\quad$ L= 3.95*10^5 J/kg

ρ =2700kg/m^3 $\quad$ T_a=773 ^{0}K $\quad$ K_l=100.8 W/m ^{0}K

K_s=180.6 W/m ^{0}K

For graphite fiber:

C_{ps}=931 J/kg ^{0}K $\quad$ K_s=143 W/m ^{0}K $\quad$ ρ=1560 kg/m^3

Application to an Axisymmetric Microscopical Unit Cell

The microscopical unit cell shown in Figure 1 consists of one graphite fiber surrounding by melting aluminum. This unit cell is designed for investigating the mushy zone evolution around a fiber under different conditions, such as different initial temperature T_0^{fiber} of preform, different cooling boundary conditions. The unit cell has the dimensions: height h= 2 mm, diameter D=0.6 mm with fiber diameter D_f=0.16 mm. The top and bottom of the unit cell are insulated. The temperature at outer boundary (r=0.3mm) is controlled by eq.(5). Finite element mesh was designed with 144 elements and 313 nodes. A dimensionless time scale parameter Λ_t is introduced as

$$\Lambda_t = tv_0/D_{fiber}$$

where v_0 is a reference velocity. To get accurate results the increment time step $\Delta\Lambda_t$ should take small value. Typically several hundred time steps are needed to complete the solidification process.

Fig. 2 shows the mushy zone evolution for initial fiber temperature T_0=500^{0}k and cooling rate parameter Q=0.1/sec. At Λ_t =0.125, two mushy zones initiate from the interface between liquid and fiber as well as near the cooling boundary (r=0.3mm)(see Fig. 2a). When time Λ_t increases to 0.531 the size of mushy zone increases and a narrow solid region formulated near the outer surface of the unit cell (see Fig. 2b). When the time parameter increases further to 2.87 and 4.93, the two mushy zones joint together and the solid zone expands towards inside. However, there is no solid zone which initiates from the interface between fiber and the mushy zone (see Fig. 2c and Fig. 2d).

Application to a Plane Microscopic Unit Cell

The microscopical unit cell shown in Figure 3a consists of eight fibers. There are infiltrated melted aluminium filling in the triangular C and square interstices B between the fibers (see Fig. 3a). This microscopical unit cell corresponds to metal matrix composites with high fiber volume fraction. This compact arrangement will give profound different characteristics of solidification from that of the above unit cell. Experimental results (Mortensen, et al., 1988) have shown that the morphology of the solidification microstructures in the triangular interstice is completely deferent from that in the square interstice. Mortensen, et al. (1982) reported: from a sample solidified at steady state with gradient G=9100 ^{0}K/m and growth rate R=203 μm/s, a controlled dendrite arm is shown in the square interstice for a compact fiber arrangement. However, the dendritic nature of the matrix is erased in the triangular interstice. This interesting result may relate to the characteristics of the temperature distributions in the two kinds of interstices. Therefore, the purpose for designing this unit cell is to see whether the temperature distributions and mushy zone evolutions in these two regions are different. Due to symmetry, only 1/8 of the region is considered see Fig. 3a,b).

Fig. 3c shows the finite element mesh in the 45^0 region which includes two half fibers and interstice B, C and A. The mushy zone evolution and temperature distribution in the square interstice B are shown from Fig. 4a to 4d. When time parameter equals to 0.0142, there are three phases. When time parameter approaches to 0.107, the whole interstice B become solid. Fig. 5a, 5b show the mushy zone evolution and temperature distribution in the triangular interstice C. We can see from these figures as well as Fig. 3d the solidification in the triangular interstice is more fast than that in the square interstice. Furthermore, the solidification in triangular interstice will start from the interstice between the fiber and the matrix, which is quite different from the one with low fiber volume fraction.

REFERENCE

Basu, B., Sekhar, J. A., 1989, "Modeling of Multidimensional Solidification of An Alloy," *Metallugical Transactions A*, 20A, pp. 1833-1845.

Fabietti, L. M. and Sekhar, J. A., 1991, "Mushy Zone Morphologies Observed During Growth of Composite Materials," *Nature and Properties of Semi-Solid Materials*, Sekar, J. A., and Dantzig, J., eds., The Minerals, Metals & Materials Society, pp. 41-67.

Lin, C. S., Sekhar, J. A., 1993, "Semi-Solid Deformation in Multi-Component Nickel Aluminide, Part 1: Equiaxed Alloys," *Journal of Material Science*, 28, pp. 3581-3588.

Lin, C. S., and Sekhar, J. A., 1993, "Semi-Solid Deformation in Multi-Component Nickel Aluminide," *Journal of Material Science*, 28, pp. 3885-3894.

Misra, M. S., Fishman, S. G., 1991, "Metal Matrix Composites-Recent Advances," *Proc. 8th Int. Conf. Comp. Mater.* Tsai, S. W. and Springer, G. S., eds.,SAMPE 18, A1-A12.

Mortensen, A., Cornie, J. A., and Flemings,1988, "Columnar Dendritic Solidification in a Metal-Matrix Composite," *Metallugical Transactions A*, pp. 709-721.

Mortensen, A., Masur, L. J., Cornie, J. A., and Flemings, M. C., 1989, "Infiltration of Fibrous Preforms by a Pure Metal: Part 1, Theory, Part 2: Experiment", *Metallurgical Transaction A*, 20A, pp. 2535-2557.

Mortensen, A., 1990, "Solidification of Reinforced Metals," *Solidification of Metal Matrix Composites*, Rohatgi, P., eds., TMS, pp. 1-21.

[9] Sekhar, J. A., Lin, C. S. and Cheng, C. J., 1991, "Castability Maps: How to design the processing of a Multi-Component Alloy from a Knowledge of the Semi-Solid Mophology and Properties," *Nature and Properties of Semi-Solid Materials*,Sekhar, J. A. and Dentzig, J., eds., the Minerals, Metals, & Materials Society, pp. 267-290.

Trivedi, R., Han, S. and Sekhar, J. A., 1990, "Microstructural Development in Interfiber Regions of Directionally Solidified Composites,"*Solidification of Metal Matrix Composites*, Rohatgi, P., eds., TMS, pp. 23-38

Fig. 1 Finite Element Model For Axisymmetric Unit Cell

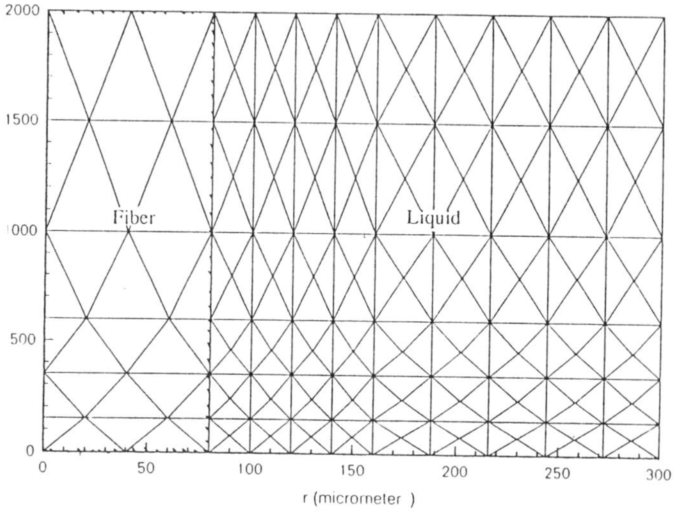

Fig. 2a Temperature Distribution (time parameter = .125)
Q=.1 & Initial Fiber Temp. of 500 Degrees K

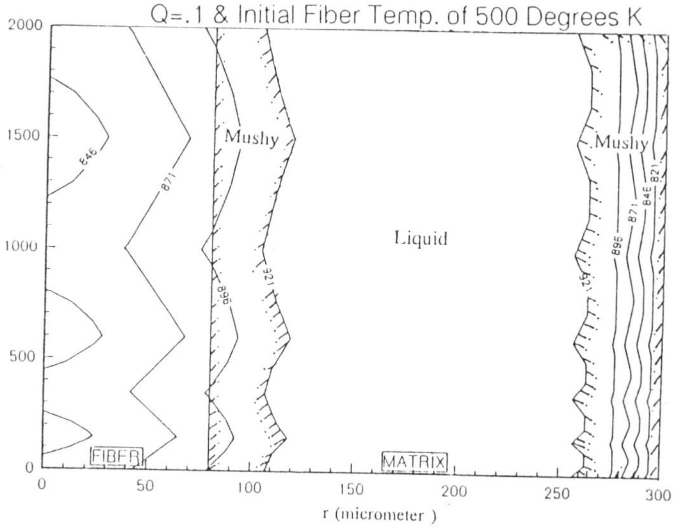

Fig. 2b Temperature Distribution (time parameter = .531)
Q=.1 & Initial Fiber Temp. of 500 Degrees K

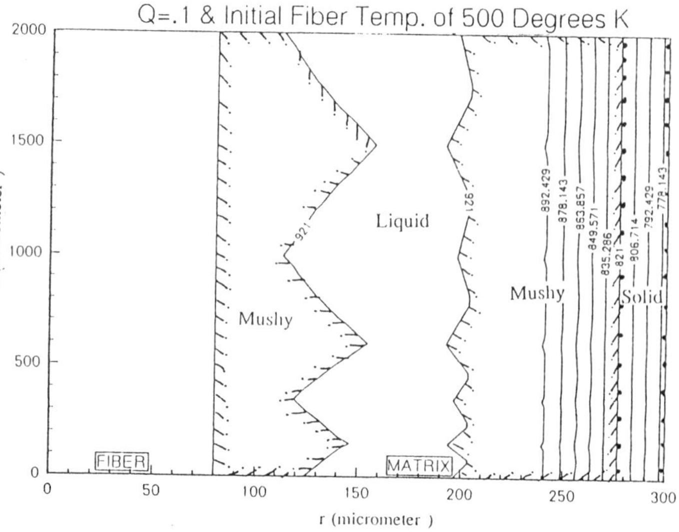

Fig. 2c Temperature Distribution (time parameter = 2.87)

Q=.1 & Initial Fiber Temp. of 500 Degrees K

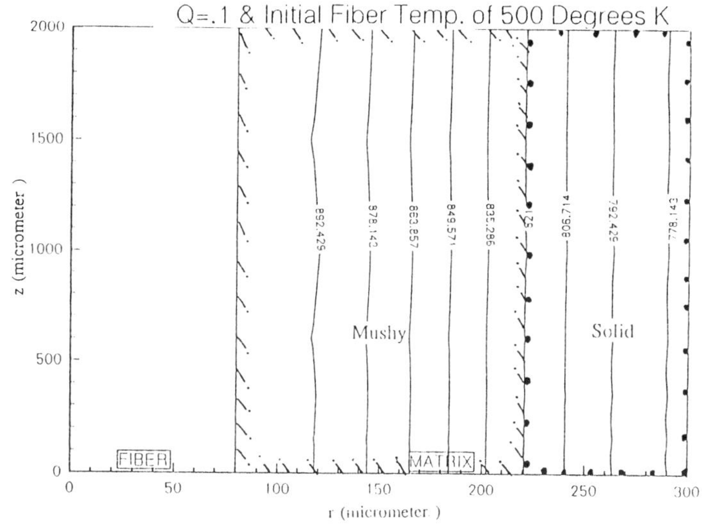

Fig. 3c Finite Element Model For Plane Unit Cell

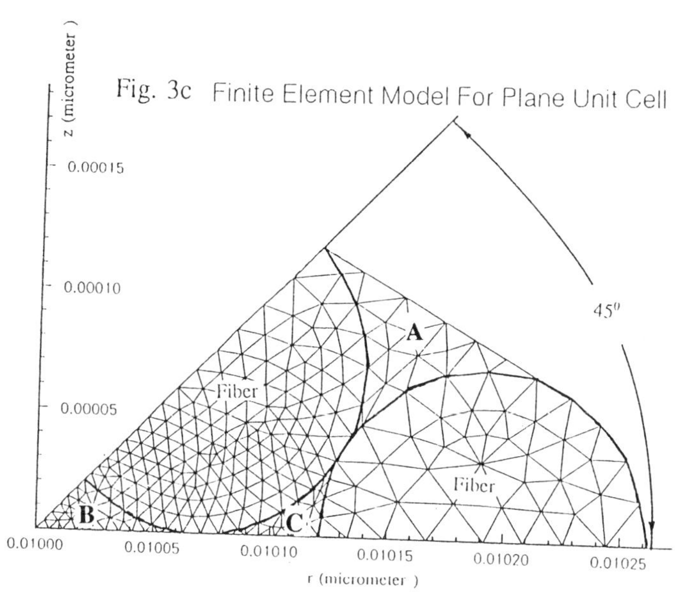

Fig. 2d Temperature Distribution (time parameter = 4.93)

Q=.1 & Initial Fiber Temp. of 500 Degrees K

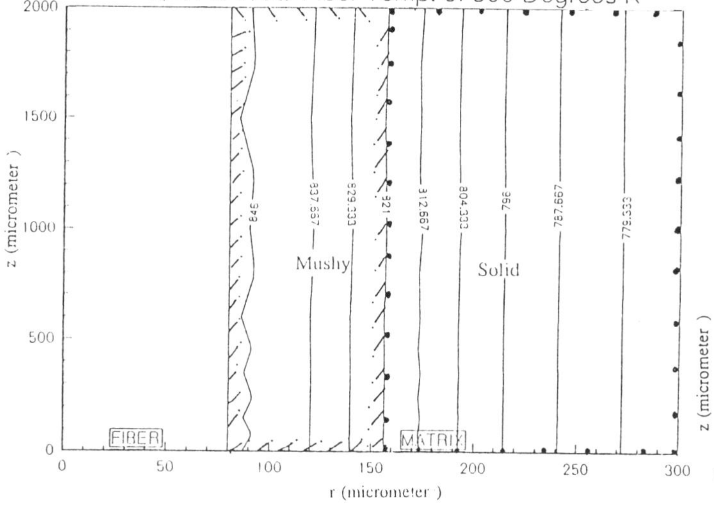

Fig. 3d Temperature Distribution in Interstices B and C

Temperature Distribution

Time Parameter = .0142

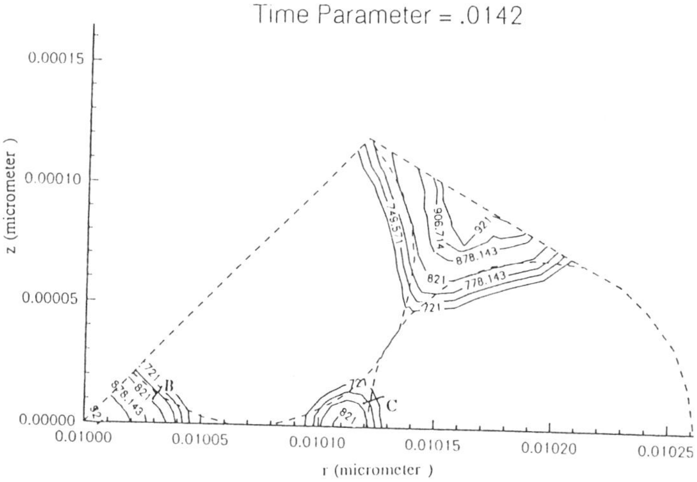

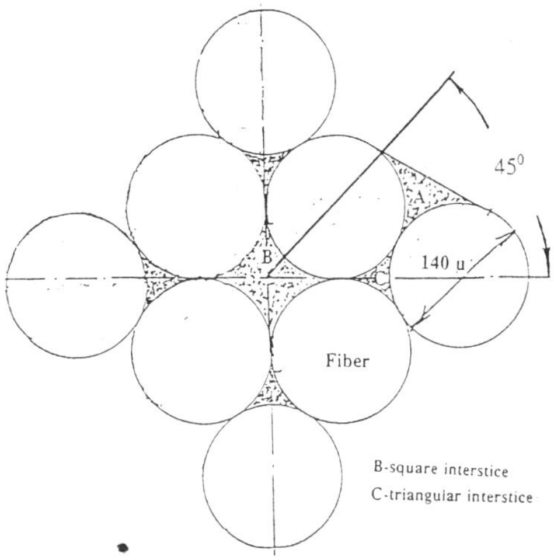

Fig. 3a Plane Unit Cell with 8 Fibers

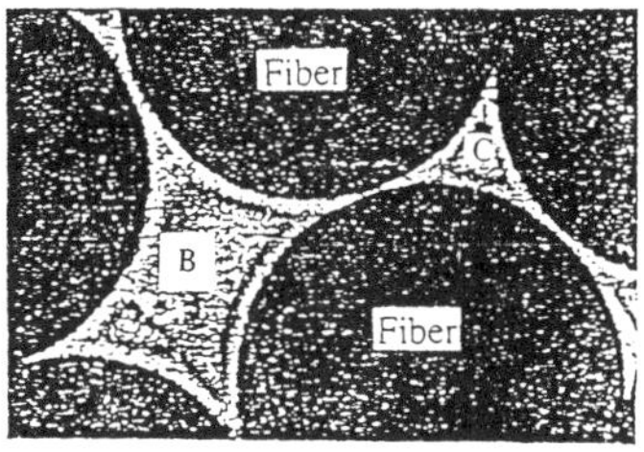

Fig. 3b Microstructures
(Reffered from Mortenson, 1990)

Fig. 4a Temperature Distribution in Square Interstice B

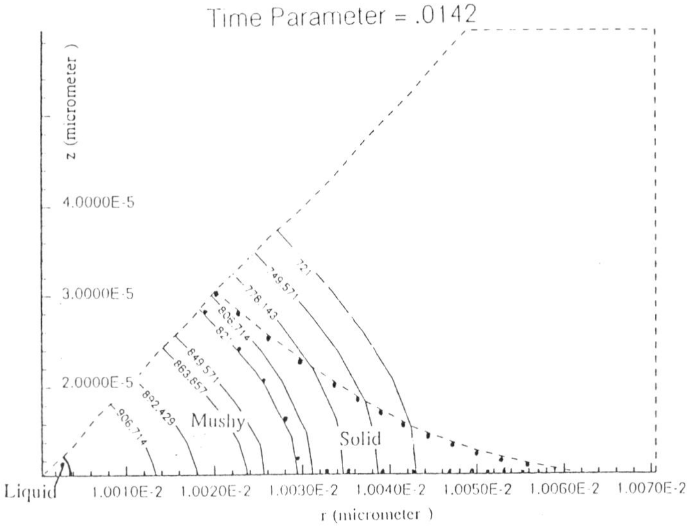

Fig. 4b Temperature Distribution in Square Interstice B

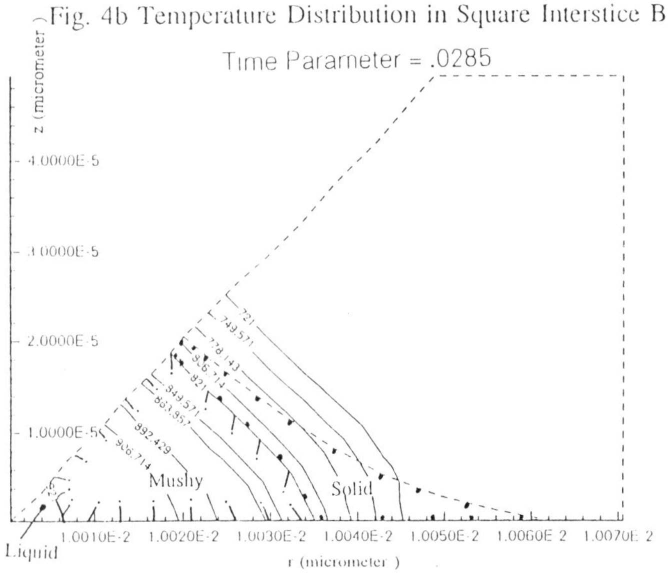

Fig. 4c Temperature Distribution in Square Interstice B

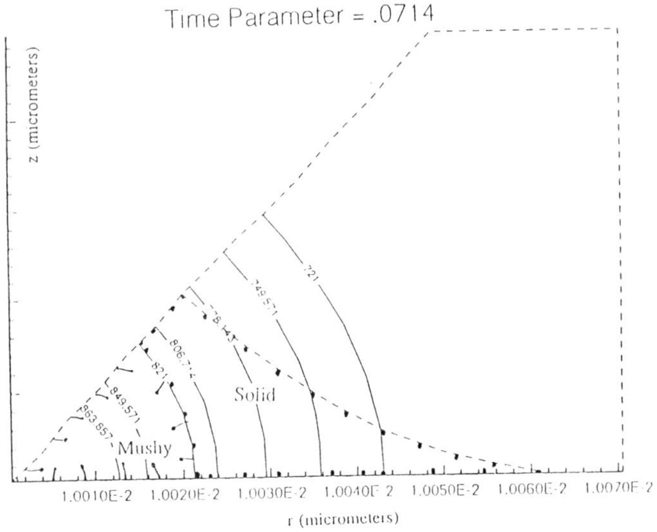

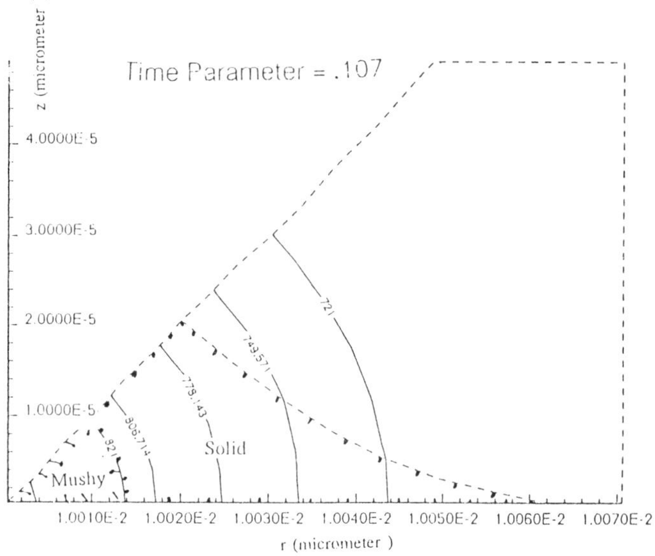

Fig. 4d Temperature Destribution in Square Interstice B
Temperature Distribution in Region B

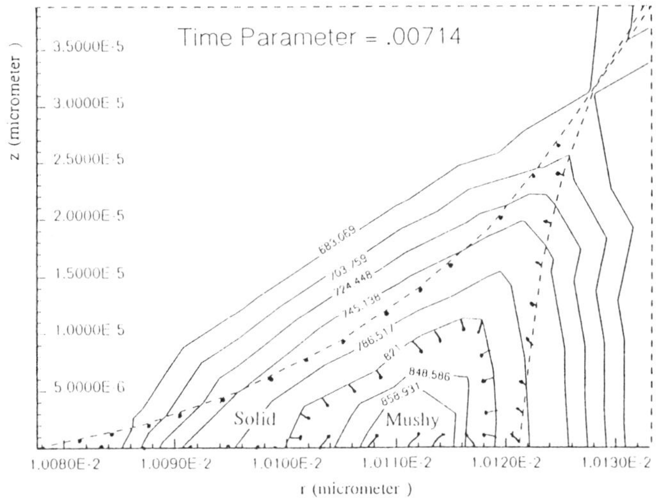

Fig. 5a Temperature Distribution in Triangular Interstice C

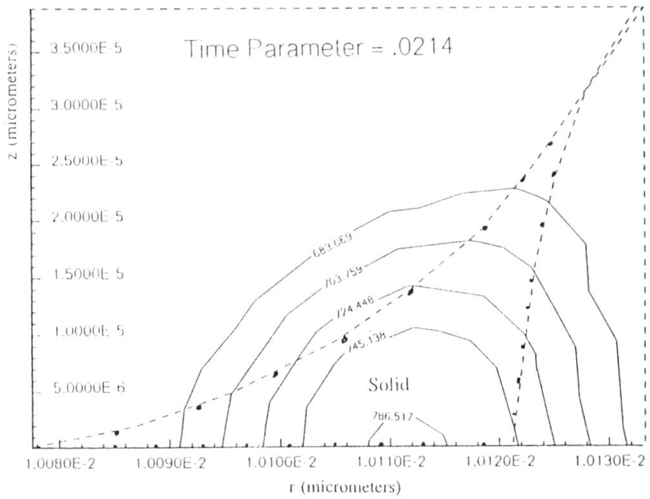

Fig. 5b Temperature Distribution in Triangular Interstice C

HTD-Vol. 284/AMD-Vol. 182, Transport Phenomena in Solidification
ASME 1994

SUSPENSION OF CERAMIC PARTICLES IN LIQUID METALS FOR SYNTHESIS OF COMPOSITES

P. K. Rohatgi, C. S. Narendranath, and M. A. Khan
Dept. of Materials
College of Eng. and Applied Science
University of Wisconsin
Milwaukee, Wisconsin

R. Asthana
NASA Lewis Research Ctr.
Cleveland, Ohio

M. S. Sohal
Idaho National Engineering Laboratory
EG&G Idaho, Incorporated
Idaho Falls, Idaho

ABSTRACT

Dispersion of ceramic particles in metallic melts using mixing impellers is a widely used technique to fabricate metal matrix composites. Uniformity in spatial distribution of particles in the liquid and the rate at which the particles settle down or float up will strongly influence the final cast structure and mechanical properties of the composites.

This paper discusses some aspects of the creation of a homogeneous liquid-particle mixture, by considering various parameters of stirrers and mixing conditions. A cold model of 'vortex' technique for dispersing particles has been used to examine the influence of impeller blade angle and dimension of baffles on the homogeneity of particles in the melt.

The model was constructed using SiC and water, to examine the influence of impeller blade angle and impeller speed on the homogeneity of particle mixing in melts. The volume fraction of SiC in stirred mixtures was determined as a function of radial and axial positions in the mixing vessel, from weight fractions of mixture pipetted out. It was observed that once a homogeneous mixture was obtained, the effects of changes in impeller speed and blade angles on the mixing quality were insignificant. Radial impellers consumed the least power for achieving homogeneous suspensions, but gave relatively high variations in concentrations at higher speeds, whereas the impellers with varying pitch blades consumed the highest power to achieve a homogenous suspension.

INTRODUCTION

Dispersion of ceramic particles in metallic melts using mixing impellers is a widely used technique to fabricate cast metal matrix composites (MMC)[1]. The process essentially consists of introducing reinforcing particles into the melts while the metal is stirred. Since it is a mechanical mixture of liquid metal and the reinforcing particles, the distribution of particles in the liquid metal and subsequently, in the solidified metal profoundly depend on the relative dimensions of stirrer and crucible, stirring speed, the settling or floatation behavior and particle pushing during solidification. If the reinforcement is not homogeneously distributed in the liquid while stirring, the volume fractions of reinforcements will vary from point to point in the melt, as well as in the solidified metal. Clusters in the melt while mixing will amplify the settling behavior. The denuded or reinforcement free zones caused by settling largely depend on the volume fraction and the initial distribution of particles. Studies on settling of silicon carbide particles in liquid aluminum produced by a stirring technique indicates that size of the denuded zones, due to settling, increases with increase in time. This is illustrated in Figure 1. However, the rate of formation of denuded zones is expected to be minimized by improving the quality of suspension. In addition, during stirring, the fine particles may flocculate resulting in clusters of particles which settle or float at much faster rates. Since it is always a less than perfect distribution of particles in the liquid state, the solidified metal exhibits a structure in which particles are not uniformly distributed. A typical microstructure of aluminum − 10 vol. % silicon carbide metal matrix composites is shown in Figure 2. It is apparent from the figure that particles are not uniformly distributed throughout the matrix. Coagulation of particles is observed, as well as particles being pushed to the boundary by growing dendrites.

At high temperatures, there is an additional problem of gas pick-up during vortex mixing which impairs the quality of the composite casting. It has been shown [3-5] that porosity content in melt-particle slurries depends on mixing parameters such as depth of immersion of the impeller in the melt, impeller speed, and the design of the impeller.

The dispersion synthesis of MMC's [Fig. 3(a)] typically involves three steps (1) particle introduction in the melt, (2) creation of a homogeneous mixture prior to casting, and deaggregation of flocculated particles, and (3) solidification of suspension. The first step is controlled by surface thermodynamics, the second by fluid dynamic effects and the third step, primarily, by the solidification factors and the interactions of particles with solidifying interfaces. In addition, other factors such as the dimensions of the crucibles, types of stirrers, blade angle, relative dimensions of the crucibles and blades and the rpm of the stirrers significantly influence the quality of suspension. It is extremely difficult to study the quality of suspension in actual systems because of the operating temperature and by virtue of their opacity. However, it is possible to understand the influence of stirrer dimensions with respect to crucibles and rpm and influence of fluid dynamics on the quality of suspensions through modeling using transparent liquids.

Considerable work has been done earlier in the field of chemical engineering [6] on various aspects of solid-liquid mixing in agitated slurries. Some of these basic principles have been applied to metal-ceramic composite slurries [3-8]. Several studies have been made on solid-liquid mixing in non-metallic systems. Zwietering [9] has used a model consisting of fine sand and sodium chloride particles as dispersoids, suspended in water, acetone, CCl_4, and oil. He has used paddle type, turbine, vaned disc and propeller types of stirrers to stirr the particles. Several investigators have studied the influence of various mixing parameters, such as the nature of stirrers, their critical dimension on uniformity of distribution of particles in a liquid medium [11-23]. The results indicate that the relative dimensions between crucibles, and stirrers, number of baffels, blade angles, and rpms are critical parameters which profoundly influence the quality of suspension.

The in-situ observations on dynamics of particle motion in stirred molten metals are not possible. Further, the optimum mixing conditions can not be reliably obtained from a knowledge of the final particle distribution in cast composites. Transparent models of the real system, which satisfy certain geometrical and fluid dynamic similarity criteria in the model and prototype systems, can be used to obtain practical guidelines for homogeneous mixing. Table 1 summarizes typical properties as well as experimental stirring conditions for SiC-Al and SiC-water systems. It can be observed from this table that except for the large differences in the wetting parameters (contact angle and surface tension), process temperatures and surface chemistry of stirred liquids in the two systems, the geometric and fluid dynamic parameters (Reynolds and Froude numbers) match fairly well in the real and the model systems under the experimental conditions used in the present study.

In this paper the influence of some of the experimental parameters, such as blade angle, rpm on particle distribution and power consumed, in a water-SiC system are studied and results are presented.

EXPERIMENTAL PROCEDURE

A plexiglass cylindrical tank, 12.7 cm in diameter, having an elliptical base (i.e., not a flat base) was used in combination with four rectangular baffles each 1.75 cm in width. Impellers (dia 8.9 cm) with different blade angles (±30, ±45, ±60 and 90 degrees) were used. A negative blade angle indicates that the impeller pumps downward while a positive blade angle corresponds to an upward pumping impeller. The width and thickness of the blades were constant for all blade angles. An axial flow impeller with a constant blade angle and varying pitch, known as an A-3 impeller, was also used. The tank and impeller geometry are shown schematically in Fig. 3(b). A variable speed motor controlled the rpm which was measured with the help of a stroboscope. Approximately one liter of tap water and 25 vol% SiC particles (avg size: 20 μm) were used as mixing phases. The depth of the water-SiC mixture in the tank was 11.7 cm, and the impeller height from the bottom of the tank was 2.54 cm. The samples were drawn from the stirred mixture with the help of a pipette fitted with a pipette pump for smooth and stable suction. The pipetted mixture was first weighed (to three decimal places of a gram) and then dried in an oven at 55 C and reweighed to determine the amount of dry SiC left. The samples were drawn from the stirred mixture at different depths of the tank: at the free surface of the liquid (only if the liquid surface was not very disturbed by the overturning liquid eddies), at the bottom of the tank, and two other depths intermediate between the free liquid surface and the bottom of the free liquid surface and the bottom of the tank. At each depth, three different positions in the radial directions were used to draw samples, i.e., one adjacent to the impeller shaft, midway in the radial direction and one near the wall of the tank. At least two to three readings were taken at each location.

TABLE 1. COMPARISON BETWEEN AL-SIC AND WATER-SIC SYSTEMS

Property	Al-SiC System	Water-SiC System
Surface Tension	~ 900 dynes/cm	~ 72 dynes/cm
Liquid Density	~ 2.8 g cc^{-1}	~ 1.0 g cc^{-1}
Contact Angle	157° (at 900 °C)	$\theta < 90°$
Liquid Viscosity	~ 0.014 Poise	~0.0089 Poise
Particle Density	3.2 g cc^{-1}	3.2 g cc-1
Temperature	700° C	30°C
Liquid Surface	Oxide Film Present	No Oxide Film
Effective Viscosity (25 vol.% SiC)	0.0319 Poise	0.0203 Poise
Tank Diameter/ Impeller Diameter	---	1.107
Reynolds Number	4.52 x 10^4	~ 4 x 10^4
Froude Number	~ 4.01	~ 1 to 1.5

RESULTS AND DISCUSSION

Experiments were performed for a fixed blade angle impeller at various stirring speeds. Table 2 gives a summary of experimental results. Figures 4 through 7 present typical experimental data in terms of particle volume fraction versus dimensionless depth of the mixture. It was observed that in the case of -45 degree impeller, the minimum speed required for a homogeneous suspension was found to be 181 rpm. Experiments carried out at a higher impeller speeds showed [Fig. 4] that concentration variation was practically negligible at higher impeller rpm. Some depletion of SiC was observed right above the impeller, possibly because higher angular velocities existed in this region which transported the particles toward the wall (the particle density is about 3.2 times higher than that of the liquid). This results in the crowding of particles on the walls next to the impeller. This was true for all the experiments with negative blade impellers and impellers running at higher rpm. However, the variation in SiC concentration resulting from this phenomenon is negligible (less than 0.4%) for practical purposes. The uniform particle distribution at any higher rpm and blade angles can be attributed to the use of baffles which essentially annihilates the vortex. The formation of a vortex imparts variation in magnitude of forces to different species in the mixture. The depletion of particles above the impeller and crowding next to the impeller on the wall can be minimized by attaching small fins to the tips of the impeller blades.

A -30° impeller gave a homogeneous suspension at 230 rpm, whereas a -60° impeller gave a homogeneous suspensions 315 rpm. Very high chaotic eddies were observed at the liquid surface at higher rpm and especially when the blade angle is increased from -30° to 90°. The latter causes very high angular flow which results in vary large eddies climbing the baffles and overturning at the liquid surface. These unwanted eddies tend to increase the possibility of gas pick up which is a serious problem with the actual melt processing of composites. Such eddies can be minimized by placing baffles at an angle to the tank wall.

Positive blade angle impellers [Fig. 6 and 7] gave as uniform SiC distribution as negative blade angle impellers. The impeller rpm for homogeneous suspensions produced by +30°, +45° and +60° were 415, 340, and 280, respectively. However, the impeller rpm required for homogeneous suspensions were much higher than for the negative blade angle impellers, which could be due to a major vortex forming at the top of the impeller. This produces good liquid circulatory motion above the impeller but less beneath the impeller where most of the particle are settled. All positive blade angle impellers showed good mixing at high rpm. A slight increase in the SiC concentration next to the impeller on the wall does not occur with these impellers, as was the case with negative blade angle impellers. Instead, slight particle crowding was noticed roughly 12 mm above the impeller on the wall at high speeds, which was also observed with negative blade angle impellers.

The radial flow impellers and (90° blade angle) did not perform as well as the impellers discussed above. At higher rpm, the particles were concentrated mostly at the walls and bottom of the tank. However, these impellers give homogeneous suspension at a relatively low rpm of 140, respectively. The impellers [Fig. 7] which had a constant angle and varying pitch type blades gave suspension at 372. Their performance was substantially similar to that of the negative blade angle impellers examined in the present study.

Table 2 lists the Power number (Po), Reynold's number (Re), and Froude number (Fr) for each experiment. These numbers were computed using the following relationships,

$$\text{Reynold's Number (Re)} = \rho NDL/\mu$$

$$\text{Froude Number (Fr)} = N^2D^2/gL$$

$$\text{Power Number (Po)} = P/\rho N^3D^5$$

where N is the rpm, ρ is the density, D is the diameter of the vessel, g is the acceleration due to gravity, μ is the viscosity, P is power input (in watts), and L is a characteristic dimension of the system. For computation of the above dimensionless parameters, the density of the suspension was obtained by rule of mixture, and the viscosity of suspension was obtained from Mooney's correlation [22] valid for solid fractions on the order of 0.5, and given as follows:

$$\log\left(\frac{\mu_m}{\mu_L}\right) = 2.5\ \phi_s/(1-c\,\phi_s)$$

where μ_m and μ_L are the viscosities of mixture and liquid, and ϕ_s is the volume fraction of the particles. The coefficient c usually evaluated from experimental data lies in the range 1.35 to 1.91. Table 2 shows Power consumed for different blade angle and rpms. For homogeneous suspension, the radial flow impellers consume the least power of all the impellers tested in this study. Among the negative blade impellers, -45°, and among the positive blade angle impellers, +60°, consumed the least power for homogeneous suspension. The impellers with varying pitch blade consume the most power for the same purpose. Turbulent flow roughly occurs at Re > 4 x 10^4. Below this Re, the flow could be treated as laminar. In the present situation, the flow may be laminar or turbulent.

CONCLUSIONS

The present study has shown quantitatively that solid-liquid mixtures remain practically homogeneous at impeller speeds higher than the speed at which homogeneity is achieved, irrespective of impeller geometry. The small (0.2% in 25 vol%) variations in SiC concentrations around the impellers can be avoided by placing the impeller in a draft tube or by attaching fins to the blades of the impeller. The radial flow impellers consume the least power for achieving a homogeneous suspension. The axial impellers consume the most power among the impellers tested for creating a complete and uniform suspension. It is also observed that turbulent flow conditions are reached during impeller mixing at Reynold's numbers in excess of 4 x 10^4. The Power number remains approximately constant for a given impeller speed for any blade angle.

TABLE 2. RPM: POWER CONSUMPTION AND DIMENSIONLESS PARAMETERS FOR PARTICLE MOTION

θ	N RPM	P W	Po	Re x 10^4	Fr
-30°	200	22.75	71.69	2.03	0.076
	230	28.35	58.74	2.34	0.101
	565	91.8	12.83	5.74	0.608
+30°	378	25.55	11.93	3.84	0.272
	415	30.0	10.58	4.21	0.328
	655	68.2	6.12	6.65	0.817
-45°	124	21.2	280.31	1.26	0.029
	181	32.016	136.11	1.84	0.062
	200	34.675	109.27	2.03	0.076
	612	75.0	8.25	6.21	0.714
	1210	175.33	2.50	1.23	2.789
+45°	315	26.0	20.97	3.2	0.189
	340	30.1	19.31	3.45	0.220
	560	58.8	8.44	5.69	0.597
-60°	285	24.4	26.57	2.89	0.155
	315	30.1	24.28	3.2	0.189
	595	78	9.34	6.04	0.674
+60°	225	18.75	41.50	2.28	0.096
	280	24.78	28.45	2.84	0.149
	595	74.75	8.95	6.04	0.674
90°	115	17.5	290.08	1.17	0.025
	140	23.2	213.15	1.42	0.037
	486	59.5	13.07	4.93	0.45
Blades with varying pitch	315	28.48	22.97	3.2	0.189
	372	33.95	16.62	3.78	0.264
	840	104.4	4.42	8.53	1.344

REFERENCES

1. P. K. Rohatgi, R. Asthana and S. Das, *Int. Metals Revs.*, 31(3), 1986, 115.
2. D. M. Schuster, M. D. Skibo and W. R. Hoover, *Light Metal Age*, Feb. 1989, 15.
3. J. Y. Oldshue, *Fluid Mixing Technologies*, McGraw-Hill Publ. Co., NY (1983).
4. G. S. Hanumanth and G. A. Irons, *J. Mater. Sci.*, 28 (1993) 2459.
5. P. K. Ghosh and S. Ray, *Trans. Jpn. Inst. Met.*, 29 (1988) 502.
6. P. K. Ghosh and S. Ray, *Trans. AFS*, 88 (1988) 775.
7. S. Mohan, V. Agarwall and S. Ray, *Z. Metallkde.*, 80 (1989) 612.
8. N. El-Kaddah and K. E. Chang, *Mater. Sci. Eng.*, A144 (1991) 221.
9. Th. N. Zwietering, *Chem. Eng. Sci.*, 8 (1958) 244.
10. A. W. Nienow, *Chem. Eng. Sci.*, 23 (1968) 1453.
11. J. Weisman and L. E. Efferding, *AIChE Journal*, 419.
12. G. E. H. Joosten, J. G. M. Schilder and A. M. Broere, *Trans. I.Ch.E.*
13. A. Q. Quraishi, R. A. Mashelkar, and J. J. Ulbrecht, *AIChE Journal*, 23 (1977) 487.
14. A. W. Nienow and D. Miles, *Chem Eng. J.*, 15 (1978) 13.
15. G. Baldi, R. Conti and E. Alaria, *Chem. Eng. Sci.*, 33 (1978) 21.
16. C. M. Chapman, A. W. Nienow, M. Cook and J. C. Middleton, *Chem. Eng. Res. Des.*, 61 (1983) 71.
17. P. A. Shamlou and M. F. Edwards, *Chem. Eng. Sci.*, 40 (1985) 1773.
18. W. Chudacek, *Chem Eng. Sci.*, 40 (1985) 385.
19. R. Kuboi and A. W. Nienow, *Chem. Eng. Sci.*, *41* (1986) 123.
20. T. P. K. Chang, A. T. Watson and G. B. Tatterson, *Chem. Eng. Sci.*, 40 (1985) 269.
21. T. P. K. Chang, A. T. Watson and G. B. Tatterson, *Chem. Eng. Sci.*, 40 (1985) 277.
22. J. Mooney, *J. Colloid Sci.*, 6 (1951) 162.

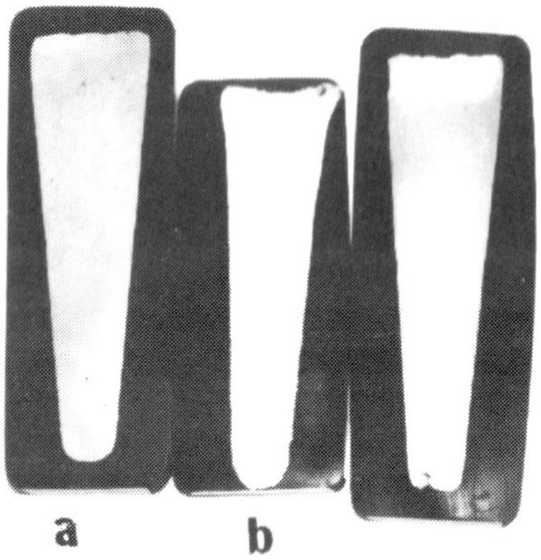

FIG. 1. DENUDED ZONES FORMED DUE TO SETTLING OF PARTICLES IN ALUMINUM-SILICON CARBIDE COMPOSITES AT DIFFERENT TIME INTERVALS.
(a) 10 MIN., (b) 45 MIN., (c) 60 MIN.

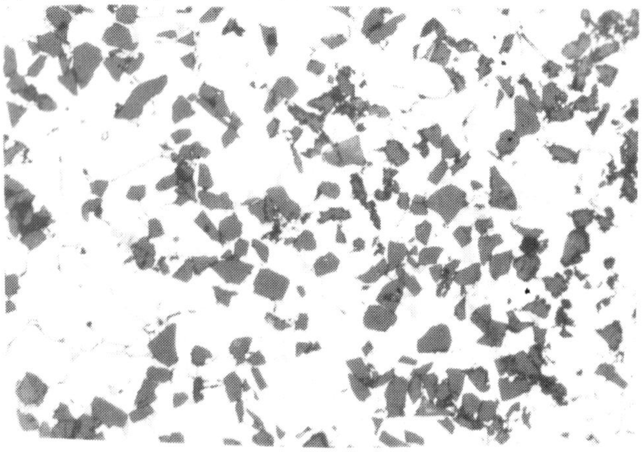

FIG. 2. A TYPICAL MICROSTRUCTURE OF ALUMINUM-SILICON CARBIDE COMPOSITES SHOWING NON-UNIFORM DISTRIBUTION OF PARTICLES.

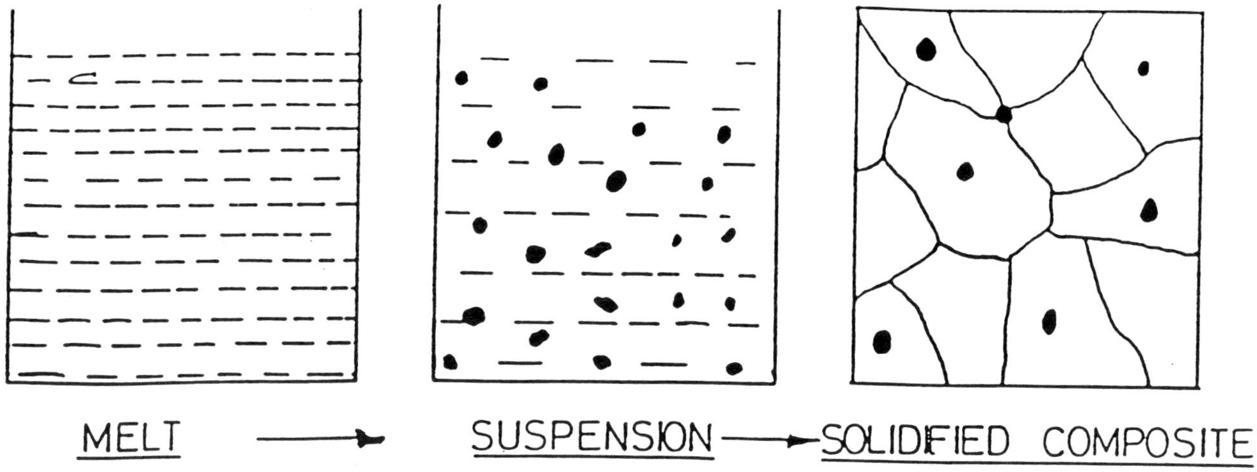

A

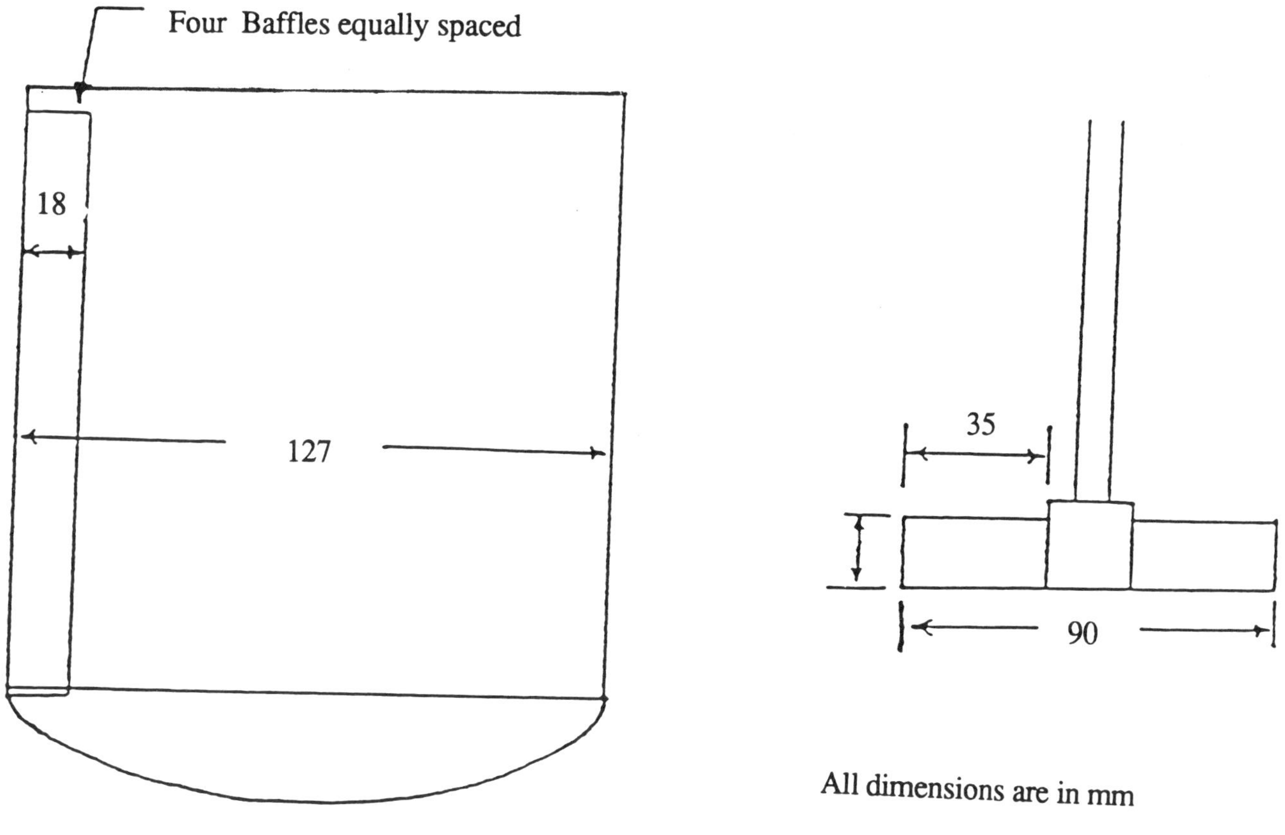

B

FIG. 3. (A) SCHEMATIC DIAGRAM SHOWING THE DISPERSION TECHNIQUE OF SYNTHESIZING CAST MMC'S USING THE VORTEX TECHNIQUE, AND (B) SCHEMATIC DIAGRAM OF TANK AND IMPELLER ARRANGEMENT USED IN THE PRESENT STUDY.

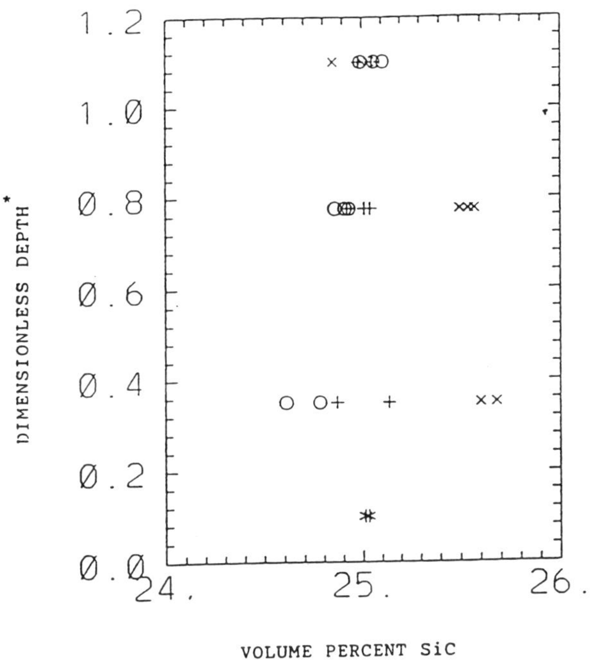

FIG. 4 VARIATION OF VOLUME FRACTION OF SIC (20 μm SIZE) WITH THE DIMENSIONLESS DEPTH OF MIXTURE IN A 25% SIC-WATER MIXTURE STIRRED AT 612 RPM WITH A -45° IMPELLER. THE SYMBOLS REPRESENT SAMPLES DRAWN FROM: [*]-BOTTOM, [X]-WALL, [O]-MID-RADIUS, AND [+]-SHAFT.

$$^{*}\text{Dimensionless Depth} = \frac{\text{Liquid Depth}}{\text{Diameter of the Tank}}$$

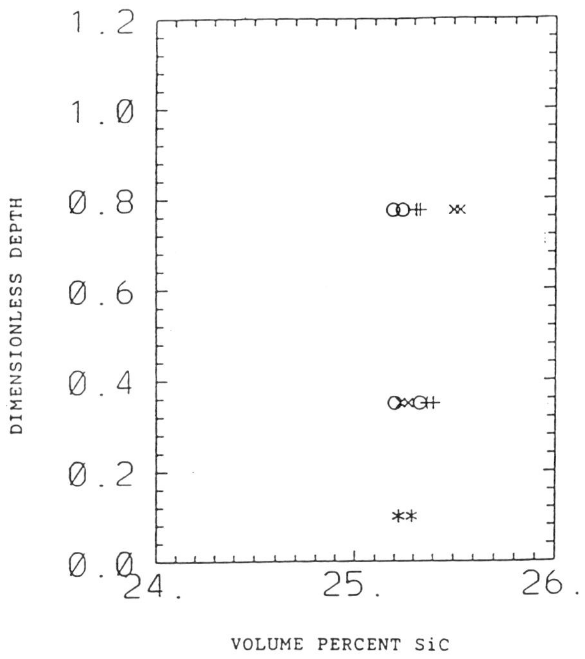

FIG. 6. VARIATION OF VOLUME FRACTION OF SIC (20 μm SIZE) WITH THE DIMENSIONLESS DEPTH OF MIXTURE IN A 25 VOL.% SIC-WATER MIXTURE STIRRED AT 655 RPM WITH A +30° IMPELLER. THE SYMBOLS REPRESENT SAMPLES DRAWN FROM: [*]-BOTTOM, [X]-WALL, [O]-MID-RADIUS, AND [+]-SHAFT.

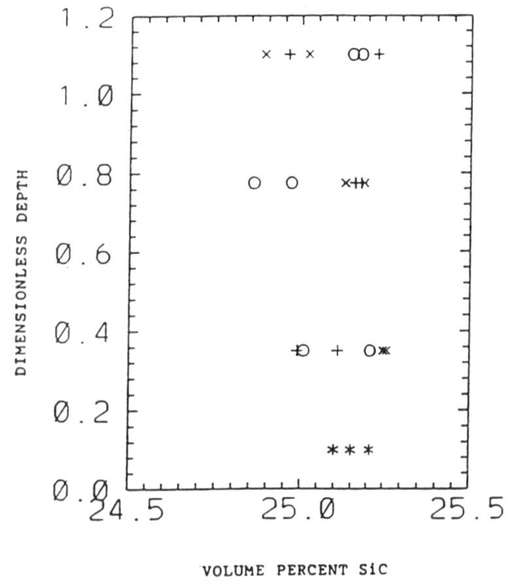

FIG. 5. VARIATION OF VOLUME FRACTION OF SIC (20 μm SIZE) WITH THE DIMENSIONLESS DEPTH OF MIXTURE IN A 25 VOL. % SIC-WATER MIXTURE STIRRED AT 315 RPM WITH A +45° IMPELLER. THE SYMBOLS REPRESENT SAMPLES DRAWN FROM: [*]-BOTTOM, [X]-WALL, [O]-MID-RADIUS, AND [+]-SHAFT.

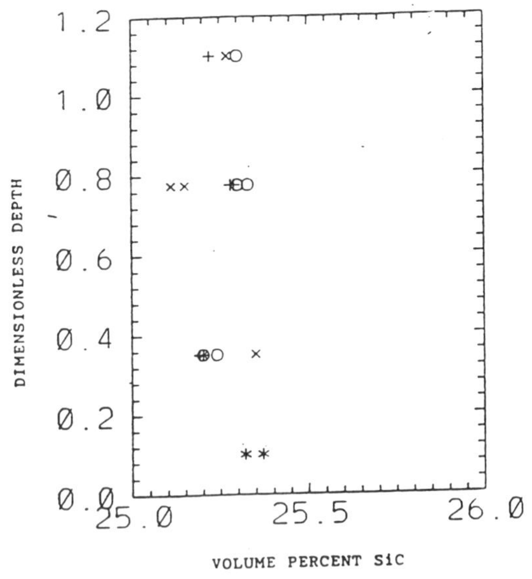

FIG. 7. VARIATION OF VOLUME FRACTION OF SIC (20 μm SIZE) WITH THE DIMENSIONLESS DEPTH OF THE MIXTURE IN A 25 VOL. % SIC-WATER MIXTURE STIRRED AT 372 RPM WITH AN A-3 IMPELLER. THE SYMBOLS REPRESENT SAMPLES DRAWN FROM: [*]-BOTTOM, [X]-WALL, [O]-MID-RADIUS, AND [+]-SHAFT.

HTD-Vol. 284/AMD-Vol. 182, Transport Phenomena in Solidification
ASME 1994

CFD STUDY OF THE MOULD FILLING OF A HORIZONTAL THIN WALL ALUMINUM CASTING

R. van Tol, H. E. A. van den Akker, and L. Katgerman
Delft University of Technology
Delft, The Netherlands

THE RESULTS ARE PRESENTED OF A STUDY AIMED AT VALIDATING NUMERICAL SIMULATIONS OF MOULD FILLING PHENOMENA IN A THIN WALL HORIZONTAL CASTING. THE FLOW IS STUDIED USING CONTACT MEASUREMENTS AND THE RESULTS ARE COMPARED WITH CFD CALCULATIONS. THE EFFECT OF SURFACE TENSION AND DIFFERENT INLETS ARE CONCERNED. THE TIME OF SOLIDIFICATION IS COMPARED TO VALUES MEASURED BY THERMOCOUPLES.

INTRODUCTION

Using shape castings for structural applications is attractive, because it enables design of multi-functional products, which are sometimes impossible to construct otherwise. In the automotive and aerospace industry in particular, there is an increasing demand for lighter products. This implies that with reduced material consumption, equivalent or even improved product performance should be attained. To achieve this, shape castings are designed to be as thin as possible. For foundries this creates a market for thin wall castings with a high guaranteed quality requirement. However, because of the high surface to volume ratio of thin wall castings, casting defects occur more easily. This makes manufacturing of thin wall castings complicated.

Computer simulations have turned out to be a powerful tools for optimizing the characteristics of the product and for studying the reproducibility of the manufacturing process. (Adams et al., 1992; Piwonka, Voller and Katgerman, 1993). Mould filling simulations take a special place in CFD, because a free surface tracking algorithm is required. Over the past decade two methods, MAC (Welch et al., 1966) and SOLAVOF (Hirt and Nichols, 1981), are extended to 3-D and compared by Chin-Wen Chen et al, 1993.

The robustness of calculational methods for mould filling simulations is generally tested in simple geometries (Van der Graaf et al, 1993; Xu and Mampaey, 1993; Pei et al, to be published). While a vertical plate has been used rather often for validation studies, this paper aims at validating mould filling simulations of a horizontal thin wall casting.

Such a casting exhibits a strong interaction between heat transfer (solidification), surface tension and the gravitational force. The gravitational force is orthogonal to the plane of flow and has therefore no influence on the shape of the free surface in the plane of flow.

The shape of the propagating flow is measured in time from an experiment and compared to CFD calculations using different inlet conditions. The heat transfer from metal to mould is modelled as well to allow the liquid metal to solidify on the mould wall during mould filling.

THREE KEY ISSUES

While solving the equations of motion and tracking the position of the free surface have become routine-like procedures, the success of simulating mould filling, particularly of horizontal thin-wall castings, critically depends on how the heat transport into the (sand) mould is modelled and how the surface tension is taken into account. A third important issue concerns the effectiveness and size of the computational effort. The relevance of these three key issues with a view to predicting solidification processes will be discussed first.

The metal near the metal-air surface that has been in contact with the mould cavity for some time has lost more of its internal energy to the mould than the metal that just has entered the mould cavity at the end of the mould filling period. The last metal entering the mould cavity does not only spend the shortest period of time in the mould it also cools down at the location where the mould is the warmest. Both these effects contribute to differences in local temperature history in thin wall sand castings originating from the mould filling period.

Therefore, assuming a uniform temperature field at the moment the mould is completely filled, is quite unrealistic for thin wall aluminium castings. The initial temperature distribution after mould filling can be studied by CFD methods.

In simulating mould filling of thin wall aluminium castings, fluid flow and heat flow have to be calculated simultaneously. Solidification can occur during filling, due to the high area-to-volume ratio, and the flow can be interrupted locally or totally, resulting in a cold run. Fluid flow and heat transfer are therefore highly coupled. This process is analytically evaluated by Schröder, 1982, 1983. The necessary requirement is that the latent heat released per unit time is known. Numerical calculations do not suffer from this constraint.

The numerical calculation of horizontal mould fillings is even more complex, because of the high surface tension of aluminium. Combined with bad wetting of sand moulds by liquid aluminium, the metal maintains a natural height (Nieswaag and Deen, 1989). This height normally exceeds the thickness of thin wall castings and causes the metal to be in permanent contact with the top surface. This effect cannot be neglected in mould filling calculations, because this contact influences largely the heat flow to the top mould.

Detailed CFD simulations require substantial amounts of memory and CPU-time. The computational domain or the number of computational cells sometimes has to be limited to keep it within the available hardware limits. The computational resolution in the casting becomes poor if the whole feeding and running system are to be included. Hence, it looks attractive to try and lump the feeding and running system into a simple boundary condition (BC), the details of upstream processes being ignored.

In this study, various options of lumping the gating system of a thin wall gravity casting into single BC have been investigated. Various ways of dealing with the surface tension have been studied as well.

For this study a horizontal horse shoe was chosen. The casting, the gating system and the pouring cup are shown in Figure 1. The thickness of the horse shoe is 5 mm.

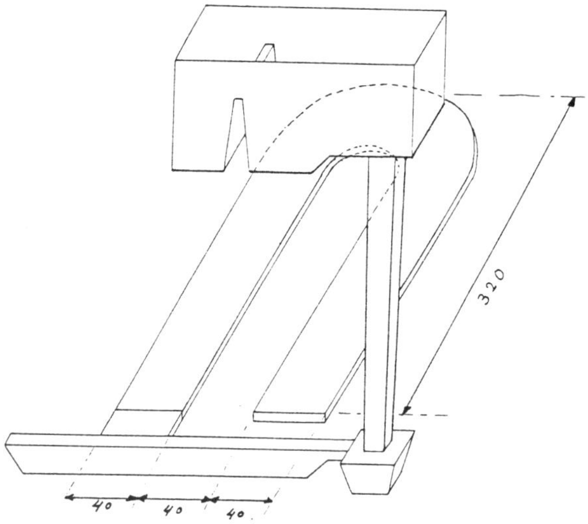

Figure 1. Geometry of the casting and gating system.

COMPUTATIONAL MODEL

To calculate the mould filling of the casting, the conservation laws for mass, momentum and energy are solved, together with a fluid advection equation for the interface. For the last equation a volume of fluid method is used (Hirt and Nichols, 1981). The equations are discretisized in a finite volume mesh and solved using an explicit time dependent algorithm. The convergence of the pressure iterations is speeded up by using line interpolation in the direction of the plate thickness.

The flow is assumed to be laminar. During the flow calculation the fraction of solid produced has to be calculated. The solid fraction produced is modelled as a linear function of the temperature. A latent heat enthalpy formulation is used to calculate the solid fraction. The solid fraction is assumed always to be in rest with respect to the computational mesh. A friction coefficient is used to model the impact of the solidified material on the flow.

At the external boundaries of the mesh a zero heat

transfer BC is applied. The material parameters are assumed to be constant with temperature. The calculations are done with FLOW-3D,[1] a dedicated commercial software code for free surface type CFD problems. The free-surface behaviour and heat transfer have been separately studied before by Bahkudarov et al., 1991 and 1993.

Heat transfer at the metal-mould interface

Since the coefficients of thermal conductivity of metal and mould differ by two to three orders of magnitude, the heat transfer through the mould wall is mainly limited by the heat transfer in the sand. Therefore, the local temperatures in the sand have to be included in the calculation. To ensure the computational domain comprises a sufficiently large volume of sand, the heat penetration depth was estimated. A depth of 7 mm was obtained, using a typical maximum contact time of 100 seconds in the calculations. A thickness of about 15 mm of the sand mould was therefore included to be on the safe side.

In numerical routines the temperatures are evaluated at the cell centres. The heat transport in the sand mould is computed dynamically by means of a heat transfer coefficient that can be estimated from h=k/l, where k denotes the thermal conductivity of the sand and l the distance. At the metal-sand interface, l has to be taken equal to the distance from the interface to the first cell centre in the sand. The computations become more accurate with decreasing cell size.

Near to the free propagating surface, the heat transfer to the wall is very large as a result from the steep gradient in the sand, see Figure 2. The time t=0 in the figure is the moment the metal contacts the mould wall. This results in solidification of metal on the mould wall and heat is released close to the flow tip, see Figure 3 (Campbell, 1988). Due to this complex process near the flow tip it is difficult to make a good approximation of the heat transfer coefficient during mould filling. Accounting for a solidified layer on the mould wall requires small cell sizes on the metal side of the wall.

Due to the finite volume formulation that is used, the fine mesh cells, that are only needed on both sides of the interface, may extend to the rest of the computational domain (where not needed) and may therefore lead to small time steps. As an alternative the stationary approximation was used, which gives a value of 240 J/m^{2}sK for the heat transfer coefficient for a wall cell size of 5 mm. This value is used in the calculations of the cooling after mould filling is completed.

During mould filling a value of 500 J/m^{2}sK was used. This value was found to give cold shuts at approximately the correct time compared to experiments.

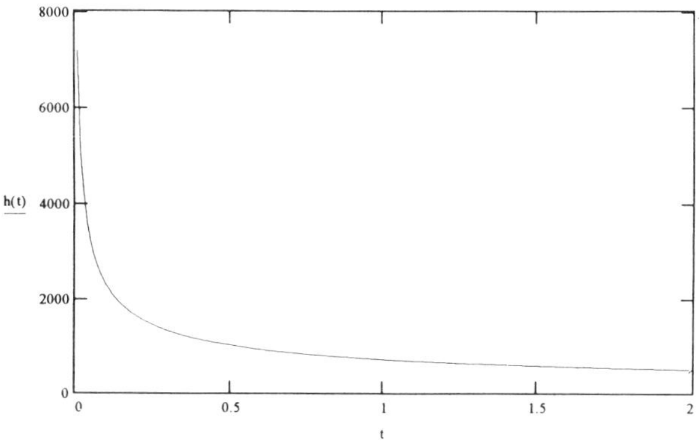

Figure 2. Heat transfer coefficient approximated by penetration theorie.

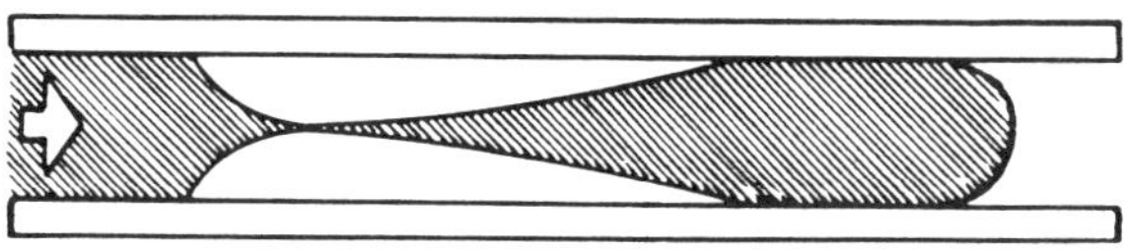

Figure 3. Solidification on the mould wall. The white parts represent solidified material on the mould wall.

The metal-air interface

To perform calculations with more then one cell in the thickness of the casting, surface tension forces at the interface have to be included.

The parameters describing the metal-air interface, contact angle and surface tension, can be obtained from the measured height h of an aluminium stream. This height was measured to be around 11 mm (Nieswaag and Deen, 1989). Application of the equation below gives a contact angle θ of 140° at a surface tension of 0.84 N/m. These values were used for the calculations.

$$\cos\theta = 1 - \frac{\rho g h^2}{2\sigma}$$

[1] FLOW-3D is a registered trademark of Flow Science, Inc., Los Alamos NM(USA).

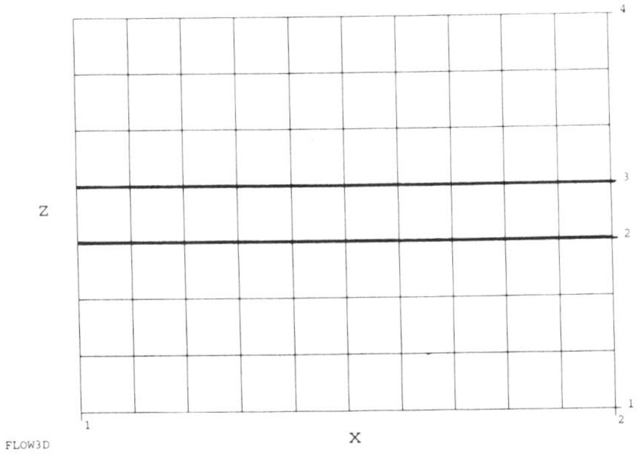

Figure 4a. Grid with one cell in the thickness of the horse shoe.

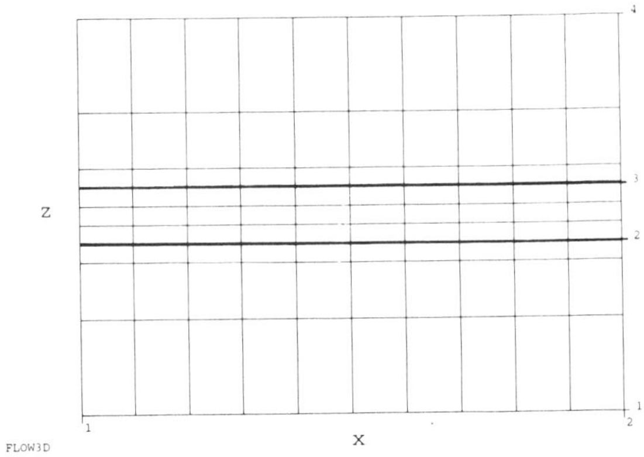

Figure 4b. Grid with three cells in the thickness of the horse shoe.

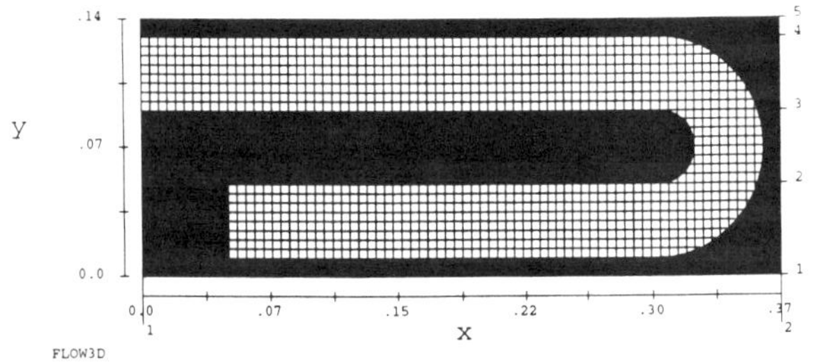

Figure 5. Grid in the plane of the horse shoe.

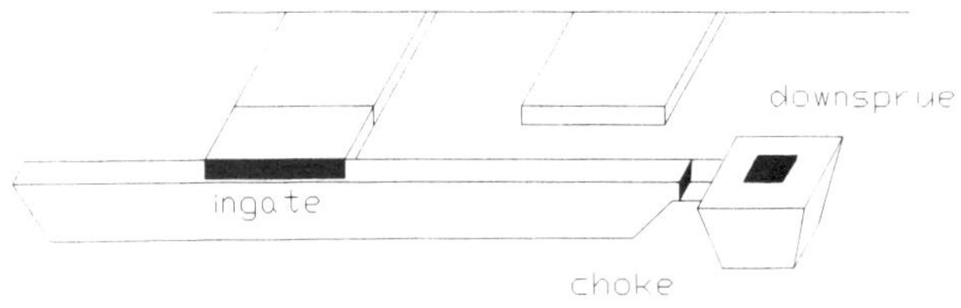

Figure 6. Locations for the boundary conditions.

The assumption of no heat transfer is made at the metal-air interface, ignoring radiation. Gas pressure effects, due to heating and cooling of the mould cavity, are not taken into account.

Computational details

The mesh finally selected to model the horse shoe contained 28 * 74 cells in the horizontal plane and 1 or 3 cells in the direction of the thickness of the horse shoe, as shown in Figure 4. In both cases three computational cells above and under the horse shoe were used to model the sand. Additional cells were used to model parts of the gating system.

The grid is chosen such that the cell faces coincide with the horizontal interfaces between metal and sand mould. Along the vertical straight edges of the horse shoe this was done similarly, but the bend of the horse shoe is described with a porosity model, see Figure 5.

Boundary conditions

With the view of reducing the domain in which the flow and heat transfer equations have to be solved, it is attempted to represent the gating system of the horse shoe by a single BC at either the ingate, or the choke, or the bottom of the down sprue (see Figure 6).

The magnitude of the uniform velocities at these locations is obtained from the measured value of the inflow rate. The velocities and areas at the boundaries are given in Table 1.

location	area [cm^2]	velocity [cm/s]
ingate	2	31.5
choke	0.75	83.9
downsprue	1	62.9

Table 1. The BC velocity at the different locations.

Using constant velocity BC's has the disadvantage that if cold runs occur or the mould is filled, pressures will go to infinity and the calculation collapses. This would not occur if a pressure BC is used. Because the pressure is not known anywhere in the gating system during filling, a pressure BC cannot be used to model the gating system. A (constant) pressure boundary condition can

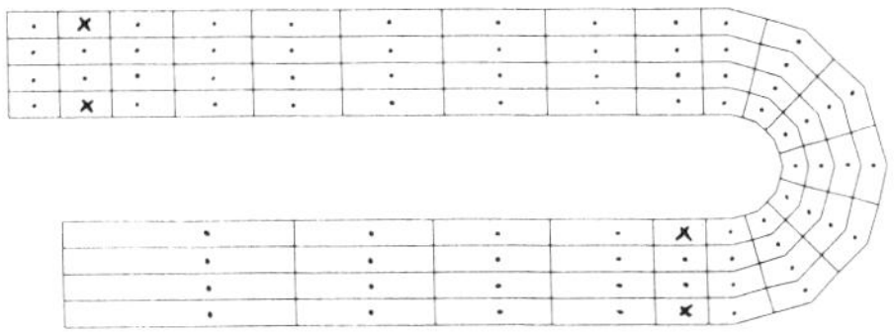

Figure 7. Locations of the contacts.

	measured	calculated
ingate	40	33
bend	30	25

Table 2. Local solidification time in seconds.

only be applied at an external boundary; that would require the whole running and gating to be included.

To prevent the solution from diverging when constant velocity BC's are used the calculation is interrupted at the moment in time the pressure suddenly starts to rise; from that moment onwards the BC velocities are set to zero.

This enables one to calculate the temperature history after the mould has been filled: the heat transport equation is solved for conduction only, but with the heat release due to solidification properly taken into account. For these calculations zero heat flux is assumed at the inlet.

The temperature at the inlet is difficult to measure during the mould filling period. It can be obtained from analytical approximations or a simulation of the gating system separately from the casting. This was not considered during this study. A constant inflow temperature of 700 °C was set at the inlet during the mould filling period.

EXPERIMENTAL CONDITIONS

The simulations relate to experiments performed with a casting made of an Al-12wt%Si alloy using a silicate bonded sand mould. The gating system is filled from a pouring cup.

To register the mould filling of the casting as a function of time, 84 copper wires are installed into the top mould, shown by the dots in Figure 7. On contact with the liquid metal the time is stored in a PC.
The sample rate is 500 Hz. The top mould can be used, because the metal is permanently in contact during the whole filling period as discussed earlier. This method registers only the propagation of the metal-air surface.

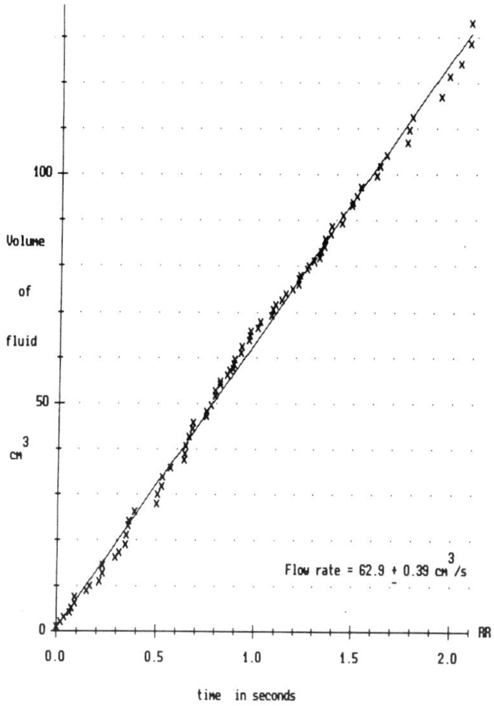

Figure 8. Volume of fluid as a function of time.

The flow rate is experimentally detected by assigning areas to all the contacts as shown in Figure 7. The total area at any time in contact with the fluid, multiplied by the thickness of the plate, gives the fluid volume as a function of time (see Figure 8). The slope of the curve shows an inflow rate of 62.9 cm^3/s. At the scale of the filling time of the mould this rate could be considered constant.

The filling of the plate, as detected by the contact measurements, is given in Figure 9. Near the ingate, after the bend and at the end of the horse shoe, the free surface on the outside is ahead of the free surface at the inside.

Additional to the contact measurements, thermocouples are used to measure the time of solidification. The locations are given in Figure 7 (crosses). The sample rate was 1 Hz. The measured solidification times are given in Table 2.

COMPUTATIONAL RESULTS AND DISCUSSION

One cell in the thickness of the horse shoe.

Simulation results of the filling of the horse shoe without the runner are shown in Figure 10. Compared with the experimental results, the shape of the interface

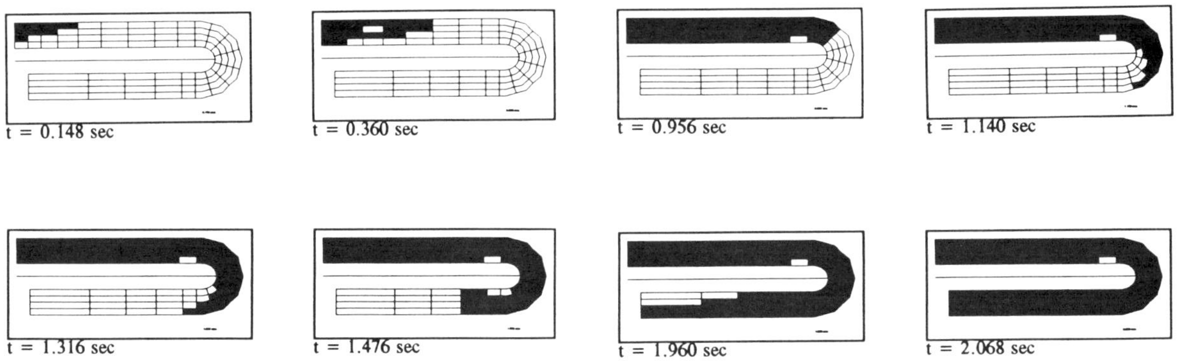

Figure 9. Experimentally detected mould filling.

through and after the bend is similar such that the fluid is ahead at the end of the bend and spreads out over the width of the horse shoe after the bend.

Near the ingate the first entrance of the metal on the outside of the horse shoe is evidently not found in the calculations, because the runner, which makes a 90° angle with the ingate, is not included in the simulation.

In Figure 11 the inflow is shown when the runner is also considered. If the BC location is at the choke, the flow from the ingate does not spread to the inner side of the horse shoe as found by the experiments.

The flow was assumed laminar, with a Reynolds number of about 2000, using the hydraulic diameter. The experimental results however suggests that the flow might be slightly turbulent and that the difference in spreading of the interface between calculations and experiments can be explained by local turbulence effects. This is demonstrated in Figure 12, where a Prandtl mixing length model was used, with a length of 1 mm. Then a much better agreement with the experiment is obtained.

In Figure 13 the sloped runner end was replaced by a vertical wall. In relation to Figure 11, the fluid now spreads from the ingate over the width of the horse shoe. This shows that small changes in the runner geometry can have a remarkable influence on the shape of the free surface in the horse shoe.

The pouring well was also taken into account by applying BC's at the bottom of the downsprue, using the sloped runner. Then the filling of the horse shoe differed hardly from that represented in Figure 11.

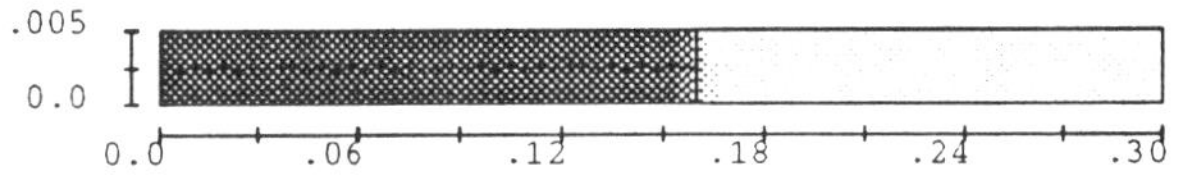

One cell without surface tension.

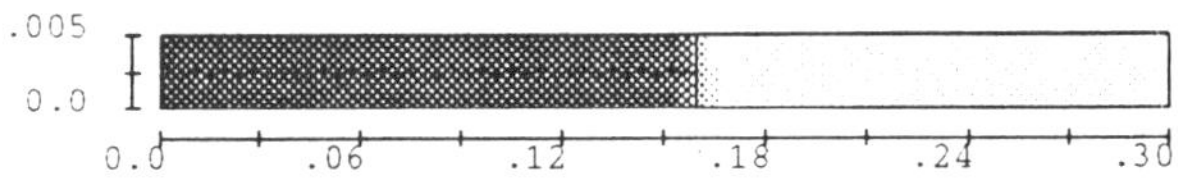

One cell with surface tension.

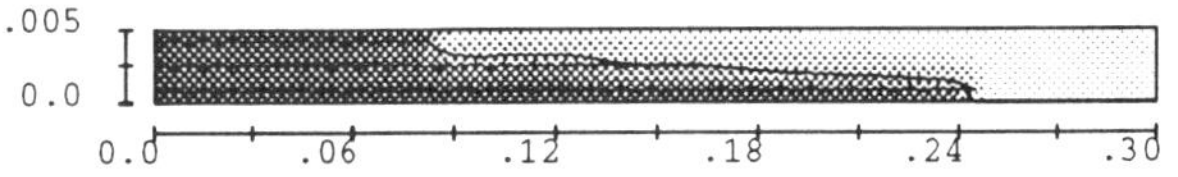

Three cells without surface tension.

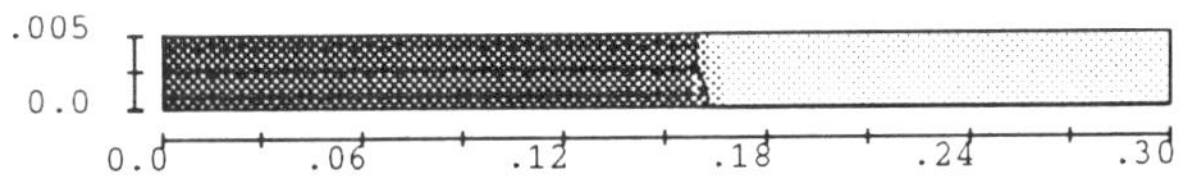

Three cells with surface tension.

Figure 14. Influence of the surface tension on the shape of the metal air interface.

2D results considering surface tension.

The effect of surface tension and contact angle on the shape of the metal-air interface for one and three cells in the plate thickness is shown in Figure 14. In 2D-calculations with only one cell in the plate thickness the

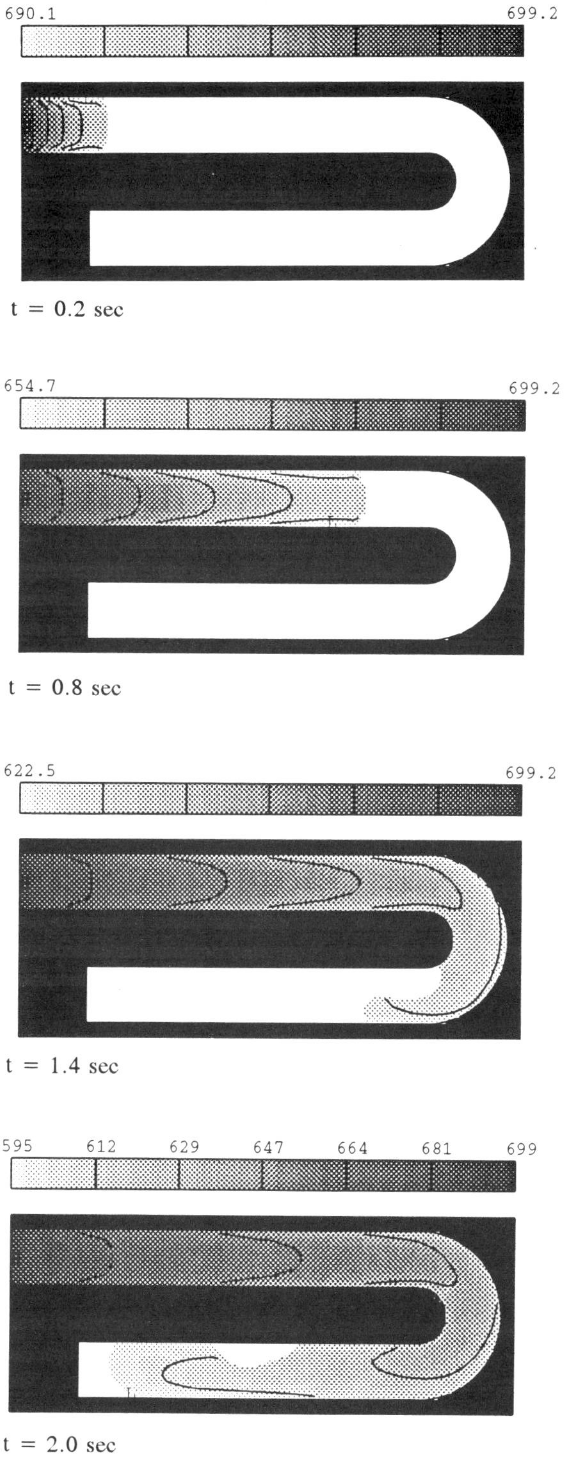

Figure 10. Computational results for filling, without runner and onecell in the thickness direction of the horseshoe.

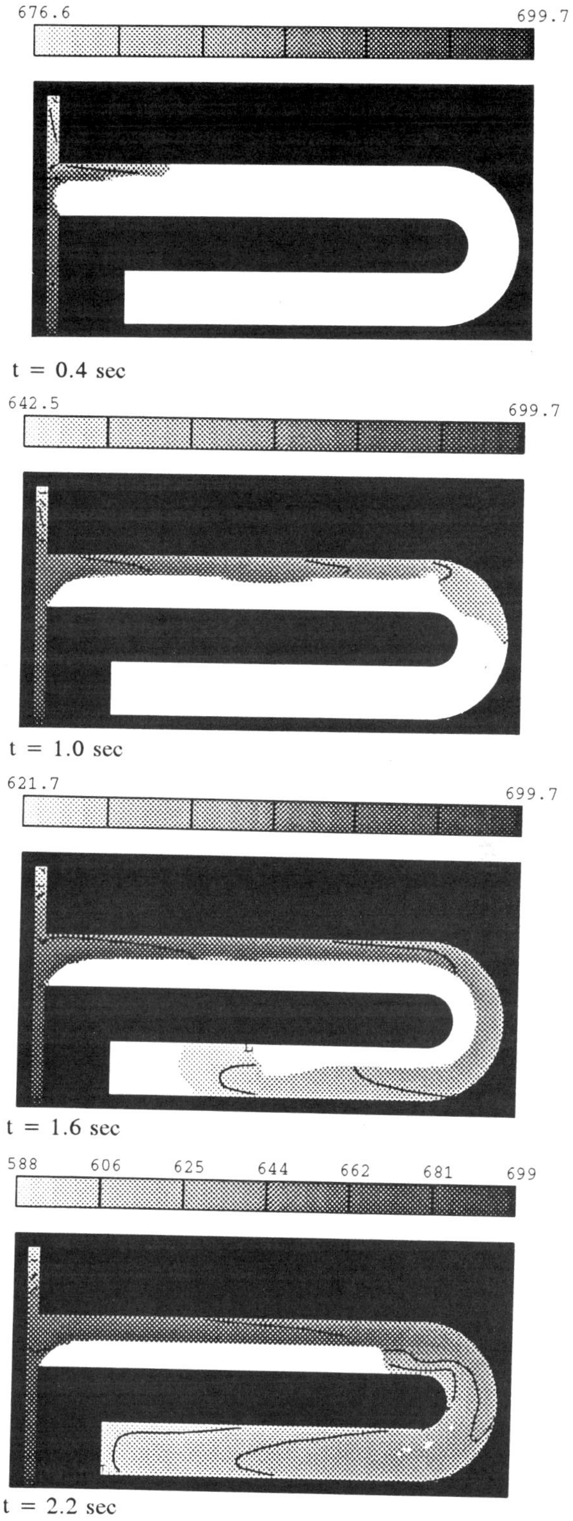

Figure 11. Computational results for filling, with runner and onecell in the thickness direction of the horseshoe.

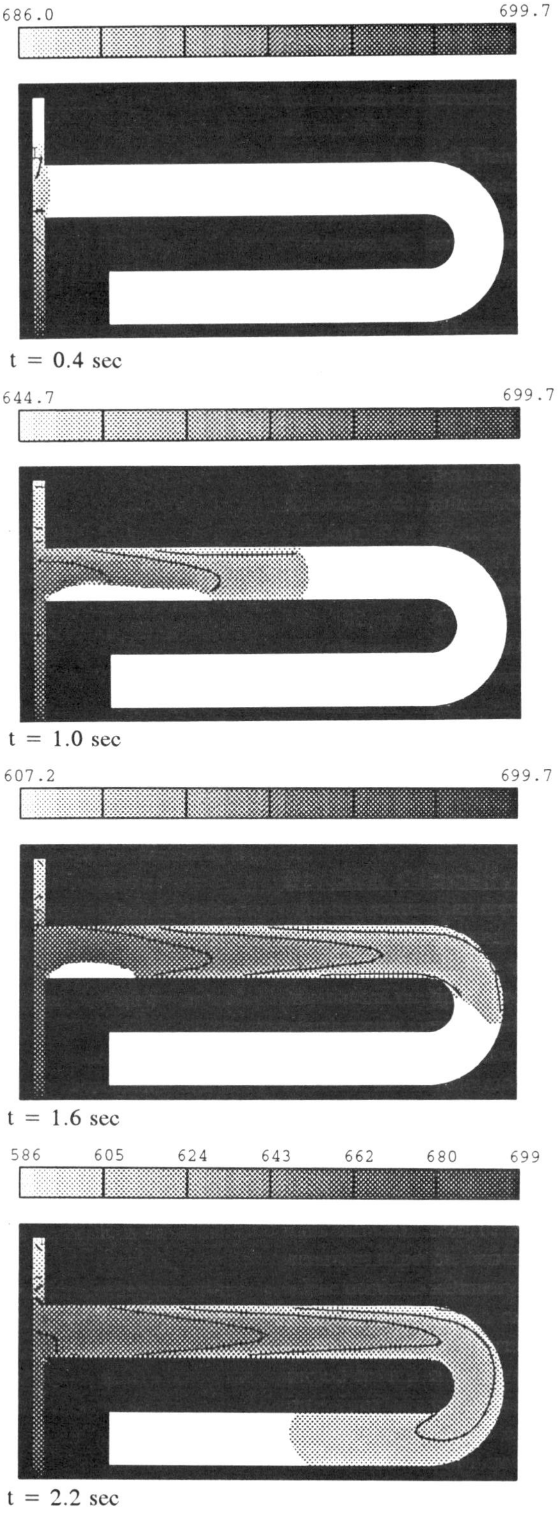

Figure 12. Computational results for turbulent filling, without runner and one cell in the thickness direction of the horseshoe.

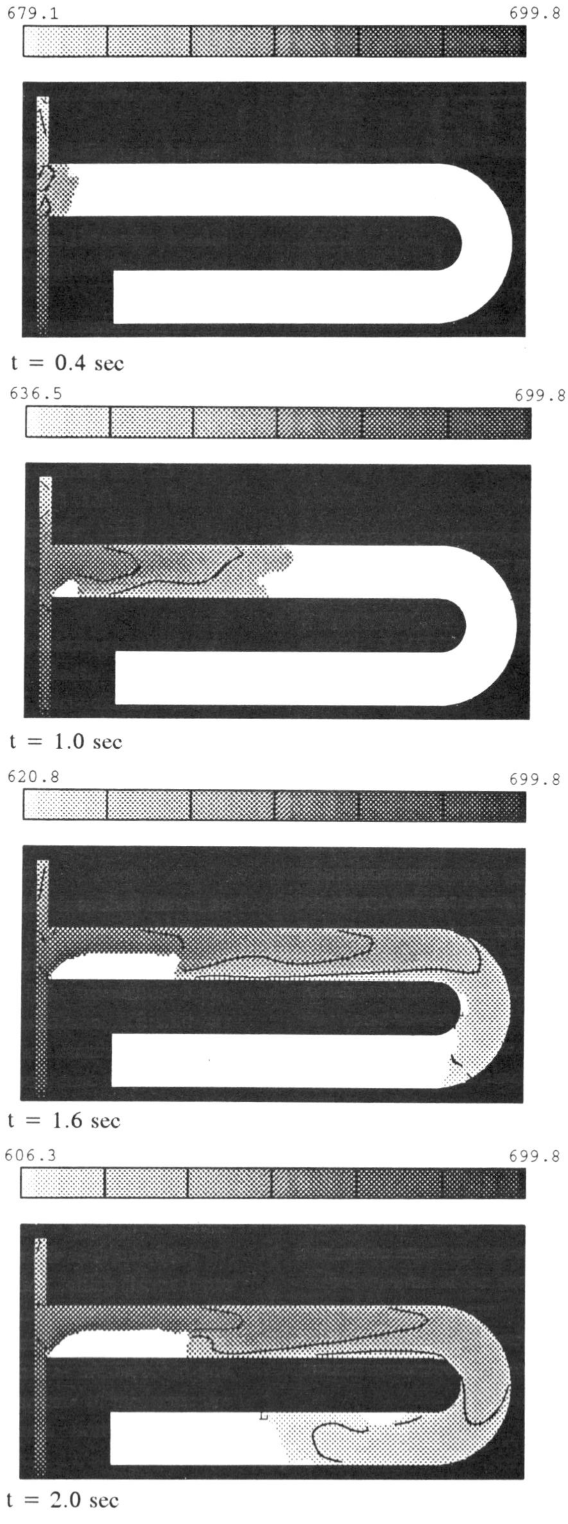

Figure 13. Computational results for filling, with slightly changed runner and one cell in the thickness direction of the horseshoe.

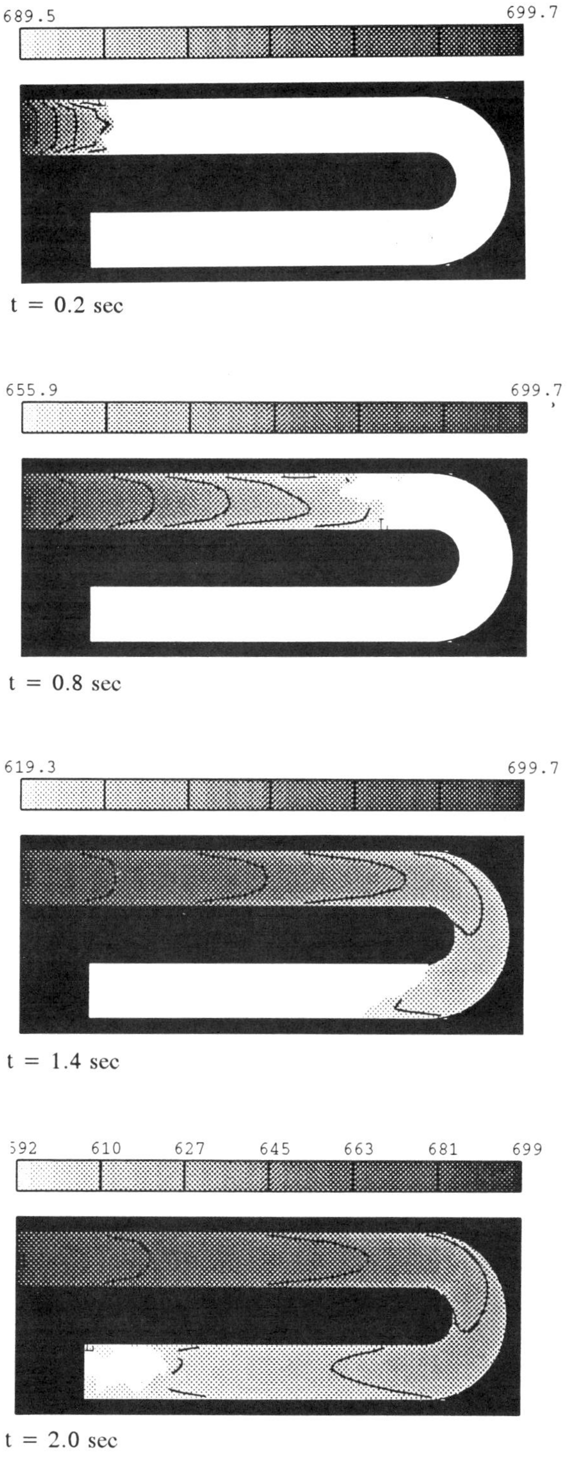

Figure 15a. Computational results for filling, without runner and three cells in the thickness direction (centre plane).

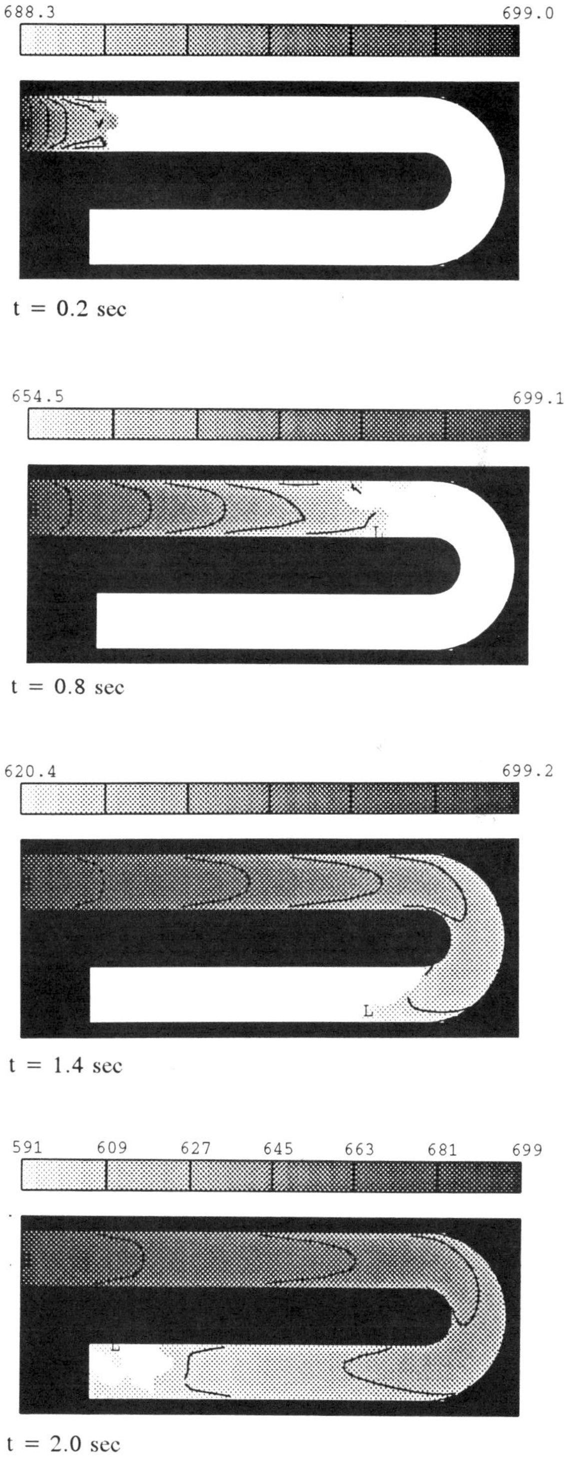

Figure 15b. Computational results for filling, without runner and three cells in the thickness direction (bottom plane).

fluid is always in contact with bottom and top cell faces, because the orientation and curvature of the interface are not resolved by the computational mesh in this direction. Only a tendency to broaden in the plane of flow is found as a result from the surface tension force. Similar effects are reported by Mampaey and Xu, 1993.

In calculations with more cells in the plate thickness the surface tension keeps the metal in contact with the top mould as discussed earlier. When the surface tension is ignored, the fluid spreads over the bottom of the cavity.

BC's at the ingate with three cells in the direction of the thickness.

Another calculation of the horse shoe was carried out with the inlet at the ingate, but with the grid of Figure 4b, which has three cells in the plate in the direction of the thickness. The results are shown in Figure 15 for the centre and bottom planes. In both planes the free surface is always at the same location due to the surface tension effect, its propagation is also similar to that of the two dimensional case in Figure 14. The free surface now exhibits instabilities. These irregular surface shapes are never found in castings after a cold run. So these instabilities are assumed to be artefacts resulting from numerical instabilities.

The solidification time.

For calculations with the one cell in the plate thickness and the inlet at the ingate the solidification of the plate was calculated. The thermocouples at the inside and at the outside of the horse shoe show the same solidification time. (The solidification time is defined as the time passing while moving from the first to the second arrest along the cooling curve.) The thermocouples located near the ingate give a difference in solidification time. Solidification times are measured and calculated are given in Table 2.

The calculated solidification time is only 80% of the measured solidification. The solidification time after the bend is about 75% of the solidification time 30 mm downstream of the ingate in both the calculation and the measurement.

CONCLUDING REMARKS

Replacing running and gating system by single boundary conditions looks as an attractive option for simulating the general filling behaviour of thin wall aluminium castings. We have found, however, that non-uniform velocities during the filling operation can only be found by incorporating the runner in the simulation domain. Taking the inlet further upstream than the choke results in the same global filling behaviour and seems unnecessary at this stage.

For calculations with multiple cells in the plate thickness the surface tension needs to be included to keep the metal in contact with the top of the mould cavity. This effect is found in 2D and in 3D calculations; the surface tension description used in the FLOW-3D calculations results in instabilities at the free surface in the 3D calculations.

The solidification time measured just after the bend is 75% of the solidification time measured 3 mm downstream of the ingate. As this was found in the calculations as well, the ratio of these times is calculated correctly.

The solidification times in the calculations was 80% of the solidification times measured. This suggests that a heat transfer coefficient of 180 J/m^2sK is more appropriate than 240 J/m^2sK .

The computer simulations allow for details in the flow field and temperature distribution, where experimental data are not available yet. The simulations clearly show the lower temperature at the front of the liquid. More detailed experimentation is required for a rigorous validation of the computations and, eventually, for optimization of the casting design.

References

D. Adams, G. Butlin, G. Higginbottom, L. Katgerman, A.W.D. Hills and J.A. Charles, "Modelling of Castings: Developments in the UK", Metals and Materials, September 1992, 496-500

M. Barkhudarov, H. You, J. Beech, S.B. Chin, D. H. Kirkwood, "Validation and developement of Flow-3D for castings", EPD Congress 1992, editor J.P. Hager, The Minerals, Metals & Materials Society (1991)

M. Barkhudarov, H. You, J. Ortega, J. Beech, S.B. Chin, D.H. Kirkwood, "Experimental Validation and Developement of Flow-3D for Casting Problems", "Modelling of Casting and Welding Processes VI", TMS, Warrendale (1993)

J. Campbell, "Thin wall castings", Materials Science and Technology **4** (1988), 194-204.

Chin-Wen Chen, Hung-Yih Chou, Ching-Ren Li, Chih-Tzung Shei, Weng-Sing Hwang,"Comparison of Different Computational Fluid Dynamics Techniques on Their Applications to the modelling of Mould Filling in Casting", Trans. Jap. Foundrymen's Soc., vol. 12 (1993), oct.

G. van der Graaf, H.E.A. van den Akker, L. Katgerman,"Flow phenomena of mould filling for thin wall castings", 60th World Foundry Congress 1993 (The Hague).

C.W. Hirt and B.D. Nichols, "Volume of fluid (vof) method for dynamical boundaries", Journal of Computational Physics **39** (1981), 201-225.

H. Nieswaag and H.J.J. Deen, "Mould filling experiments on mould flow in thin wall castings", Exchange paper 57th World Foundry Congress 1990 (Osaka).

T.S. Piwonka, V. Voller and L. Katgerman, editors, "Modelling of Casting and Welding Processes VI", TMS, Warrendale (1993).

Q.X. Pei, H.E.A. van den Akker, L. Katgerman, H. Nieswaag,"3-D Mould filling simulation and experimental verification for a complex casting system.", To be published.

A. Schröder,"Theoretische Betrachtungen zum Fließvermögen von Schmelzen beim Gießen in verlorene Formen", Giesserei forschung (1982), heft 4, 143-146.

A. Schröder,"Versuche zum Fließvermögen von Gußschmeltzen in sandformen", Giesserei forschung (1983), heft 1, 31-34.

J. E. Welch, F.H. Harlow, J.P. Shannon, B.J. Daly,"The MAC Method: A computing Technique for Solving Viscous, Incompressible, Transient Fluid-Flow problems Involving Free Surfaces," Los Alamos Scientific Laboratory report LA-3425 (1966).

Z.A. Xu and F. Mampaey, "A study of mould filling for castings", Exchange paper 60th World Foundry Congress 1993 (The Hague).

HTD-Vol. 284/AMD-Vol. 182, Transport Phenomena in Solidification
ASME 1994

FAST-ACTING SIMULATION OF SIMULTANEOUS FILLING AND SOLIDIFICATION

Yi F. Zhang
Keane, Incorporated
Albany, New York

Hsin P. Wang
GE R&D Center
Process Physics Laboratory
Schenectady, New York

Wing K. Liu
Department of Mechanical Engineering
Northwestern University
Evanston, Illinois

ABSTRACT

For cast filling process, the Navier-Stokes equation and the continuum equation can be reduced to the transient Bernoulli equation and potential equation, which results in a significant saving of computer running time and storage requirement. The volume of fluid (VOF) are combined with finite element method for solving casting filling problems. The enthalpy method with 1-D heat conduction model is used to determine the temperature distribution and the thickness of the filling. Numerical examples for prediction of filling patterns and parametric study are presented.

1. INTRODUCTION

The development of a fast-acting process simulator for analyzing the simutaneous filling and solidification phenomena is critically needed for improving today's tooling design productivity. None of the casting filling simulation software available today satisfy this industry need because of the excessive computational requirement in both CPU time and memory for solving the full Navier-Stokes equations.

One of the most challenging problems for casting filling is the complexity of the free and moving boundaries. Considerable progress has been made in the solutions of free and moving boundary problems. Among them the height function method[1], line segment method[2], marker particles method[3] belong to the fixed mesh technique. However, these methods can not handle complex geometries or require huge amount of computer time and storage. An arbitrary Lagrangian-Eulerian(ALE) Petrov-Galerkin finite element technique has recently been developed to study nonlinear continua [4]-[5] including nonlinear viscous fluids under large free surface wave motion. The moving boundaries can be tracked with the accuracy characteristic of the Lagrangian methods and the mesh can conserve its regularity in avoiding element entanglement. However, this technique is only efficient for the problems in which the total volume of the fluid keeps constant and the initial shape covers a major portion of the mold. The practical application of this technique for volume-changing molding process remains to be explored.

In this development, the fast-acting simulation models of thin-walled casting processes which couple the velocity potential approach with a transient Bernoulli equation are developed. The volume of fluid method is combined with the finite element method for solving cast filling problems.

The enthalpy method is applied to phase change heat transfer of the filling material. For thin-walled cast filling, heat conduction can be considered only in z(thickness) direction. Therefore, 1-D conduction element s are used.

Example calculations are given. The parametric studies are conducted and the results provide useful insights into process design.

2.MATHEMATICALFORMULATION

2.1 Dimensional analysis

We assume the molten metal is homogeneous and that the flow is incompressible. The conservation equations of mass, momentum and energy are:

Continuity:

$$u_{i,i} = 0 \qquad (2.1)$$

Momentum:

$$\rho(u_{i,t} + u_{i,j}u_j) = t_{ij,j} + b_i \qquad (2.2)$$

Energy:

$$\rho c_p(T_{,t} + u_i T_{,i}) = q_{i,i} \qquad (2.3)$$

where u_i is the velocity; r is the density; t_{ij} is the component of the Cauchy stress; b_i is the body force; T is the temperature; c_p is the specific heat; q is the heat flux; m is the viscosity; and t is the time. Indices i and j denote the space dimension. Repeat indices denote summations over the appropriate range. A comma designates a partial derivative with respect to space or time.

To solve the coupled equations (2.1)-(2.3) for a multi-dimensional flow and complex geometry is extremely difficult. However, in reality, some forces are several orders of magnitude less than other forces and can be neglected if we understand the nature of the process. We now simplify the momentum equation by dimensional analysis.

Let l_o, u_o, m_o be the characterized length, velocity, viscosity, respectively. All the variables in momentum equation (2.2) can be written in terms of the proper reference quantities by defining dimensionless variables as follows : $u_i^* = u_i/u_o$, $u_i^* = x_i/l_o$, $p^* = p/\rho u_0^2$, $m^* = m/m_o$, considering

$$t_{ij} = -p\delta_{ij} + m\, u_{i,j}$$

the resulting dimensionless momentum equations is:

$$\frac{\partial u_i^*}{\partial t^*} + u_j^* \frac{\partial u_i^*}{\partial x_j^*} = -\frac{\partial p^*}{\partial x_i^*} + \frac{1}{R_e}\frac{\partial}{\partial x_j^*}\left(m^* \frac{\partial u_i^*}{\partial x_j^*}\right) + \left(\frac{1}{F_r^2}\right) 1_i \qquad (2.4)$$

The material properties of a typical liquid metal (Titanium) at 1973 K are:

ρ =4133 (Kg/m^3), m =4.5x10^{-3} (N-s/m^2), c_p = 786 (J/Kg-K), a = 1.1x 10^{-5}

Typically, for a thickness of 0.0005m and velocity of 0.5m/s, $Re \approx 10^5$ .Therefore, The viscous force can then be neglected during the process and the flow can be treated as an inviscid and inertia dominated flow. If the flow has no initial rotation, the flow is then an irrotation flow . For thin-walled cavities, the thickness integrated conservation equations can be obtained which further simplify the 3-D problem into a 2-D problem. correspondingly, variables such as velocity U,V, pressure P and potential Φ become mean variables averaged through the mold cavity gap[6].

2.2. Governing Equations

1. Laplacian Equation

Since the flow is assumed to be irrotational, potential Φ can be defined as $U = \frac{\partial \Phi}{\partial x}$ and $V = \frac{\partial \Phi}{\partial y}$.

The thickness integrated continuity equation becomes the Laplacian equation:

$$\nabla H \nabla \Phi = 0 \qquad (2.5)$$

where H is the cavity thickness,Φ is the mean potential averaged through the cavity gap.

2. Transient Bernoulli Equation

By integration of momentum equation, we obtain

$$\frac{\partial \Phi}{\partial t} + \frac{P}{\rho} + gy + \frac{\bar{V}^2}{2} = \frac{\partial \Phi_{gate}}{\partial t} + \frac{P_{gate}}{\rho} + gy_{gate} + \frac{\bar{V}^2_{gate}}{2} \qquad (2.6)$$

where $\bar{V} = \sqrt{U^2+V^2}$, U and V are mean velocities averaged through the cavity gap.

If we denote the gate, side wall and free surface by Γ_g, Γ_w and Γ_s, the boundary conditions for the Laplacian equation are as follows:

1. $$\frac{\partial \Phi_{gate}}{\partial \mathbf{n}} = v_{gate} \text{ on } \Gamma_g \qquad (2.7)$$

where **n** is the outward unit normal vector.

2. $$\frac{\partial \Phi}{\partial \mathbf{n}} = \mathbf{0} \text{ on } \Gamma_w \qquad (2.8)$$

3. $$\Phi = \bar{\Phi} \quad \text{on } \Gamma_s \qquad (2.9)$$

The prescribed potential $\bar{\Phi}$ changes with time and can be derived in the following way. We define $\Phi_{n+1} = \Phi(t_{n+1})$ and $\Phi_n = \Phi(t_n)$ where t_n = n Dt, n and Dt are the step number and time step. As depicted in Fig 2.1, if an explicit time integration is used, we obtain

$$\Phi_{n+1} = \Phi_n + \frac{d\Phi}{dt}\Big|_{t=t_n} Dt$$

$$= \Phi_n + \left(\frac{\partial \Phi}{\partial \mathbf{n}}\frac{\partial \mathbf{n}}{\partial t} + \frac{\partial \Phi}{\partial t}\right)\Big|_{t=t_n} Dt$$

$$\approx \Phi_n + \frac{\partial \Phi}{\partial n}\Big|_{t=t_n} \cdot \bar{V}^n Dt + \frac{\partial \Phi}{\partial t}\Big|_{t=t_n} Dt$$

$$= \Phi_n + (\frac{\partial \Phi}{\partial n} \cdot \frac{\partial \Phi}{\partial n})\Big|_{t=t_n} Dt + \frac{\partial \Phi}{\partial t}\Big|_{t=t_n} Dt \quad (2.10a)$$

where

$$\frac{\partial \Phi}{\partial t}\Big|_{t=t_n} = \frac{\Phi_{n+1} - \Phi_n}{Dt}$$

which can be computed from the transient Bernoulli equation (2.6). Considering $p = 0$ at the free surface, then

$$\frac{\partial \Phi}{\partial t}\Big|_{t=t_n} = \frac{p_{gate}}{r} + gy_{gate} + \frac{\bar{V}^2_{gate}}{2} - gy - \frac{\bar{V}^2_n}{2} \quad (2.10b)$$

therefore,

$$\Phi_{n+1} = \Phi_n + Dt\,[(\frac{\partial \Phi}{\partial n} \cdot \frac{\partial \Phi}{\partial n})\Big|_{t=t_n} + \frac{p_{gate}}{r} + gy_{gate} + \frac{\bar{V}^2_{gate}}{2} - gy - \frac{\bar{V}^2_n}{2})] \quad (2.10c)$$

The initial condition is

$$\Phi(0) = 0 \text{ on } \Gamma_g \text{ at } t = 0 \quad (2.11)$$

3. Enthalpy equation

During casting process, liquid metal releases its heat to the mold and then is solidified when it reaches its melting point. Therefore, the heat transfer during the casting process includes phase change. The enthalpy method is employed in conjunction with a finite element method to solve for the solidification in our study. For thin-walled cavities, because heat conduction is only dominated in z direction and convection is only dominated in x-y plane, the enthalpy equation may take the form

$$\rho \frac{\partial I}{\partial t} = k \frac{\partial^2 T}{\partial z^2} - q \quad \text{in} \quad \Omega^{s+1} \quad (2.12)$$

where $q = \rho c_p (U\frac{\partial T}{\partial x} + V\frac{\partial T}{\partial y})$,ρ, k , I , T is the density, conductivity, enthalpy and temperature, separately. Ω^{s+1} is the domain including both solid and liquid parts.

The boundary conditions are $T = T_c$ at $z = h$, $\frac{\partial T}{\partial z} = 0$ at $z = 0$ if the flow is symmetric to Z (see Fig. 2.2) where T_c is the contact temperature between the ceramic mold surface and the liquid metal and can be calculated from the following formula [7]:

$$T_c = \frac{\sqrt{\rho_M c_{p_M} k_M}\, T_{sup} + \sqrt{\rho_c c_{p_c} k_c}\, T_{pre}}{\sqrt{\rho_M c_{p_M} k_M} + \sqrt{\rho_c c_{p_c} k_c}} \quad (2.13)$$

where the subscript M and C indicate properties of the cast metal and ceramic mold separately. T_{sup} is the superheat temperature of the casting metal and T_{pre} is the preheat temperature of the ceramic mold.

In the cast filling, the initial condition refers to the initial temperature condition at the flow front. . In our study, we adopt the "fountain flow" model by which a divergent flow at the front is simulated as shown in Fig. 2.2. We specify the centerline temperature of previous time step as the initial temperature of the current flow front.

3. FINITE ELEMENT FORMULATIONS

In the following, we will be only concentrated in the enthalpy equation since the finite element formulations for the Laplace potential equation are well known.

A thin-walled mold can be seen as composed of many tri-prizms shown in Fig.3.1. Heat conduction only occurs along z direction of each prism. one-dimensional elements can be used for computing heat conduction. In this study, ten 1-D elements are used for each "prizm", which is enough to catch the temprature distribution in the thickness direction. Heat convection which is only considered in x-y plane will be evaluated at the previous time step and served as a source term for the conduction equation.. The resulting semidiscrete finite element equation for this transient heat conduction with phase change is then:

$$\mathbf{M}\dot{\mathbf{I}} + \mathbf{KT} = \mathbf{F} \quad (3.1)$$

where

$$M = [M_{ij}] = \int_0^H \rho N_i N_j \, dz \quad (3.2)$$

$$K = [K_{ij}] = \int_0^H KN_{i,k} N_{j,k} \, dz \quad (3.3)$$

$$F = [F_i] = -\int_0^H N_i q dz - \int_0^H KN_{i,k} N_{NEQ+1,k} \, dz \quad (3.4)$$

N is the shape function, K is the conductivity and NEQ is the numer of equations.

If the midpoint rule is used for time integration, we obtain

$$\mathbf{M}\ \mathbf{I}^{n+1} = \alpha\Delta t\ \mathbf{K}\mathbf{T}^{n+1} + \alpha\Delta t\ \mathbf{F}^{n} - \mathbf{M}\ \mathbf{I}^{n} \qquad (3.5)$$

$$\hat{\mathbf{I}}^{n+1} = \mathbf{I}^{n} + (1-\alpha)\Delta t\ \mathbf{v}^{n} \qquad (3.6)$$

$$\mathbf{v}^{n+1} = (\mathbf{I}^{n+1} - \hat{\mathbf{I}}^{n+1})/\alpha\Delta t \qquad (3.7)$$

where $\alpha = 0.5$

4.CONTACT OF ISO-THERMAL MULTIPLE FREE SURFACE

The jet in a mold will impinge a rigid wall first. However, as the free surface reaches another rigid wall, the jet will turn back and finally impacts the original free surface and the process continues until a vent is identified.

Surfaces of discontinuity are allowable in the potential flow of an inviscid flow although not in a real fluid. As indicated in Fig 4.1, there is a distinct difference in velocity at the interface for potential flow but a large number of eddies or vertices are developed in real fluid. The equilibrium condition requires that the pressure at the both sides of the interface must be the same, but the velocities both in direction and magnitude and the potentials may be different on both sides. The double-node technique is introduced to treat this problem. In Fig 4.2, Φ, P, V and Φ', P',V' represent potential, pressure and velocity at both sides of the interface.

Assuming that the pressure difference between both sides of the interface reduces quickly after the impingement occurs and the movement of the interface is small, we treat the interface as an inflexible wall. Therefore, $\frac{\partial \Phi}{\partial n} = 0$ is the boundary condition for both sides of the interface in this study.

The potential of the flow front keeps increasing as it moves. There exists a distinct difference between the potentials of the flow front and the original jet when they impact each other. A proper value of this difference of potential is used as a criterion for establishing the double nodes. Once the double nodes are established, the connectivity of the related elements is also accordingly changed.

The implementation of the double-node scheme is also shown in Fig. 4.2. When the flow front finally turns back and reaches node 7, we find by checking the potential difference between node 7 and 1(node 1 was occupied by the original stream), that the head of the flow front starts to impinge the original stream. Node 1 is then transformed into a double-node which consists of number 1 and 2. Accordingly, the connectivity for element A is also changed from 7,1,8 to 7,2,8. The flow front then turns upward. By checking the potential difference between node 8 and 2, we find the impact also occurs between node 8 and 2, therefore node 2 has to be transformed into a double-node which consists of number 3 and 4, and the connectivity of element B changes from 2,3,8 to 2,4,8. Similarly, as the flow moves on, nodes 3,4,....are transformed to double-nodes and the connectivity of elements C,D,...is also changed. On both sides of the double-nodes 1(2),3(4),5(6),... velocities and potentials are different. These double-nodes act as a rigid wall and force the flow front to move upward.

5. EXAMPLE CALCULATIONS

The properties of the material (Titanium) used in the following examples are tabulated in Table.1

Table. 1 Properties of filling material

Density	4133	Kg/M^3
Specific Heat	786	J/Kg-K°
Thermal Conductivity	35.8	W/M-K°
Latent Heat	30000	J/Kg
Saturated Temperature	1913	K°

5.1. L-type and 3-D mold

The computer code has been tested for a rectangular mold in [8] in which the results with this code are compared with: (1) the experiments for filling a cavity with a water jet and (2) solution of other numerical simulations using full Navier - Stokes equation.

Fig. 5.1 shows the flow pattern in a L-type mold. The flow starts from the left lower corner. The flow makes right turn when it hits the top wall. However, when the flow hits the right wall of the L-type, it starts to flow towards the right and down direction. The right part of the mold is first filled.

Our codes are also applied on simple real 3-D mold. As shown in Fig.5.2 and Fig.5.3, the 3-D mold makes flow pattern change. In Fig.5.3, the right side represents 3-D flow pattern. When the flow reaches the slope and moves upwards, the velocity of the flow front starts to slow down which makes the flow pattern wider.

This fast-acting simulation needs less than 60 seconds on the HP 720. The Marker-and-Cell method for full Navier-Stocks equation requires 1000 seconds on VAX8600 machine.

5.2. Parametric studies

Figure 5.4 shows the relation between fraction solidified and superheat and contact temperatures for a 0.5cm thick part with a 10.0 cm/s melt velocity. The vertical axis represents the maximum solidified fraction of the total cavity thickness during the filling process. The variation in melt superheat temperature is shown on the horizontal axis. Different curves are plotted for each of the contact temperatures (thus mold preheat temperatures). The figure indicates that the maximum solidified fraction is decreased as the superheat temperature increased. It also indicates that as the contact temperature (hence the mold preheat temperature) increases, for a given superheat temperature, the solidified layer thickness decreases. The smallest solidified layer, that will interfere with the flow pattern the least, can be achieved with highest superheat and preheat temperatures.

Figure 5.5 predicts the freeze-off area at different operational conditions. It indicates that the 'area' of the process window decreases as the melt velocity is decreased. If the process conditions are located above the 'window', complete filling of the part should be produced with some solidified layer formed during the process. If the process conditions are located within the 'window' area, flow would freeze off before it completely fills the cavity. Increasing the superheat and contact (preheat) temperature will decrease the size of the freeze-off area. For thin-walled castings, misruns or cold shuts often occur under poor process conditions such as low pouring rate.

Figure 5.6 shows the effects of the process parameters on the filling length. As can be seen, for a given part thickness the melt velocity plays much a more important role than other conditions such as superheat and contact temperatures.

These parametric studies can provide useful insights into investment process design and help the engineers design molds more effectively.

5. CONCLUSIONS

1. The dimensional analysis indicates that for casting filling process, the Navier-Stokes equation and the continuum equation can be reduced to the transient Bernoulli equation and potential equation, which leeds to a significant saving of computer time and storage;
2. The derivation of the momentum and continuity equations for thin-walled cavities further simplifies the model and makes the process modeling of the 3-D casting of an arbitrary shape thin-walled cavity practical;
3. The combination of VOF algorithm and the finite element method leeds to an extremely powerful modeling technique;
4. The filling process for 2-D L-type and 3-D rectangular mold are simulated and the parametric studies are also conducted. The results provide useful insights into process design.

References

[1] C.W. Hirt, etal, SOLA - A Numerical Solution Algorithm for Transient Fluid Flows, Los Alamos Scientific Laboratory report LA-5852, 1975,

[2] B.D. Nichols and C.W. Hirt, Improved Free Surface Boundary Conditions for Numerical Incompressible Flow Calculations, J. Comp. Phy., Vol. 8, 1971.

[3] F.H. Harlow and J.E. Welch, Numerical Calculation of Time-Dependent Viscous Incompressible Flow of Fluid with Free Surface, The Physics of Fluids, 8, No. 12, 2182-2189, 1965.

[4] A.Huerta and W.K, Liu, Viscous Flow with Large Free Surface Motion, 69,277-324, 1988

[5] W.K.Liu, Adaptive ALE Finite Elements with Particular reference to external work rateon frictional interface, computer Methods in Applied Mechanics and Engineering, 93, 189-216,1991.

[6] H.P. Wang, Numerical Algorithms for Casting Filling Analysis of Thin-Walled Cavities, G.E. Cooperate Research and Development, 1990.

[7] H.P. Wang and E.M. Perry, An Interactive Parametric Analysis Tool for Thin-Walled Investment Casting, Modeling of Casting, Welding and Advanced Solidification Processes V, Edited by M.Rappaz, eta, The Minerals, Metals & Materials Society, 1991.

[8] Y.F.Zhang, W.K.Liu and H.P.Wang: Casting Filling Simulations of Thin-Walled Cavities with Solidification, Eng. Foundation, Modeling of Casting, Welding and Advanced Solidification Processes VI, March 21,1993.

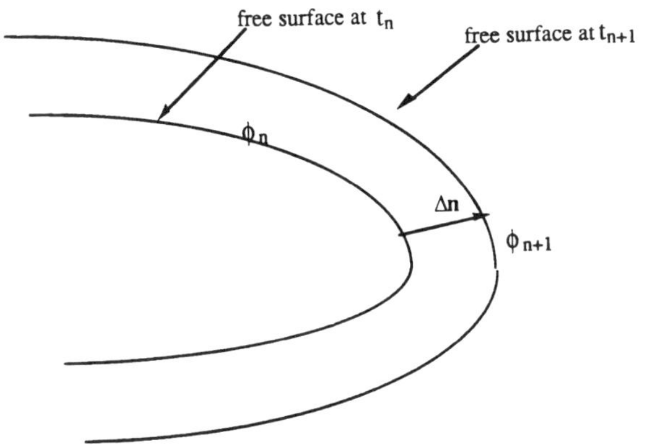

FIGURE 2.1 DERIVATION OF THE FREE SURFACE BOUNDARY CONDITION

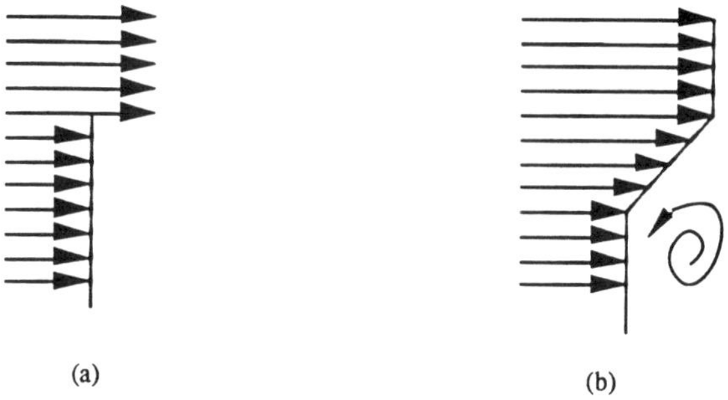

FIGURE 4.1 FREE SURFACE CONTACTS FOR (a) AN IDEAL FLUID AND (b) A REAL FLUID

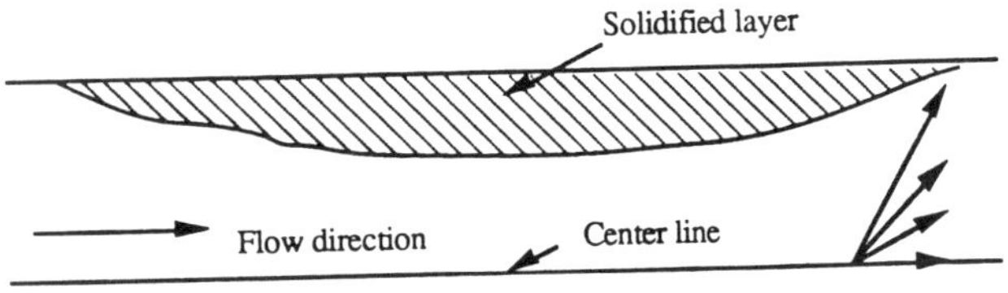

FIGURE 2.2 SCHEMATIC ILLUSTRATION OF THE INITIAL CONDITION BY 'FOUNTAIN FLOW MODEL'

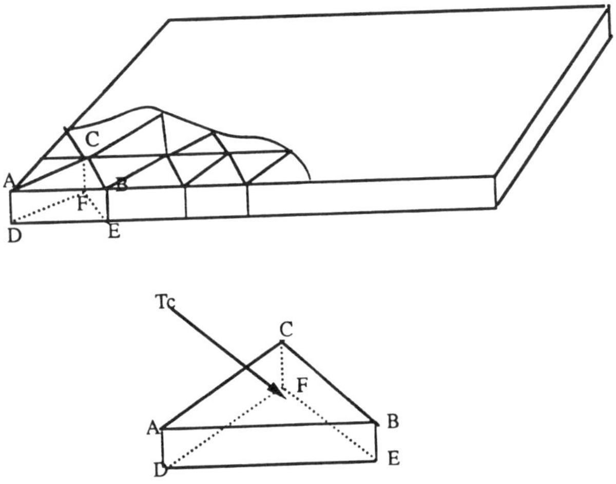

FIGURE 3.1 ONE DIMENSIONAL HEAT CONDUCTION MODEL

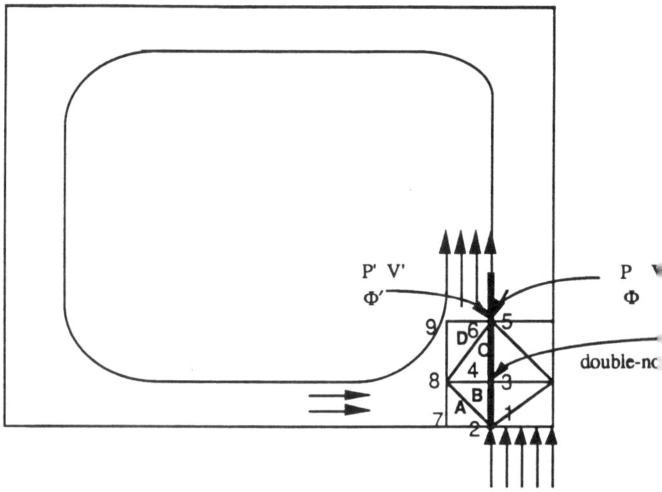

FIGURE 4.2 DOUBLE-NODE SCHEME

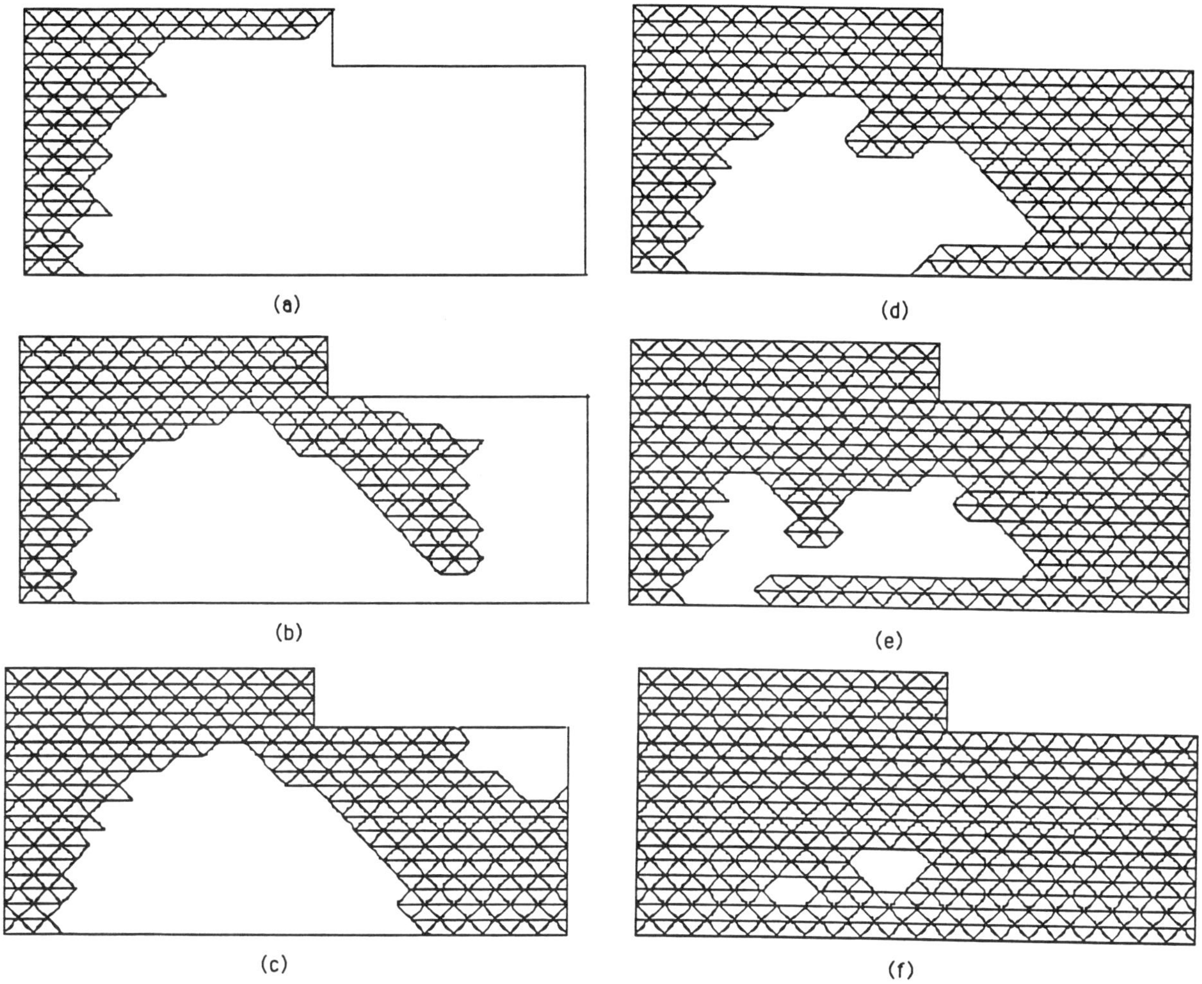

FIGURE 5.1 FLOW PATTERN IN A L-TYPE MOLD

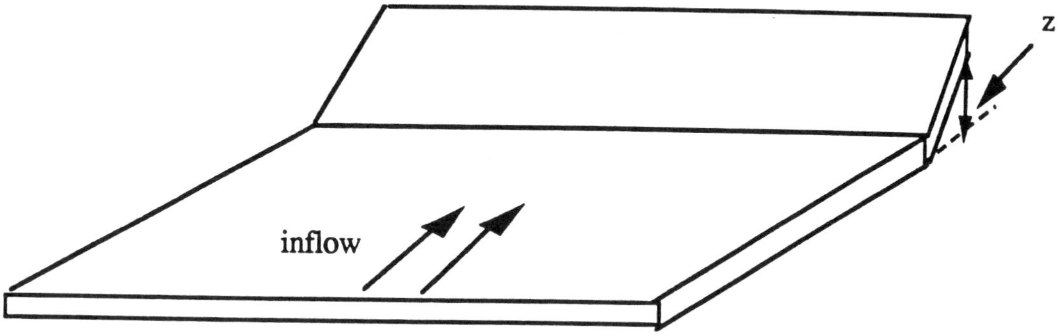

FIGURE 5.2 3-D MOLD

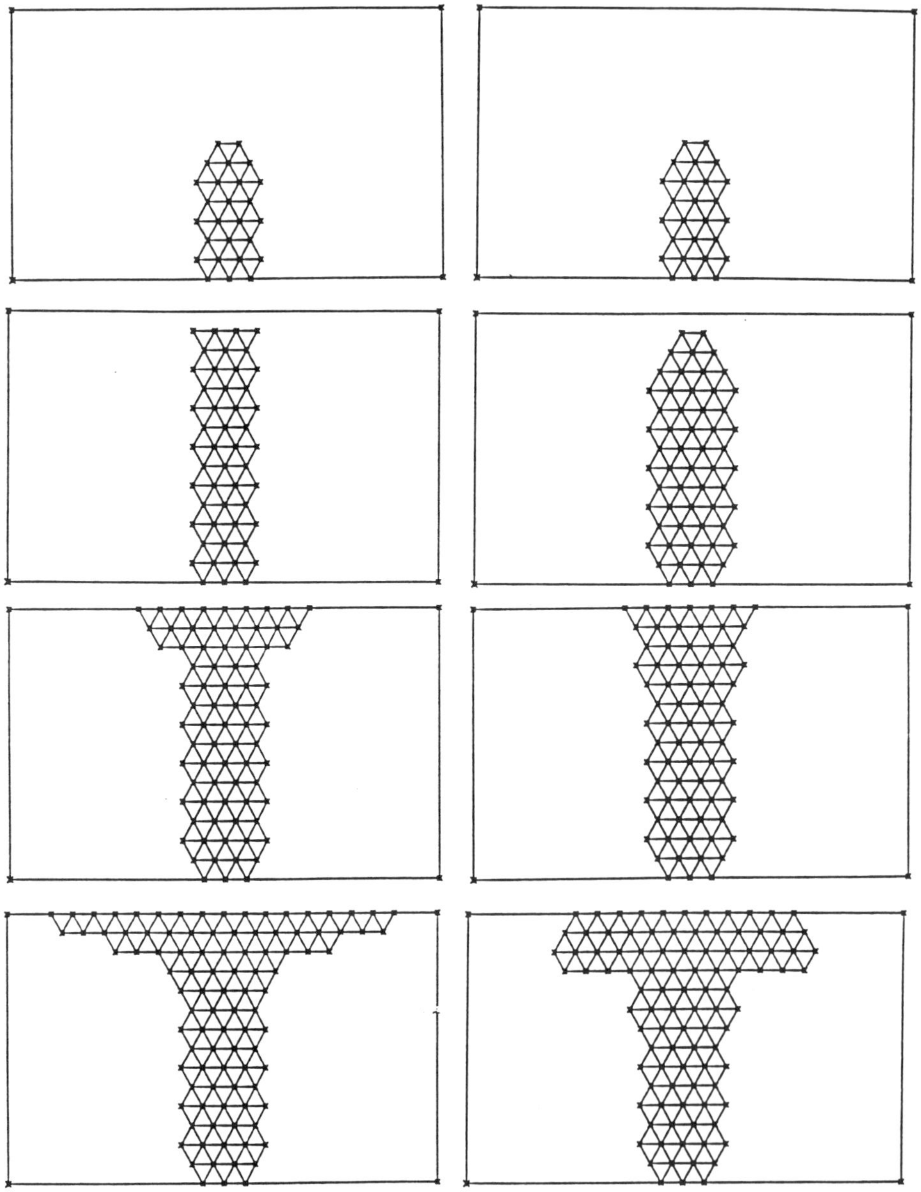

2-D MOLD 3-D MOLD

FIGURE 5.3 COMPARISON OF PATTERNS BETWEEN 2-D AND 3-D MOLDS

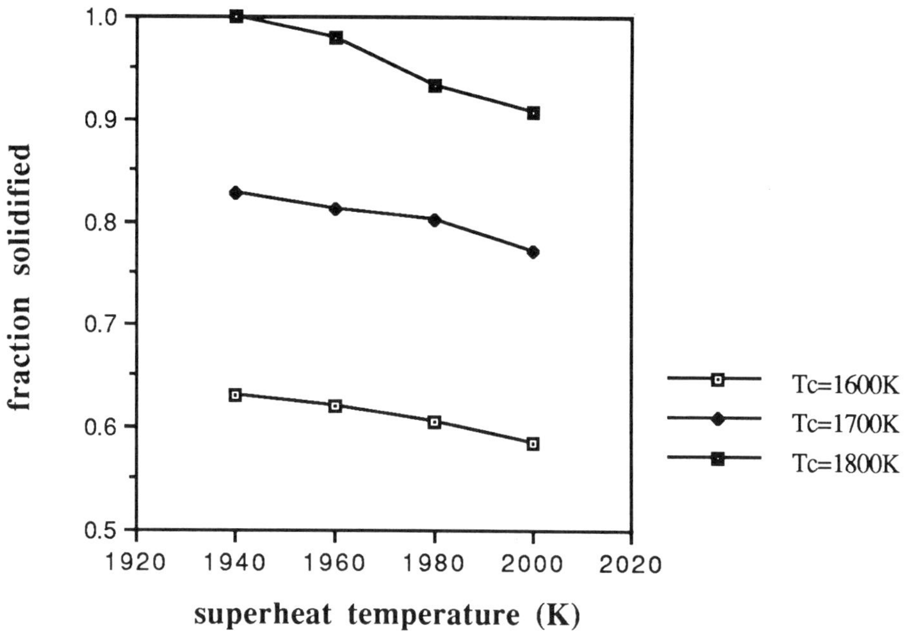

FIGURE 5.4 PARAMETRIC ANALYSIS RESULTS

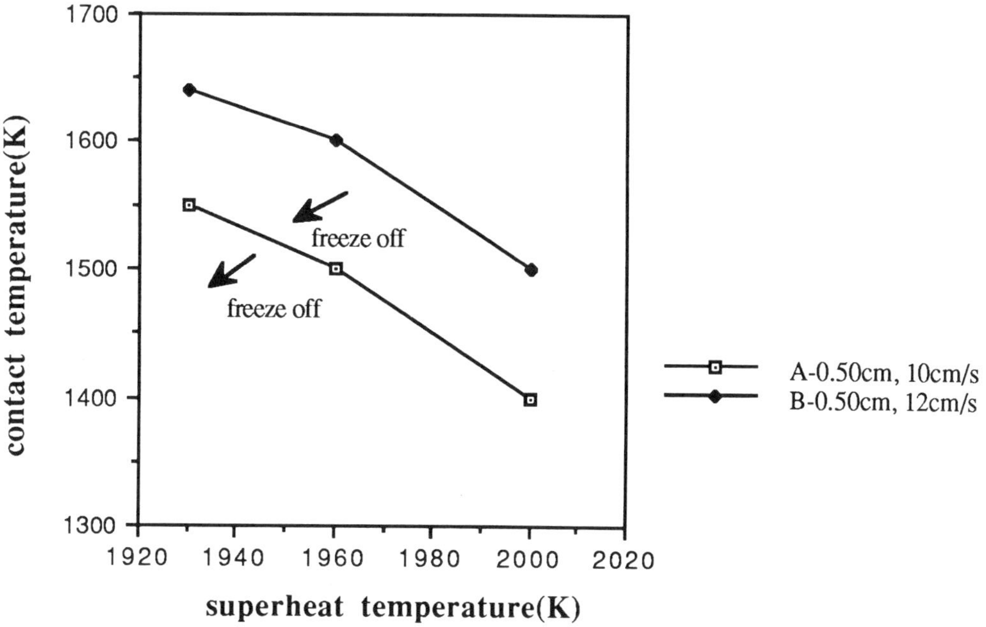

FIGURE 5.5 FREEAE-OFF MAP(a)

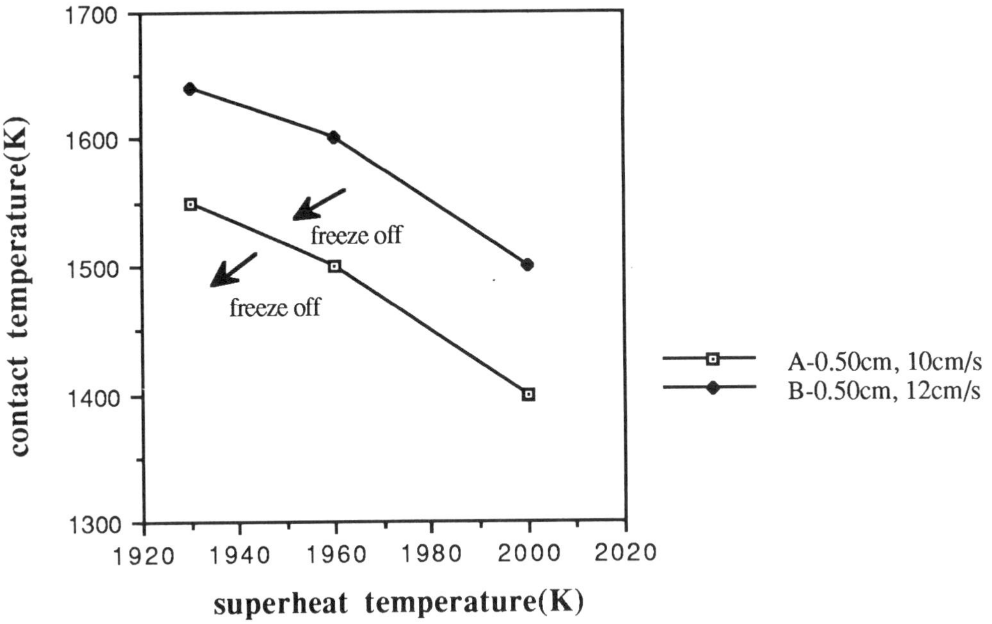

FIGURE 5.5 FREEZE-OFF MAP(b)

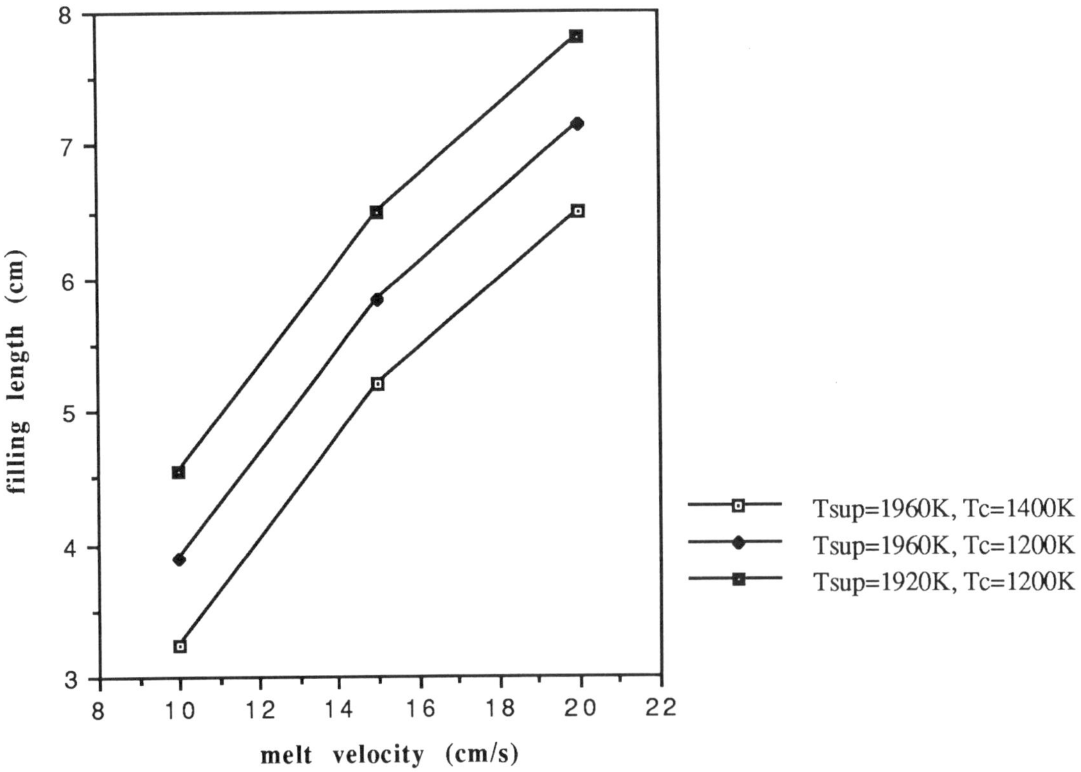

FIGURE 5.6 FILLING LENGTH PREDICTION FOR A THIN PART

HTD-Vol. 284/AMD-Vol. 182, Transport Phenomena in Solidification
ASME 1994

NUMERICAL AND EXPERIMENTAL STUDY OF TRANSPORT PHENOMENA IN DIRECTIONAL SOLIDIFICATION OF SUCCINONITRILE

Henry C. de Groh III
NASA Lewis Research Center
Cleveland, Ohio

Minwu Yao
Ohio Aerospace Institute
Brook Park, Ohio

ABSTRACT

A numerical and experimental study of the growth of succinonitrile (SCN) using a horizontal Bridgman furnace and transparent glass ampoule was conducted. Two experiments were considered: one in which the temperature profile was fixed relative to the ampoule (no-growth case); and a second in which the thermal profile was translated at a constant rate (steady growth case). Measured temperature profiles on the outer surface of the ampoule were used as thermal boundary conditions for the modelling. The apparent heat capacity formulation combined with the variable viscosity method was used to model the phase change in SCN. Both 2-D and 3-D models were studied and numerical solutions obtained using the commercial finite element code, FIDAP[1]. Comparison of the numerical results to experimental data showed excellent agreement. The complex 3-D shallow-cavity flow in the melt, differences between 2-D and 3-D models, effects of natural convection on the thermal gradient and shape of the solid/liquid interface, and the sensitivity of simulations to specific assumptions, are also discussed.

1. NASA does not endorse commercial products. Details about the products named in this paper were included for completeness and accuracy. No endorsement or criticism of these products by NASA should be assumed.

INTRODUCTION

The manufacture of electronic materials and optoelectronic devices demands high-quality crystals. It is known (Brown, 1988) that the quality of crystals grown from the melt is strongly influenced by the interaction between heat and mass transport and fluid flow during the solidification process. Consequently, vigorous experimental and numerical research activities have been conducted in recent years in order to enhance the understanding of transport phenomena and fluid motion during crystal growth (Sparrow, et al., 1979, Chang and Brown, 1984, Pimputkar and Ostrach, 1981, Langlois, 1984, Glicksman et al., 1986, Yeoh et al., 1990).

Horizontal Bridgman growth is a widely used technique in crystal growth research. During horizontal Bridgman growth under terrestrial conditions (1-g), the so-called "shallow-cavity" convective flow can be quite strong (Arnold et al., 1991, Chait, 1990). Generally, shallow-cavity flow is complex, three-dimensional in nature, and about two orders of magnitude stronger than convection during vertical Bridgman growth. Previous studies show that this gravity-driven convective flow can have a significant impact on growth rate, solid/liquid (s/l) interface shape and segregation of impurities (Brown, 1988, Sparrow, et al., 1979, Chang and Brown, 1984, Pimputkar and Ostrach, 1981, Langlois, 1984, Glicksman et al., 1986, Yeoh et al., 1990).

Among the materials used for understanding solidification and crystal growth behavior, a transparent plastic material called succinonitrile (SCN) has been gaining increasing interest from experimentalists (Mennetrier et al., 1991, Chopra and Glicksman, 1988, Inotomi et al., 1993). The main advantages of SCN for laboratory study of crystal growth are as follows. First, SCN is widely used as an analog to metals. For example, a SCN-acetone alloy can be used as a model material for metallic solidification study. Second, because of its transparency, the fluid motion can be simultaneously observed through a transparent ampoule. Thus some other important physical characteristics, such as the growth rate, interface shape, strength of convective flow and even the concentration profile, can be quantitatively determined using optical devices. Third, it has a conveniently low melting point ($T_m = 58.24°C$) and grows non-faceted. Finally, its physical and chemical properties have been well established (Chopra et al., 1988).

In previous publications (Mennetrier, 1991, Yeoh et al., 1992, Yao and de Groh, 1993), the authors and their co-workers have reported the effects of natural convection on interface shape during horizontal Bridgman growth of SCN. Fairly good agreement was achieved among experiments and two numerical simulations, one based on the finite element method (FEM) and a second used the finite difference method (FDM). However, those works were restricted to study of the no-growth case. In addition, the study of interface shape was limited to a mid-center vertical plane (symmetry plane), and no direct temperature measurements were available from inside the ampoule.

In the present work, we consider two new experiments (de Groh and Lindstrom, 1994). They are a refined no-growth experiment with temperature being measured inside the SCN sample and a steady growth solidification experiment with non-zero growth rate. In the steady growth case experimental conditions were measured after steady state was achieved. However, the numerical simulation also models the transient between zero and steady growth. For the two experiments, the interface shape was measured not only at the mid-center vertical plane but also at other two-dimensional planes, which together provide a three-dimensional picture of the s/l interface. Measured temperature profiles on the outer surface of the ampoule are imposed as thermal boundary conditions for the FEM modelling.

The primary objectives of this work are as follows: to determine quantitatively how conduction and convection influence interface shape, to evaluate the numerical model and computer code through comparison with experiments, to address some relevant issues in the numerical modelling, such as the difference between 2-D and 3-D models, and to provide benchmark numerical and experimental data for researchers in this field.

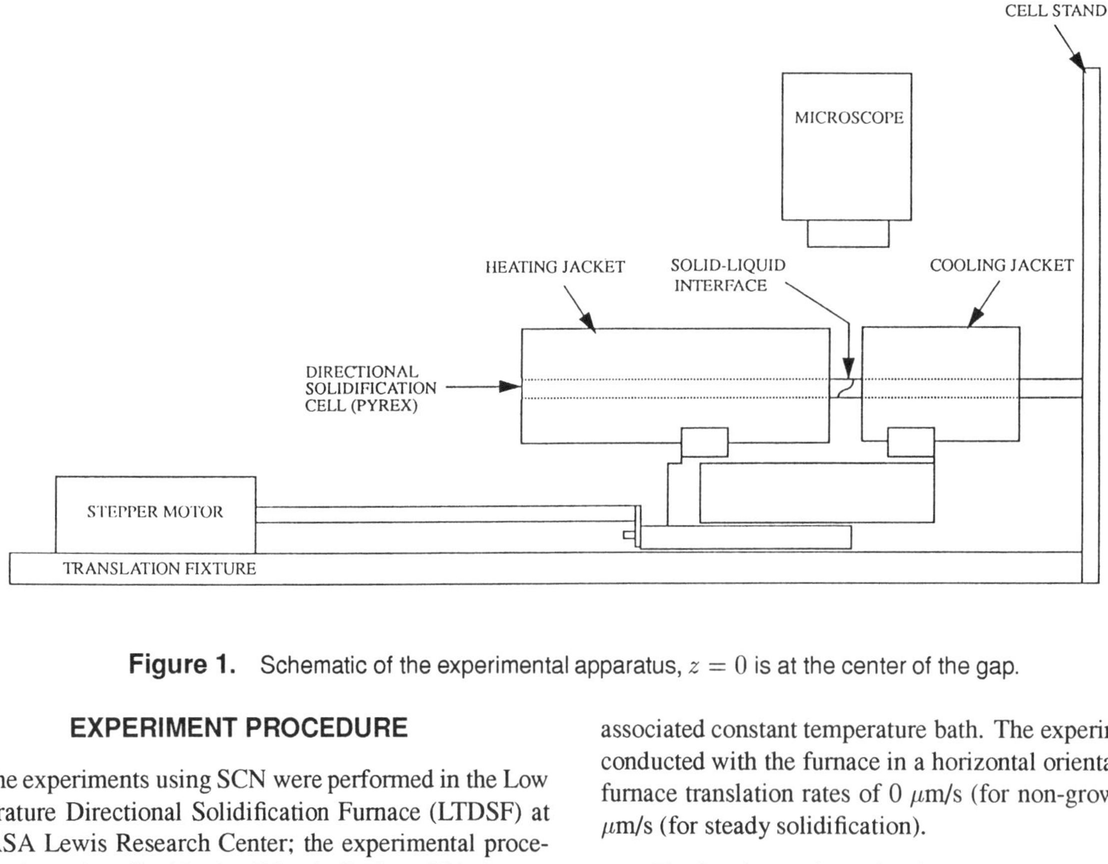

Figure 1. Schematic of the experimental apparatus, $z = 0$ is at the center of the gap.

EXPERIMENT PROCEDURE

The experiments using SCN were performed in the Low Temperature Directional Solidification Furnace (LTDSF) at the NASA Lewis Research Center; the experimental procedure has been described in detail by de Groh and Lindstrom (1994) and Yeoh (1992). A schematic of the experimental apparatus is shown in Figure 1. The LTDSF is a Bridgman type furnace employing two copper jackets, each of which has an associated constant temperature bath. The experiments were conducted with the furnace in a horizontal orientation and at furnace translation rates of 0 μm/s (for non-growth) and 40 μm/s (for steady solidification).

The heating and cooling jackets have a 1.1 cm square hole into which the ampoule fits. The borosilicate glass ampoules used have an outer square cross section of 0.775 cm and are 15 cm long with a wall thickness of approximately

0.0925 cm. The corners of the ampoule are slightly rounded as depicted in Fig. 2(a). The ampoule was filled under vacuum with SCN which was purified to eliminate solutal convection. The physical properties of SCN and of the glass ampoule have been listed elsewhere (de Groh and Lindstrom, 1994). In this paper we shall consider two experiments: the no-growth experiment (referred to as SCN-4) and the steady solidification experiment (SCN-8). (In addition to these two experiments, work by de Groh and Lindstrom (1994) also includes a steady melting experiment. Because of the limited space, this third experiment will be analyzed in a future publication).

In all experiments, the heating and cooling jackets were maintained at a temperature difference of $63°C$ with a hot zone temperature of $78°C$ for no-growth and $75°C$ during solidification. The temperature distributions on the outer surface of the ampoule were measured with type K (Chromel-Alumel) thermocouples attached to the top, bottom, front and corners of the ampoule as shown in Fig. 2(b). The temperature of the ampoule was influenced by the furnace set point, by convection and conduction in the sample, and by natural convection in the ambient air environment around the ampoule. These effects caused the temperature distribution to vary among the top surface, the vertical sides and the bottom of the ampoule.

To measure the temperature distribution, the furnace was moved relative to the ampoule in discrete steps during no growth. After each step movement of the furnace, the system was allowed to equilibrate for about 10 minutes before temperature measurements were taken. This gave the temperature distribution of the ampoule as a function of distance from the s/l interface. The temperature and position measurement accuracies are estimated to be approximately $\pm 1°C$ and ± 0.5 mm.

In the no-growth case, temperature was also measured inside the SCN sample with one thermocouple located at the center and the other between the center and the upper wall. These two thermocouples, designated in Fig. 2(b) by T_c and T_u respectively, provided temperature distributions along two longitudinal directions, i.e. the lines $(0, 0, z)$ and $(1.54mm, 0, z)$.

A microscope and camera were used to examine the s/l interface. The interface location and shape was quantitatively analyzed at the mid-center vertical plane (MCP), upper-center horizontal plane (UCP), top surface (TS) and the front surface of the SCN sample (FS). In the coordinate system shown in Fig. 2, the MCP corresponds to the $(x, 0, z)$ plane. UCP is in the yz plane at $x = 1.5$mm for SCN-4 and $x = 1.0$mm for SCN-8. TS represents the intersection between the S/L interface and the inner top wall, namely the interface shape in the plane. FS refers to the intersection between the s/l interface and the inner front ampoule wall, the interface at the $(2.95mm, y, z)$ plane. Photographs were taken of the s/l interface only when steady state conditions were reached. The photographs were then traced on an electromagnetic digitizer. The shape of the interface was obtained from the digitized data. To minimize the inconsistency of the measured temperature and interface positions caused by experimental uncertainties, a simple averaging technique was used to adjust the raw experimental data. These adjusted temperature and interface position data are listed in de Groh and Lindstrom (1994).

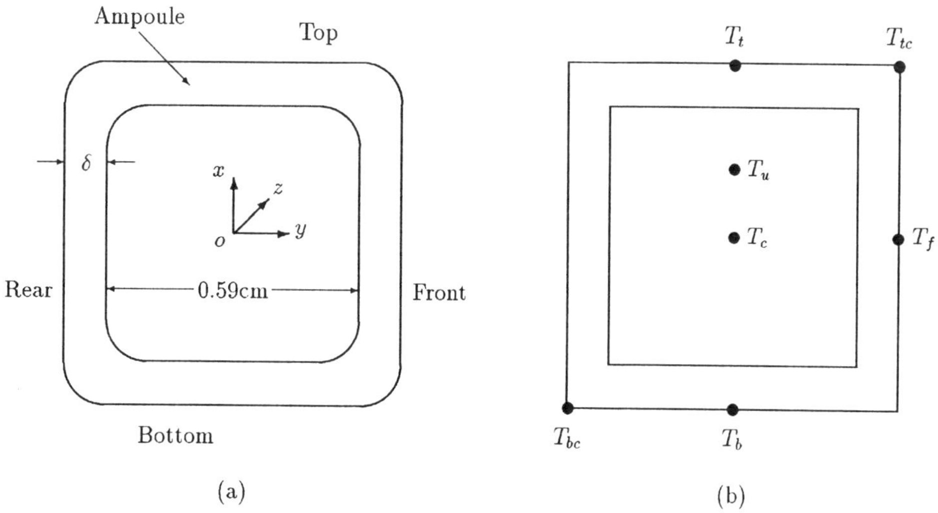

Figure 2. Schematic of the cross-section of glass ampoule and arrangements of thermocouples. (a) The rounded-corner ampoule actually used in the experiment and definition of co-ordinate system. $z = 0$ is defined as the center of the gap between hot and cold zones and the positive z-axis is directed towards the solid. $\delta = 0.0925$cm is the thickness of ampoule wall. (b) The simplified sharp-corner model used in the simulation.

The Prandtl number, $Pr = \nu/\alpha$, for SCN is approximately 23, where $\nu = 2.6 \times 10^{-6} m^2/s$ is the kinematic viscosity and α is thermal diffusivity. The thermal Grashof number is given by:

$$Gr_T \equiv \frac{g\beta_T \Delta T L^3}{\nu^2}$$

where $\beta_T = -8.1 \times 10^{-4}/K$, is the coefficient of thermal expansion. Since we are considering horizontal growth, $\Delta T = 18K$ is the temperature difference between the hot zone and the melting temperature, and the distance over which is L, the characteristic length of the system ($L = 2cm$). Under these conditions at unit gravity, $g = 9.8m/s^2$, the thermal Grashof number is about 1.7×10^5.

NUMERICAL MODELING

Governing Equations

The mathematical model used in the present work considers heat transport in both SCN and the glass ampoule, fluid motion in the melt, and phase change at the S/L interface. The liquid SCN is assumed to be Newtonian and its motion is described by the following Navier-Stokes equation:

$$\rho_0 \left(\frac{\partial \mathbf{u}}{\partial t} + \mathbf{u} \cdot \nabla \mathbf{u} \right) = -\nabla p + \nabla \cdot [\mu(\nabla \mathbf{u} + (\nabla \mathbf{u})^T)] + \rho_0 \mathbf{g}[1 - \beta_T(T - T_0)] \quad (1)$$

where $\mathbf{u}$ is the velocity vector, t is time, ρ_0 is fluid density, p is pressure, μ is viscosity, T is temperature, T_0 is a reference temperature, g is the acceleration of gravity, β is the volumetric expansion coefficient and the Boussinesq model is adopted to approximate the buoyancy force caused by density variation with temperature. The incompressibility condition for liquid SCN is given by

$$\nabla \cdot \mathbf{u} = 0 \, . \quad (2)$$

The heat transport is controlled by the balance of thermal energy

$$\rho_0 c_p \left(\frac{\partial T}{\partial t} + \mathbf{u} \cdot \nabla T \right) = \nabla \cdot (\kappa \nabla T) \quad (3)$$

where c_p is specific heat, κ is thermal conductivity. To model the borosilicate glass ampoule we treat the ampoule walls as solid and consider only the heat conduction equation (3) within the wall regions. Since the temperature levels considered were low, radiative heat transfer was neglected in this work.

The boundary conditions associated with eqn. (1) are the no-slip conditions imposed at the SCN/ampoule interface. For eqn. (3), the interpolated temperature profiles based on the experimental measurements are specified on the outer surface of the ampoule. Note that the numerical simulation incorporates conduction through the ampoule.

At the s/l interface, the following phase change conditions need to be satisfied:

$$T_s[S(t), t] = T_l[S(t), t] = T_m \, , \quad (4)$$

$$(\kappa_s \nabla T_s - \kappa_l \nabla T_l) \cdot \hat{\mathbf{n}} = \rho L \frac{dS}{dt} \, . \quad (5)$$

The subscripts, s and l, refer to the solid and liquid regions, respectively; $S(t)$ is the spatial position of the S/L interface; T_m is the melting temperature; $\hat{\mathbf{n}}$ is the unit outward normal of the solid region; and L is the latent heat of fusion. Since at the atomic level the interfaces studied are flat, we shall not consider the influence of interface curvature on melting point (Flemings, 1974) and assume solidification to occur at the equilibrium melting temperature.

The FEM Model

In the horizontal Bridgman configuration, the longitudinal axis of the furnace is perpendicular to the gravity vector as shown in Fig. 3. Since it is reasonable to assume that the heat and flow fields are symmetric with respect to the middle center plane, only half of the ampoule is modelled in the 3-D Simulation. We consider two ampoule cross-sections. One has rounded corners, which is closer to the real ampoule used in the experiment, while the other has sharp corners.

In selecting the length of the computational domain, we considered only the central 6.25 cm of the total 15 cm length of the ampoule. Beyond the region modeled, the experimental data indicated that the temperature variations are very small and should not affect the solution near the interface.

The 2-D FEM mesh was built with the 4-node bilinear element, in which the velocity and temperature were approximated by bilinear shape functions and the pressure was approximated as piecewise constant. The typical 2-D mesh used in the modelling has 954 bilinear elements and 1026 nodes.

For the 3-D FEM model, we used the 8-node linear brick element, in which the velocity and temperature are assumed to be trilinear and the pressure to be piecewise constant. The FEM meshes were generated by FIMESH, a mesh generator provided in FIDAP. A total of four 3-D meshes were created for our computation. For each of the sharp corner and rounded corner models, we had a corresponding fine mesh and a coarser mesh. The two fine meshes are shown in Fig. 4.

In this work numerical solutions were obtained using the FEM program FIDAP, a general fluid dynamics analysis package (Engleman, 1993). For steady-state problems, the discretized FEM equations can be reduced to a set of nonlinear algebraic equations in the following matrix form

$$\mathbf{K}(\mathbf{U})\mathbf{U} = \mathbf{F} \quad (6)$$

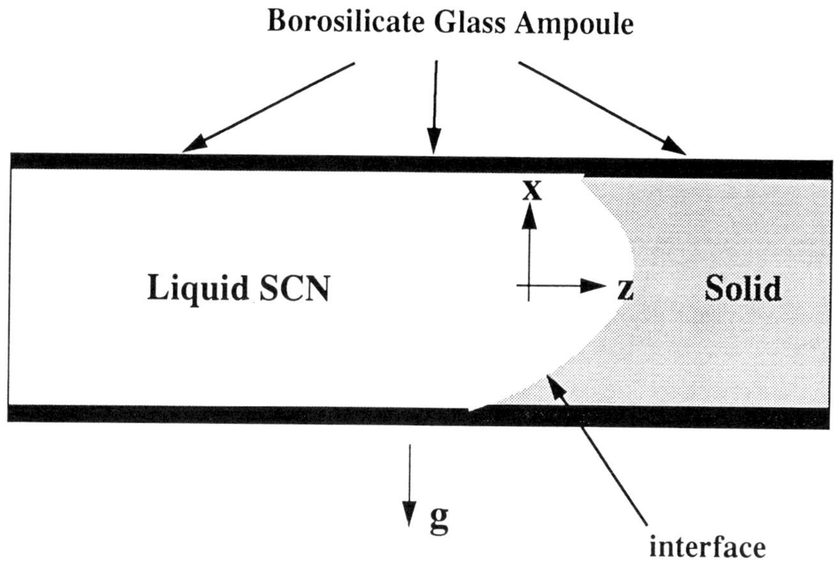

Figure 3. Schematic diagram of the simplified 2-D FEM model for the directional SCN growth experiment. For the 3-D model this diagram represents the mid-center vertical plane, i.e. the xz plane at $y = 0$.

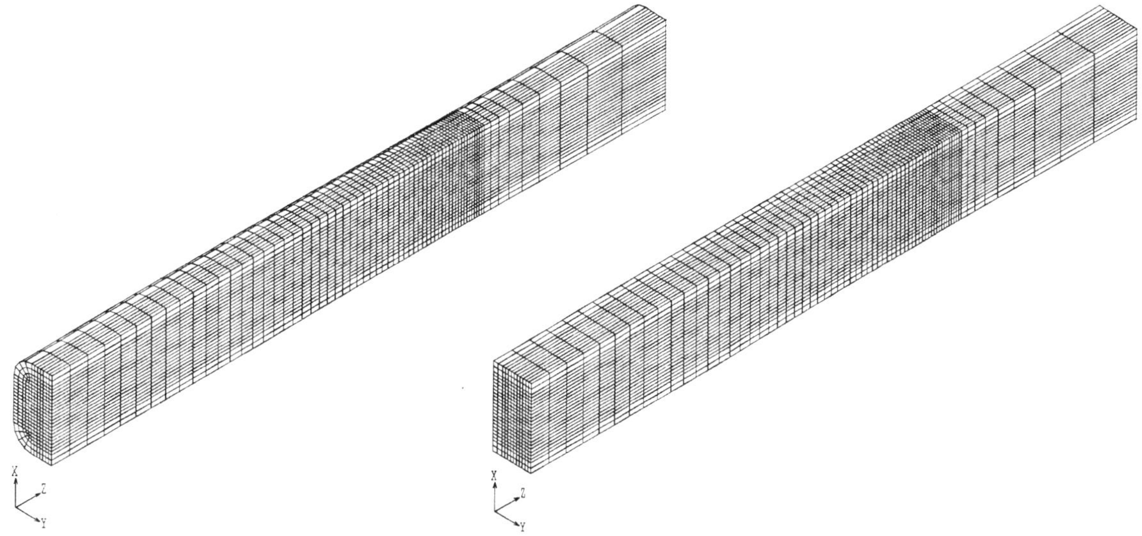

Figure 4. The two finer 3-D meshes used. On the left is the rounded corner mesh. This mesh has 18090 8-node linear brick elements with a total of 20468 nodal points. On the right is the sharp corner mesh built with 19872 elements and 22750 nodes.

where $\mathbf{K}$ is the global system matrix, $\mathbf{U} = (\mathbf{u}, p, T)$ is the global vector of unknowns (velocities, pressure and temperature), and $\mathbf{F}$ is a vector that includes the effects of body forces and gradient type boundary conditions. For the problem we considered, there is strong coupling between the momentum and the energy equations through the buoyancy term as well as through the convective terms.

The Enthalpy Method

To model the phase change in SCN, we used the enthalpy method (Crank, 1984). As a fixed domain approach, the enthalpy method avoids tracking the s/l interface by incorporating the Stefan condition (5) into the following definition of enthalpy:

$$H(T) = \int_{T_{\text{ref}}}^{T} \rho c_p(\tau) d\tau + \rho f(T) L \tag{7}$$

where T_{ref} is an arbitrary reference temperature and f is the *local liquid volume fraction* (Crank, 1984, Voller and Swaminathan, 1990). For an isothermal phase change, f is given by the Heaviside step function

$$f(T) = \begin{cases} 0, & T < T_m \\ 1, & T > T_m \end{cases} . \tag{8}$$

In numerical solutions, H as given in (7) usually needs to be smoothed. The following linear approximation (Yao and Chait, 1993) is used in our computation:

$$H_\varepsilon(T) \equiv \begin{cases} \rho_s c_p^s T, & T < T_m - \varepsilon \\ \rho_s c_p^s (T_m - \varepsilon) + & T_m - \varepsilon < T < T_m + \varepsilon \\ + \left(\dfrac{\rho_s c_p^s + \rho_l c_p^l}{2} + \dfrac{\rho_s L}{2\varepsilon} \right) [T - (T_m - \varepsilon)], & \\ \rho_s c_p^s T_m + \rho_l c_p^l (T - T_m) + \rho_s L & \\ & T > T_m + \varepsilon . \end{cases} \tag{9}$$

In this approximation, the latent heat is released over a small temperature interval $[T_m - \varepsilon, T_m + \varepsilon]$, and the value of ε corresponds to the half-length of a transition zone.

Based on the definition of enthalpy an *apparent heat capacity* (AHC) can then be defined as (Crank, 1984)

$$C^A(T) \equiv \frac{\partial H}{\partial T} = \rho c_p + \rho L \delta(T - T_m) \tag{10}$$

where δ is the Dirac function. Numerical schemes based on (10) are often referred to as the *apparent heat capacity method* (AHCM). We use the following temporal averaging scheme (Morgan et al., 1978, Dantzig, 1989) to approximate the AHC:

$$C^A \approx C_\varepsilon^A = \frac{H_\varepsilon(T^k) - H_\varepsilon(T^{k-1})}{T^k - T^{k-1}}, \tag{11}$$

where k represents iteration number.

One of the difficulties inherent to the AHCM is the selection of parameter ε involved in the calculation of C_ε^A or H_ε. Detailed studies about the effect of ε value on solution accuracy and convergence with mesh refinement can be found in Shamsundar (1978), Yao and Chait (1993a), (1993b). For the AHCM with the linear approximation given in (9), numerical tests in Yao and Chait (1993a) shows that the accuracy of solutions varies with the value of ε and there exists an optimum ε at which the best accuracy may be obtained for a particular spatial and time discretization. Unfortunately, the analytical prediction of the optimum ε is not available in practice. The general rule recommended by Bonacina (1973) is to select the value of ε so that the transition zone embraces one or two complete elements. This rule was used for selecting ε values in our computations. Our study suggests that this rule produces results that are very close to the optimum ε. In enthalpy method, the s/l interface is usually recovered by computing its isotherm; its resolution is determined by the value of ε. For the no-growth case the resolution of interface is about $2\varepsilon = 0.1°C$ which is smaller than the estimated accuracy of measured temperature.

At the s/l interface or in the transition region, the fluid velocity diminishes to zero. Clearly then, the enthalpy formulation must be able to account for this velocity behavior in the vicinity of the phase-change front. There are a number of methods available in the literature (Voller, 1987). In our computation, a so-called variable viscosity method (Voller et al., 1987, Gartling, 1980) is used to model the velocity behavior. In this method, the liquid SCN is treated as a Newtonian fluid whose viscosity is a function of temperature and takes an artificially high value when T is below the melting point. This treatment has the effect of immobilizing the solid portion of the SCN so that any predicted velocities in the solid region are negligible.

Implementation of the variable viscosity method is very simple. It requires only the specification of a viscosity-temperature curve. However the artificially introduced large discontinuity in the viscosity may cause some numerical difficulties in convergence of the nonlinear iteration, especially when the segregated solution approach is used and the convection is strong (as in this work). Consequently, an incremental solution procedure is used. In this solution process, we begin with a viscosity jump across the interface of about 10^4. Then we restart from the previous solution each time with a viscosity jump increase of 10 or 10^2. Our computation stops when a viscosity discontinuity of 10^8 is reached, since our experience shows that the solution accuracy is good enough at this point.

Segregated Solution Approach

In general there are two distinct solution approaches available for solving the nonlinear system (6). The first approach solves the whole system in a simultaneous coupled manner, while the second approach solves each equation separately in a sequential segregated manner. Fully coupled solution approaches, such as successive substitution and Newton-Raphson, usually require formation of the global system matrix which includes all the unknown degrees of freedom. While this strategy is cost-effective for most 2-D problems, the peripheral storage required for 3-D problems can become excessive.

In contrast to the fully-coupled approach, the segregated solution algorithm (Haroutunian et al., 1991a and 1991b) avoids the direct formation of a global system matrix. Instead, the global matrix is decomposed into smaller sub-matrices, each governing the nodal unknowns associated with only one conservation equation. These smaller sub-matrices are then solved in a sequential manner. As the storage of the individual sub-matrices is considerably less than that needed to store the global system matrix, the storage requirements of the segregated approach are substantially less than that of the fully coupled approach. This makes it possible to solve large-scale 3-D simulation problems on a workstation. All the 3-D computations presented in this work were done on a Sparcstation.

RESULTS AND DISCUSSION

In this section we present our numerical simulation results and compare them with experiments.

No-Growth Experiment (SCN-4)

2-D FEM Modeling

It is natural to start from a simplified 2-D model which considers the mid-center vertical plane of the ampoule (MCP) only. The measured temperature profiles given by the thermocouples T_t and T_b are imposed on the top and bottom boundaries of the 2-D model. Since the resulting global system (6) is much smaller than that in the 3-D case, the fully coupled solution approach is used for solving the nonlinear system.

The numerical results suggest that the heat and flow fields predicted by the simplified 2-D model are fairly good for the no-growth experiment. For example, the 2-D solution of temperature along the center z-axis, T_c, is very close to the 3-D solution and to experimental data, as shown in Fig. 5. The S/L interface shape of the 2-D model also compares well with the 3-D solution and the measured data, as can be seen in Fig. 6. Our results indicate that solutions of the 2-D model can provide reasonable approximations for temperature, velocity and interface shape on the symmetric planes (MCP) of the ampoule.

Visualization of 3-D Flow in the Melt

The information obtained from the 2-D model is limited to the MCP. Although the 3-D model requires much more computational effort and resources, it can provide much more detail on the interface shapes, transport phenomena and fluid flow in the whole domain. The flow pattern on the MCP indicates that the dominant flow is the so-called *shallow-cavity flow* (Arnold et al., 1991), which agrees with the experimental observation and literature. The primary characteristic of shallow-cavity flow is the single recirculating cell in the vertical (xz) planes as shown in Mennetrier et al. (1991), Yeoh (1992), and Yao and de Groh (1993). This strong convective flow cell forces hot liquid to flow along the top wall, raising and homogenizing the top wall temperature as well as directing hot liquid against the upper portion of the interface. The above mentioned fluid motion can be visualized using a trace of a particle path as shown in Fig. 7, in which a particle is released at the point $x = 0.26$, $y = -0.1$ & $z = -0.6$. As seen in the side view in Fig. 7(a), the liquid particle turns downward when confronted by the interface. After being cooled by the interface and the imposed thermal gradient, it returns along the bottom wall of the ampoule. The isometric perspective view in Fig. 7(b) illustrates the complex three-dimensional particle trajectory in the space between the MCP and the rear wall. Note that the spatial position of the particle in Fig. 7 is plotted at each time step. Since the time step is fixed, the distance between two particle symbols actually indicates how far the particle travels in one time step. Therefore it is clear, by examining the distance between the circular symbols on the path, that the particle flows much faster near the interface than at the other end of the domain.

Another important feature of the 3-D flow field is secondary flow in the planes perpendicular to the z-axes (i.e. the xy planes). A visualization of the secondary flows is shown in Fig. 8 in which we plot velocity vectors on different xy planes. The plot at $z = 0$ cuts the interface in the middle and captures the liquid SCN on the upper portion only. The blank lower portion in the $z = 0$ plot is the solid SCN. Moving away from the interface along the negative z-direction, a flow cell is first developed on the upper portion around $z = -0.2$cm. This flow cell grows stronger on the xy planes further away from the interface. After reaching the maximum strength, the upper cell starts decaying. Meanwhile, a second flow cell is formed in the lower part as shown by the $z = -0.4$ plot. This lower cell rotates in an opposite direction to the upper cell and is stronger in planes deeper in the hot zone. At around $z = -0.6$cm (about one seventh of the total liquid SCN length) the two counter rotating cells are about of equal strength. Then the upper cell becomes weaker and weaker, being pushed to the upper corner at $z = -3.2$ and vanishing at about $z = -3.9$. At $z = -4.1$cm, the flow is dominated by the primary flow pattern again with liquid coming along the bottom wall, changing direction and flowing upwards along

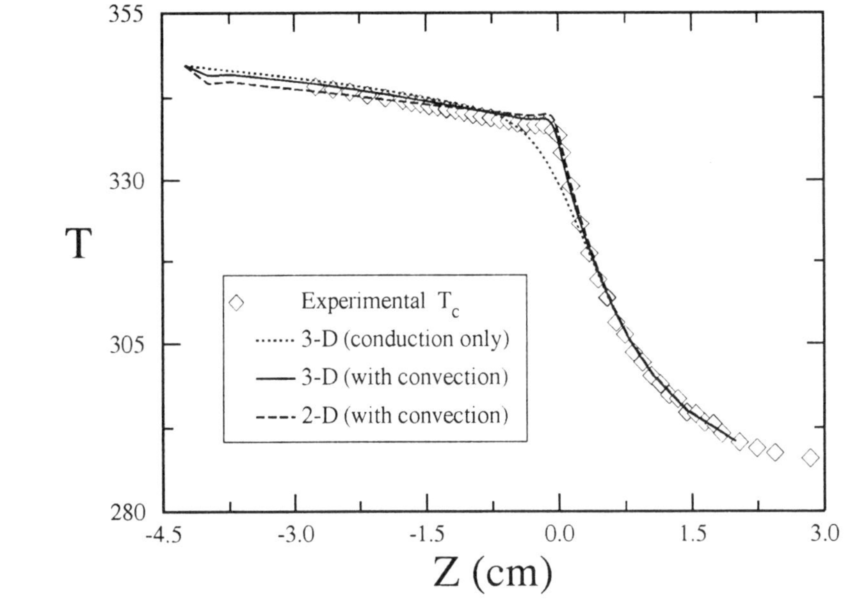

Figure 5. Comparison of 2-D and 3-D FEM solutions of temperature variation of T_c along the center z-axis, i.e. line $(x = 0, y = 0, z)$, with the experimental data.

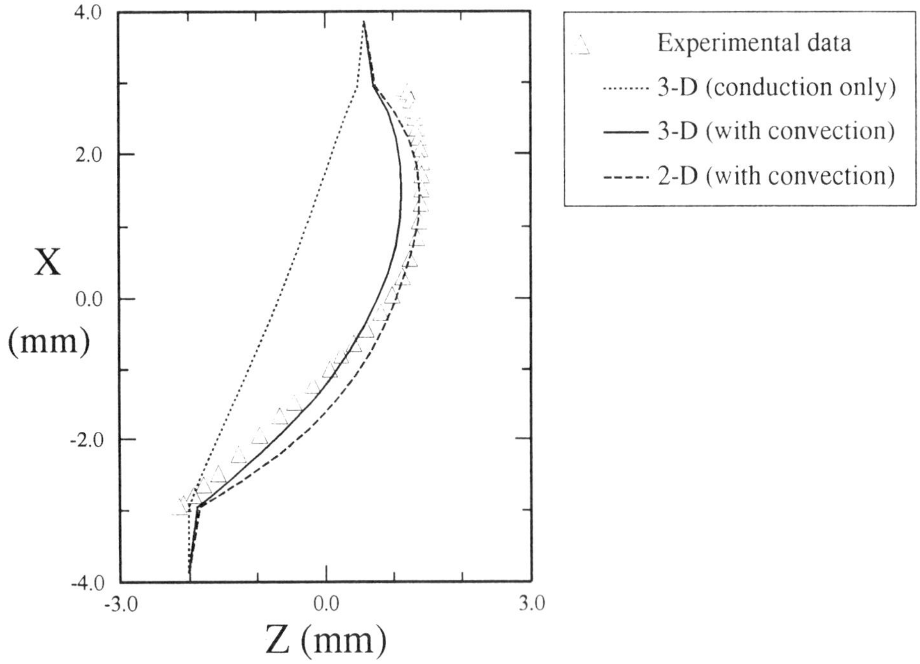

Figure 6. Simulated s/l interface shapes on the MCP based on 2-D and 3-D FEM models and comparison with the no-growth experiment (SCN-4) data.

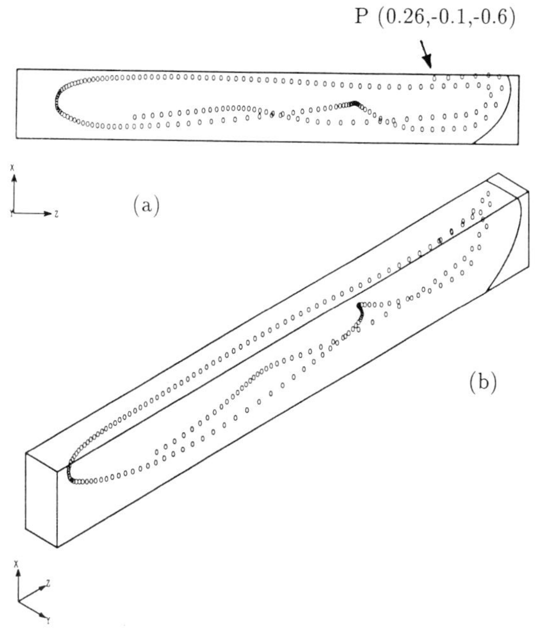

Figure 7. The particle path plotted from time 0 to 220 sec. with a fixed time step $\Delta t = 1.2$ sec for SCN-4. The particle, labelled as P, is released near the interface and MCP. (a) The side view; (b) The isometric perspective view. Note that only the liquid SCN part of the computational domain is displayed here.

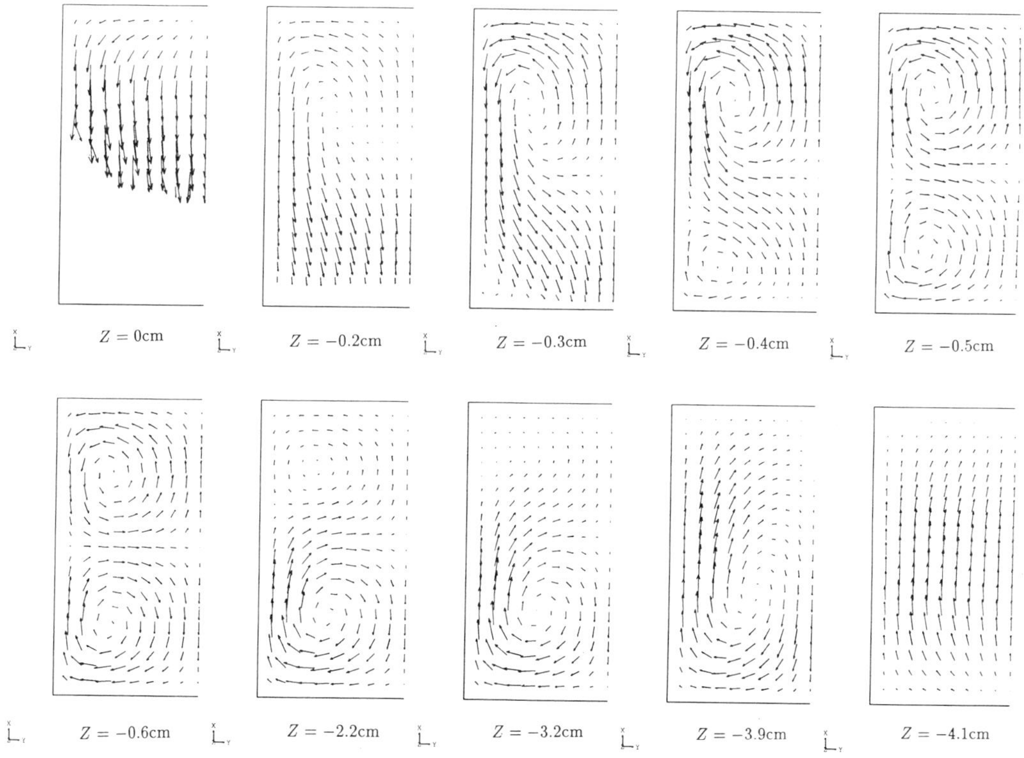

Figure 8. Visualization of the secondary flows on different xy planes for the no-growth SCN-4 experiment. The plots are based on the finer mesh for the simplified sharp corner model. Note that the plots are viewed from negative z-direction and the hot end of ampoule is $z = -4.2$cm.

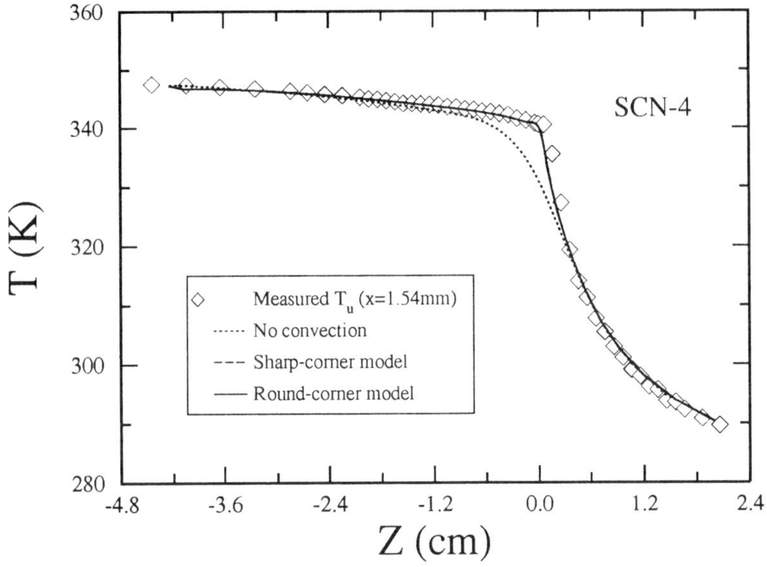

Figure 9. Computed no-growth 3-D FEM solutions of temperature variation of T_u along the upper z-axis, i.e. line $(x = 1.54mm, y = 0, z)$ using the finer round-corner and the sharp-corner meshes.

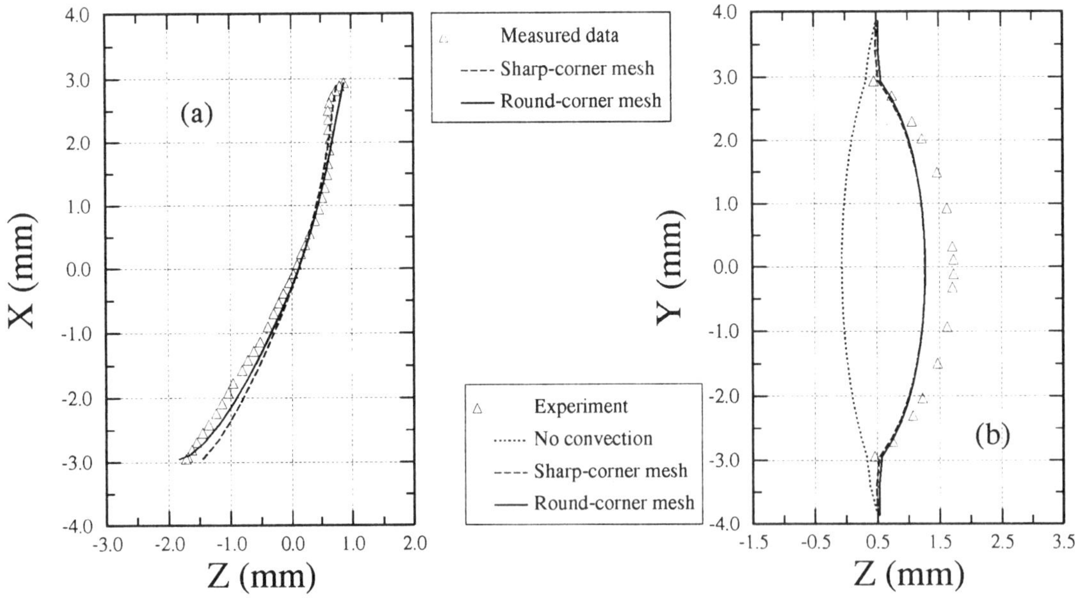

Figure 10. Modelled S/L interface shapes during no-growth solidification using the round-corner and the sharp-corner FEM meshes and comparison with the experimental measurements. (a) On the front surface of the SCN sample (FS, $y = -2.95$mm); (b) The upper center plane (UCP, $x = 1.54$mm).

the hot end of the ampoule, then changing direction again and flowing back along the top wall toward the interface.

Effects of Natural Convection

Our previous studies and the present work indicate that the convective flow in the melt has a great impact on the shape of s/l interface. This is shown in Fig. 6 and 12 where the interface obtained from the conduction-only solution is flat; the interface is highly curved when convection is included.

Another interesting phenomenon related to natural convection is the temperature distribution in the neighborhood of the interface. As seen in Fig. 5, the temperature variation is smooth near the interface (around $z = 0$) with a relatively wide diffusion layer when no convection is considered. However, when convection is added, there is a sharp change in the slope of the temperature curve and the diffusion layer becomes much narrower near the interface. Note the good agreement between the simulation with convection and the experimental data in Fig. 5. This narrow diffusion boundary layer and the dramatic change in slope render a great challenge to numerical modeling. We believe this phenomenon may be one of the main causes of difficulty in attaining convergence.

As noted earlier, for the cases considered, the thermal Grashof number was about 1.7×10^5 and the Prandtl number is about 23. At first, this Gr_T seems moderate, at least compared to some other horizontal systems examined by de Groh and Nelson (1994). However, SCN's relatively large Prandtl number enables larger transverse thermal gradients to develop, thus making possible the highly curved interface. Materials having a lower Prandtl number tend to result in flatter isotherms and interfaces (Gadonniex et al., 1994 and Rouzaud et al., 1993). This is reflected in the Rayleigh number, $Ra_T = Gr_T \times Pr$, which was about 4×10^6 in this study. For two other cases of horizontal plain front solidification using Bi-Sn alloys, which resulted in flatter interfaces, Rayleigh numbers were in the range of 4×10^5 (de Groh and Nelson, 1994). Thus for SCN the buoyant force/viscous force ratio is comparatively larger as compared to metals, making SCN generally more sensitive to gravity driven convection than metals.

Effects of Ampoule Corner Shape

To study the effects of ampoule shape on the thermal and flow fields, and especially the effects on the interface shapes, we examined both round-corner and simplified sharp-corner meshes as depicted in Fig. 1. The comparison between the two sets of solutions indicates that the shape of the ampoule corner has very little effect on the numerical solution. For example, on the MCP, the modelled temperature, velocity and interface shape based on the two meshes are almost identical. As a typical check, the temperature distribution of T_u on the MCP in Fig. 10 shows less than 1% difference between the solutions of T_u from the round-corner and sharp-corner meshes.

Slight differences are observed only in the vicinity of the corners. In Fig. 10(a) we compare the interface shape at the front surface of the SCN sample (FS). As shown, the interface shape given by the round-corner mesh is slightly closer to the experiment than the sharp-corner mesh solution. Another comparison of interface shape on the UCP is presented in Fig. 10(b), in which only a very small difference can be observed near the ampoule wall (at $y = \pm 2.95$mm).

Steady Solidification Experiment (SCN-8)

2-D FEM Modeling

As in the no-growth case, the 2-D model is adopted to simulate the middle center plane (MCP) of the ampoule. The measured temperature profiles of the thermocouples T_t and T_b (shown in Fig. 11) are used to specify thermal boundary conditions on the top and bottom boundary of MCP. A linear interpolation is used when the nodes fall between the raw experimental data points. To model the movement of the furnace (and hence the transient thermal environment), we assume the temperature profiles of T_t and T_b do not change with time, but translate towards the hot end with the same constant speed of 0.04mm/sec as the furnace. Since there is no direct experimental data available for an initial solution we use the steady (no-growth) analysis results as the initial condition. In our computation the Euler backward scheme with a fixed time step $\Delta t = 2$ sec is used for the time integration. The resulting global FEM system is solved by the Newton-Raphson iteration scheme.

To check the validity of the 2-D model we compare the solutions of interface location on MCP with experiment and present the results in Fig. 12. The conduction-only solution does not agree well with the experimental results and shows once again the significance of natural convection effects on the interface shape. In section 4.1 we have shown that the 2-D model provides a very good approximation for the interface shape on MCP in simulating the no-growth experiment (SCN-4). However this conclusion does not hold for modelling the solidification with non-zero growth rate. Fig. 12 shows the maximum difference between the 2-D solution (at $t = 400$sec) and the experiments to be about 3mm. This rather large difference is considered unacceptable and is much greater than the uncertainty in interface location in the experiments, which was estimated to be ± 0.5mm.

3-D FEM Simulation

The main reason for the inadequacy of the 2-D model during growth at the MCP is that the 2-D model does not have any knowledge of the 3-D effect from the rear and front ampoule walls. This does not seem to be a problem when the interface is not moving, such as the case in SCN-4 because there is less curvature in the yz plane. However when the interface moves, the 3-D effects become much more important. Our study suggests that a full 3-D model has to be used for simulating the growth of SCN-8.

Because the segregated solution approach is currently

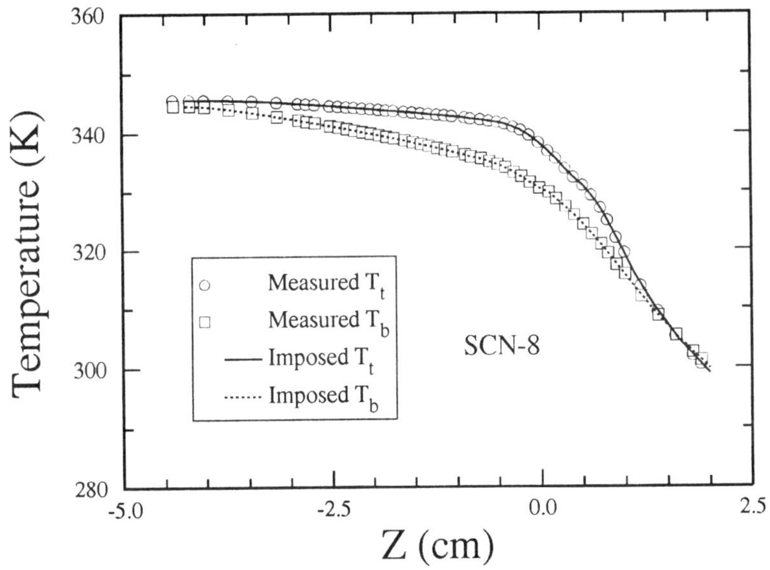

Figure 11. The measured temperature distribution of T_t and T_b along the ampoule axis. The imposed T_t and T_b are obtained by linear interpolation between experimental data points and used in the 2-D modeling as the top and bottom temperature boundary conditions. During growth the two curves are translated with a steady speed of 0.04mm/sec towards hot end.

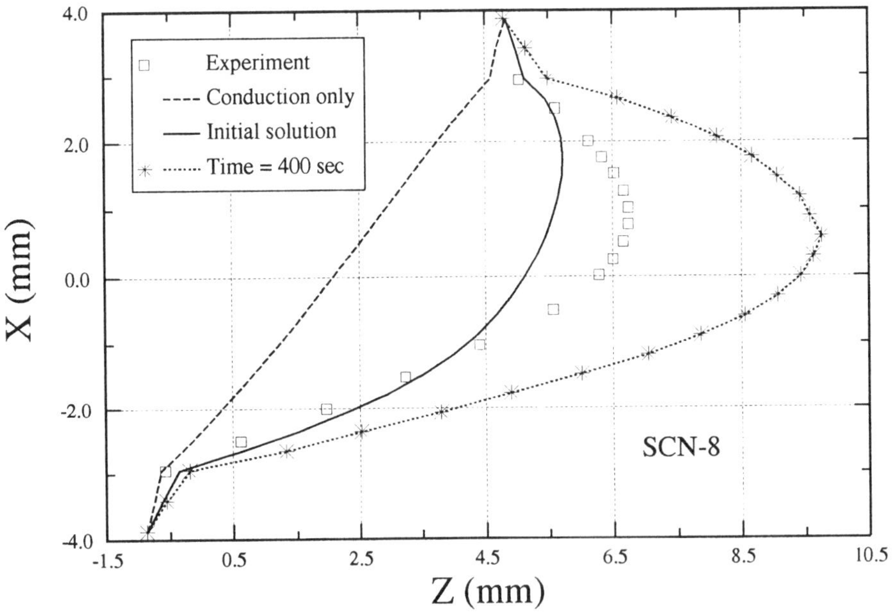

Figure 12. Simulated S/L interface shapes on the middle center plane (MCP) based on the 2-D FEM model and comparison with the experiment. The conduction-only solution is based on steady analysis with no convection. The initial solution is obtained by steady analysis considering both conduction and convection but no growth. The transient solution considers conduction, convection and a steady translation of the furnace (steady growth).

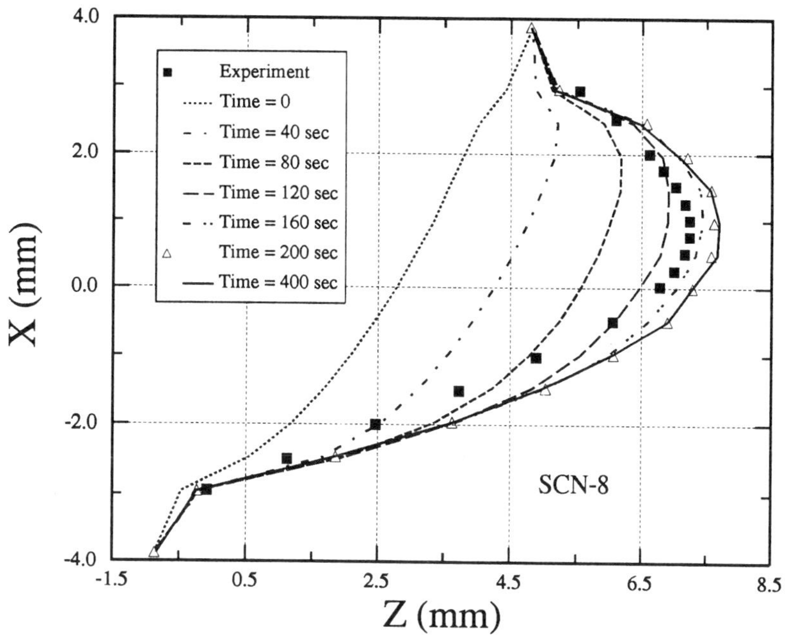

Figure 13. Development of S/L interface shapes on the MCP given by the transient 3-D FEM solidification analysis and comparison with experiment during horizontal solidification.

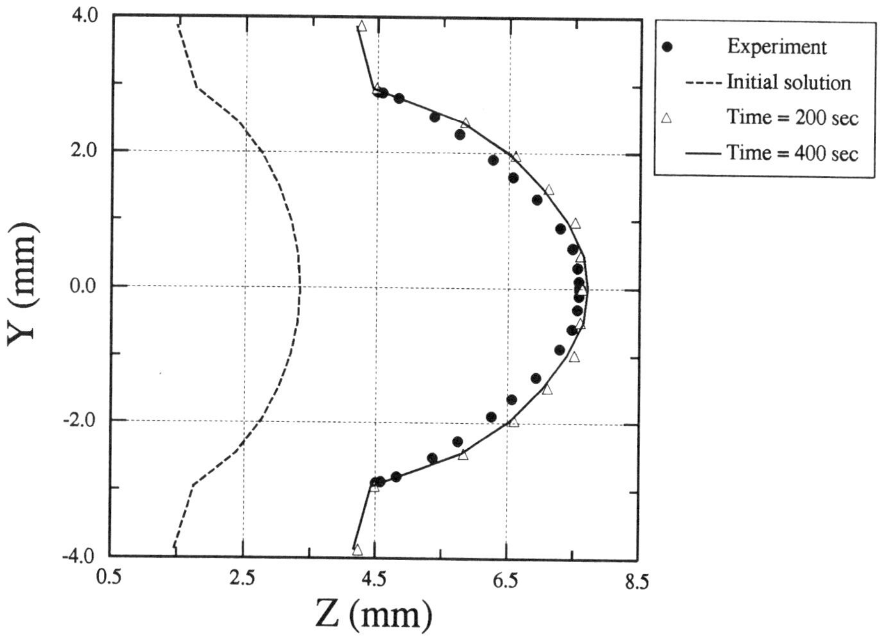

Figure 14. Simulated S/L interface shapes during solidification on the upper center plane (UCP, $x \approx 1.0$mm) and comparison with experiment.

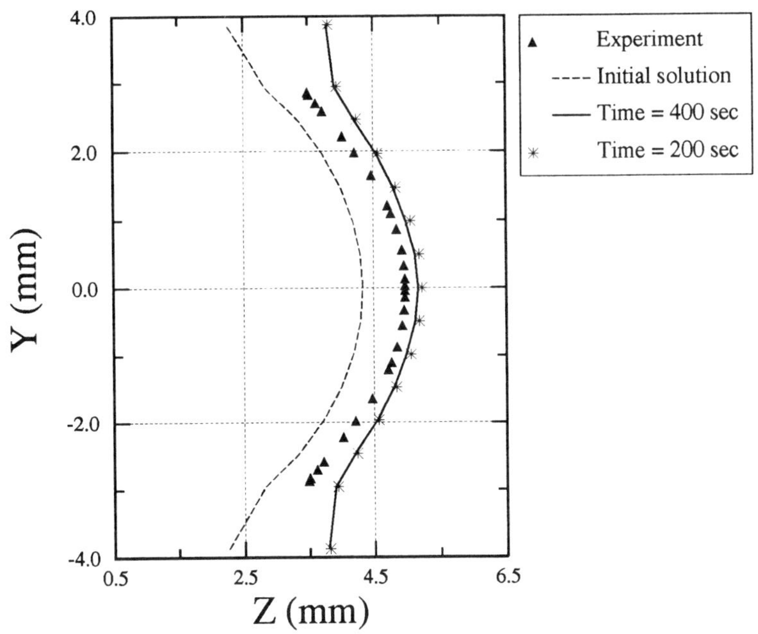

Figure 15. Computed interface shapes on the top surface of the SCN sample (TS, $x = 2.95$mm) based on 3-D transient analysis for SCN-8 and comparison with experiment.

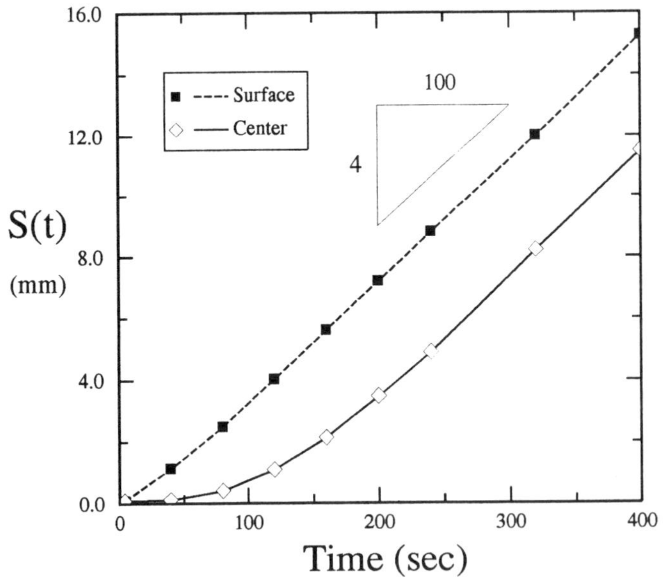

Figure 16. Time history of the interface position at the center of top surface ($x = 2.95, y = 0$) and the center ($x = 0, y = 0$) of SCN sample. The speed of the moving interface is given by the slope of the curves.

not available for transient analysis in FIDAP, the 3-D results presented in this section were obtained using the fully coupled solution approach and based on the coarse 3-D mesh with the simplified sharp corners.

The numerical evolution of the interface shape at the MCP is shown in Fig. 13. Our results indicate that the solution becomes steady after about 200 seconds. The interface shapes at $t = 200$ and 400 sec are quite close to the measured data (Fig. 13). The simulated interface shapes on the UCP and TS planes are presented in Fig. 14 and 15, respectively. The agreement between the 3-D numerical solution and the experiment is excellent.

The time history of two interface positions are shown in Fig. 16. One is at the top surface of SCN sample, i.e. along the line ($x = 2.95$mm, $y = 0, z$) and shown by the curve referred to as "surface" in Fig. 16. The other is at the center of the SCN sample. The slope of the two $S(t)$ curves represents the simulated growth rate, and the vertical distance between these two curves indicates the interface deflection between the top surface and the center. As we can see from Fig. 16, the interface shape is fully developed and the movement of the interface becomes steady when $t > 200$sec. The predicted growth rate, which is 0.04 mm/sec, is equal to the furnace translation speed used in the experiment.

CONCLUSIONS

Perhaps the most obvious advantage of using SCN for crystal growth research is its transparency, which allows quantitative determination of the s/l interface shape and simultaneous observation of important transport phenomena. The numerical and experimental investigation presented in this paper provides two complete benchmark tests for the horizontal Bridgman growth of SCN under terrestrial conditions. The excellent agreement between the numerical results and experimental measurements not only serves as a validation of the numerical model but also demonstrates the importance of the collaboration between numerical modeling and experiment.

For the two cases examined, shallow-cavity convective flow is confirmed, by our numerical and experimental observation, to be the primary flow pattern. This convective flow and its dominance in heat transfer have a significant impact on the shape of the s/l interface. As viewed from the liquid side, the s/l interface in both cases is concave in the upper half of the ampoule. This is due to the above-mentioned convecting flow which brings relatively warm liquid from the hot zone and rams it against the upper part of the interface. This flow of warm liquid moving toward the interface along the top ampoule wall with cooler liquid returning along the bottom wall, results in a dominating thermal gradient in the x-direction (with the top hotter) and interface asymmetry as viewed in the vertical (xz) planes. During solidification, as the longitudinal thermal gradient is translated along the ampoule in the negative z-direction, the liquid SCN gets cooled immediately near the ampoule wall and the s/l interface in contact with the ampoule moves with the same translation speed. However, the inner regions of the sample must conduct the heat through the poorly conducting SCN, causing solidification near the ampoule center to lag behind the outer edges. This results in a much more deflected (curved) interface for the solidification case. In addition to the effect on interface shape, natural convection in the melt has also a significant effect on the temperature distribution near the interface. Our experimental and numerical results indicate that the convection causes a very sharp thermal gradient in the liquid near the interface.

Another interesting aspect of the complex 3-D flow motion in the melt is the secondary flows in the planes perpendicular to the ampoule axes. The flow visualization based on our numerical simulation shows a complex flow structure with multiple flow cells in the xy planes which vary along the ampoule axes. The typical pattern of the secondary flow consists of two counter rotating flow cells on each side of the mid-center vertical (symmetric) plane (MCP). The upper flow cell flows down along the vertical rear (and front) wall and up at the MCP. The lower flow cell brings the fluid up along the vertical ampoule walls and down at the MCP.

In the no-growth case, the 2-D model provides a good approximation for the interface shape and the primary flow pattern on the MCP. However, for non-zero growth rate, the 2-D model is not adequate and 3-D modeling should be considered. Comparisons between the two sets of solutions obtained from the round-corner and the simplified sharp-corner meshes also suggest that the shape of the ampoule corner does not have a significant effect on the numerical solution.

Our experimental examination is continuing with 3-D fluid flow velocity measurements in the SCN liquid near the interface. The valuable experience gained from our comparisons between experiments and simulations, and the good agreement achieved thus far, enables us to more confidently apply the code to other modelling cases (Yao et al., 1993, Yao and de Groh, 1994).

ACKNOWLEDGMENTS

This work was supported by NASA's Microgravity Science and Application Program (grant code # NCC 3-208). Thanks are due T. Lindstrom for extensive assistance with the SCN solidification experiments. The authors also thank T. Glasgow, E. Nelson from NASA Lewis Research Center and the other two anonymous reviewers for their comments and corrections on the manuscript.

REFERENCES

Arnold, W.A., Jacqmin, D.A., Gaug R.L. and Chait, A., 1991, "Three-Dimensional Flow Transport Modes in Directional Solidification During Space Processing," J. Spacecraft Rockets , vol. 28, pp. 238-243.

Brown,R.A., 1988, "Theory of Transport Process in Single Crystal Growth from the Melt," AIChE J., Vol. 34 (6), pp. 881-911.

Chait, A., 1990, "Transport Phenomena in Space Processing: A Modelling Approach," presented at the XX ICHMT Int'l Symposium on Manufacturing and Materials Processing , Dubrovnik, Yugoslavia,.

Chang, C.J. and Brown, R.A., 1984, "Natural Convection in Steady Solidification: Finite Element Analysis of a Two-Phase Rayleigh-Benard Problem," J. Comp. Phys., vol. 53 pp. 1-27.

Chopra, M.A. and Glicksman, M.E., 1988, "Measurement of the Diffusion Coefficient of Acetone in Succinonitrile at Its Melting Point," J. Crystal Growth , vol. 90, pp. 543-546.

Chopra, M.A., Glicksman, M.E. and Singh, N.B., 1988, Met. Trans. A , vol. 19A, pp. 3087-30xx.

Crank, J., 1984, Free and Moving Boundary Problems, Clarendon Press, Oxford, chapters 3 and 6.

Dantzig, J.A., 1989, "Modeling Liquid-Solid Phase Changes with Melt Convection, Int. J. Num. Meth. Eng. , Vol. 28, 1769-85.

de Groh III, H.C. and Lindstrom, T., 1994, "Interface Shape and Convection during Solidification and Melting of Succinonitrile, NASA Tech. Memorandum 107724, NASA Lewis Research Center, (in press).

de Groh III, H.C. and Nelson, E.S., 1994, "On Residual Acceleration During Space Experiments," submitted to the 1994 ASME Winter Annual Meeting, Chicago IL, Nov. 13-18.

Engleman, M., 1993, FIDAP Theoretical Manual (version 7), Fluid Dynamics International, Inc., 500 Davis St. Suite 600, Evanston, IL 60201.

Flemings, M.C., 1974, Solidification Processing, McGraw-Hill, p. 95.

Gartling, D.K., 1980, "Finite element analysis of convective heat transfer problems with change of phase," in Computer Methods in Fluids, Morgan, K. et al. (eds), Pentech, London, pp. 257-284.

Gadonniex, D., Gokhale, A. and Abbaschian, R. 1994, "Morphological Stability of Faceted Solid/ Liquid Interfaces in Dilute Bi-Sn Alloys," 32nd Aerospace Sci. Meeting, AIAA 94-0791.

Glicksman, M.E., Coriell, S.R. and McFadden, G.B., 1986, "Interaction of Flows with the Crystal-Melt Interface," Ann. Rev. Fluid Mech. , vol. 18, 307-335.

Haroutunian, V., Engelman, M. and Hasbani, I., 1991a, "Segregated Finite Element Algorithms for the Numerical Solution of Large-Scale Incompressible Flow Problems," presented at the Fourth International Symposium on Computational Fluid Dynamics, Davis, California, September; also submitted to Inter. J. Num. Methods in Fluids.

Haroutunian, V. M. Engelman and I. Hasbani, 1991b, "Three Segregated Finite Element Solution Algorithms for the Numerical Solution of Incompressible Flow Problems, Proceedings of the Sixth International Conference in Australia on Finite Element Methods, Sydney, Australia, July, vol. 1, G.P. Steven, C. McIvor and D.W. Kelly (eds.), University of Sydney, Australia, pp. K102-K122, .

Inotomi, Y., Miyashita, H. et. al., 1993, "Influence of Mixing in Liquid on Unidirectional Solidification Rate in Transparent Organic Alloy," J. Crystal Growth , vol. 130, pp. 85-95.

Langlois, W.E., 1985, "Buoyancy-Driven Flows in Crystal Growth Melts," Ann. Rev. Fluid Mech., vol. 17, pp. 191-215.

Mennetrier, C., Chopra, M.A. and de Groh III, H.C., 1991, "Effect of Thermal Convection on the Shape of a Solid-Liquid Interface," FED-vol. 111, Forum on Microgravity Flows, ASME , pp. 5-10.

Mogan, K., Lewis R.W. and Zienkiewicz, OZ., 1978, "An Improved Algorithm for Heat Conduction Problem with Phase Change," Int'l J. Num. Methods Eng., Vol. 12, pp. 1191-1195.

Pimputkar, S.M. and Ostrach, S., 1981, "Convective Effects in Crystals Grown from Melt," J. Crystal Growth , vol. 55, pp. 614-646.

Rouzaud. A., Comera, J., Contamin, C., and J.J. Favier, 1993, "Ground Results of the MEPHISTO Program: Benefits and Space Experiments Orientation," Microgravity sci. technol. VI/2, pp. 84- 87.

Shamsundar, N., 1978, "Comparison of Numerical Methods for Diffusion Problems with Moving Boundaries", in Moving Boundary Problems, Wilson D.G. and Boggs, P.T. (eds), Academic Press, New York, pp. 165-185.

Sparrow, E.M., Ramsey, J.W. and Harris, S., 1979, "Freezing Controlled by Natural Convection," J. Heat Transfer , vol. 101, pp. 578-584.

Voller, V.R. and Swaminathan, C.R., 1990, "Fixed Grid Techniques for Phase Change Problems: A Review," Int'l J. Numer. Methods Eng., Vol. 30, pp. 875-898.

Voller, V.R., Cross, M. and Markatos, N.C., 1987, "An Enthalpy Method for Convection/Diffusion Phase Change," Int'l J. Num. Methods Eng., Vol. 24, pp. 271-284.

Yao, M. and de Groh III, H.C., 1993, "A Three-Dimensional

Finite Element Method Simulation of Bridgman Crystal Growth and Comparison with Experiments," Num. Heat Transfer, Part A: Applications , vol. 24, pp. 393-412.

Yao, M. and Chait, A., 1993a, "An Alternative Formulation of the Apparent Heat Capacity Method for Phase Change Problems," Num. Heat Transfer, Part B: Fundamentals , vol. 24, pp. 279-300.

Yao, M. and Chait, A., 1993b, "Application of the Homographic Approximation in the Enthalpy Method for Phase Change Problems," Int. J. Num. Methods Heat & Fluid Flow, vol. 3, pp. 157-172.

Yao, M., Matthiesen, D.H. and Chait, A., 1993, "A Numerical Simulation of Heat and Mass Transport in the GTE GaAs Experiment," Proceedings of the 5th FIDAP Users Conference, May 2-4, Chicago, Illinois.

Yao, M. and de Groh III, H.C., 1994 "Numerical Modelling of Bridgman Growth in Space with MEPHISTO, prepared for 1994 ASME Winter Annual Meeting.

Yeoh, G.H., Behnia, M., de Vahl Davis, G. and Leonardi, E., 1990, "A Numerical Study of Three-Dimensional Natural Convection During Freezing of Water," Int'l J. Num. Meth. Eng. , vol. 30, pp. 899-914.

Yeoh,G.H., de Vahl Davis, G., Leonardi, E., de Groh III, H.C. and Yao, M., 1992, "A Numerical and Experimental Study of Natural Convection and Interface Shape in Crystal Growth," 1st International Conference on Transport Phenomena in Processing, PIThE, Hawaii.

Yeoh, G.H., 1992, "Natural Convection in A Solidifying Liquid," Chapter 7, Ph.D. Thesis, University of New South Wales, Australia.

HTD-Vol. 284/AMD-Vol. 182, Transport Phenomena in Solidification
ASME 1994

COMBINED HEAT TRANSFER AND FLUID FLOW ANALYSIS OF SEMI-TRANSPARENT CRYSTALS IN LOW-G AND 1-G SOLIDIFICATION

M. Kassemi
Space Materials Science and Engineering Section
Jet Propulsion Laboratory
Pasadena, California

M. H. N. Naraghi
Department of Mechanical Engineering
Manhattan College
Riverdale, New York

ABSTRACT

A combined conduction-convection-radiation model is presented for solidification of two important oxide crystals BSO and YAG which are transparent to radiation below 6 microns and opaque to radiation in the rest of the spectrum. The numerical model tracks the solidification front and as the geometry changes the necessary view factors for radiation exchange inside the crucible are updated. Numerical results show that, for both materials, radiation is the dominant heat transfer mechanism through the solid crystal. Nonuniform radiative loss from the solidification front can determines the shape of the interface and increases its curvature significantly. The extent of the interface stretching and curvature depend strongly on the value of the refractive index. Numerical simulations also indicate that while there is little difference between the 1-g and low-g results for YAG, there is a significant difference between the 1-g and low-g results for BSO.

NOMENCLATURE

A	= surface area, (m^2)
Bi	= Biot number, $(\frac{hR}{K_a})$
C	= specific heat, (J / kg K)
F	= radiation function
Gr	= Grashof number, $\left(\frac{g_o \beta R^3 T_h}{\nu^2}\right)$
K	= thermal conductivity, (W / m K)
L	= heat of fusion, (J / kg)
$\hat{n}$	= unit normal vector
n	= index of refraction
Nr_s	= radiation-conduction number, $\left(\frac{n^2 \sigma T_h^3}{K_s}\right)$
Nr_a	= crucible radiation-conduction number, $\left(\frac{\sigma T_h^3}{K_a}\right)$
Pr	= Prandtl number, $(\frac{\nu}{\alpha})$
Pe	= Peclet number, $(\frac{U_p R}{\alpha})$
q	= dimensionless radiative flux, $\left(\frac{\bar{q}}{\sigma T_h^4}\right)$
R	= radius, (m)
St	= Stanton number, $\left(\frac{L\rho_s}{T_h}\right)$
T	= temperature, (K)
$\vec{V}$	= velocity vector, $\left(\frac{\bar{V}}{(Gr)^{1/2}}\right)$

Greek

α	= thermal diffusivity, $(\frac{\rho C}{K})$
β	= expansion coefficient, (1 / K)
ε	= emissivity

λ, λ_c = wavelength, cut-off wavelength, (microns)

μ = dynamic viscosity, ($N\ s / m^2$)

ν = kinematic viscosity, ($N\ s/ m^2$)

ρ = density, (kg / m^3)

σ = Stefan Boltzmann constant, ($W / m^2\ K^4$)

θ = dimensionless temperature (T / T_h)

Subscripts

a = crucible

c = cold zone

h = hot zone

l = melt

m = melting point

s = crystal

r = radial

z = axial

∞ = ambient parameter

Radiation View Factors

$\overline{WW}$ = wall-to-wall radiation exchange factor

$\overline{WS}$ = wall-to-interface radiation exchange factor

$\overline{SW}$ = interface-to-wall radiation exchange factor

$\overline{SS}$ = interface-to-interface radiation exchange factor

INTRODUCTION

Oxide crystals have become an important part of many modern day devices in computing, information processing, and lasers due to their desirable optical, electrical, magnetic, and acoustic properties. The performance of these devices depends directly on the quality of the crystals used, which, to a large extent, is determined by the uniformity of temperature and concentration at the growth interface. Consequently, heat and mass transfer to and from the interface during growth, and their relationship to the thermal environment established by the furnace and the fluid flow in the melt, play key roles in controlling the solidification process. There has been a tremendous drive in the past decade to optimize and improve the conditions, configurations, and procedures for growing and processing crystals. This drive has also instigated a significant effort to understand and isolate the effects of the various interacting transport mechanisms through numerical modeling.

Oxide crystals have been usually grown by the Czochralski technique. In the Czochralski process, heat is supplied radially from the side to the crucible containing the charge and removed axially at the solidification front. This sets up an unsteady three-dimensional destabilizing buoyancy-driven convection which may result in periodic fluctuations of the interface and generation of rotational impurities. Since the requirement for uniformity is more stringent for oxide crystals (with length scales on the order of centimeters) than for semiconductors, researchers have been forced to exploit other techniques for growing these materials. The vertical Bridgman technique has been a favored alternative because, with the crucible aligned with the gravitational vector, convection in the melt is quite weak. In addition, the axisymmetric heat input and extraction from the sides results in a more stable axisymmetric solid-liquid interface with lower microscopic and macroscopic compositional variations.

In this paper, we present a comprehensive numerical model for solidification of two important oxide crystals, BSO and YAG, by the vertical Bridgman technique. Bismuth Silicon Oxide (BSO) is an optically active semi-insulating material that is photo-conductive and has widespread applications in optical information processing and computing components, such as spatial light modulators and volume holographic optical elements and filters. Yitrium Aluminum Oxide Garnet (YAG) is another important optically active oxide crystal which is used in many laser devices. These two materials were chosen because they have well-defined experimental counterparts, their thermophysical and radiative properties are relatively well-known, and last but not least because of the interest to grow BSO crystals in the low-gravity environment of space (Witt, 1993).

Most of the numerical models developed for solidification of crystals have neglected the effects of radiation heat transfer within the crucible. Brown (1988) has made a comprehensive review of the papers published in this area. In general, these studies apply to solidification of semiconductors and cannot be generalized to represent the behavior of oxide crystals. The earliest investigations of the effect of radiation on nonopaque crystals is due to Viskanta and coworkers (Tarshis et al.; 1969 and O'Hara et al.; 1968, Viskanta; 1975). In these studies, the formidable general problem is reduced to a one-dimensional analysis of steady-state conduction and radiation heat transfer as it occurs between two partially transparent media in intimate thermal contact. The models implemented in these works neglect many of the complexities of the actual growth process.Nevertheless, they show that the temperature distributions and the net thermal fluxes in a growing semi-transparent crystal are drastically modified by the participation of the media in the radiation transfer process. These investigations also conclude that radiative heat transfer stabilizes the interface. This occurs because the temperature gradients at the interface are steeper in combined radiative-conductive systems than for the purely conductive cases. This conclusion is later disputed by Abrams and Viskanta (1974). Again, through a one-dimensional radiation-conduction analysis, they show that for a range of parametric values encountered in melting and solidification of many optical materials, radiation can force the temperature profile within the liquid phase to assume a shape which leads to unstable interfacial growth. This finding is corroborated by two more recent papers due to Antonov et al.(1980) and Yuferev and Vasil'ev (1987). These two investigations present a more realistic treatment of conduction and radiation heat transfer for growth of sapphire by the Stepanov's method. The analyses are still one-dimensional. But, they again show that radiation heat transfer can lead to instability in the crystallization front. It is also postulated that the pronounced stretching of the solid-liquid interface observed experimentally may be due to radiative transfer. Interaction of multi-dimensional radiation exchange with convection and conduction was studied by Kassemi and Duval (1989, 1990) in the context of crystal growth by vapor transport. They used a finite-difference control-volume approach to discretize the diffusive and convective terms and an element-to-node zonal approach to represent the radiative exchange. The results show that, through interaction with convection, radiation significantly affects the crystal shape. It was also shown that surface and internal radiation exchange have opposing effects on the interface curvature. The first studies to focus on solidification of semi-transparent oxides from melt in realistic crystal growth configuration has been due to Brandon and Derby (1991, 1992). They developed a rigorous finite-element model for solidification of oxide crystals which included interactions among conduction and radiation in the solid and convection in the melt. They also clearly showed that radiation loss through the solid can produce significant stretching of the interface. Finally, Lin and Motakef (1993) considered solidification of BSO in a vertical Bridgman configuration. They solved the combined radiation conduction convection problem indirectly by iterating between the finite element code ABAQUS to solve the radiation-conduction problem in the solid and the fluids code FIDAP to solve the conduction-convection problem in the melt. The movement and change in the interface shape was accounted for by iterating between the two codes. That is, the interface location was calculated by the user from the temperature contours generated by ABAQUS and then used as input into FIDAP to calculate new temperature and velocity fields.

The main objective of this paper is to investigate the role of radiative heat transfer and convection on solidification of BSO and YAG. Radiation exchange through the solid is modeled using an exchange factor method which can be easily incorporated in both finite-element and finite-difference formulations. Since there is also interest in growing BSO crystals in space, attention will be focused on simulating solidification experiments for both BSO and YAG under typical low gravity conditions. In this way, the roles of radiation and convection, which are normally intricately coupled, can be distinctly isolated and studied.

MATHEMATICAL FORMULATION

Physical model

A cross-sectional view of the cylindrical ampoule in a typical vertical Bridgman furnace configuration is shown in

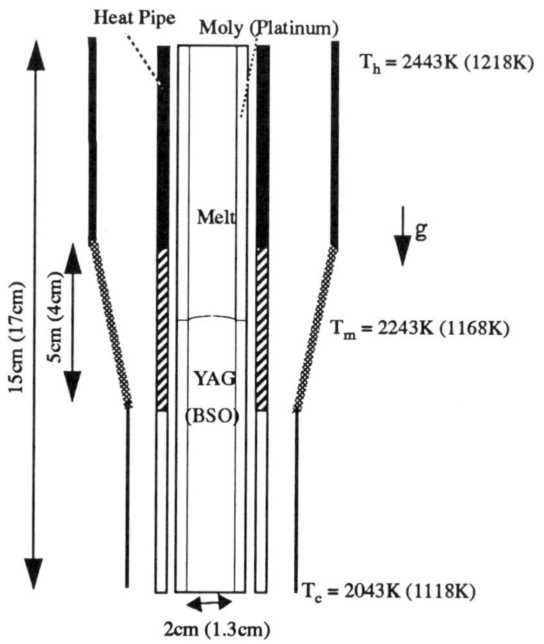

Figure 1: Cross Sectional View of the Crucible in a Vertical Bridgman Furnace

Fig. 1. In this setup, the ampoule, which encapsulates both the solid and the melt, is pulled downwards in the gravitational field through the temperature profile maintained along the bore of the furnace, at a constant velocity, U_p. The three-zone furnace consists of a hot section separated from the cold section by an insulated region. The temperature in the hot and cold zones are maintained by heat pipes; therefore, they are uniform at temperatures T_h and T_c, respectively. The insulated region is not actively controlled; thus, the temperature of the bore surface in this region varies linearly between the hot and cold ends. As a result, the bore surface temperature is assumed to be given by the piecewise continuous profile in Fig. 1. Although the same basic configuration is used for solidification of both YAG and BSO, the details of the geometry, materials, temperature levels, and thermophysical and radiative properties are different. The details are given in Tables 1 and 2. The information provided in Table 1 relates to the experimental set-up used at MIT (Witt, 1993) for solidification of BSO, and the information in Table 2 refers to the system at Lawrence Livermore National Laboratory for solidification of YAG as described and adopted by Brandon and Derby (1992).

Table 1. Geometric Configurations and Thermophysical Properties For BSO (Witt, 1993)

Crucible Length	0.17 m
Adiabatic Zone Length	0.04 m
Crucible Inner Radius	0.01 m
Crucible Thickness	0.002 m
Crucible Pull Rate	1 (10^{-6}) m/s
Biot Number (Side)	0.025
Biot Number (Ends)	0.083
Hot Zone Temperature	1218 K
Cold Zone Temperature	1118 K
Melting Temperature	1168 K
Melt Expansion Coefficient	$7(10^{-5})$ 1 / K
Melt Viscosity	0.022 Pa s
Melt Prandtl Number	48.0
Heat of Fusion	50,000 J / kg
Thermal Conductivity (Solid)	0.18 W / m K
Thermal Conductivity (Melt)	0.27 W / m K
Thermal Conductivity (Molybdenum)	75.0 W / m K
Density (Solid)	9200 kg / m^3
Density (Melt)	7630 kg / m^3
Specific Heat (Solid)	294 J / kg K
Specific Heat (Melt)	393 J / kg K
Crucible Emissivity (Outer Surface)	0.15
Crucible Emissivity (Inner Surface)	0.15
Crucible Emissivity (Interface)	0.50
Index of Refraction	1-2.54

Table 2. Geometric Configurations and Thermophysical Properties For YAG (Derby, 1992)

Crucible Length	0.15 m
Adiabatic Zone Length	0.05 m
Crucible Inner Radius	0.0065 m
Crucible Thickness	0.003175 m
Crucible Pull Rate	1 (10^{-6}) m/s
Biot Number (Side)	$2.925(10^{-4})$
Biot Number (Ends)	$9.75(10^{-4})$
Hot Zone Temperature	2443 K
Cold Zone Temperature	2043 K
Melting Temperature	2243 K
Melt Expansion Coefficient	2. $7(10^{-5})$ 1 / K
Melt Viscosity	0.04 Pa s
Melt Prandtl Number	8.0
Heat of Fusion	455,500 J / kg
Thermal Conductivity (Solid)	10.0W / m K
Thermal Conductivity (Melt)	5.0 W / m K
Thermal Conductivity (Molybdenum)	100.0 W / m K
Density (Solid)	4300 kg / m^3
Density (Melt)	4300 kg / m^3
Specific Heat (Solid)	1000 J / kg K
Specific Heat (Melt)	1000 J / kg K
Crucible Emissivity (Outer Surface)	0.30
Crucible Emissivity (Inner Surface)	0.30
Crucible Emissivity (Interface)	1.0
Index of Refraction	1.8

Radiation heat transfer

In the solidification of semiconductors, usually both the crystal and the melt are opaque to thermal radiation. Furthermore, both phases typically have relatively high thermal conductivities. Therefore, conduction is the dominant mode of heat transfer in both the solid and the melt. Oxide crystals, on the other hand, are usually semi-transparent to thermal radiation in the solid phase and almost opaque in the melt. They also have relatively low thermal conductivities in both phases. Therefore, heat transfer during the solidification of oxide crystals is governed by an intricate balance between convection and conduction in the melt and conduction and radiation in the solid. In a sense, the solid acts a light pipe through which the interface loses a considerable amount of heat (by emission) to the cold sections of the crucible wall or directly to the furnace (if the crucible is also transparent).

The radiation transmittance properties of BSO and YAG are shown in Figs. 2 and 3. It is evident that BSO and YAG have very similar radiative characteristics, especially for wavelengths below 6 microns. They are nearly transparent to radiation in the visible and near-infrared spectrum and opaque in the rest of the infrared region. The cut-off wavelength for both materials is about 6 microns. As indicated in Fig. 2, the transmittance of the 1.5mm and 3mm samples are quite similar for BSO, indicating that the loss in transmission for wavelengths below 6 microns is mostly due to surface reflection and that internal absorption is negligible. For BSO, there is an intermediate absorption band between 6.5 and 8 microns. But at melting temperatures of BSO, less than 5% of the total emission occurs in this band. Therefore, for the purposes of this analysis a semi-gray model is adopted for both materials where the crystals are assumed to be fully transparent to radiation below the cut-off wavelength of 6 microns and opaque to the infrared radiation above it. There is almost no quantitative data available on the radiative properties of these materials in the molten phase. From the limited qualitative data which is discussed in the literature it is evident that the absorptivity of oxide crystals increases by orders of magnitude in the molten state. Therefore, the liquid phase is assumed to be opaque for both BSO and YAG. Finally, it should be noted that because of the high melting temperatures of these two materials, nearly 80% of the radiation for BSO and 90% of the radiation for YAG is emitted by the interface in the transparent window below 6 microns. Therefore, there is considerable radiation exchange between the hot interface and the cooler crucible wall through the solid.

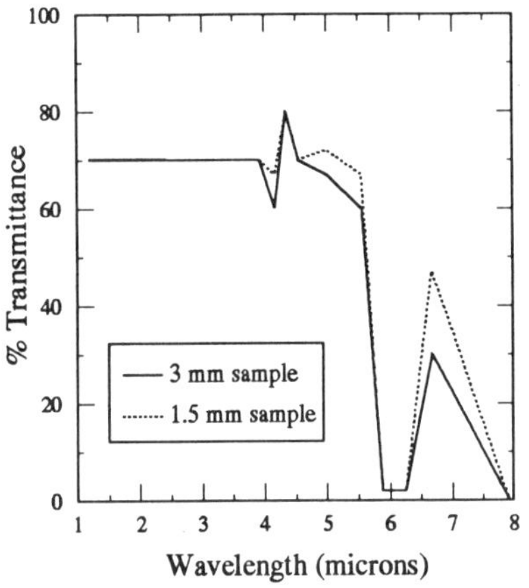

Figure 2: Spectral Transmittance of BSO as a Function of Wavelength (Lin and Motakef, 1993).

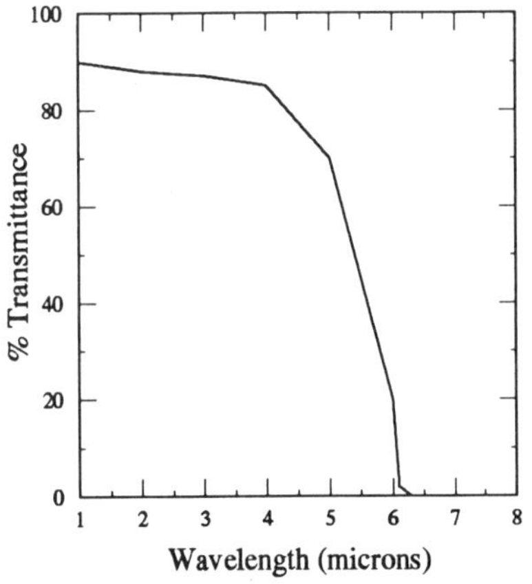

Figure 3: Spectral Transmittance of YAG as a Function of Wavelength (Cockayne, 1969)

Governing Equations

The heat transfer mechanisms which govern the solidification of oxides are complicated. There is a strong heat transfer link through radiation and natural convection between the furnace and the crucible. Consequently, the axial temperature distribution of the bore surface is approximately imposed on the outer surface of the crucible. Heat transfer inside the crucible is dominated by conduction and convection in the opaque melt, and by conduction and radiation through the semitransparent crystal. Therefore, at the inner crucible surface, in the melt region, there is a balance between the conductive fluxes. Similarly, at the inner crucible surface, in the crystal, there is a balance among the radial conductive fluxes through the ampoule and the crystal and the net radiative flux at the wall surface. Since the pulling velocity of the ampoule is extremely small, a quasi-steady approach is adopted, and the advective terms which arise due to the ampoule motion are not considered. The final location and shape of the interface (at quasi-steady-state) is of course determined by a balance among the conductive fluxes on both sides of the solidification front, the net radiative flux at the interface, and the released heat of fusion. For the materials considered here, and again due to the very slow pulling speed, the latent heat of fusion is negligible compared to the other terms in the energy balance, but it is still retained in the interface equation for the sake of completeness. Furthermore, since it is assumed that the longitudinal axis of the ampoule is aligned with the gravitational vector, and the bore temperature profiles established by the furnace are circumferentially uniform, axisymmetric conditions are exploited. Following the quasi-steady approach, the energy equations describing heat transfer in the melt, the crystal and the ampoule are written as follows.

1. Crystal

$$\nabla^2\theta + (Nr_s)\int_0^\infty (\nabla \bullet q_{r_\lambda})\, d\lambda = 0 \qquad (1)$$

2. Melt

$$(Pr\frac{K_l}{K_s}(Gr)^{1/2})\vec{V}\bullet\nabla\theta = (\frac{K_l}{K_s})\nabla^2\theta \quad (2)$$

3. Ampoule

$$\nabla^2\theta = 0 \quad (3)$$

These equations are subject to the following thermal boundary conditions:
1. Melt-Ampoule Interface:

$$(\frac{K_l}{K_s})\nabla\theta\bullet\hat{n}_{al} = (\frac{K_a}{K_s})(\nabla\theta\bullet\hat{n}_{al}) \quad (4)$$

2. Crystal-Ampoule Interface:

$$-(\nabla\theta)\bullet\hat{n}_{as} = -(\frac{K_a}{K_s})(\nabla\theta\bullet\hat{n}_{as}) + (Nr_s)\int_0^\infty (q_{a_\lambda}\bullet\hat{n}_{as})\,d\lambda \quad (5)$$

3. Ampoule-Air-Furnace Interface:

$$-(\frac{K_a}{K_s})(\nabla\theta\bullet\hat{n}_{a\infty}) = (Bi)(\theta-\theta_\infty) + (Nr_a\frac{K_a}{K_s})\varepsilon_{a\infty}(\theta^4-\theta_\infty^4) \quad (6)$$

4. Ampoule Top and Bottom:

$$\theta = \theta_c, \theta_h \quad (7)$$

In addition to these boundary conditions, the energy equation is also subject to the following interface conditions:

$$\theta = \theta_m \quad (8)$$

and

$$-(\frac{K_l}{K_s})(\nabla\theta)\bullet\hat{n}_{ls} = -\nabla\theta\bullet\hat{n}_{ls} + (Nr_s)\int_0^\infty (q_{s_\lambda}\bullet\hat{n}_{ls})\,d\lambda - (St)(Pe) \quad (9)$$

Using the radiative properties of YAG and BSO as estimated from Figs. 2 and 3, the total divergence of radiative flux reduces to

$$\int_0^\infty (\nabla\bullet q_{r_\lambda})\,d\lambda = 0 \quad (10)$$

The net radiative flux at the wall is given by

$$\int_0^\infty (q_{a_\lambda}\bullet\hat{n}_{as})\,d\lambda = \varepsilon_{as}F_{0-\lambda_c}(\lambda_c, T_a)\,\theta_a^4 - \int_{A_a}\varepsilon_{as}F_{0-\lambda_c}(\lambda_c, T_a)\,\theta_a^4(r')\,\overline{WW}(r',r)\,dA - \int_{A_s}\varepsilon_{ls}F_{0-\lambda_c}(\lambda_c, T_m)\,\theta_m^4(r')\,\overline{SW}(r',r)\,dA \quad (11)$$

Similarly, the net radiative flux at the interface is given by

$$\int_0^\infty (q_{s_\lambda}\bullet\hat{n}_{ls})\,d\lambda = \varepsilon_s F_{0-\lambda_c}(\lambda_c, T_m)\,\theta_m^4 - \int_{A_a}\varepsilon_{as}F_{0-\lambda_c}(\lambda_c, T_a)\,\theta_a^4(r')\,\overline{WS}(r',r)\,dA - \int_{A_s}\varepsilon_s F_{0-\lambda_c}(\lambda_c, T_m)\,\theta_m^4(r')\,\overline{SS}(r',r)\,dA \quad (12)$$

The fluid flow in the melt, which is primarily driven by the buoyancy force, is described by the continuity and balance of momentum equation and is subject to non-slip boundary conditions at all solid boundaries:
1. Continuity:

$$\nabla\bullet\vec{V} = 0 \quad (13)$$

2. Momentum:

$$(Gr^{1/2})\vec{V}\bullet\nabla\vec{V} = -\nabla P + \nabla^2\vec{V} + (Gr^{1/2})(\theta-\theta_m) \quad (14)$$

3. Non-Slip Boundary Condition:

$$\vec{V} = 0 \quad (15)$$

Finally, these equations are subject to symmetry conditions along the centerline of the ampoule:

$$\vec{V}\bullet\hat{n}_r = 0, \quad \vec{V}\bullet\hat{n}_z = 0 \quad (16)$$

In writing these equations, it was also assumed that: (a) the thermophysical properties of the solid and the melt, although different, are constant throughout each phase; (b) the gap between the furnace bore and the crucible wall is small so that the external radiation exchange between elements on these two surfaces is basically one-to-one (i.e. view factor is one); and (c) all surfaces in the model are treated as diffuse for the radiation exchange calculations.

Numerical Formulation

The finite-element code FIDAP was adopted to solve the solidification problem. FIDAP was significantly modified in order to incorporate a radiative heat transfer model based on an exchange factor scheme, similar to the DEF method described by Naraghi and Kassemi (1989) into the code. The diffusive and convective terms in the governing differential equations were discretized based on the regular Galerkin formulation. Discretization of the integral terms describing radiation exchange using the exchange factor method results in a set of algebraic equations which can be easily incorporated in both finite element and finite difference codes. Moreover, exchange factor methods have been already used with both finite element and finite difference techniques and have produced very accurate results (Kassemi and Naraghi 1993, Saltiel and Naraghi 1990). Nine-node quadratic continuum elements and three-node quadratic surface elements were used throughout the mesh. A nine-node gaussian integration scheme was used to integrate all the terms. The radiation flux terms were evaluated at these integration points.

The resulting set of discretized algebraic equations are solved using a segregated approach which tackles every degree of freedom individually (Engleman, 1993). That is, the solution matrix is decomposed into smaller loosely connected sub-matrices, each associated with only one conservation equation. The smaller matrices are then solved in a sequential manner using gaussian elimination. Because these matrices are loosely connected, the method has slower convergence rate compared to the coupled direct solvers. However, the scheme is fairly robust because it has a large radius of convergence and does not require a good starting guess. In addition, because the degrees of freedom are decoupled, it is much less demanding with regard to computer storage needs as compared to coupled solvers.

The solidification problem is treated by tracking the interface as a free surface. In contrast to the coupled solvers where the new interface position is part of the solution vector, in the segregated approach an iterative scheme is adopted. First, the conservation equations are solved assuming a fixed interface location and using the continuity of temperature at the interface (Eq. 8) as a boundary condition to the energy equation. Next, the required change in the interface location is determined by satisfying the interface energy balance condition (Eq. 9). The updated interface position is then used again to solve the conservation equations. This iterative process is continued until a converged solution is attained. During each simulation, as the solidification front moves and changes shape, the interface position is tracked and the position of the nodes are changed along straight lines (spines) in proportion to the movement of the interfacial nodes. As an example, the meshes at the start and end of a typical simulation are shown in Figs. 4. Because of this change in geometry and nodal position, new radiation exchange factors have to be calculated at every iteration. For calculation of these exchange factors the reader is referred to Naraghi and Kassemi (1989).

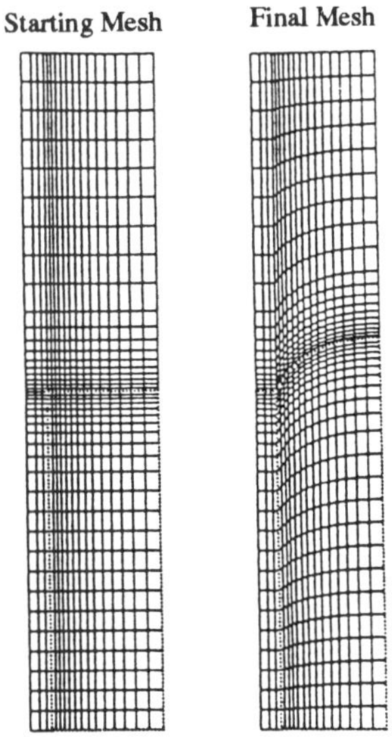

Figure 4: Finite Element Meshes at Beginning and End of a Typical Simulation

The simulation presented in this paper used 870 elements based on a 85x25 mesh with nodes which were unevenly distributed as indicated in Fig. 4. The convergence criterion for the free surface was 10^{-4} and for the temperature, pressure and velocities was 10^{-6}. Depending on the values of Nr and Gr, it took between 40 -100 free surface updates to achieve a converged solution.

RESULTS AND DISCUSSION

The results presented in this section are focused on isolating the effects of radiation and convection in solidification of YAG and BSO. Radiation effects are isolated through parametric variation of the conduction-radiation number, Nr, and convection effects will be isolated by performing low-g and 1-g simulations by varying the Grashof number, Gr. It will be shown that because of the slight differences between the radiative and thermophysical properties of YAG and BSO, the extent of interaction between convection and radiation for the two systems and its effect on interface shape is different.

Simulations for the low-gravity experiments will be considered first. The temperature profile and streamlines for solidification of BSO in a typical low-g experiment with $g_o = 1 \times 10^{-4}$ is shown in Figs. 5 and 6. In order to isolate the interacting mechanisms, the effects of radiation are neglected by setting Nr = 0 in Fig. 5. Since there is a mismatch between the thermal conductivities of the melt, the crystal, and the platinum crucible, the interface is slightly curved. Because for BSO the conductivity of the crystal is smaller than the conductivity of the melt, the interface is convex into the solid region and is positioned slightly closer to the cold end. Since continuity of fluxes must be satisfied at the interface the temperature gradients on the solid side (which has a lower conductivity) are slightly steeper than on the melt side as shown in Fig. 5. The curvature of the interface and the radial gradients near the solidification front drive two small but quite strong convection cells in that area with the flow rising from the middle of the crucible. There are also two large weak secondary cells which are mainly driven by the sharp change in the furnace temperature profile.

When the effects of radiation are included for an Nr = 5 (based on index of refraction, n = 1.0), there is a drastic change in the interface shape and the fluid flow structure as shown in Fig. 6. The interface which is modeled as an opaque surface at a melting temperature, T_m, loses a significant amount of heat through the semitransparent solid in the wavelength region below 6 microns (where about 80% of the emission takes place). Since the solid acts like a light pipe, this radiant heat impinges upon the crucible wall (which is relatively cooler) and is removed from the crucible. The mid-section of the interface has a better view of the cold sections of the crucible wall than the end regions. Consequently, more heat is lost from this central portion and the center of the interface moves considerably towards the hot end. Since the conductivity of platinum is very high (about 400 times larger than conductivity of the crystal or the melt) and there is a strong radiative and convective link between the crucible and the furnace, the temperature of the crucible wall is only slightly affected by the internal radiation exchange. Therefore, the location of the two ends of the interface which are in contact with the crucible are pinned down by the temperature field maintained in the crucible wall. This nonuniform radiative loss, forces the interface to attain a highly curved shape which becomes convex into the melt. The temperature contours of Fig. 6 also show that since most of the heat lost from the interface is by radiation, the dome section of the crystal, which is encompassed by the interface at a temperature, T_m, is at a very uniform temperature. In contrast, because the increased radiative loss through the solid has to be balanced by supply of heat by convection and conduction through the melt, there are sharp temperature gradients on the melt side of the interface. These gradients drive two vigorous convection cells as shown in Fig. 6 which rotate with the flow rising from near the walls (as opposed to the purely convective case of Fig. 5). Note, also that due to the movement of the interface into the hot zone and the increased strength of the two vortices near the interface, the two weaker and larger cells of Fig 5 disappear. These results clearly show that radiation exchange not only changes the shape of the solidification front for BSO, but also results in significant modification of the flow structure.

Solidification of YAG in reduced gravity is considered in Figs. 7 and 8. The thermophysical properties of YAG are slightly different from that of BSO as indicated in Table 2. In Fig. 7, the effects of radiation are neglected by setting Nr = 0.0. Again, because of the mismatch in the thermal conductivities of the solid, the melt, and the crucible, the interface is curved. But this time, because the conductivity of the melt is smaller than the conductivity of the solid, the interface moves slightly towards the hot end and is curved convex into the melt (in contrast to Fig. 5). The streamline patterns of Fig. 7 show two smaller strong vortices near the interface which, again in contrast to Fig 5 for BSO, are rotating with the flow rising from near the walls. The two larger and weaker vortices driven by the discontinuity in the furnace profile are also present.

When the effects of radiation are included by setting Nr = 1.87 (n = 1.8) for YAG as in Fig. 8, the interface shape and the flow structure drastically change. Even at a moderate value of Nr = 1.87, radiation is the dominant heat transfer mode. Because of the uneven radiative loss from the solidification front through the solid, the interface becomes again highly stretched, parabolic and convex into the melt. Similarly, the large radial temperature gradients in the melt drive two intense vortices near the interface. Comparison between Figs. 5 and 7 and Figs. 6 and 8 indicate that while there is quite a difference between the interface shape and flow structure for YAG and BSO when radiation effects are neglected, there is a striking similarity between the flow structure and interface shape when radiation effects are included. This underscores the fact that in low-g environment, radiation heat transfer clearly dominates the solidification process and therefore slight differences between the thermophysical properties of the two materials do not affect the general characteristics of the growth process.

The temperature contours and streamlines for solidifica-

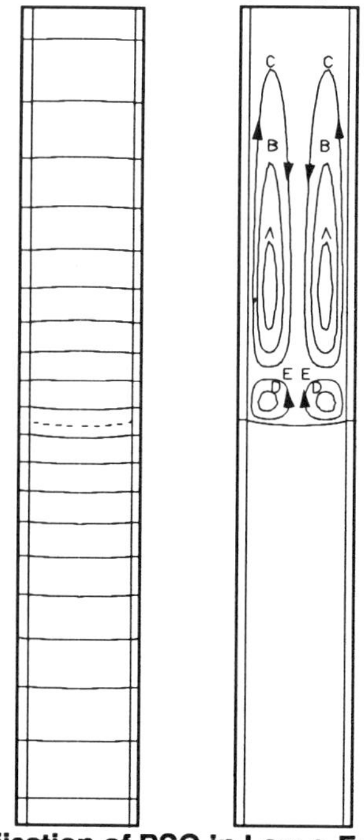

Figure 5: Solidification of BSO in Low-g Environment for Gr = 10, Nr = 0.0: a) Temperature Contours; Minimum = 0.918, Maximum = 1.0, First Contour = 0.920, Increment = 0.0041. b) Streamline Contours; A = -0.5816(10^{-5}), B = -0.3604(10^{-5}), C = -0.1391(10^{-5}), D = 0.8211(10^{-6}), E = 0.3033(10^{-5}).

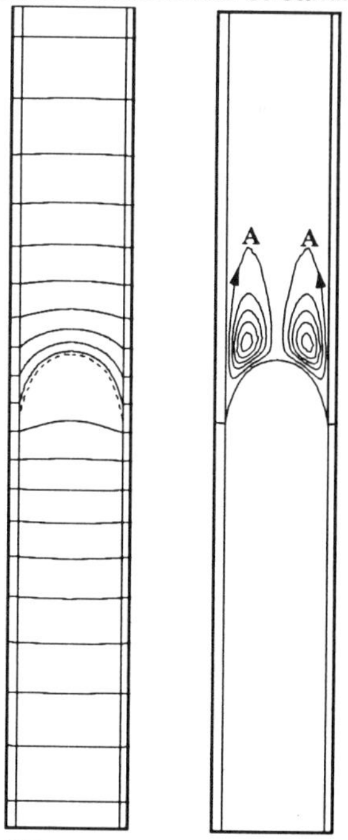

Figure 6: Solidification of BSO in Low-g Environment for Gr = 10, Nr = 5: a) Temperature Contours; Minimum = 0.918, Maximum = 1.0 First Contour = 0.920, Increment = 0.0041. b) Streamline Contours; A = -0.7811(10^{-5}), Increments = 0.1598(10^{-4}).

tion of BSO in typical ground-based experiments are shown in Fig. 9. There is again a significant stretching of the interface due to the nonuniform radiation loss from the interface. However, the interface is fairly flat in the central region even in the presence of strong radiation effects. This is mainly because of the important role played by convection in the BSO melt. Convection is quite strong for BSO at 1-g (Gr = 100736). Since BSO has a very low conductivity and high Pr number (Pr = 48) in the liquid phase, the temperature field is easily affected by the strong convection which flattens the temperature contours near the interface. Physically, this implies that the hot fluid brought down by the recirculating vortices from the upper region of the crucible, uniformly heats the temperature in the central portion of the ampoule and, therefore, prevents the solid from growing into that region. Comparison between Figs, 6 and 9 shows that, for BSO, as a result of this opposing and competing effects of convection and radiation, the interface becomes much flatter (less parabolic) in ground-based experiments as compared to the low-gravity processing.

The temperature contours and streamlines for solidification of YAG in typical ground-based experiments are shown in Fig. 10. Because of the relatively high conductivity of the materials and the relatively low Grashof number for the flow, conduction and radiation are the dominant modes of heat transfer for YAG, even in the 1-g case. Therefore, there is no noticeable difference between the temperature contours presented in Fig 8 and Fig 10. Of course, the intensity of fluid flow in the low-g case of Fig. 8 is lower than the 1-g results of Fig 10. But, in both cases, the flow does not affect the interface shape appreciably due to the relatively high conductivity of the melt. It should be mentioned that the results presented in Fig. 10 are in very good qualitative agreement with the experimental findings of Cockayne et al. (1969) for YAG and DyAG, and in excellent quantitative agreement with predictions of Brandon and Derby (1992).

The extent of stretching of the interface depends directly on the amount of nonuniform radiative loss from the emitting interface through the solid. Physically, since the solid acts as a light pipe, its efficiency at removing heat from the interface depends on its index of refraction. Parametrically, this heat loss depends primarily on the value of the radiation-conduction number, Nr, which increases according to the square of the refractive index. The results presented for BSO, so far, were all generated for an index of refraction of 1. The value of the index of refraction for BSO at its melting temperature is not exactly known but there is some evidence that it might be as high as 2.54. The results presented in Fig. 11 demonstrate the sensitivity of the interface shape to the value of the refractive index. This clearly underscores the need for measuring radiative properties of these materials at high temperature. Accurate predictions for solidification of oxide crystals are possible only if accurate radiative properties are used in the models.

Crystal growers always desire a slightly convex growth interface in order to minimize stresses and improve the quality of the emerging crystal. All of the preceding results showed that for vertical Bridgman growth of both YAG and BSO (and by extension, other semi-transparent oxide materials as well), nearly all of the interfacial curvature is due to the uneven radiative loss from the interface. Naturally, if one was interested in eliminating this stretching, the most efficient way would be to resupply all the heat lost by radiation back to the interface. The practicality of this task is, of

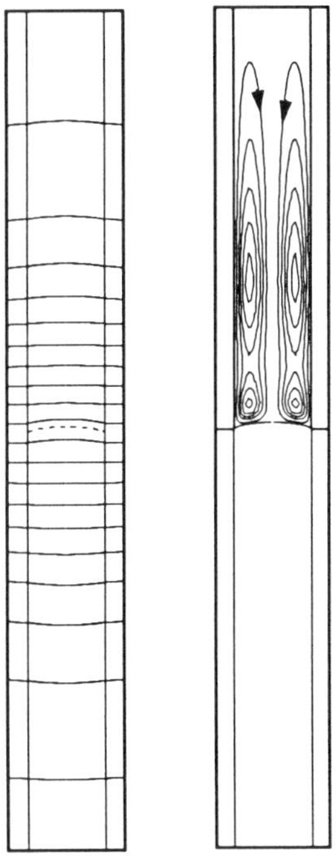

Figure 7: Solidification of YAG in Low-g Environment for Gr = 1, Nr = 0.0: a) Temperature Contours; Minimum = 0.8360, Maximum = 1.0, First Contour = 0.8401, Increment = 0.0082. b) Streamline Contours; Innermost Contours on Top and Bottom Cells = -0.2585(10^{-3}), Increments = 0.5740(10^{-4}).

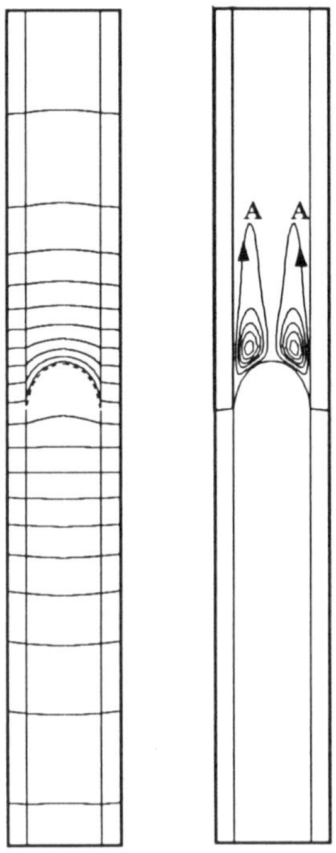

Figure 8: Solidification of YAG in Low-g Environment for Gr = 1, Nr = 1.87: a) Temperature Contours; Minimum = 0.918, Maximum = 1.0 First Contour = 0.920, Increment = 0.0041. b) Streamline Contours; A = -0.2531(10^{-5}), Increments = 0.5068(10^{-5}).

course, questionable. But just as a thought experiment, the easiest way to achieve this end would be through the use of a crucible with a highly reflective interior surface as shown in Fig 12. If the inside surface of the crucible is perfectly reflective, all the heat lost by the interface through emission will be redirected by the crucible wall back to the interface. As a result, the interface remains relatively flat as in Fig 12. Unfortunately, although the concept of a perfectly reflective interface is conceptually easy to grasp, it is practically very hard to achieve.

CONCLUSIONS

A combined radiation conduction convection numerical model was developed to study solidification of oxide crystals in a vertical Bridgman furnace. The model was applied to the processing of both YAG and BSO under realistic experimental conditions. From the 1-g and low-g simulations the following conclusions can be drawn:

1. Under the experimental conditions considered in this paper, radiation is the dominant heat transfer mode at the interface for solidification of BSO and YAG.

2. For both BSO and YAG, the interface attains a highly stretched parabolic shape largely because of the nonuniform radiative loss from the interface. In both cases, the interface is convex into the melt and there are two vortices rotating near the interface with the flow rising from the region near the wall.

3. If radiation is neglected or the crystal is treated as opaque, the interface is only very mildly curved due to the mismatch among the thermal conductivities. The interface is also convex into the phase with the lower conductivity. In the absence of radiation effects, the flow structure indicates two large vortices in the upper portion of the melt and two smaller vortices near the interface. The direction of the rotation of the smaller vortices depends on the shape of the interface.

4. For YAG, because of its higher conductivity, conduction and radiation are the dominant heat transfer mechanisms. Therefore, the temperature contours and the shape of the interface remains relatively the same in both 1-g and low-g environments.

5. For BSO, convection plays a more important role and there is a considerable difference between the temperature contours and the interface shape of the 1-g and low-g cases. In 1-g applications, the recirculating flow can compensate for a significant amount of the radiant heat loss from the center of the interface. Therefore, the interface is much flatter in ground-based applications than in the low-g environment.

REFERENCES

Abrams, M. and Viskanta R., 1974, "The Effects of Radiative Heat Transfer Upon Melting and Solidification of Semi-Transparent Crystals," *J. of Heat Transfer*, Vol. 96, p.184.

Antonov, P.I., Bakholdin, S.I., Tropp, E.A, and Yuferev, V.S., 1980, "An Experimental and Theoretical Study of Temperature Distribution in Sapphire Crystals Grown from the Melt by Stepanov's Method," *J. Crystal Growth*, Vol. 50, p.62.

Brandon, S., and Derby, J.J., 1991, "Internal Radiation Transport in the Vertical Bridgman Growth of Semitransparent Crystals," *J. Crystal Growth*, Vol. 110, p. 481

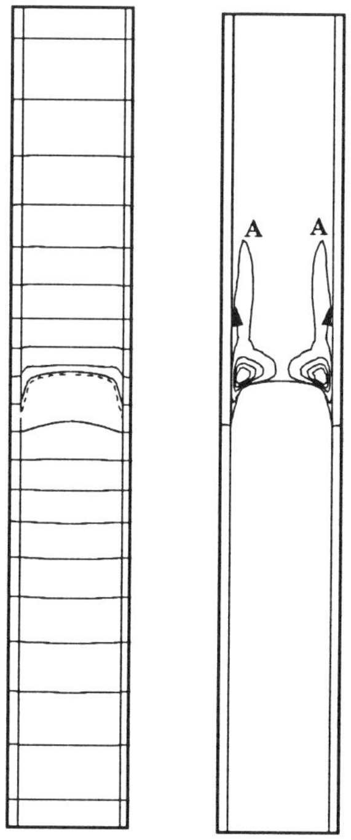

Figure 9: Solidification of BSO in 1-g Environment for Gr = 100736, Nr = 5.0: a) Temperature Contours: Minimum = 0.918, Maximum = 1.0, First Contour = 0.920, Increment = 0.0041. b) Streamline Contours; A = -0.5068(10^{-3}), Increments = 0.1215(10^{-3}).

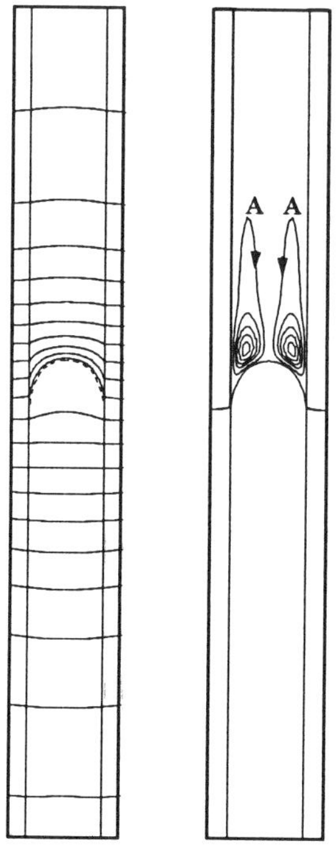

Figure 10: Solidification of YAG in 1-g Environment for Gr = 2053, Nr = 1.87: a) Temperature Contours; Minimum = 0.918, Maximum = 1.0 First Contour = 0.920, Increment = 0.0041. b) Streamline Contours; A =- 0.1951(10^{-2}), Increments = 0.434(10^{-3}).

Brandon, S., and Derby, J.J. 1992, "Heat Transfer in Vertical Bridgman Growth of Oxides: Effects of Conduction, Convection, and Internal Radiation," *J. Crystal Growth*, Vol. 121, p. 473

Brown, R. A., 1988, "Theory of Transport Processes in Single Crystal Growth from the Melt," *AIChE J.*, Vol. 34, p. 8.

Cockayne, B., Chesswas, M., and Gasson D.B., "Faceting and Optical Perfection in Czochralski Grown Garnets and Ruby", *J. Mat. Science*, Vol. 4, p. 450.

Engleman, M., 1993, "FIDAP 7.0: Fluid Dynamics Analysis Package," FDI Inc., Evanston, IL.

Kassemi, M. and Duval, W.M.B., 1990, "Interaction of Surface Radiation with Convection in Crystal Growth by Vapor Transport," *J. Thermophysics and Heat Transfer*, Vol. 11, p. 454.

Kassemi, M. and Duval, W., 1989, "Effect of Gas and Surface Radiation on Crystal Growth from the Vapor Phase," *PhysicoChemical Hydrodynamics*, Vol. 11, p. 737.

Kassemi, M., and Naraghi, M.H.N., 1993, "Analysis of Radiation-Natural Convection Interactions in 1-g and Low-g Environments Using the Discrete Exchange Factor Method", *Int. J. Heat and Mass Transfer*, Vol. 36, No. 17, p. 4141.

Lin, C., and Motakef S., 1993, "Modelling of Directional Solidification of BSO," *J. Crystal Growth*, Vol. 128, p. 834.

Naraghi, M.H.N. and Kassemi, M., 1989, "Analysis of Radiative Transfer in Rectangular Enclosures Using a Discrete Exchange Factor Method", *ASME J. Heat Transfer*, Vol. 111, p. 1117.

O'Hara, S., Tarshis, L.A., and Viskanta R., 1968, "Stability of the Solid-Liquid Interface of SemiTransparent Materials," *J. Crystal Growth*, Vol. 3-4, p. 583.

Saltiel, C., and Naraghi, M.H.N., 1990, "Combined-Mode Heat Transfer in Radiatively Participating Media Using the Discrete Exchange Factor Method with Finite Elements," *Heat Transfer 1990*, Hemisphere Publication, Vol. 6, p. 391.

Tarshis, L.A., O'Hara, S. and Viskanta R., 1969, "Heat Transfer by Simultaneous Conduction and Radiation for two Absorbing Media in Intimate Contact," *Int. J. Heat Mass Transfer*, Vol. 12, p. 333.

Viskanta, R., and Anderson E.E., 1975, "Heat Transfer in Semitransparent Solids," *Advances in Heat Transfer*, (Eds. T.F. Irvine and J.P. Hartnett, Academic Press), Vol. 11, p. 318.

Viskanta, R. and Anderson E.E., 1975, "Heat Transfer in Semitransparent Solids," *Advances in Heat Transfer*, (Eds T.F. Irvine and J.P. Hartnett, Academic Press), Vol. 11, p.318.

Witt, A. F., 1993, Personal Communication.

Yuferev, V.S. and Vasil'ev, M.G., 1987, "Heat Transfer in Shaped Thin-Walled Semitransparent Crystals Pulled from the Melt," *J. Crystal Growth*, Vol. 82, p. 31.

ACKNOWLEDGMENT

We are indebted to the detailed information and guidance provided by Prof. A. Witt of MIT and Dr. S. Motakef of CAPE Inc. with regard to BSO solidification and furnace configurations. The support of Microgravity Science & Applications Division at National Aeronautics and Space Administration and the support of Mr. Tom Glasgow and Dr. Arnon Chait of the Processing Science and Technology Branch is greatly appreciated. Finally, the valuable system-related assistance of Ron Gaug and Dave Thompson of the Computational Materials Laboratory at Lewis Research Center are gratefully acknowledged.

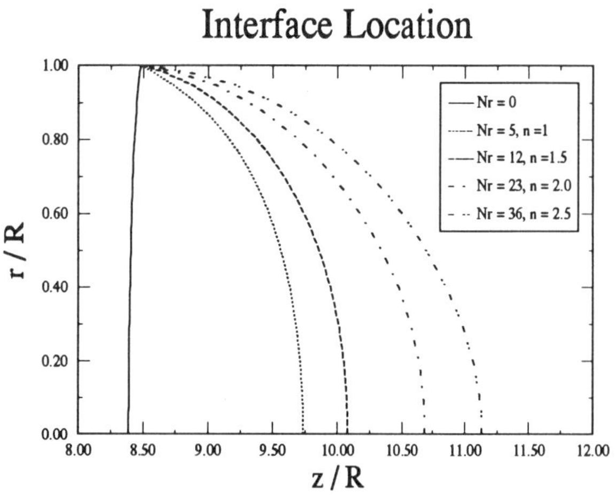

Figure 11: Effect of Index of Refraction on the Interface Shape for Solidification of BSO in Low-g Environment; Gr = 10.

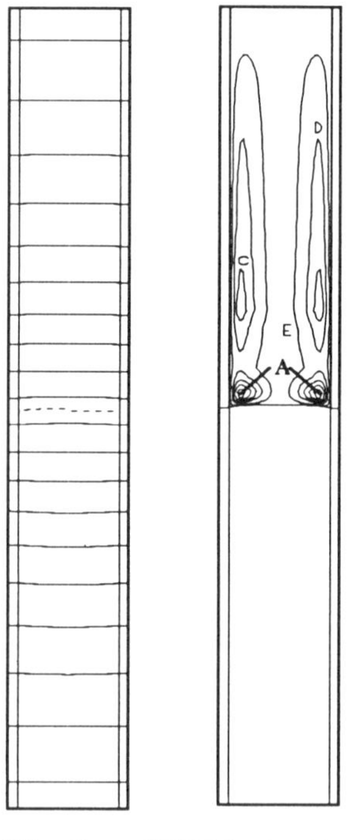

Figure 12: Solidification of BSO in 1-g Environment in a Perfectly Reflecting Crucible for Gr = 100736, Nr = 5.0: a) Temperature Contours; Minimum = 0.918, Maximum = 1.0, First Contour = 0.920, Increment = 0.0041. b) Streamline Contours; A =0.3663(10^{-4}), E = 0.3171(10^{-5}), Increments = 0.8370(10^{-5}).

HTD-Vol. 284/AMD-Vol. 182, Transport Phenomena in Solidification
ASME 1994

HEAT AND MASS TRANSFER IN SOLIDIFICATION BY THE SUBMERGED HEATER METHOD

A. G. Ostrogorsky, Z. Dragojlovic
Mechanical Engineering, Aeronautical Engineering & Mechanics
Rensselaer Polytechnic Institute
Troy, New York

ABSTRACT

The submerged disk-shaped device, located close and parallel to the solid/liquid interface, is used to control heat and solute transfer in the vertical Bridgman configuration. The Grashof number of the melt is reduced by a factor of ~ 10^3 (compared to the Bridgman configuration without the submerged heater), a reduction which is comparable to reducing the gravitational acceleration to 10^{-3} of earth gravity. An axisymmetric model of heat, momentum and solute transfer during solidification by the Submerged Heater Method was developed. For Sn-1% wt. Bi alloy, the model reveals weak convective interference with segregation. The onset of convective interference with segregation can not be predicted using the solutal Peclet number. A nondimensional group named the Segregation number is proposed as a substitute. Our numerical and experimental results indicate that segregation characteristic of ideal diffusion-controlled steady state growth can be achieved in ground based experiments using the Submerged Heater Method.

NOMENCLATURE

A	= area, cm
C	= $C_L/(z,r)\ C_\infty$, dimensionless melt concentration
C	= concentration, atoms/cm^3
D	= diffusion coefficient, cm/s^2
g	= gravitational acceleration
H	= height, cm
k	= $C_S(0)/C_L(0)$, equilibrium segregation coefficient
k	= conductivity, W/cm-K
L	= characteristic length, cm
r	= *r*/L, dimensionless radial distance
Se	= $(VD)/(V_S{}^2L)(1-k)/k$, segregation number
T	= temperature, K
ΔT	= destabilizing temperature difference, K
V	= velocity
z	= *z*/L, dimensionless axial distance
α	= thermal diffusivity, cm/s^2
β	= coefficient of thermal expansion, 1/K
δ_D	= thickness of solute boundary layer, cm
ν	= kinematic viscosity, cm/s^2
ρ	= melt density, g/cm^2
θ =	$[T(z,r) - T_m]/(T_{max} - T_m)$, dimensionless temperature

Subscripts

L	= liquid
m	= melting point
max	= maximum value
min	= minimum value
S	= solidification, solid
SH	= submerged heater
r	= radial
zone	= zone melt
∞	= value at infinity or inflow

INTRODUCTION

Single crystals are grown from the melt by slow plane-front directional solidification. The heat transfer goal of directional solidification is to i) melt the polycrystalline charge, ii) impose an axial temperature gradient along the melt and, iii) slowly move the melt relative to the axial temperature gradient (or move the gradient relative to the melt).

In all currently used melt growth processes (e.g., Czochralski, Bridgman, Floating Zone), solidification occurs inside tube-type furnaces. Heat is supplied to the melt radially, across the crucible side walls. Because of the heat exchange across the crucible side walls, radial temperature gradients must exist in the melt. In the presence of gravity, radial temperature gradients always generate buoyant forces which result in hydrostatic instability and convection. It is established that radial temperature gradients:

- result in curved solid-liquid interfaces (Holmes and Gatos, 1981);

- cause thermal stresses and dislocations in the growing crystal (Jordan et al., 1986);
- promote axial and radial segregation, caused by melt convection (Müller, 1988);

and upon exceeding a critical value;

- drive the unsteady natural convection causing microscopic inhomogeneities in the crystal (Müller, 1988).

Because the heat is supplied radially, reduction of radial temperature gradients reduces the total amount of heat flowing through the solid/liquid interface, weakening the desirable axial temperature gradient normal to the growth interface.

The recently proposed Submerged Heater Method, SHM, (Ostrogorsky, 1990) results in close-to-purely-axial heat flow in the melt. The main feature of this method is a submerged baffle, situated close and parallel to the growth interface in the vertical Bridgman configuration, Figure 1. The baffle controls the axial flow of heat and solute. It contains thermocouples while in some applications, a powered baffle was used (i.e., "submerged heater", Ostrogorsky et al., 1991; 1993; Ostrogorsky and Müller, 1994). A single or a multi-zone (tube-type) guard heater, controls the radial heat flow.

The heat is extracted from the growing crystal downward, through a support pedestal, attached to the water cooled shaft. During growth, the radial (destabilizing) temperature gradients are maintained at $\partial T/\partial r \sim 0.1$ K/cm. Within the guard heater, the heat flow is close to one-dimensional (purely axial). The destabilizing ΔT is < 1 K.

The enclosure between the solid/liquid interface and the baffle is shallow. It contains a small portion of the melt. Above the baffle is the large top melt. The annular gap between the crucible and the baffle is $\sim$ 0.05 cm .

The melt is solidified by lowering the crucible, while the tubular furnace and the submerged heater remain at a fixed elevation. While the crucible is lowered, the large top melt feeds solidification. During growth, the temperature of the submerged heater, T_{SH}, is held constant at $\approx$ 10 K above T_m, the melting point of the charge. As a result, the freezing interface is at a small constant distance H_{zone} below the bottom surface of the submerged heater,

$$H_{zone} = \frac{T_{SH} - T_m}{\partial T / \partial z} \qquad (1)$$

In most experiments, the axial temperature gradient below the submerged heater was $\partial T/\partial z \approx 10$ to 30 K/cm. For $T_{SH} = T_m + 10$ K, $H_{zone} \approx 0.3$ to 1 cm. Since the diameter of the used crucibles is in the range d = 3.6 to 6 cm, the zone melt is shallow, ($H_{zone}/d < 1$).

The dimensionless Grashof number, Gr, scales the ratio between the buoyancy forces (driving the flow) and viscous forces (opposing convection),

$$Gr = \frac{g\beta \ \Delta T \ L^3}{\nu^2} \qquad (2)$$

where g is the gravitational acceleration, β is the coefficient of thermal expansion, ΔT is the destabilizing temperature difference, L is characteristic length scale and ν is the kinematic viscosity. The melt properties ν and β can not be altered. Thus, the buoyancy forces and melt convection can be attenuated by reducing g, L^3 or ΔT.

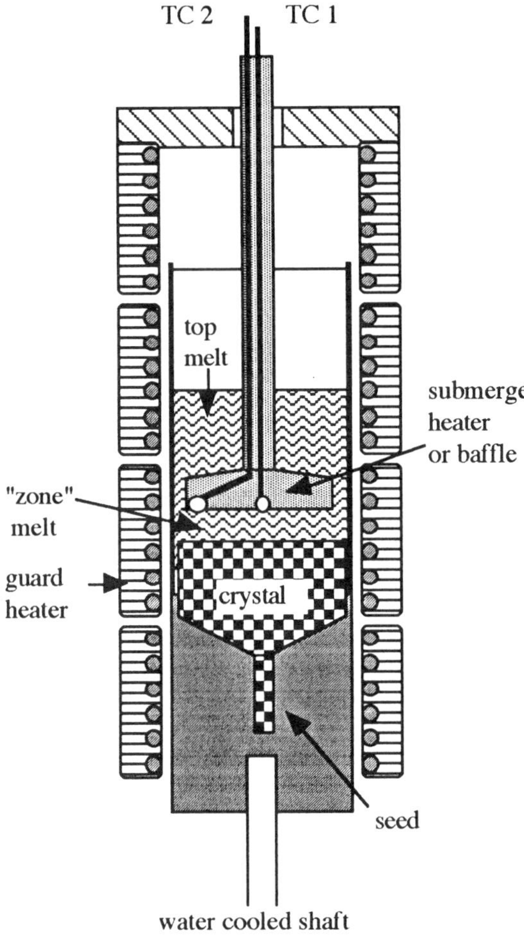

Fig. 1. Schematic of the experimental apparatus for crystal growth by the Submerged Heater Method (SHM).

The baffle and the interface form a shallow horizontal enclosure, where the characteristic length scale is the enclosure height, equal to H_{zone}. H_{zone} is one order of magnitude smaller than the crucible diameter or the height of the melt without the baffle (Ostrogorsky et al., 1991, 1993). As a result, the Grashof number is reduced by three orders of magnitude. Furthermore, in the zone melt, the radial temperature difference ΔT driving the convection is notably reduced. This implies that the baffle reduces the ratio between buoyancy forces and viscous forces by three to four orders of magnitude, a reduction which had the same effect as decreasing the gravitational acceleration to 10^{-3} to 10^{-4} of the earth gravity g_0.

Using the SHM, we obtained segregation characteristic of diffusion-controlled steady state growth in 5.8 cm crucibles (Sn-1% Bi specimens, Ostrogorsky et al., 1991) and (Te-doped InSb specimens, Ostrogorsky et al., 1993). Diffusion-controlled steady-state segregation was previously reported only in space experiments (Te-doped InSb in 1.28 cm ampoule, Witt et al. 1975).

Here we present a simple axisymmetric model of heat, momentum and solute transfer during solidification by the Submerged Heater Method.

NUMERICAL MODEL OF SEGREGATION DURING GROWTH BY THE SUBMERGED HEATER METHOD

The finite element program FIDAP was used to simulate the heat transfer, fluid flow and solute segregation during directional solidification by the SHM (FIDAP, 1993). The geometry of the melt and the submerged heater matches the one used in experiments, fig. 2. The height of the melt L is set equal to the diameter, d = 5.8 cm. The annular gap between the submerged heater and the crucible wall was set equal to 0.05 cm. The solid-liquid interface is assumed to be flat, as found in most of our experiments. Axial symmetry is assumed. The melt and the baffle are divided into 391 finite elements (23 in axial x 17 in radial direction). The submerged heater is simulated with solid elements, allowing only for heat conduction. The governing equations (continuity, momentum, energy and species concentration) were nondimensionalized using L, α/L and $\rho\ \alpha^2/L^2$ (α is the thermal diffusivity and ρ is melt density):

$$\nabla \cdot \mathbf{V} = 0 \qquad (3)$$

$$\mathbf{V} \cdot \nabla\mathbf{V} = -\nabla p + \Pr\nabla^2\mathbf{v} + Gr \cdot \Pr^2 \cdot \theta\ \mathbf{e}_z \qquad (4)$$

$$\mathbf{V} \cdot \nabla\theta = \nabla^2\theta \qquad (5)$$

$$\mathbf{V} \cdot \nabla C = \frac{\Pr}{Sc}\nabla^2 C \qquad (6)$$

where $\nabla \equiv \mathbf{e}_z\partial/\partial z + \mathbf{e}_r\partial/\partial r$. The dimensionless groups are defined in Table 1. The nondimensional temperature θ and concentration C are defined as:

$$\theta \equiv \frac{T(z,r) - T_m}{T_{max} - T_m} \qquad (7)$$

$$C \equiv \frac{C_L(z,r)}{C_\infty} \qquad (8)$$

where T_{max} is uppermost melt temperature and $C_L(z,r)$ is the dimensional solute concentration, [atoms/cm^3]. C_∞ solute concentration at the top of the melt [atoms/cm^3].

The following boundary conditions are imposed on the solid-liquid interface (z=0, 0<r<1), which is assumed to be planar:

$$\theta = 0 \qquad (9)$$

$$\mathbf{V} \cdot \mathbf{e}_r = 0 \qquad (10)$$

$$-\mathbf{V} \cdot \mathbf{e}_z = \frac{V_S L}{\alpha} \qquad (11)$$

$$\frac{\partial C}{\partial z} = \frac{Pe\ Sc}{\Pr}(1-k)\ C \qquad (12)$$

where V_S [cm/s] is the rate of lowering the crucible. The equilibrium segregation coefficient, k is defined as,

$$k = \frac{C_S(0)}{C_L(0)} \qquad (13)$$

where the $C_S(0)$ is solute concentration in the solid and $C_L(0)$ solute concentration in the melt at the interface (at z=0). The equation (10) is the no-slip condition, (11) imposes a uniform outflow from the melt due to freezing. The equation (12) represents the solute conservation at the solid-liquid interface.

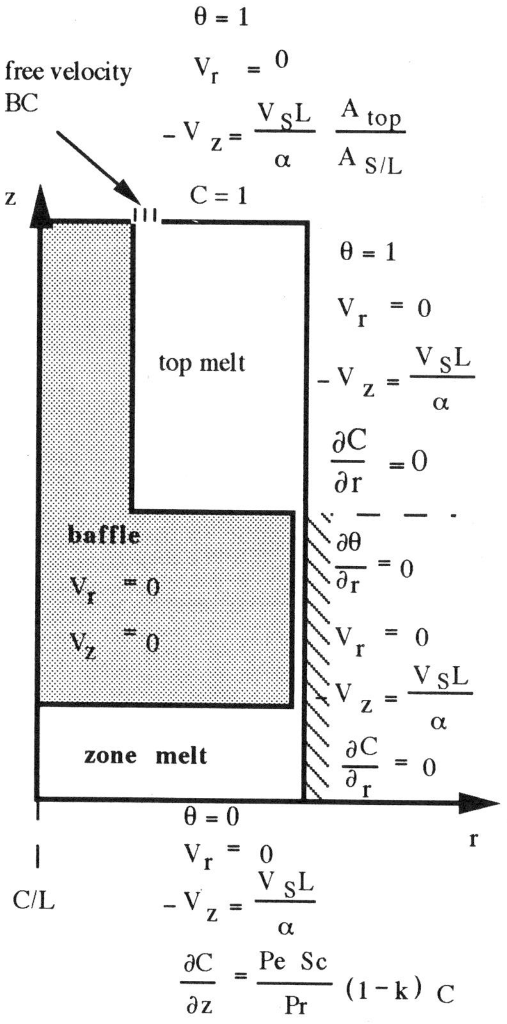

Fig. 2. A model of melt geometry and dimensionless boundary conditions of the solidification experiments reported by Ostrogorsky et al., (1991). The submerged heater in vertical Bridgman configuration produces no heat (it acts as a baffle).

The boundary conditions imposed on the top of the melt are:

$$\theta = 1 \quad (15)$$

$$\mathbf{V} \cdot \mathbf{e}_r = 0 \quad (16)$$

$$-\mathbf{V} \cdot \mathbf{e}_z = \frac{V_S L}{\alpha}\left(\frac{A_{top}}{A_{S/L}}\right) \quad (17)$$

$$C = 1 \quad (18)$$

were A_{top} is the area of the top melt surface, and $A_{S/L}$ is the interface area. To satisfy the continuity equation, three elements had to be left free of imposed axial velocity (17). All boundaries of the baffle are assumed to be impermeable to the solute and the melt:

$$\theta = \theta_{SH} \quad (19)$$

$$\frac{\partial \theta}{\partial z} = \left(\frac{k_{SH}}{k}\right)\frac{\partial \theta_{SH}}{\partial z} \quad (20)$$

$$\frac{\partial \theta}{\partial r} = \left(\frac{k_{SH}}{k}\right)\frac{\partial \theta_{SH}}{\partial r} \quad (21)$$

$$\mathbf{V} \cdot \mathbf{e}_r = 0 \quad (22)$$

$$\mathbf{V} \cdot \mathbf{e}_z = 0 \quad (23)$$

$$\frac{\partial C}{\partial z} = 0 \quad (24)$$

$$\frac{\partial C}{\partial r} = 0 \quad (25)$$

where k_{SH} [W/cm-K] is thermal conductivity and θ_{SH} is temperature of the baffle. The baffle, made out of a high conductivity graphite, has $k_{SH}/k = 1.5$.

We assumed that the freezing rate is equal to the rate of lowering the crucible V_S. Therefore, the boundary conditions at the melt side boundaries are:

$$\frac{\partial \theta}{\partial r} = 0 \qquad 0<z<0.5 \quad (26)$$

$$\theta = 1 \qquad 0.5<z<1 \quad (27)$$

$$\mathbf{V} \cdot \mathbf{e}_r = 0 \quad (28)$$

$$\mathbf{V} \cdot \mathbf{e}_z = \frac{V_S L}{\alpha} \quad (29)$$

$$\frac{\partial C}{\partial z} = 0 \quad (30)$$

Within the guard heater, the side boundaries of the melt were modeled as insulated, equation (26).

RESULTS

The above system of governing equations (eq. 3 to 6) and boundary conditions (eq. 9 to 30) were solved for geometry and properties used in experiments with Sn-1% wt Bi (Ostrogorsky et al., 1991). The thermo-physical properties of Sn-1%Bi are given in Table 2. In the interest of simplicity, in all simulations reported here, the submerged heater was assumed to produce no power.

Table 1. Dimensionless parameters and their values for the Sb-Bi system

Group	Definition	Value
Radial distance	$r = r/L$	0 to 0.5
Axial distance	$z = z/L$	0 to 1
Temperature	$\theta \equiv \frac{T(z,r) - T_m}{T_{max} - T_m}$	0 to 1
Concentration	$C \equiv \frac{C_L(z,r)}{C_\infty}$	1 to C_∞/k
Prandtl number	$Pr \equiv \frac{\nu}{\alpha}$	0.015
Schmidt number	$Sc \equiv \frac{\nu}{D}$	162
Grashof number	$Gr = \frac{g\beta \ \Delta T \ L^3}{\nu^2}$	2.7 $\times 10^6$
Rayleigh number	$Ra = \frac{g\beta \ \Delta T \ L^3}{\alpha \nu}$	4.2 $\times 10^4$
Segregation number	$Se \equiv \frac{V}{V_S^2}\frac{D}{L} \cdot \frac{1-k}{k}$	~ 0.1

Table 2: Thermo-physical Properties of Sb-1%Bi System

Property	Value
Melting point, T_m[°C]	232
Melt density, ρ[g/cm^3]	7.0
Kinematic viscosity, ν[cm^2/s]	0.0026
Thermal diffusivity, α[cm^2/s]	0.171
Diffusion coefficient, D [cm^2/s]	1.6 $\times 10^{-5}$
Thermal conductivity, k[W/cm-K]	0.30
Thermal expansion, β [1/K]	8.75 $\times 10^{-5}$
Equilibrium segregation coefficient k	0.35
Growth rate V_S,[cm/s]	4.16 $\times 10^{-4}$

The temperature field is shown in Figure 3. The maximum temperature difference was set to ΔT = 20 K, yielding axial temperature gradient $\partial T/\partial z \approx 10$ K/cm. The radial temperature gradient which resulted in the melt was $\partial T/\partial r \approx 0.1$ K. Both are close to the gradients found in our Sn-Bi experiments (Ostrogorsky et al., 1991). The heat transfer is dominated by conduction. Only the isotherms $\theta = 0.85$ and $\theta = 0.95$ reveal weak presence of advection in the top melt. Note that, at the adiabatic boundary ($r = 0.5$, $0 < z < 0.5$), the temperature varies approximately linearly from $\theta = 0$ to $\theta = 1$.

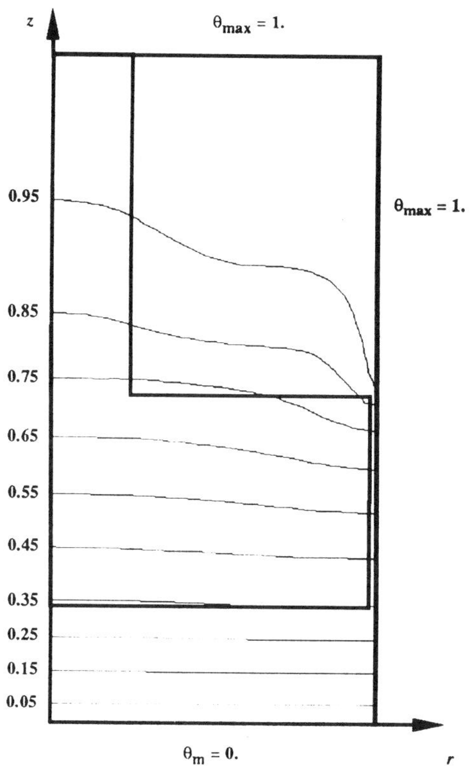

Fig. 3 Dimensionless temperature $\theta = [T(z,r) - T_m]/(T_{max} - T_m)$ in the melt and the submerged heater (baffle). $T_m = 232$ °C, $T_{max} = 252$ °C.

Figure 4 shows the velocity field in the melt, in the presence of the unpowered submerged heater. The maximum dimensional velocity in the top melt is $V_{max,top} = 0.607$ cm/s, corresponding to Reynolds number, $Re = V_{max,top}L/\nu \approx 700$. The downward motion of the crucible ($V_S = 4.16 \times 10^{-4}$ cm/s) and the velocity field in the zone melt, are too low to notice.

The convective flow velocity at the freezing boundary strongly depends on the zone height, H_{zone}. Thus, in Figure 5, radial velocity $V_r(z,r)$ is shown separately, for different values of H_{zone}. For $H_{zone} = 1$ cm, the radial velocity is $V_r = 66.5$ μm; for $H_{zone} = 0.6$ cm, the radial velocity is $V_r = 21.3$ μm .(~ 300 times lower than in the top melt). The solute layer $\delta_D \sim 0.1$ cm (see figures 6 and 7) is shown in the same figure. Note that only within the solute layer, convection causes net solute transport (outside the solute boundary layer, the concentration field is uniform). For $H_{zone} \leq 0.4$ cm, the radial velocity in the solute layer is lower than the solidification rate ($V_r << V_S$).

A three-dimensional view of Bi concentration is given in fig. 6. The submerged heater is impermeable. In the top melt $C = 1$ (C_L is uniformly equal to $C_\infty = 1$ [wt. %]). This implies

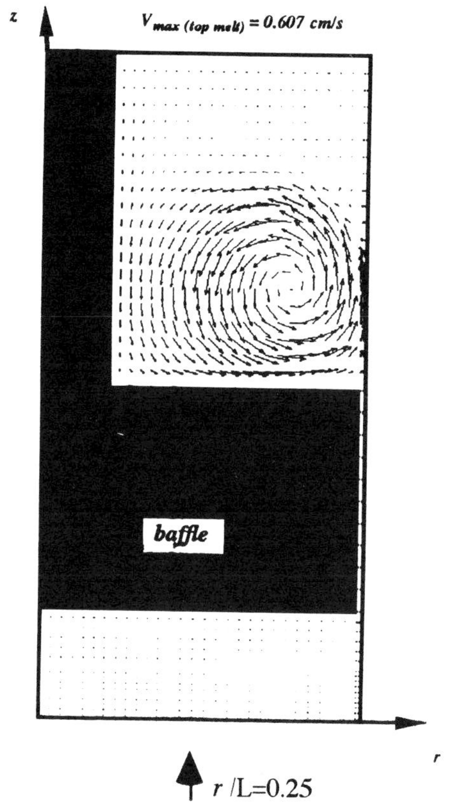

Fig. 4. Velocity in the presence of an unpowered submerged heater for the boundary conditions given in fig. 2.. The maximum velocity in the top melt is $V_{max,top} = 0.607$ cm/s ($Re \approx 700$, $Pr = 0.015$)

that there is no back diffusion from the zone into the top melt. All solute rejected at the freezing interface stays in the zone, and eventually is absorbed by the interface.

Since there is no back diffusion, solute conservation requires that the average concentration at the freezing interface is $C_{L,\ average} = C_\infty/k = 2.86$ wt. %. The solute fields shown in Figure 6 satisfy this requirement.

The solute boundary layer at the interface is slender. Outside of the solute layer ($z > \delta_D \sim 0.1$ cm) there is no net solute transport because concentration field is uniform.

Solute distribution of at the melt center line, is plotted as a function of distance ahead of the interface, fig. 7. The lines with symbols + and × were obtained using the present model, for Hzone = 1.0 cm and Hzone = 0.4 cm, respectively. In the same figure, we show for comparison, the analytical solution for convection-free normal freezing (lines with symbols ■ ; Tiller, 1953),

$$\frac{C_L}{C_\infty} = 1 + \frac{k-1}{k} \cdot \exp(-\frac{V_S}{D} z) \qquad (28)$$

Eq. (28) was computed using $k = 0.35$, $V_S = 4.16 \times 10^{-4}$ cm/s and $D = 1.6 \times 10^{-5}$ [cm^2/s]. (same parameters as in the model). The lines virtually overlap, indicating that convection -free solidification is possible using the Submerged Heater Method.

Figure 8 shows Bi concentration [wt. %], at the solid/liquid interface (z=0), as a function of radial distance. Top line is concentration in the liquid C_L(0,r) obtained from the model. The bottom line is the concentration in the solid, calculated using equation (13). The data (shown with error bars) were obtained using the Auger spectroscopy with accuracy ± 10 % of the measured value (Ostrogorsky et al., 1991). The data shown in Figure 8 a) were taken from the portion of the specimen which was solidified with H_{zone} ≈1 cm. The absolute value of the calculated concentration in the solid C_S agrees well with the data. However, the model did not capture the "w" shape of the data profile.

The data shown in Figure 8 b) were taken from the portion of the specimen which was solidified with H_{zone} ≈ 0.5 cm. Again, the calculated concentration C_S is close to the data.

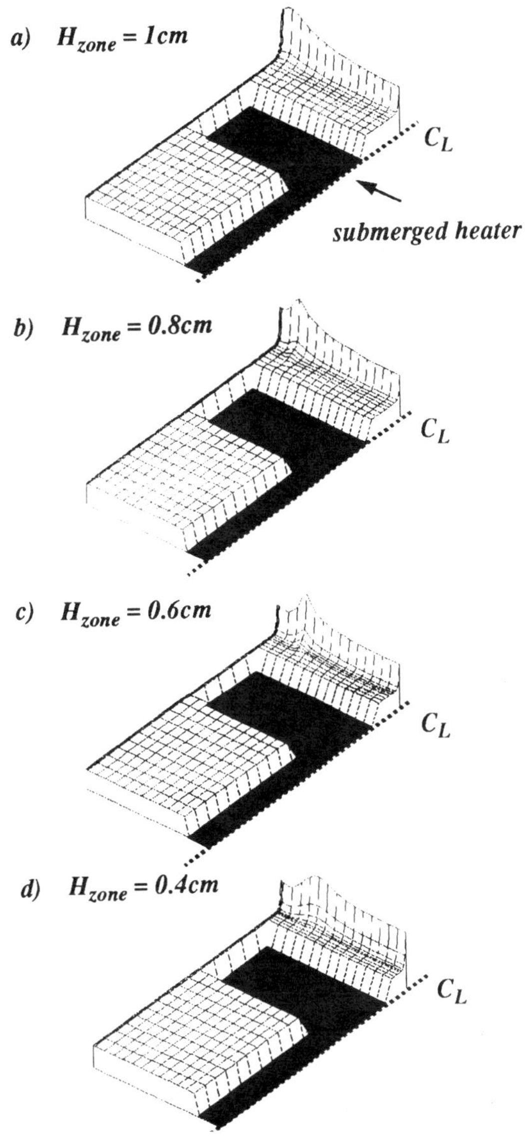

Fig. 5 Radial velocity profiles V_r (z,r) in zone melt, at the radial location, r = 1.45 cm (r = r/L = 0.25). The solute layer at the solid/liquid interface δ_D ~ 0.1 cm (see fig. 6 and 7).

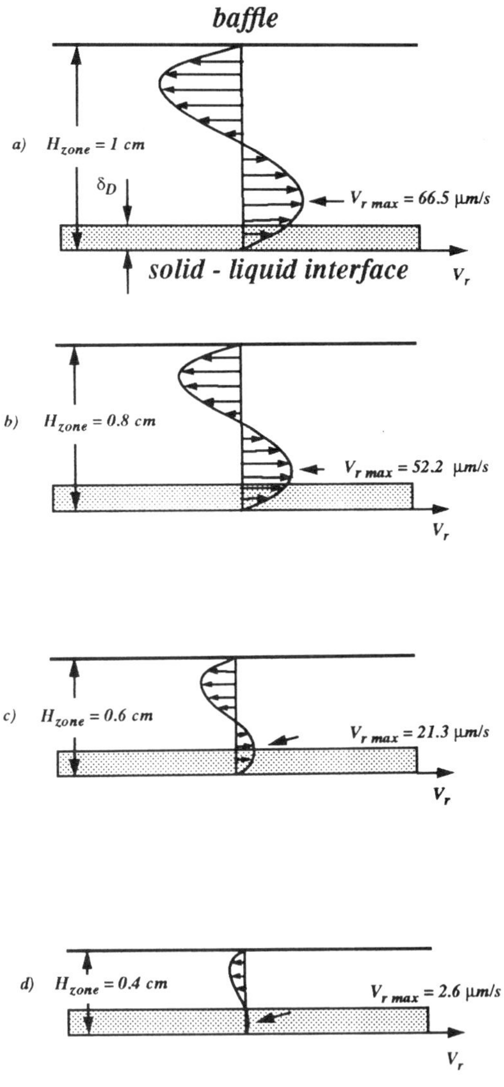

Fig. 6 Dimensionless concentration $C = C_L(z,r)/C_\infty$ of Bi in the Sn melt. In the top melt, $C = C_\infty = 1$ (no back diffusion). At the interface is $C_{average} = C_\infty/k$. $\delta_D \sim D/V_S \sim 0.1$ cm ; $D = 1.6 \times 10^{-5}$ cm^2/s; $V_S = 4.16 \times 10^{-4}$ cm/s; k = 0.35; Sc = 162.

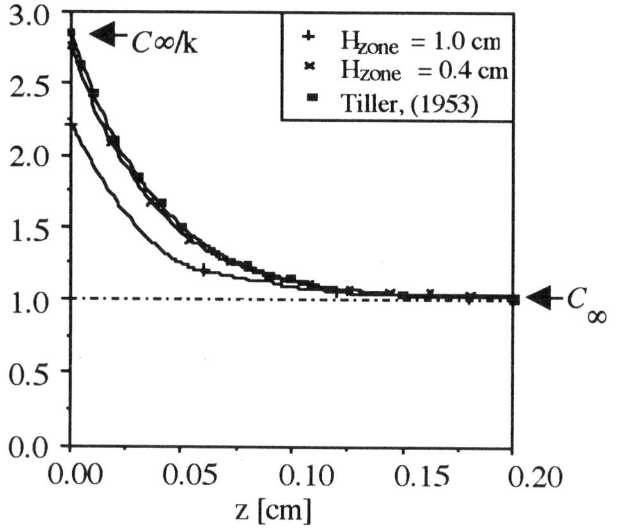

Fig. 7. Axial distribution of the Bi at center line, plotted versus distance from the solid-liquid interface. The line with symbols ▪ is calculated using the one-dimensional analytical solution for convection free solidification (Tiller, 1953). Lines with symbols × and + are calculations using the present model, for H_{zone} = 1.0 cm and H_{zone} = 0.4 cm, respectively.

DISCUSSION AND CONCLUSIONS

The Submerged Heater Method offers a unique, axial heat transfer environment suitable for crystal growth. The Grashof number of the melt is reduced by a factor of ~ 10^3 (compared to the vertical Bridgman configuration without the submerged heater), a reduction which is comparable to that of reducing the gravitational acceleration to 10^{-3} of earth gravity. As a result, the level of convection at the freezing interface is reduced by a factor of 10^2 to 10^3 (depending on the height of the zone).

An axisymmetric model of heat, momentum and solute transfer during solidification by the Submerged Heater Method was developed. Steady buoyancy forces and low levels of convection, enable accurate numerical simulations. For the Sn-1% Bi alloy, the model reveals weak convective interference with segregation. The model predicts a radial nonuniformity, located close to the entrance region of the zone melt. At this point, it is not clear why this nonuniformity was not revealed by experiments (Ostrogorsky et al., 1991; 1993).

The solute distribution ahead of the advancing solid-liquid interface (fig. 7.) is close to the one-dimensional distribution described in the famous Tiller's paper (1953). Weak radial segregation is observed for $0.6 < H_{zone} < 1$. When zone height is reduced to H_{zone} less than 0.6, solute concentration at the freezing interface becomes equal to,

$$C_L(0) = C_\infty/k \tag{31}$$

confirming the absence of convective interference with segregation (excluding in the entrance region). Accordingly, the solute concentration in the solid is uniformly equal to C_∞,

$$C_S(0) = k \cdot C_L(0) = C_\infty \tag{32}$$

When (32) is satisfied, solute inflow into the zone melt is equal to the outflow (into the crystal), resulting in the ideal steady-state segregation. Previously, the ideal diffusion-controlled steady-state segregation was reported only in a few space experiments.

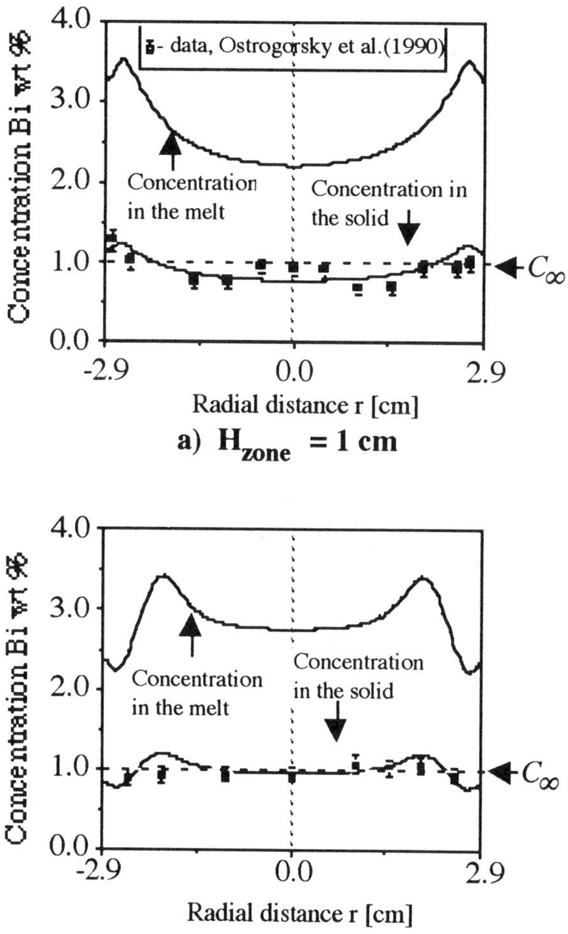

Fig. 8 Bi concentration [wt. %], as a function of radial distance, at the solid/liquid interface (z=0). Top line is the calculated concentration in the in the liquid phase $C_L(0,r)$. The bottom line is the concentration in the solid, $C_S(r)$ ʃ k • $C_L(r)$. The data are from Ostrogorsky et al., 1991.
a) Calculations were performed for H_{zone} = 1 cm. The data were taken from a portion of the specimen solidified from the zone melt having height, H_{zone} ≈1 cm.
b) Calculations were performed for H_{zone} = 0.4 cm. The data were taken from a portion of the specimen solidified from the zone melt having height, H_{zone} ≈ 0.5 cm.

The solutal Peclet number, which scales the importance of convective solute transport to diffusion,

$$Pe = \frac{\text{convective solute transport}}{\text{solute transport by diffusion}} = \frac{V \cdot L}{D} \quad (29)$$

may lead to erroneous conclusions on importance of convection in segregation. In contrast to our experiments (Ostrogorsky et al., 1991) and the present results (fig.6 and fig.7) substitution of the convective velocity $V = 21.3 \times 10^{-4}$ cm/s (fig. 5 c), $L = d/2 = 2.9$ cm and $D = 1.6 \times 10^{-5}$ cm^2/s into (29) yields,

$$Pe \approx 300.$$

which indicates convection dominated transport. Note that Pe number computed by (29) indicates that lateral convection is 300 times larger than lateral diffusion. Still, there is little radial segregation, because the lateral convection is small compared to the axial transport due to freezing.

Furthermore, in the limit, the Peclet number approaches infinity, as $D \rightarrow 0$. This is an erroneous behavior, since an infinitely low diffusion coefficient yields an infinitely thin solute layer, unaffected by convection.

The level of convective interference with segregation can be estimated by comparing the amount of solute which enters the solute layer due to freezing (Ostrogorsky and Müler, 1992),

$$J_{solidification} = V_S\, C_\infty\, L \quad (30)$$

to the amount of solute removed from the solute layer by convection, fig. 9,

$$J_{convection} = V \cdot \delta_D (C_\infty / k - C_\infty) \quad (31)$$

Dividing (31) by (30) defines a non-dimensional parameter,

$$Se \equiv \frac{J_{convection}}{J_{solidification}} = \left(\frac{V}{V_S}\right)\left(\frac{\delta_D}{L}\right)\left(\frac{1-k}{k}\right) \quad (32)$$

that may be named the segregation number, Se. The convection-free segregation occurs when $J_{convection} << J_{solidification}$, or $Se << 1$.

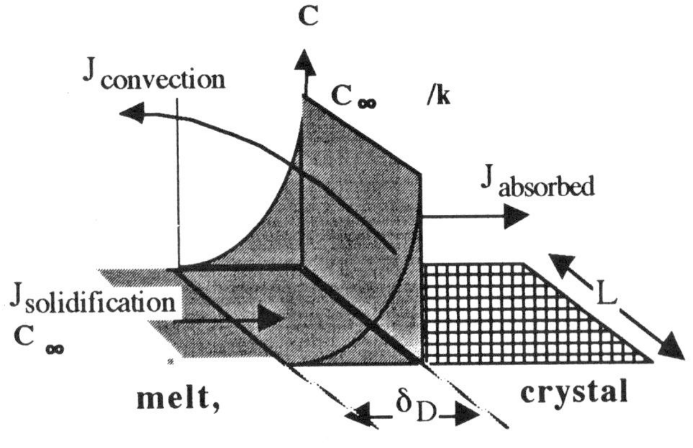

Fig. 9 Conservation of solute in the boundary layer at the growth interface

The first term on the right hand side of (32) is, $V/V_S = 5.12$ (for $H_{zone} = 0.6$ cm, $V = 21.3 \times 10^{-4}$ cm/s $V_S = 4.16 \times 10^{-4}$ cm/s). The second term, δ_D/L, is the aspect ratio of the solute layer. The thickness of the solute layer in the absence of convection is of the order,

$$\delta_D \sim \frac{D}{V_S} \sim 0.04 \text{ cm} \quad (33)$$

so that, $\delta_D/L \sim 10^{-2}$. The last term in (32) is equal to: $(1-k)/k = 1.86$. Therefore, the segregation number is of the order,

$$Se \sim 0.1$$

indicating that only ~ 10 % of the solute which approaches solid-liquid interface and enters the solute boundary layer will be removed by convection. The remaining 90 % will be incorporated in the solid, resulting in close to convection free segregation (i.e., low radial segregation). Although the convective velocity is ~ 5 times higher than the solidification rate, the segregation is close convection-free.

Substitution of (33) in (32), yields,

$$Se \equiv \frac{V}{V_S^2}\frac{D}{L} \cdot \frac{1-k}{k} \quad (34)$$

In contrast to the space growth where the magnitude and direction of the residual acceleration (and thus buoyancy forces) continuously vary, the buoyancy forces during growth by the SHM remain constant and normal to the growth interface. This is an important feature of the SHM, since numerical simulations have demonstrated that acceleration parallel to the growth interface causes one to two orders of magnitude higher melt velocities than acceleration acting along the axis of the crucible (Alexander et al., 1989).

The use the SHM in space laboratories, would result in the combined reduction of g (for a factor of ~10^3 to 10^4), ΔT (for a factor of ~ 10) and L^3 (for a factor of ~10^2 to 10^3), lowering Gr and buoyancy forces by as much as a factor of 10^6 to 10^8.

ACKNOWLEDGMENTS

This work is sponsored by the Microgravity Science and Applications Division of the National Aeronautics and Space Administration (award NAG 8-952).

REFERENCES

Alexander, J.I.D., Ouazzani,J. and Rosenberger,F., 1989, "Analysis of the Low Gravity Tolerance of Bridgman-Stockbarger Crystal Growth I", *Journal of Crystal Growth*, Vol. 97, pp. 285-302.

FIDAP 7.0 Users Manual (1993).

Holmes, D.E. and Gatos, H.C., 1981,"Convective Interference and "Effective" Diffusion-Controlled Segregation under Stabilizing Vertical Temperature Gradients" *Journal of Electrochemical Society*, Vol. 128, pp. 429-437.

Müller, G, 1988, in *Crystals: Growth, Properties and Applications*, Vol. 12, Springer, Berlin.

Jordan, A.S., Caruso, A.R. and Von Neida, A.R., 1986, " A Thermoelastic Analysis of Dislocation Generation in Pulled GaAs Crystals", *Bell System Technical Journal*, Vol. 59, pp. 359-371.

Ostrogorsky,A.G., 1990, "Numerical Simulation of Single Crystal Growth by Submerged Heater Method" *Journal of Crystal Growth* , Vol. 104 (1990) 233-238.

Ostrogorsky,A.G., Mosel, F. and Schmidt, M.T., 1991, "Diffusion-Controlled Distribution of Solute in Sn-1%Bi, "*Journal of Crystal Growth* , Vol. 110, pp. 950-954.

Ostrogorsky,A.G., Sell, H.J., Scharl, S. and Müller, G, 1993, "Convection and Segregation During Growth of Ge and InSb Crystals by the Submerged Heater Method", *Journal of Crystal Growth* , Vol. 128, pp. 201-206.

Ostrogorsky,A.G., Müller, G, 1992 , "A Model of Effective Segregation Coefficient, Accounting for Convection in the Solute Layer at the Growth Interface", *Journal of Crystal Growth , Vol. 121* (1992)pp 587-598.

Ostrogorsky,A.G., Müller, G, 1994 , "Normal and Zone Solidification using the Submerged Heater Method", *Journal of Crystal Growth , Vol. 135* (1994),pp. 64-71.

Tiller, W.A. , Jackson, K.A., Rutter, J.W., and Chalmers, B., 1953, "The Redistribution of Solute Atoms During the Solidification of Metals", *Acta Metallurgica 1* , pp. 428-437.

Utech, H.P., Brower, W.S. and Early, J.G., 1966, "Thermal Convection and Crystal Growth in Horizontal Boats: Flow Pattern, Velocity Measurement, and Solute Distribution", Proceedings of an International Conference on Crystal Growth, Boston, B29., pp. 201-205.

Witt, A.F., Gatos, H.C., Lichensteiger, M.C., and Herman C.J., "Crystal Growth and Steady-State Segregation Under Zero Gravity: InSb", 1975, J. Electrochemical Society 122, pp 276-283.

HTD-Vol. 284/AMD-Vol. 182, Transport Phenomena in Solidification
ASME 1994

INTERFACE SHAPE CONTROL IN SOLIDIFICATION

Arvind Srinivasan and Celal Batur
Department of Mechanical Engineering
University of Akron
Akron, Ohio

Bruce N. Rosenthal
NASA Lewis Research Center
Cleveland, Ohio

ABSTRACT

This paper deals with the problem of controlling the solid-liquid interface shape during solidification of molten material inside a Bridgman-Stockbarger furnace. The necessary boundary conditions that would achieve the desired interface shape is found using the developments in the "Controls" area. A state-space model of the solidification process is found by utilizing the finite element method on the governing conduction equation obtained through the apparent heat capacity formulation. This model is used to design a dynamic controller that would set up a desired interface shape by making use of all available temperature measurements.

I. INTRODUCTION

In the recent years, there has been a considerable interest in directional solidification processing technique to develop materials with improved structural properties such as thermal stresses, refractive index. One way to achieve this objective is to measure the structural property of interest "on-line" and modify the control variables in the process, i.e., the temperature gradient accordingly. However, the implementation of this procedure would require:

(a) on-line measurement of the structural property,

(b) the relationship between the structural property and the temperature gradient.

It is difficult to measure structural properties on-line. There are other intermediate quantities that can be related to structural properties. The interface shape during solidification is one of the indicator of the crystal quality. For example, a flat interface would yield reduced thermal stresses in the material. Hence, the crystal quality can be significantly improved by manipulating the temperature gradient to produce the desirable interface shape during the crystal growth process.

In the past, the furnace operator would tune the temperature gradients around the ampoule to achieve the desirable interface shape. In (Dantzig and Tortorelli ,1991), an optimization approach has been taken to determine the necessary temperature gradient. This approach cannot take advantage of any on-line measurements to correct for the inevitable modeling errors or disturbances. In control terminologies, this approach just yields "open-loop" temperature gradients for the furnace.

The interface shape can be directly measured through X-rays in the case of non-transparent material or by image processing techniques for transparent furnaces. Also, it is possible to predict the interface shape on-line by measuring auxiliary quantities such as the ampoule surface temperature. These measurements can be used to correct for modeling errors.

In this paper, a new approach is proposed to control the shape of the interface by making use of all available measurements. The block diagram in Figure 1 explains how the temperatures inside the material, therefore, the interface shape is controlled. An enthalpy based finite element model of the solidification process, similar to the formulation in (Srinivasan et al., 1994), is obtained by considering conduction heat transfer only. This model is utilized to predict the interface shape (in situation where interface shape cannot be directly measured) and is

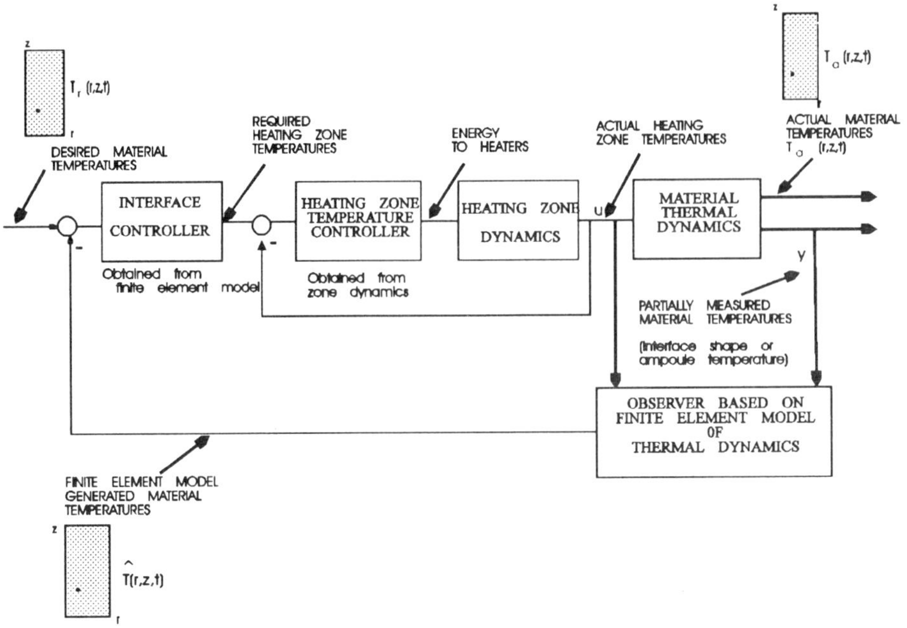

Figure 1. Proposed method to control the shape of the interface.

also used to determine the required temperature gradients that would produce the desired shape.

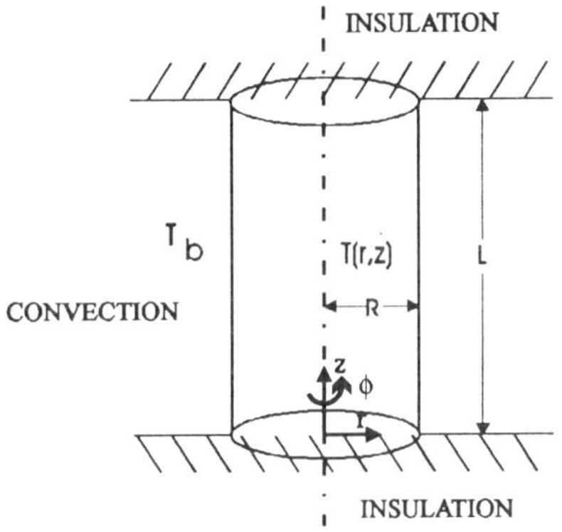

Figure 2. Material inside a cylindrical ampoule.

2 GOVERNING EQUATIONS FOR THE SOLIDIFICATION PROCESS

The dynamics of the crystal growth process inside an ampoule in a vertical furnace is primarily governed by the conduction equation given below

$$\rho c \frac{\partial T}{\partial t} = \nabla \cdot (k \nabla T) \quad , \tag{1}$$

where ρ is the density, c is the heat capacity, k is the thermal conductivity of the material and T is the temperature. In any crystal growth problem, the material undergoes a phase change. The mathematical model for the heat conduction problem with phase change, also known as the Stefan's problem includes two heat conduction equations; one each for solid and liquid region. In addition, a third equation describes the heat conduction at the solid/liquid interface. The model is described by the following set of equations (Crank, 1984)

$$\rho_l c_l \frac{\partial T}{\partial t} = \nabla \cdot (k_l \nabla T) \qquad \text{Liquid region}$$

$$\rho_s c_s \frac{\partial T}{\partial t} = \nabla \cdot (k_s \nabla T) \qquad \text{Solid region}$$

$$k_s \frac{\partial T}{\partial n} - k_l \frac{\partial T}{\partial n} = \rho L v_n \qquad \text{At the Interface} \quad , \tag{2}$$

where the subscript 'l' correspond to properties of material in the liquid region and subscript 's' corresponds to material properties in the solid region. n denotes the unit vector that is normal to the interface with the positive direction of n pointing into the liquid region, v_n is the velocity of the interface along the unit normal, and L is the latent heat of solidification. There are additional boundary conditions that depend on the geometry of the ampoule, and the type of the furnace. Figure 2 depicts a typical ampoule inside the Bridgman-Stockbarger furnace. The material is inside an axi-symmetric cylindrical ampoule. The top and the bottom of the ampoule are insulated. The furnace is capable of establishing an axi-symmetrical temperature profile with varying temperatures along the length of the cylinder. Heat transfer from the furnace into the material occurs through convection. The BC's for this configuration is given by

$$\left.\frac{\partial T}{\partial z}\right|_{z=0} = 0$$

$$\left.\frac{\partial T}{\partial z}\right|_{z=L} = 0$$

$$\left. k \frac{\partial T}{\partial r} + h(T - T_b)\right|_{r=R} = 0 \tag{3}$$

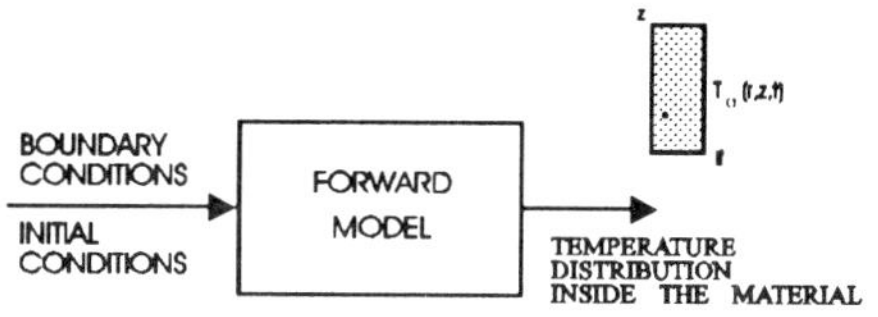

Figure 3. Representation of forward problem.

3. FORWARD PROBLEM

It is imperative to find the temperature distribution inside the material or the interface location for a given set of boundary conditions and initial conditions as illustrated in Figure 3. In this work, this is known as the "forward" problem. A number of research articles have appeared in the last few years (Crank, 1984)-(Shamsundar and Sparrow, 1975) to solve the forward problem. The main difficulty in solving the forward problem is the movement of the interface surface. The interface either moves into the liquid region when the material solidifies or moves into the solid region when melting occurs. The rate at which this movement occurs depends on the rate at which heat is removed at the interface surface. The heat removal rate is dependent on the material properties that is usually temperature dependent or at least depends on the state[1] of the material. This phenomenon introduces non-linearity into the problem. Further, the rate of travel of the interface is not known *a priori*. This rate is needed to make a heat balance across the interface to solve for the temperature distribution. Hence, an iterative scheme is needed to solve the forward problem. This introduces yet another non-linearity.

3.1 Apparent Heat Capacity Formulation

The transient heat conduction problem with phase change for arbitrary geometries is solved using numerical techniques such as Finite Element Method (FEM) or Finite Difference Method (FDM). The fixed grid method is the most widely used technique as it modifies the moving boundary value problem to a non-linear heat conduction problem without change of phase through the definition of total enthalpy. For this reason, these methods are also known as the enthalpy methods. A comprehensive survey of the fixed grid techniques is provided by Voller et al. (1990). In this method, the total enthalpy is defined as

$$H(T) = \int_{T_{ref}}^{T} \rho c \, d\theta + \rho g(T) L \quad , \qquad (4)$$

where H is the total enthalpy dependent on the temperature T, T_{ref} is the arbitrary reference temperature and $g(T)$, for problems with distinct interface, is the Heaviside step function given by

$$g(T) = \begin{cases} 0, & T < T_m \\ 1, & T > T_m \end{cases} \quad , \qquad (5)$$

where T_m is the melting point of the material. A modification in $g(T)$ is necessary to use this procedure to solve the mushy phase change problem. In basic enthalpy formulation, the governing equation for the phase change problem is given by

$$\frac{\partial H}{\partial t} = \nabla \cdot (k \nabla T) \quad . \qquad (6)$$

The properties ρ, c at any spatial location are dependent on the state[2] of the material and is given by

$$\rho = (1 - g(T))\rho_s + g(T)\rho_l$$
$$c = (1 - g(T))c_s + g(T)c_l \quad . \qquad (7)$$

The enthalpy formulation given by (6) is equivalent to the conduction energy formulation given by (2). The proof to the general 3-D case can be found in (Shamsundar and Sparrow, 1975).

As outlined in (Voller et al., 1990), there are several ways to solve (6). In the Apparent Heat Capacity (AHC) formulation (Bonacina et al., 1973), the rate of change of enthalpy is written

$$\frac{\partial H}{\partial t} = \frac{\partial H}{\partial T} \frac{\partial T}{\partial t} \quad . \qquad (8)$$

Further from (3),

$$c^A(T) \equiv \frac{\partial H}{\partial T} = \rho c + \rho L \delta(T - T_m) \quad , \qquad (9)$$

where c^A is the Apparent Heat Capacity (AHC), $\delta(.)$ is the delta-dirac function. Using (8) and (9), the basic enthalpy formulation equation (6) is transformed to

$$c^A(T) \frac{\partial T}{\partial t} = \nabla \cdot (k \nabla T) \quad . \qquad (10)$$

Note that the above governing equation is the same as the conduction energy equation in (1). The AHC is temperature dependent; therefore (10) is non-linear. Further, the AHC function defined in (9) has a singularity at $T = T_m$.

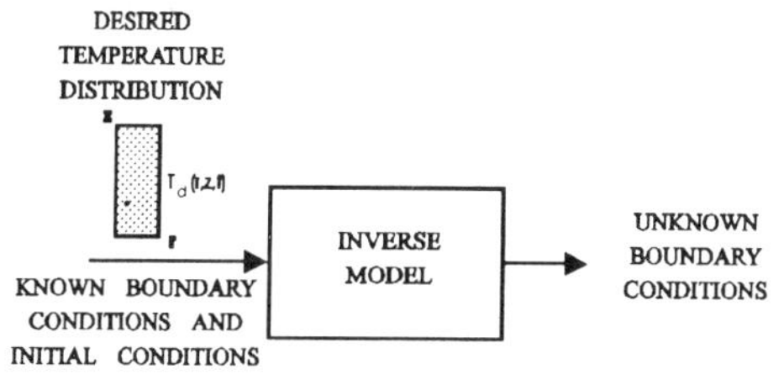

Figure 4. Representation of inverse problem.

[1] solid or liquid state

[2] solid or liquid

4. INVERSE PROBLEM

The "inverse problem" corresponds to finding the necessary boundary conditions for a desired temperature distribution or interface location as illustrated in Figure 4. Inverse problems are generally more difficult to solve than the forward problem. Some results regarding inverse heat conduction problems can be found in (Beck, 1973). Even for simple heat conduction problems, the inverse problem solutions are non-unique and numerically ill-conditioned. Taghavi and Duval (1989) solved the inverse heat transfer problem analytically for a simplified furnace in order to determine a furnace temperature profile that would result in a flat interface. Dantzig and Tortorelli (1991) used the enthalpy based FE model of the furnace to find the necessary temperature profile for a flat interface. The necessary furnace zone temperatures in their case are found as a solution to an optimization problem. These two methods can be used to determine the necessary temperature profile off-line. However, due to inevitable modeling errors, these solutions may not produce the desirable interface shape.

In the controls area, the shortcomings associated with the use of inverse solution are very well understood. The basic approach to overcome such difficulty is to use on-line measurements to compensate for the modeling errors. For the crystal growth problem, the on-line measurements are used to determine the necessary temperature gradient to produce the desirable interface shape. Obviously, in order to implement such an idea, it is necessary to have sensors and heater actuators to establish the necessary temperature gradient around the ampoule. A procedure to determine the necessary temperature gradient on-line by making use of all available measurements is proposed in this paper.

4.1 Distributed Parameter Systems

A significant amount of research has been reported in a controls area known as the "Distributed Parameter Systems (DPS)" to solve inverse problems similar to the one on hand, i.e., the boundary control of the solid-liquid interface shape. A general survey of the modeling and control issues of DPS can be found in (Wang , 1964), (Balas, 1982), (Goodson and Polis, 1974), and (Tzafestas and Stavroulakis, 1983).

In classical control, the system to be controlled is represented in the form of Ordinary Differential Equations (ODE). The model of the system is usually described in the Laplace domain or the state-space domain. The DPS, on the other hand are characterized by PDE's. The DPS theory can be broadly divided into two main groups: modeling, and control.

The modeling aspect includes obtaining a model for the controller design or for the simulation of the system. Most of the practical modeling approaches approximate the DPS by a set of ODE's. This is performed by using lumping techniques such FDM, FEM or modal approximation. In this paper, we use the FEM to obtain a lumped state-space model of the DPS.

The control aspect of DPS includes issues such as stability, controllability, observability, and trackability. Definition for these concepts can be found in (Friedland, 1986). Any practical control design approach requires a transfer function or a state-space model of the DPS. This model can be used to design a controller whose output would be a solution to the inverse problem, i.e., the necessary BC.

5. GENERAL HEAT CONDUCTION PROBLEM

In the AHC formulation, the solidification problem is transformed into a regular heat conduction problem with temperature dependent coefficients. Almost all control design methods are developed for linear systems. Therefore, it is necessary to linearize the non-linear equation in (10). Before linearizing the system, it will be worthwhile to see how the control algorithm performs for linear heat conduction problem with no phase change. This would provide us with enough intuition to solve the non-linear problem. Also, it is easier to illustrate many control issues on a linear problem. Hence, as a first step, the linear heat conduction system with no phase change is considered.

5.1 Finite Element Based State-Space Model

The general heat conduction problem is described in terms of a PDE along with appropriate BC's. In the inverse problem, it is required to determine the controllable BC[3] that would set up a desired distribution inside the region of interest. The FEM can be used to obtain a lumped model of the heat conduction problem including the BC's and is given by

$$M\dot{T} + KT = F, \qquad (11)$$

where M, K, and F are the mass, stiffness, and force matrices respectively and T is the temperature at certain key points (nodes). The above equation can be used to determine the solution to the forward problem. However, solving the inverse problem is difficult using equation (11) as the relation on how the BC's affects the temperatures are embedded in the force matrix F.

In (Srinivasan et al., 1994), an approach to parameterize the three main BC's namely the insulation BC, convection BC and Dirichlet BC are proposed. In the case of Dirichlet BC, the parametrization is done in terms of the nodal temperature on the Dirichlet boundary. Similarly, the

[3]The required BC are set up by a command to the heater actuator.

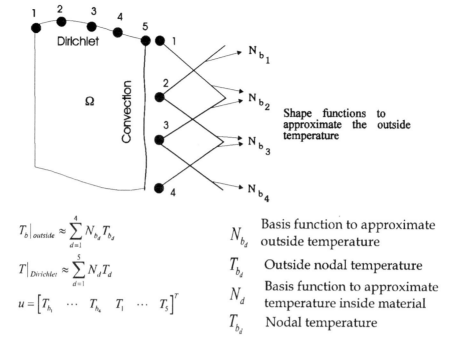

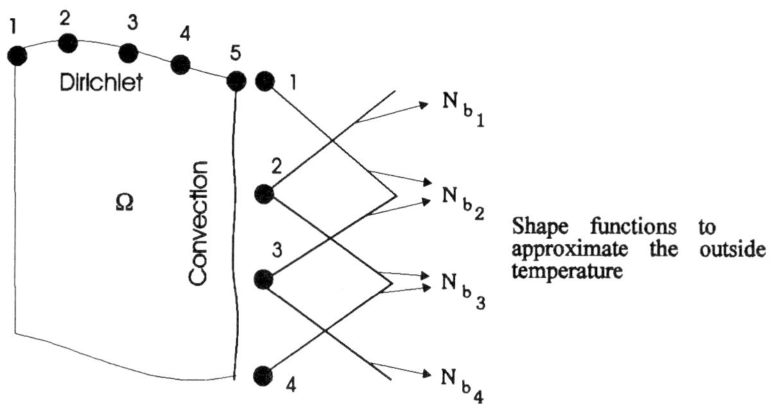

$$T_b\big|_{outside} \approx \sum_{d=1}^{4} N_{b_d} T_{b_d}$$

$$T\big|_{Dirichlet} \approx \sum_{d=1}^{5} N_d T_d$$

$$u = \begin{bmatrix} T_{b_1} & \cdots & T_{b_4} & T_1 & \cdots & T_5 \end{bmatrix}^T$$

N_{b_d} Basis function to approximate outside temperature

T_{b_d} Outside nodal temperature

N_d Basis function to approximate temperature inside material

T_{b_d} Nodal temperature

Figure 5. Parameterization of convection and Dirichlet Boundary conditions.

convection BC is parametrized in terms of the nodal outside temperature (See Figure 5). With this parameterization, the FE model for the heat conduction problem is given by

$$M\dot{T} + KT = Bu, \qquad (12)$$

where u is a m-dimensional vector that contains the parametrized BC's and B is n by m matrix with n being number of unknown nodal temperatures. Following the technique in (Srinivasan et al., 1994), the above equation can modified to yield a state-space model as given below

$$\dot{T} = \tilde{A}T + \tilde{B}u \qquad (13)$$

The transformation from (12) to (13) can be achieved by inverting the mass matrix M. The use of a lumped mass matrix would reduce the computational effort significantly in this regard. There is an evolving field in the controls area known as the "descriptors systems" in which controllers can be designed using (12) directly. Therefore, it is possible to design controllers without inverting the rather large mass matrix M. We do not pursue this approach in this paper and use (13) for the purpose of controller design.

Only a few of the members of u can be varied as desired by a command to the heater actuators and these are included in the vector u^c and all other non-varying parameters are included in u^e. Consequently, $\tilde{B}$ is decomposed appropriately to satisfy

$$\tilde{B}u = \tilde{B}^c u^c + \tilde{B}^e u^e. \qquad (14)$$

Substituting the above relation into the state-space finite element model given by equation (12) to yield

$$\dot{T} = \tilde{A}T + \tilde{B}^c u^c + \tilde{B}^e u^e \qquad (15)$$

Any temperature measurement can be described in terms of the nodal temperature as

$$y = \tilde{C}T + \tilde{D}^c u^c + \tilde{D}^e u^e \qquad (16)$$

In the next section, equation (15) and (16) are used to design a controller.

5.2 Control Objective and Design Procedure

The main objective of the inverse heat conduction problem is to determine the BC's that can be varied to establish a desired temperature distribution inside the continuum. All variable BC are parametrized and included in the vector u^c. Hence the inverse problem can be stated as follows: "Find $u^c(t)$, $0 < t < \tau$ such that $T(\tau)=T_d$, where T_d is the desired temperature distribution inside the material." Most of the times, we require the steady-state reference following, i.e., $\tau \rightarrow \infty$.

This paper utilizes developments in the "controls area" to solve the inverse problem. The control solution utilizes feedback, i.e., it uses measured quantities to determine u^c. Conceptually, any controller can be represented by the following equation

$$u^c(t) = f(y,t), \qquad (17)$$

where $f(.)$ is any function and y is a vector that contains all the measurements. The function f is usually designed as a linear function of y, or a solution of a system of linear differential equation.

The main advantage of feedback is that the reference tracking can be exact in the presence of any reasonable modeling error or disturbances. Further, the transient dynamics of the system can be altered as desired. The transient dynamics of the open-loop system (u^c=0) in (15) from arbitrary initial conditions is determined by the eigenvalues of the $\tilde{A}$ matrix. In addition, if the open-loop system is unstable, i.e., $\tilde{A}$ has eigenvalues with positive real parts, feedback can be used to stabilize the system.

5.2.1 State-Feedback Controller. State-feedback is the most general linear control law and is given as

$$u^c = K_s T + u_b, \tag{18}$$

where K_S is the state-feedback constant gain matrix. An additional bias input u_b is included in (18) to have non-zero steady-state temperature distribution inside the material. The closed-loop system of (15) after applying the control in (18) is given by

$$\dot{T} = \left(\tilde{A} + \tilde{B}^c K_s\right)T + \tilde{B}^c u_b + \tilde{B}^e u^e. \tag{19}$$

The transient dynamics of the controlled system is determined by eigenvalues of $\left(\tilde{A} + \tilde{B}^c K_s\right)$. Therefore, the state-feedback gain matrix can be selected to shape the transient response. However, some modes of the $\tilde{A}$ matrix cannot be manipulated by the controller. These are known as the uncontrollable modes.

5.2.2 Implementation of State-Feedback Controller through Observers. To implement the control law in (18), it is necessary to measure all the states, i.e., the nodal temperatures T. Only a few of the states[4] can be measured and therefore all other states must be reconstructed from these measurements. The control law in (18) is modified as

$$u^c = K_s \hat{T} + u_b \tag{20}$$

where $\hat{T}$ is the estimated state and is found by the observer equation (Friedland, 1986)

$$\dot{\hat{T}} = \tilde{A}\hat{T} + \tilde{B}^c u^c + \tilde{B}^e u^e + L(y - \tilde{C}\hat{T} - \tilde{D}^c u_c - \tilde{D}^e u_e). \tag{21}$$

Here L is the observer gain matrix that is selected by the designer to shape the estimated state transient response. It is possible that some of the modes cannot be estimated using the available measurements. These are known as unobservable modes.

If there are uncontrollable and / or unobservable modes, it may not be possible to design and implement the controller given by (20). Also, it is possible to have states (or a linear combination of states) that are either weakly controllable or weakly observable. Qualitatively, a state is said to be weakly controllable, if a small change in the state requires a very large input. Hence, if a controller tries to alter a weakly controllable state, it would request a large control input from the heater actuators, i.e., the controller gain will be high. Similarly, a state is said to be weakly observable, if a small change in the output is created by a very large change in the state. This would make the observer gain L very high thereby becoming sensitive to sensor noise. A judgment on the number of weakly controllable and observable states can be made by computing the Hankel singular values of the system σ_i's, which are given by

$$\sigma_i = \sqrt{\lambda_i\left(\tilde{W}_c \tilde{W}_o\right)}, \tag{22}$$

with $\sigma_1 \geq \sigma_2 \cdots \geq \sigma_n \geq 0$. $\tilde{W}_c$ and $\tilde{W}_o$ are the controllability and observability Grammians of the system and are found by solving the following Lyapunov equations

$$\tilde{A}\tilde{W}_c + \tilde{W}_c\tilde{A}^T + \tilde{B}^c\left(\tilde{B}^c\right)^T = 0 \tag{23}$$

$$\tilde{A}^T\tilde{W}_o + \tilde{W}_o\tilde{A} + \tilde{C}^T\tilde{C} = 0. \tag{24}$$

If σ_i drop significantly after the k th singular value, then there are (n-k) weakly observable or controllable states.

A practical controller that tries to alter the dynamics of the weakly controllable or observable modes will either saturate the actuators due to high control gain or be too sensitive to sensor noise due to high observer gain. Both saturation of actuators, and sensitivity to sensor noise are undesirable in any control system. In this situation, the controller is designed using a subsystem of (15) in which all the weakly controllable and observable modes are eliminated.

This elimination involves finding an invertible transformation matrix P which transforms the system to a balanced system of coordinates (Moore, 1981) such that

$$T^l = P^{-1}T. \tag{25}$$

Here T^l is the new state-vector containing a linear-combination of the nodal temperatures T. In the new coordinates, all system matrices are transformed as

$$\dot{T}^l = AT^l + B^c u^c + B^e u^e$$
$$y = CT^l + D^c u^c + D^e u^e,$$

where

$$A = P^{-1}\tilde{A}P, \quad B^c = P^{-1}\tilde{B}^c, \; B^e = P^{-1}\tilde{B}^e$$
$$C = \tilde{C}P, \quad D^c = \tilde{D}^c, \quad D^e = \tilde{D}^e \tag{26}$$

A kth order subsystem containing the modes associated with k largest Hankel singular values can be obtained by partitioning the transformed system as

[4] or a linear combination of the states are measured

$$T^l = \begin{bmatrix} T_1^l \\ T_2^l \end{bmatrix} \quad A = \begin{bmatrix} A_{11} & A_{12} \\ A_{21} & A_{22} \end{bmatrix} \quad B^c = \begin{bmatrix} B_1^c \\ B_2^c \end{bmatrix} \quad B^e = \begin{bmatrix} B_1^e \\ B_2^e \end{bmatrix}$$

$$C = [C_1 \quad C_2] \quad D^c = [D_1^c \quad D_2^c] \quad D^e = [D_1^e \quad D_2^e]$$

$$P = [P_1 \quad P_2] \tag{27}$$

where $A_{11} \in \Re^{k \times k}$, $A_{22} \in \Re^{(n-k)\times(n-k)}$ and all other matrices are of appropriate dimension. The subsystem after elimination $(n\text{-}k)$ weakest controllable\observable modes are given by

$$\dot{T}_1^l = A_{11} T_1^l + B_1^c u^c + B_1^e u^e$$
$$y \approx C_1 T_1^l + D_1^c u^c + D_1^e u^e \tag{28}$$

The observer based state-feedback controller designed using the most controllable and observable subsystem given by (28) is similar to (20) and is given as

$$u^c = K_s \hat{T}_1^l + u_b \tag{29}$$

where $\hat{T}_1^l$ is the estimated state and is found by the observer equation

$$\dot{\hat{T}}_1^l = A_{11}\hat{T}_1^l + B_1^c u^c + B_1^e u^e + L(y - C_1\hat{T}_1^l - D_1^c u^c - D_1^e u^e) \tag{30}$$

The separation principle (Friedland, 1986) allows us to determine the controller gain K_S and the observer gain L independently. The state-feedback controller is designed as a Linear Quadratic Regulator (LQR). The LQR is found by minimizing the following quadratic performance

$$J = \int_0^\infty \left((T_1^l)^T Q T_1^l + (u^c)^T R u^c \right) dt \tag{31}$$

where Q and R are weighing matrices of appropriate dimension. The state-feedback gain that minimizes the cost in (31) is given by

$$K_s = R^{-1} (B_1^c)^T X \tag{32}$$

where $X \geq 0$ is the solution of the following Riccati equation

$$A_{11}^T X + X A_{11} - X B_1^c R^{-1} (B_1^c)^T X + Q = 0 \tag{33}$$

The weighing matrices Q and R are the design parameters that can be selected to give a reasonable transient response.

The observer is designed as a Linear Quadratic Estimator (LQE) using the reduced order model (28). The LQE is a dual problem of the LQR. Analogous to (31), the LQE weighing matrices Q_0, R_0 are design matrices and the observer gain L is found as

$$L = -R_o^{-1} C_1 X_o, \tag{34}$$

where $X_o \geq 0$ is the solution of the following Riccati equation

$$A_{11} X_o + X_o A_{11}^T - X_o C_1^T R_o^{-1} C_1 X_o + Q_o = 0 \tag{35}$$

The closed-loop system is given by

$$\begin{pmatrix} \dot{T}_1^l \\ \dot{T}_2^l \\ \dot{\hat{T}}_1^l \end{pmatrix} = \underbrace{\begin{pmatrix} A_{11} & A_{12} & B_1^c K_s \\ A_{21} & A_{22} & B_2^c K_s \\ 0 & 0 & A_{11} + B_1^c K_s - LC_1 - LD_1^c K_s \end{pmatrix}}_{A_{cl}} \begin{pmatrix} T_1^l \\ T_2^l \\ \hat{T}_1^l \end{pmatrix}$$
$$+ \begin{pmatrix} B_1^c \\ B_2^c \\ B_1^c - LD_1^c \end{pmatrix} u_b + \begin{pmatrix} B_1^e \\ B_2^e \\ B_1^e - LD_1^e \end{pmatrix} u^e + \begin{pmatrix} 0 \\ 0 \\ I \end{pmatrix} y \tag{36}$$

The transient response of the controlled system is determined by the A_{cl} matrix.

In addition to shaping the transient response, the controller has to establish the desired temperature distribution inside the material in the steady-state. This requirement can be represented by the following equation

$$T(t) = T_d \quad t \to \infty, \tag{37}$$

where T_d is the desired nodal temperature. From (25), it can be observed that in the balanced coordinates, achieving (37) is equivalent to satisfying

$$T^l(t) = P^{-1} T_d \quad t \to \infty. \tag{38}$$

The states of the controlled balanced system in the steady state is given by the solution to the following system of equations

$$\begin{bmatrix} A_{11} + B_1^c K_s & A_{12} \\ A_{21} + B_2^c K_s & A_{22} \end{bmatrix} T^l(\infty) = B^c u^b + B^e u^e \tag{39}$$

Note the above equation is obtained as the steady-state solution of (36) using the fact $\hat{T}_1^l(t) = T_1^l(t)\ t \to \infty$. The bias input that would achieve (39) must satisfy the following matrix equation

$$B^c u^b = -\begin{bmatrix} A_{11} + B_1^c K_s & A_{12} \\ A_{21} + B_2^c K_s & A_{22} \end{bmatrix} P^{-1} T_d + B^e u^e \equiv v \tag{40}$$

A bias input u^b exist, if the vector v lies in the range space of B^c. A formal set of conditions for the existence of the bias input for an arbitrary reference can be found in (Srinivasan, 1994).

5.3 Example

The conduction problem inside the ampoule shown in Figure 2 is modeled in this section. The ampoule contains Lead Bromide. It is assumed the temperature are such that there is no phase change in the material. The BC's for this problem are given by (3). Due to axi-symmetry, it is sufficient to find the temperature for the surface $\phi = 0$ as shown in Figure 6. The control problem is to determine the boundary temperature T_b so that a prescribed temperature distribution can be established inside the material. In order to obtain a FE Model, the domain has to be discretized. The domain is discretized into a 5 by 9 grid resulting in 45 nodal points and 32 elements as in Figure 6. Since this problem has no Dirichlet BC, all the nodal temperatures are unknowns and hence the state space model has 45 states. The outside temperature T_b is approximated by 9 basis functions equal to the number of nodes on the boundary surface. Hence there are 9 control inputs in the system. Also, there is no exogenous input u^e. In the rest of this section, the controller design to determine the appropriate control inputs are discussed. All the computations with respect to finding the Hankel singular values, solving the LQR and LQE problem are performed using the MATLAB software package.

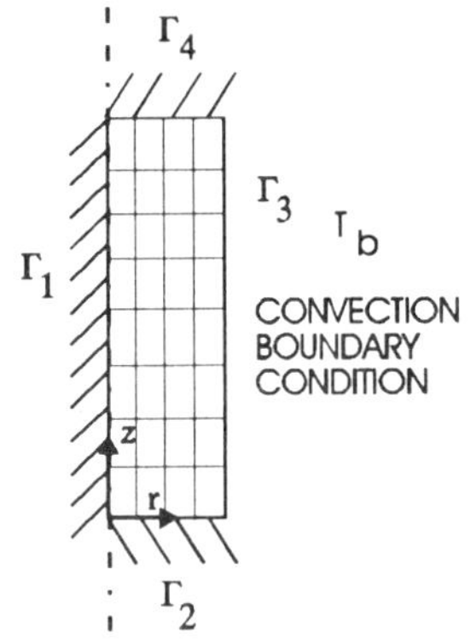

Figure 6. Discretization of axisymmetric geometry in Figure 2.

The outputs from the system are limited due to practical considerations. We consider two set of measurements and they are

(a) All nodal temperatures are measurable, i.e. $\tilde{C} = I$.

(b) Only the nodal surface temperatures Γ_3 are measurable. Actually it is not necessary for the measurements to be at the nodes as a $\tilde{C}$ matrix can be obtained for any set of measurements. This set of measurements results in a set of collocated sensors and actuators.

In practice, it is not possible to realize set (a). However, we are interested in the performance of the state-feedback controller hence we consider the set (a) of measurements. A Hankel singular values plot for the two set of measurements are given in **Figure** 7 and as expected, set (a) has larger Hankel singular values than set (b). Also, there is a significant drop in Hankel singular values for measurement set (b) around the 36th singular value. This qualitatively implies that about 9 states in (b) are very weakly observable and / or controllable with respect to other states.

Figure 8 gives the response of the open-loop (uncontrolled) system. To see the transient response, the outside nodal temperature is made 100 C for $0 < t < 12.5$ and 200 C for $t \geq 12.5$. The time constant of the uncontrolled system is about 5 minutes. Further all modes of the system are stable.

A state-feedback controller with bias as in (18) is designed to reduced the time constant of the system and to establish the desired temperature profile. In order to implement the state-feedback controller, all nodal temperatures have to be measured. This corresponds to set (a) of measurements. From the Hankel singular value plot in Figure 7, it can be seen all states are controllable. Hence, the model in (15) can be used to design the controller. The state-feedback gain matrix K is found by appropriately selecting Q and R matrices. For this system $Q = 5\,I$ and $R = I$ yielded a reasonable transient response. The bias input is found using (40) with $P = I$. In order to compare the open-loop response in Figure 8, the desired nodal temperatures are selected to be 100 C, for $t < 12.5$ and 200 C for $t \geq 12.5$. The nodal temperature transient response is shown in Figure 9 and the outside nodal temperatures that the controller requests is given in Figure 10. The time constant of the controlled system is about 2 minutes.

The same state-feedback control cannot be implemented for measurement set (b), as all the states are not available for feedback. To overcome this problem, an observer is designed and this requires all the states to be observable through the measurements. All states are observable as is evident from the Hankel singular value plot in Figure 7. However, about 9 modes are very weakly observable. Hence, the control design must be performed using a 36 th order subsystem as described in section 5.2.2. The observer and the controller gains are designed using the reduced order model. The state-feedback gain K_s is determined as before using equation (32) with appropriate Q and R matrices. The observer gain L is found using (34) and the appropriate bias input is found using (40). The nodal temperature's transient responses for the observer based control with a similar desired temperature as the state-feedback case are given in Figure 11 and the corresponding controller outputs are given in Figure 12. The observer based controller qualitatively performs very similar to the state-feedback controller. The observer based controller also has a time constant of about 2 minutes.

The outside nodal temperatures requested by the controller is implemented by a furnace temperature controller. The dynamics of the controller is not considered in this study. However, the furnace cannot provide the requested boundary temperatures at all times. For example, the sudden spikes in Figure 10 and 12 cannot be achieved by the furnace temperature controller. The main reason for this problem is that the controller has no information on what the furnace can achieve. This problem can be overcome if the furnace dynamics is included in the state-space model (15).

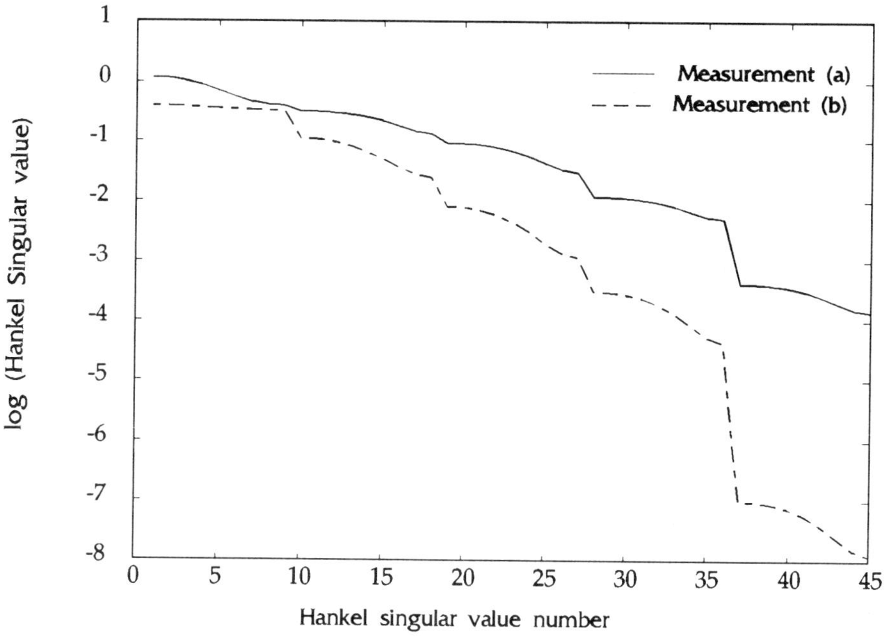

Figure 7. Hankel Singular values for measurements sets (a) and (b).

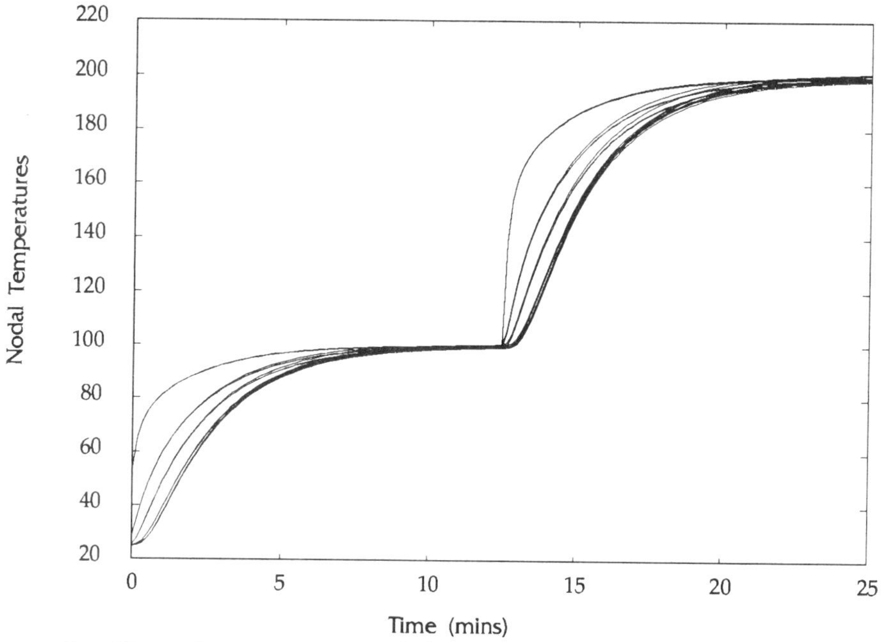

Figure 8. Open loop response of the system. Outside nodal temperatures are 100 C for $0 < t < 12.5$ and 200 C for $t > 12.5$ min

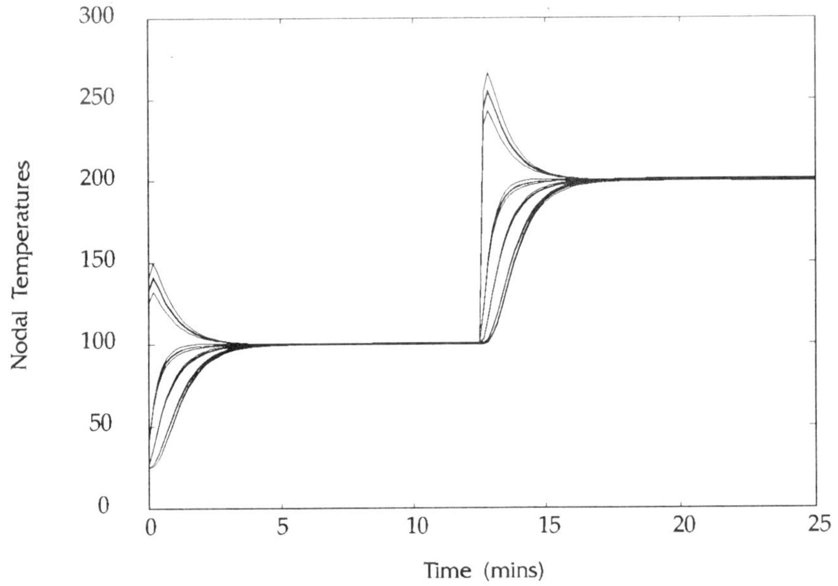

Figure 9. Transient response of the system operating with the state-feedback controller. The bias inputs are selected such that all temperatures are at 100 C for $t < 12.5$ and 200 C for $T > 25.0$.

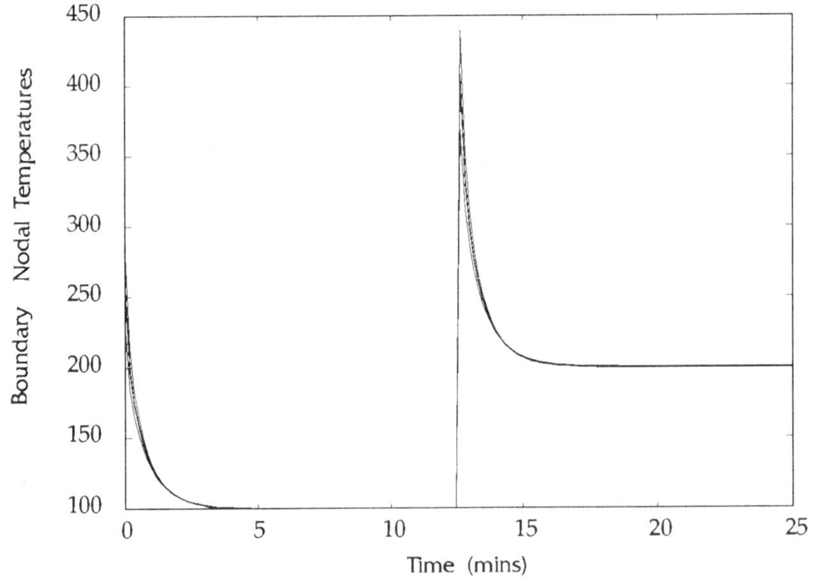

Figure 10. Outside nodal temperatures requested by the state-feedback controller.

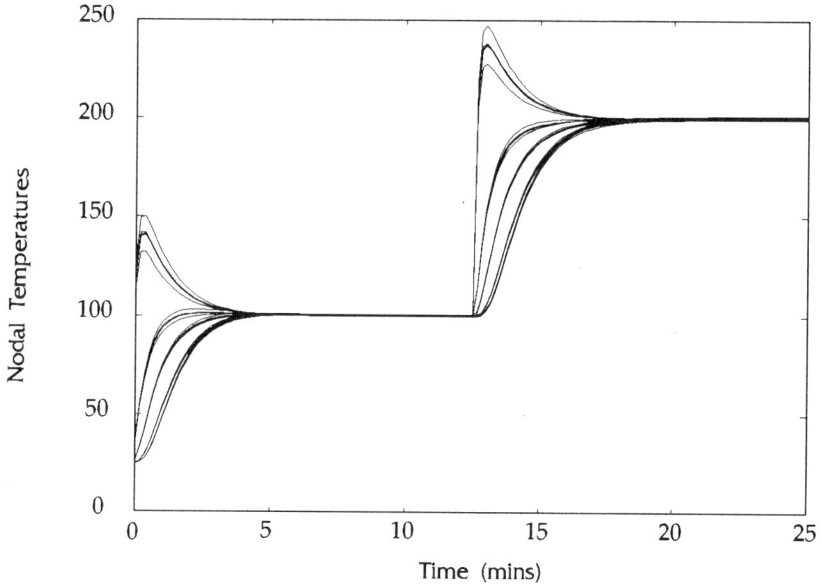

Figure 11. Transient response for the observer-based controller. The bias inputs are selected to establish the same temperatures as the state-feedback case.

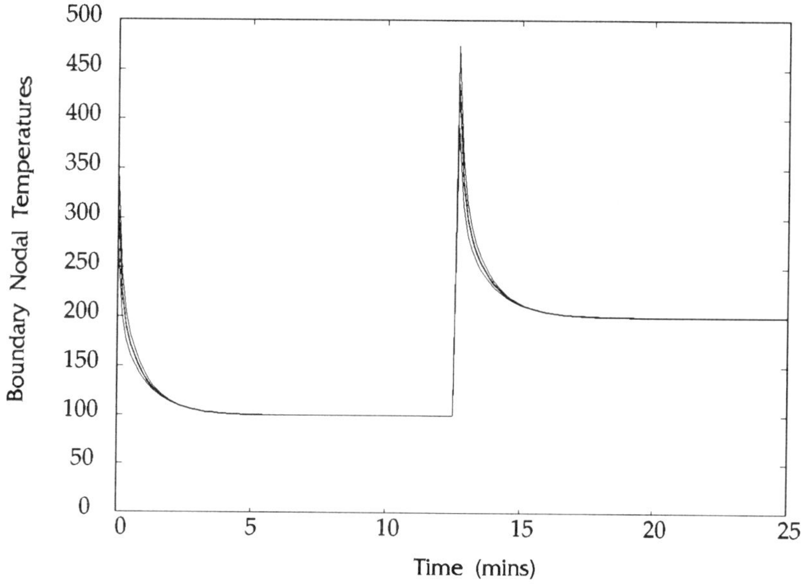

Figure 12. Outside nodal temperatures requested by the observer-based controller.

6. HEAT CONDUCTION PROBLEM WITH PHASE CHANGE

The AHC method can be used to obtain a PDE that models the phase change problem. This PDE has a form similar to that of the regular heat-conduction problem, with temperature dependent specific heat and heat conductivity coefficient. Hence, a similar procedure described in the previous section is used to obtain a state-space model of the system. However, the matrices $\tilde{A}$, $\tilde{B}^c$, and $\tilde{B}^e$ are all temperature dependent, making the state-space model non-linear. The state-space model for the heat-conduction problem with phase change is given by

$$\dot{T} = \tilde{A}(T)T + \tilde{B}^c(T)u^c + \tilde{B}^e(T)u^e \quad (41)$$

In this problem, we consider only one set of measurement, namely, the situation in which all nodal temperatures are measured, i.e. $\tilde{C} = I$. Therefore, a state-feedback type controller as designed in section 5.2.1 can be used to control the system and is given below for the sake of completeness.

$$u^c = K_s T + u_b \quad (42)$$

Since, the state-space matrices are temperature dependent (non-linear), it is reasonable to expect the state-feedback gain to be temperature dependent. However, the task of designing such a gain is very difficult. One way to overcome this difficulty is to design a constant state-feedback gain matrix and the corresponding bias input using the matrices in (41) for a given operating point, say T_f. This T_f can be the current nodal temperatures or the desired nodal temperatures. The constant state-feedback gain and the appropriate bias input are found as in section 5.3 with the same choices for the Q and R matrices. Preliminary simulation results are presented in the following section.

6.1 Simulation Results

The main aim here is to determine the outside temperatures u_b so that a flat interface is initially established at the location z=0.02m and then the crystal is grown a rate of 1 cm / hr with the constraint that the interface shape must remain flat during the growth. This is equivalent to establishing a desired temperature distribution. The desired nodal temperatures are determined to be r - independent, i.e., no temperature gradient in the r direction and a gradient of 10 C° / cm in the z-direction with the melting point of 373 C° at the desired interface location. A single state-feedback gain is determined by evaluating the model at T_f, i.e., the state-space matrices given by $\tilde{A}(T_f), \tilde{B}^c(T_f), \tilde{B}^e(T_f)$ are used for the design of the gain matrix K_s and the bias input u_b. The actual, the desired interface shape during the crystal growth and the corresponding outside temperature are shown in Figure 13.

It is clear from the Figure 13 that a reasonably flat interface shape is achieved. The controller design can be improved in different ways. For example, the control gain K_s can be re-designed from time to time instead of using a single controller. Secondly, on-line measurements are not used in determining the bias input u_b and therefore even if the measurements indicates tracking errors, the controller does not take any correction for these errors. These defects can be overcome by using the integral control design procedure. Our future work would address these issues.

7. CONCLUSION

The desired solid-liquid interface shape during crystal growth can be established by appropriately manipulating the boundary conditions. Governing equations for the solidification process is obtained using the apparent heat capacity formulation. A state-space model of the process is obtained by employing a finite element approximation to the governing equation. To gain insight into the controller design procedures, the heat conduction problem with no phase change problem is first considered. Here, a controller is designed for two different sets of measurements and an arbitrary temperature distribution is established inside the material by applying the appropriate bias input.

The same controller design procedure as above is applied for phase change problem. The desired interface shape is achieved by trying to establish an appropriate temperature distribution. The controller design is performed utilizing a linearized state-space model to establish a flat interface during crystal growth. Preliminary simulation results are encouraging with respect to controlling the interface shape.

REFERENCES

Balas, M. J., 1982, "Trends in large space structure control theory: Fondest hopes, wildest dreams", *IEEE Transaction on Automatic Control*, Vol. 27, No. 3.

Beck, J. V., 1985, *Inverse Heat Conduction: Ill Posed Problem*, John Wiley and Sons, New York.

Bonacina, C., Comini, G., Fasano, A., and Primicerio, M., 1973, "Numerical solution of phase-change problems", *Heat and Mass Transfer*, Vol. 16, pp. 1825-1832.

Crank, J., 1984, *Free and Moving Boundary Problems*, Clarendon Press, Oxford.

Dantzig, J. A., and Tortorelli, D. A., 1991, "Optimal Design for Solidification Processes",

Proceedings of the Third International Conference on Inverse Design Concepts and Optimization in Engineering, G.S. Dulikravich, Ed.

Friedland, B., 1986, *Control System Design: An Introduction to State-Space Methods*, McGraw-Hill, New York.

Goodson, R. E., and Polis, M. P., 1974, "Parameter identification in distributed systems: a synthesizing overview", *Identification of Parameters in Distributed Systems* eds. Goodson, R. E., and Polis, M. P., ASME.

Moore, B. C., 1981, "Principal component analysis in linear systems: controllability, observability, and model reduction", *IEEE Transactions on Automatic Control*, Vol. 26, pp. 17-31.

Shamsundar, N., Sparrow, E. M., 1975, "Analysis of multidimensional conduction phase change via the enthalpy model", *Journal of Heat Transfer*, Vol. , pp. 333-340.

Srinivasan, A., Batur, C., and Rosenthal, B. N., 1994, "Control of Thermal System through Finite Element Based State-Space Model", *To appear in the proceedings of the 1994 American Control Conference.*

Srinivasan, A., 1994, "Modeling and Control of Crystal Growth Using the Finite Element Technique", Ph. D. Dissertation, The University of Akron, OH.

Taghavi, K., and Duval, W. M. B., 1989, "Inverse heat transfer analysis of Bridgman crystal growth", *International Journal of Heat and Mass Transfer*, Vol. 32, No. 9, pp. 1741-1750.

Tzafestas, S. G., and Stavroulakis, P., 1983, "Recent advances in the study of distributed parameter systems", *Journal of the Franklin Institute*, Vol. 315, pp. 285-305.

Voller, V. R., Swaminathan, C. R., Thomas, B. G., 1990, "Fixed grid techniques for phase change problems: a review", *International Journal for Numerical Methods in Engineering*, Vol. 30, pp. 875-898.

Wang, P. K. C., 1964, " Control of distributed parameter system", *In the Advances in Control Systems: Theory and applications*, ed. C. T. Leondes, Vol. 1, pp. 75-172.

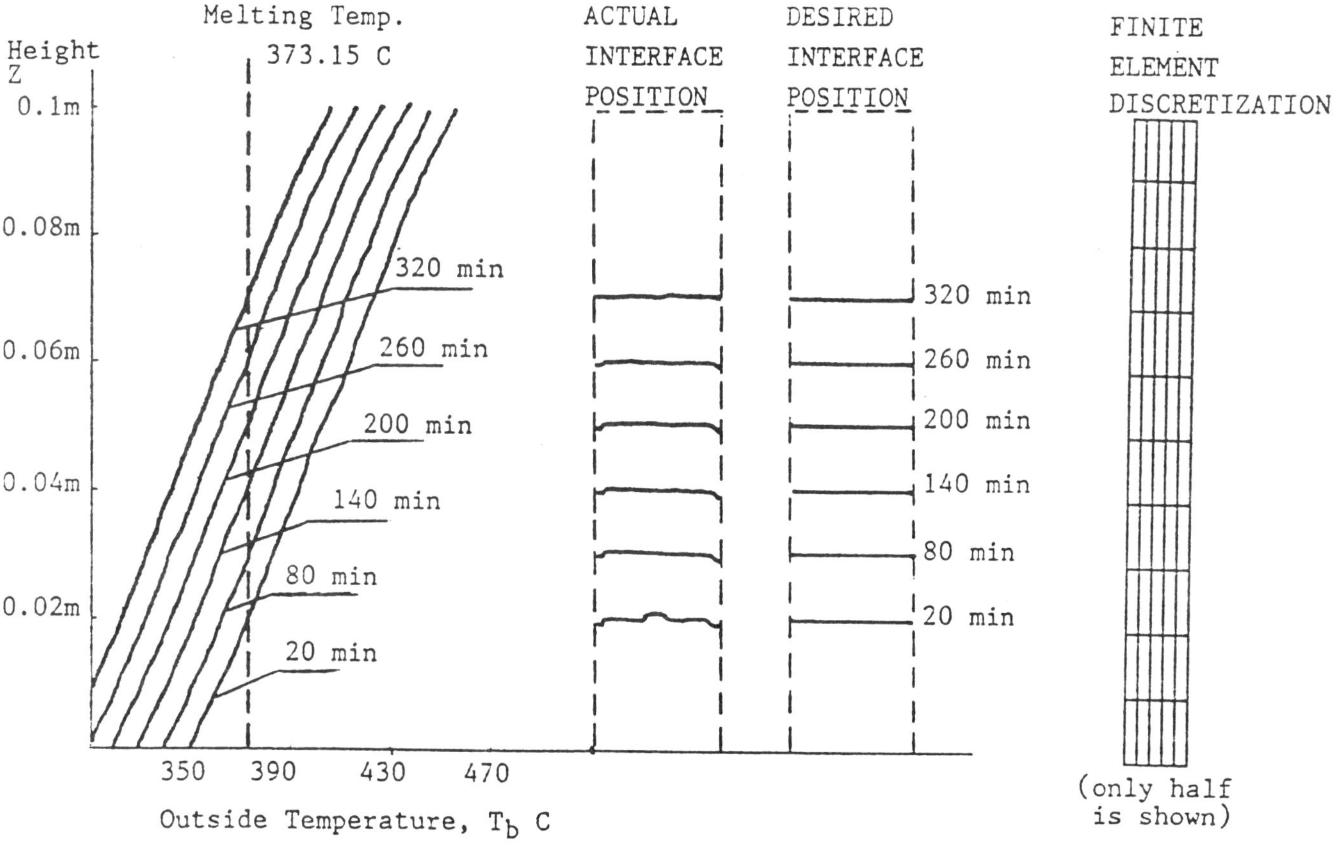

Figure 13. Manipulated boundary conditions, actual and desired interface positions.

AUTHOR INDEX

HTD-Vol. 284/AMD-Vol. 282
Transport Phenomena in Solidification

Book Number: G00887

The American Society of Mechanical Engineers

STANDING ORDER PLANS

from The American Society of Mechanical Engineers

- *Save up to 50%*
- *Get just-published information*
- *Never fill out an order form*
- *Create your own customer plan*

PLAN 1: TECHNICAL PAPERS OF ALL ASME DIVISIONS

You receive all technical papers published by ASME at an automatic 50% discount off the list price. In 1993, 961 technical papers were published with a total list price of $7,688. (Plan 1 Standing Order Price: $3,844 = Customer Savings: $3,844)

PLAN 2: SYMPOSIA / PROCEEDINGS OF ALL ASME DIVISIONS

You receive all symposia / proceedings volumes as soon as they are published at the member price - 20% to 50% off the list price. In 1993, 205 bound volumes were published at a total list price of $10,369. (Plan 2 Standing Order Price: $8,218 = Customer Savings: $2,151)

PLAN 3: TECHNICAL PAPERS AND SYMPOSIA / PROCEEDINGS OF ALL ASME DIVISIONS

You receive all papers and symposia / proceedings volumes published by ASME at the member price - 20% to 50% off the list price. In 1993, 1,166 technical papers and symposia / proceedings were published at a total list price of $18,057. (Plan 3 Standing Order Price: $12,062 = Customer Savings: $5,995)

PLAN 4: TECHNICAL PAPERS AND/OR SYMPOSIA / PROCEEDINGS OF SPECIFIC DIVISION(S)

1. Aerospace
2. Applied Mechanics
3. Management
4. Materials Handling
5. Internal Combustion Engine
6. Fuels & Combustion Technologies
7. Safety Engineering
8. Fluids Engineering
9. Bioengineering
10. Materials
11. Heat Transfer
12. Process Industries
13. Production Engineering
14. Design Engineering
15. Tribology
16. Petroleum
17. Nuclear Engineering
18. Rail Transportation
19. Power
20. Textile Industries
21. Plant Engineering & Maintenance
22. Gas Turbine
23. Environmental Engineering
24. Technology & Society
25. Dynamic Systems & Control
26. Ocean Engineering
27. Advance Energy Systems
28. Pressure Vessels & Piping
29. Solid Waste Processing
30. Solar Energy
31. Computers in Engineering
32. Noise Control & Accoustics
33. NDE Engineering
34. Electrical / Electronic Packaging
35. Offshore Mechanics & Arctic Engineering
36. Fluid Power Systems & Technologies
37. Bioprocess Engineering
38. Information Storage & Processing Systems

You receive member prices on your choice of technical papers and symposia / proceedings for any of the categories listed above. In 1993, Pressure Vessels and Piping Division published 23 proceedings volumes and 28 technical papers in 1993 at a total list price of $1,277.50. (Plan 4 Standing Order Price: $1,022 = Customer Savings: $255.52)

PLAN 5: IMECHE PUBLICATIONS

Receive a 10% discount on approximately 30 volumes published annually by Mechanical Engineering Publications (MEP), publisher for the Institution of Mechanical Engineers (IMechE), the largest UK engineering institution. Get leading European research on education and training, engineering management, engineering sciences, medical engineering, manufacturing, paper technology, power industries, process industries, reference, and transportation.

You can place your standing order by mail, fax, e-mail, or phone. . .

Mail
ASME
22 Law Drive, Box 2300
Fairfield, New Jersey
07007-2300

Fax – 24 hours
201-882-1717
201-882-5155

E-Mail – 24 hours
infocentral @ asme. org

Phone
US & Canada: 800-THE-ASME
(800-843-2763) Toll Free
Mexico: 95-800-843-2763 Toll Free
Universal: 201-882-1167